W9-AWW-573

Core Connections, Course 2
Second Edition*, Version 5.0

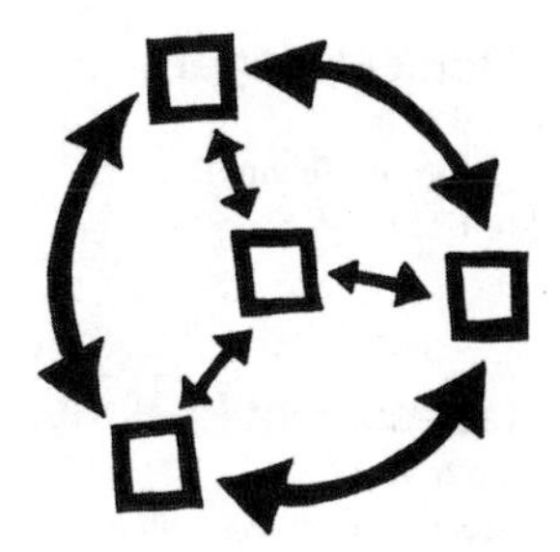

Managing Editors / Authors

Leslie Dietiker, Ph.D., Director of Curriculum (Both Editions)
Boston University
Boston, MA

Evra Baldinger (First Edition)
University of California, Berkeley
Berkeley, CA

Barbara Shreve (First Edition)
San Lorenzo High School
San Lorenzo, CA

Michael Kassarjian (2nd Edition)
CPM Educational Program
Kensington, CA

Misty Nikula (2nd Edition)
CPM Educational Program
Bellingham, WA

Contributing Authors

Elizabeth Baker
Zane Middle School

Clanci Chiu
Santa Barbara Junior High School

Kathleen Davies
Rincon Valley Middle School

Lori Hamada
CPM Educational Program

Carol Jancsi
CPM Mentor Teacher

Sarah Maile
CPM Educational Program

Bob Petersen
CPM Educational Program

Stephanie Whitney, Ph.D.
DePaul University

Tara Bianchi
American Canyon Middle School

Mark Coté
Beaver Lake Middle School

Josea Eggink
Bloomington Public Schools

Brian Hoey
CPM Educational Program

Rakesh Khanna
Hotmath, Inc.

Bruce Melhorn
International School Bangkok (ISB)

Tom Sallee, Ph.D.
University of California, Davis

Bev Brockhoff
Glen Edwards Middle School

Suzanne Cisco Cox
Turner Middle School

William Funkhouser
Zane Middle School

Janet Hollister
La Cumbre Jr. High School

Judy Kysh, Ph.D.
San Francisco State University

Chris Mikles
Post Falls Middle School

Lorna Thomas Vázquez
Neillsville, WI Math Consultant

Program Directors

Elizabeth Coyner
Christian Brothers High School
Sacramento, CA

Brian Hoey
CPM Educational Program
Sacramento, CA

Tom Sallee, Ph.D.
Department of Mathematics
University of California, Davis

Leslie Dietiker, Ph.D.
Boston University
Boston, MA

Michael Kassarjian
CPM Educational Program
Kensington, CA

Karen Wootton
CPM Educational Program
Odenton, MD

Lori Hamada
CPM Educational Program
Fresno, CA

Judy Kysh, Ph.D.
Departments of Education and Mathematics San Francisco State University, CA

*Based on *Making Connections*: *Foundations for Algebra, Courses 1 and 2*.

eBook Manager
Carol Cho
Director of Technology
Martinez, CA

eBook Programmers
Rakesh Khanna
Daniel Kleinsinger
Kevin Stein

eBook Assistants
Debbie Dodd
Shirley Paulsen
Wendy Papciak
Anna Poehlmann
Jordan Wight

Assessment Manager
Karen Wootton
Director of Assessment
Odenton, MD

Assessment Assistants
Elizabeth Baker
Zane Middle School
Eureka, CA

William Funkhouser
Zane Middle School
Eureka, CA

Assessment Website
Elizabeth Fong
Michael Huang
Daniel Kleinsinger

Illustration
Kevin Coffey
San Francisco, CA

Jonathan Weast
Sacramento, CA

Homework Help Manager
Bob Petersen
CPM Educational Program

Homework Help Website
Carol Cho
Director of Technology

Parent Guide with Extra Practice
Elizabeth Coyner
Christian Brothers High School

Brian Hoey
CPM Educational Program

Bob Petersen
CPM Educational Program

Based on the Skill Builder materials created for Foundations for Algebra (2003), created by:

Heidi Ackley
Bev Brockhoff
Scott Coyner
Brian Hoey
Robert Petersen
Kristie Sallee
Steve Ackley
Ellen Cafferata
Sara Effenbeck
Judy Kysh
Edwin Reed
Tom Sallee
Elizabeth Baker
Elizabeth Coyner
William Funkhouser
Kris Petersen
Stacy Rocklein
Howard Webb

Technical Managers
Sarah Maile
Aubrie Maze

Technical Assistants
Stephanie Achondo
Rebecca Bobell
Hannah Coyner
Matthew Donahue
Leslie Lai
Eli Marable
Alexandra Murphy
Ryan Peabody
Anna Poehlmann
Ali Rivera
Claire Taylor
Sarah Wong
Robert Ainsworth
Delenn Breedlove
Mary Coyner
Bethany Firch
Michael Li
James McCardle
Wendy Papciak
Iris Perez
Eduardo Ramirez
Andrea Smith
Christy Van Beek
Alex Yu
Bethany Armstrong
Jason Cho
Carmen de la Cruz
Dana Kimball
Jerry Luo
Nyssa Muheim
Atlanta Parrott
Steven Pham
John Ramos
Rachel Smith
Megan Walters

9 10 11 12 13 20 19 18 17 16

Version 5.0

Printed in the United States of America

ISBN: 978-1-60328-084-6

A Note to Students:

Welcome to a new year of math! In this course, you will learn to use new models and methods to think about problems as well as solve them. You will be developing powerful mathematical tools and learning new ways of thinking about and investigating situations. You will be making connections, discovering relationships, figuring out what strategies can be used to solve problems, and explaining your thinking. Learning to think in these ways and communicate about your thinking is useful in mathematical contexts, other subjects in school, and situations outside the classroom. The mathematics you have learned in the past will be valuable for learning in this course. That work, and what you learn in this course, will prepare you for future courses.

In meeting the challenges of this course, you will not be learning alone. You will cooperate with other students as a member of a study team. Being a part of a team means speaking up and interacting with other people. You will explain your ideas, listen to what others have to say, and ask questions if there is something you do not understand. In this course, a single problem can often be solved several ways. You will see problems in different ways than your teammates do. Each of you has something to contribute while you work on the lessons in this course.

Together, your team will complete problems and activities that will help you discover mathematical ideas and develop solution methods. Your teacher will support you as you work, but will not take away your opportunity to think and investigate for yourself. Each topic will be revisited many times and will connect to other topics. If something is not clear to you the first time you work on it, you will have more chances to build your understanding as the course continues.

Learning math this way has an advantage: as long as you actively participate, make sure everyone in your study team is involved, and ask good questions, you will find yourself understanding mathematics at a deeper level than ever before. By the end of this course, you will have a powerful set of mathematical tools to use to solve new problems. With your teammates you will meet mathematical challenges you would not have known how to approach before.

In addition to the support provided by your teacher and your study team, CPM has also created online resources to help you, including help with homework, and a parent guide with extra practice. You will find these resources and more at www.cpm.org.

We wish you well and are confident that you will enjoy this next year of learning!

Sincerely,

The CPM Team

Core Connections, Course 2
Student Edition

Chapter 7 Proportions and Percents 377

Chapter 8 Statistics and Angle Relationships 435

1 Introduction and Probability

CHAPTER 1 Introduction and Probability

Welcome to math class! This chapter will introduce you to several of the big ideas that you will explore during this course. You will apply your current mathematical knowledge to solve problems, some of which you will revisit later in the course using new tools.

Later in the chapter, you will focus on finding **probability**. Probability is the chance that something will happen. It is something you may have thought about in various aspects of daily life, but in this chapter you will learn how to calculate it mathematically. As you work with fish tanks, experiment with spinners, and toss coins, you will determine how to find the theoretical and the experimental probability that an event will occur. You will also review or reinforce your understanding of working with fractions and other portions.

Guiding Questions

Think about these questions throughout this chapter:

How can I work with my team to figure it out?

What questions can I ask about this problem?

How can I represent this?

How can I organize my work?

In this chapter, you will:

- Find the likelihood that a specific event will occur.
- Calculate the probabilities of two separate events to decide which is more likely to happen.
- Find both experimental and theoretical probabilities of events.
- Add and subtract fractions, as well as write equivalent fractions.

Chapter Outline

Section 1.1 This section will introduce you to several of the big ideas of the course. Each problem will require your study team to work together using several problem-solving strategies.

Section 1.2 In this section, you will learn to find the probability of a specific event. You will also learn about the meaning of probability and how it is expressed mathematically. After collecting experimental data, you will explore the difference between theoretical and experimental probability. You will then find the probabilities of two separate events.

1.1.1 What do they have in common?

Finding Shared and Unique Characteristics

Have you ever tried to learn how to play a new game just by watching other people play it? You were probably watching for patterns in the game, such as what each player did to earn points or what actions earned penalties. If you were watching a game of soccer, for example, you might have figured out that kicking the ball into the goal earned the team one point. You might also have noticed that the goalkeeper is the only player on the field allowed to use his or her hands. Noticing the patterns could help you describe some of the rules of the game. This type of observation is also called *generalizing*. When you make an observation about what objects or actions have in common, like the actions that will *always* allow you to score a point in soccer, you are making a *generalization*.

Today you will be working in a team with the goal of making generalizations about various sets of objects. As you work, keep these questions in mind:

What do the items have in common?

What makes the items different?

What are other characteristics that could describe the groups or sets?

1-1. MATH STARS

What do you have in common with your team members? What makes you unique? Today you will work with your teammates to discover some characteristics that you share and other characteristics that make each person in your team different.

Your Task: Get a copy of the Lesson 1.1.1A Resource Page and scissors. (Note: All resources pages can also be found at www.cpm.org.) Fold the resource page along the dotted lines and then cut along the solid lines. Unfold the cutout and glue it onto a piece of paper. Write each team member's name on a star.

- As a team, brainstorm something that all of you have in common that the rest of the class does not already know.
- List your team's common attribute on the paper in the center of the four stars.
- Find ways that each person in the team is unique from the others (things that are true about that person only), and write those things on each person's star.

To help you and your team members work together today, each team member has a specific job. Your job is assigned by your first name (or last name if team members have the same first name). Read the "Team Roles" information that follows and use it as a resource as you work with your team on this problem.

Team Roles

Resource Manager: If your name comes first alphabetically:

- Make sure your team has a Lesson 1.1.1A Resource Page, scissors, glue, and colored paper.
- Ask the teacher when the *entire* team has a question. *"No one has an idea? Should I ask the teacher?"*
- Make sure your team cleans up by delegating tasks. You could say, *"I will put away the ________ while you _________ ."*

Facilitator: If your name comes second alphabetically:

- Start the team's discussion of similarities and differences by asking, *"What might we have in common?"*
- Keep everyone discussing each part together by asking questions such as, *"Does anyone have ideas for what makes us each unique or different?" "What else might we have in common?"*

Recorder/Reporter: If your name comes third alphabetically:

- When your team is called on, share your team's ideas and reasons with the class.
- Help the team agree on an idea: *"Do we agree that this would not be obvious to the rest of the class?"*

Task Manager: If your name comes fourth alphabetically:

- Remind the team to stay on task and not to talk to students in other teams. You can suggest, *"Let's move on to the next part of the problem."*
- Listen for reasons and ask your teammates to justify their thinking. *"Why do you think that?"* or *"Would this be obvious to the rest of the class?"*

1-2. WHAT DO THEY HAVE IN COMMON?

In mathematics, it is sometimes useful to make general statements about sets of objects. In this problem, you will be given a set of cards (from the Lesson 1.1.1C Resource Page) with mathematical objects or information on them. With your team:

- Determine what each set has in common.
- On your paper, record what is written on the cards.
- On your paper, add two new examples that would belong to the set.
- Describe in words what all of the objects or information on the set of cards have in common.

When you are finished with a set of cards, call the teacher to your team. Explain your generalization to the teacher and get another set of cards.

1-3. **Mathography:** A mathography is a lot like your life history, except that it is focused on mathematics in your life.

a. Write a letter about yourself to your teacher. The letter will help your teacher get to know you as an individual. The letter should talk about these three general topics: you, you as a student, and you as a math student.

Remember to use complete sentences and make sure that it is neat enough for your teacher to read it easily. Start the letter with "Dear...." Make sure you sign your letter. This assignment should take 15 to 20 minutes to complete. Parts (b), (c), and (d) below have suggestions for what to write about each of the three topics.

b. **You:** Introduce yourself using the name you like to be called. Describe your hobbies, talents, and interests. State your goals or dreams. What are you proud of? What else would you like to share?

c. **You as a Student:** State the importance of school in your life. Describe yourself as a student. What kinds of classroom activities do you excel at most? What kinds of activities do you find frustrating? Explain which subjects are your favorites. Tell why you like them. How often do you finish in-class assignments? How faithfully do you do your homework?

d. **You as a Math Student:** Describe your most memorable moment in math and explain why you remember it. State your favorite math topic and name your least favorite. Explain how you feel about math this year.

1-4. Decide what the shapes below have in common. Write your answer in a complete sentence. Then draw two more shapes that belong to the same set.

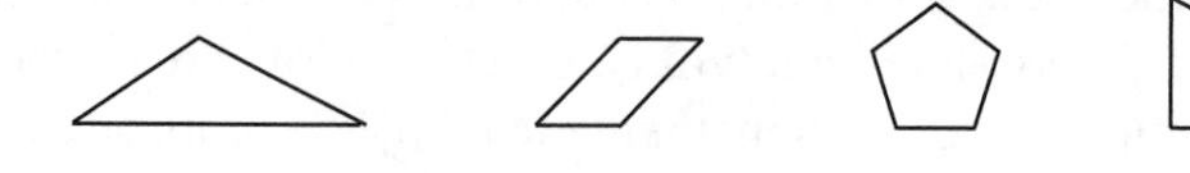

1-5. According to the diagrams below, how long is each unknown piece?

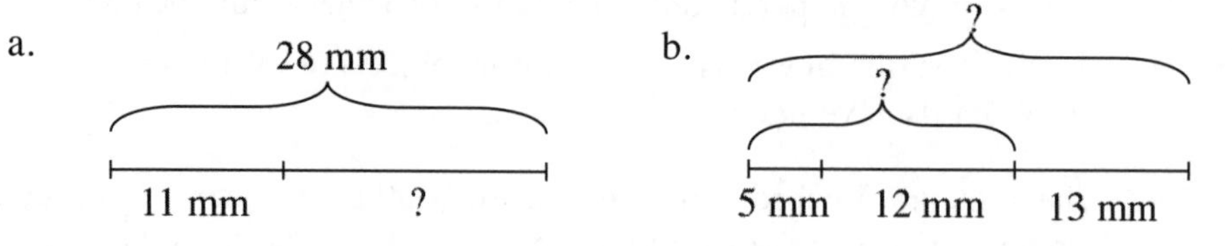

1-6. Refer to the number line shown below. List two situations or problems for which you have used a number line in the past.

–6 –5 –4 –3 –2 –1 0 1 2 3 4 5 6

1.1.2 What is the best strategy?

Analyzing a Game

Have you ever watched someone win a game again and again? Do you think that person just has good luck? In many cases, winners have strategies that increase their chances of winning. How can you develop a winning strategy? Today you will start to answer this question. Later in this course, you will learn more about analyzing a game.

Throughout this course, it will be important for you to describe and explain your ideas. In this lesson, you will play a game called Color-Rama. As you play, describe any patterns that you notice. Also explain your thinking about why certain choices might be better than others. Paying close attention to what is happening as you play can give you ideas for developing a winning strategy.

1-7. COLOR-RAMA

Your teacher will challenge your class to a game of Color-Rama! To play, a marker will be placed on the orange space on the board below. Your class will need to select *one* color for your class and *a different color* for your teacher. Then a volunteer will flip a coin three times. The coin has a "+" one side and a "–" on the other side. If the coin lands with the "+" showing, the marker will move one space to the right. If the "–" is showing, then the marker will move one space to the left. If the marker is on your class's color after three flips, your class wins. If it lands on a color no one picked, then no one wins. Which color do you think you should choose? Do you think that there is a way to predict which color the marker will land on after three moves?

Before you play, discuss the questions below with your team. When talking about strategies, be sure to describe your ideas and explain your reasoning. When your class has considered these questions, move on to problem 1-8.

Discussion Points

Does it matter which color is chosen?

Are all the colors equally likely to win? How can you decide?

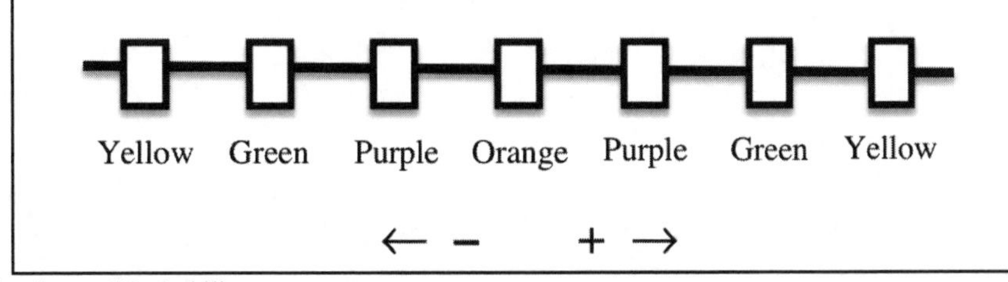

1-8. LEARNING MORE ABOUT THE GAME

Do you think one color is a better choice than the others if you want to win? Is there a color that you should not pick? One way to answer these questions is to play the game and keep track of what happens.

Your teacher will give you and a partner a Lesson 1.1.2A Resource Page and a coin with a "+" on one side and a "–" on the other side. You will need a small object such as an eraser or paper clip to use as a marker. Once you have all of your supplies, follow the directions below.

a. Play the game several times and be sure to select a different color each time. Keep track of which colors win and lose each time, not just which partner wins. What do you notice?

b. After you and your partner have played the game at least five times, join with another pair of students to form a team and discuss the following questions:

- Does the color you choose seem to affect your chances of winning?
- Is each color choice equally likely to result in a win? Explain why or why not in as many ways as you can.

c. Play the game a few more times. Do your results agree with your answers from part (b) above? Why do your results make sense?

1-9. PLAYING THE GAME

Now you get to play the game! As a class, choose two colors (one for your class, one for your teacher) that you think will improve the class's chance of winning.

a. Is there any color you could choose that would guarantee your winning the game every time you play? Explain why or why not.

b. Is there a color that would guarantee that you would *not* win? Explain why or why not.

1-10. In general, what makes a game fair? Discuss this question with your partner. Then think about whether there is a way to change the rules of Color-Rama to make it a fair game. Decide on any changes to the rules that you would recommend.

a. Play the game a few times with your new rules. Be prepared to describe the changes you made and explain your reasons for making the changes.

b. Is your new game fair? If not, could you make it fair? Work with your team to find a way to explain how you know your game is fair or why you cannot make it fair.

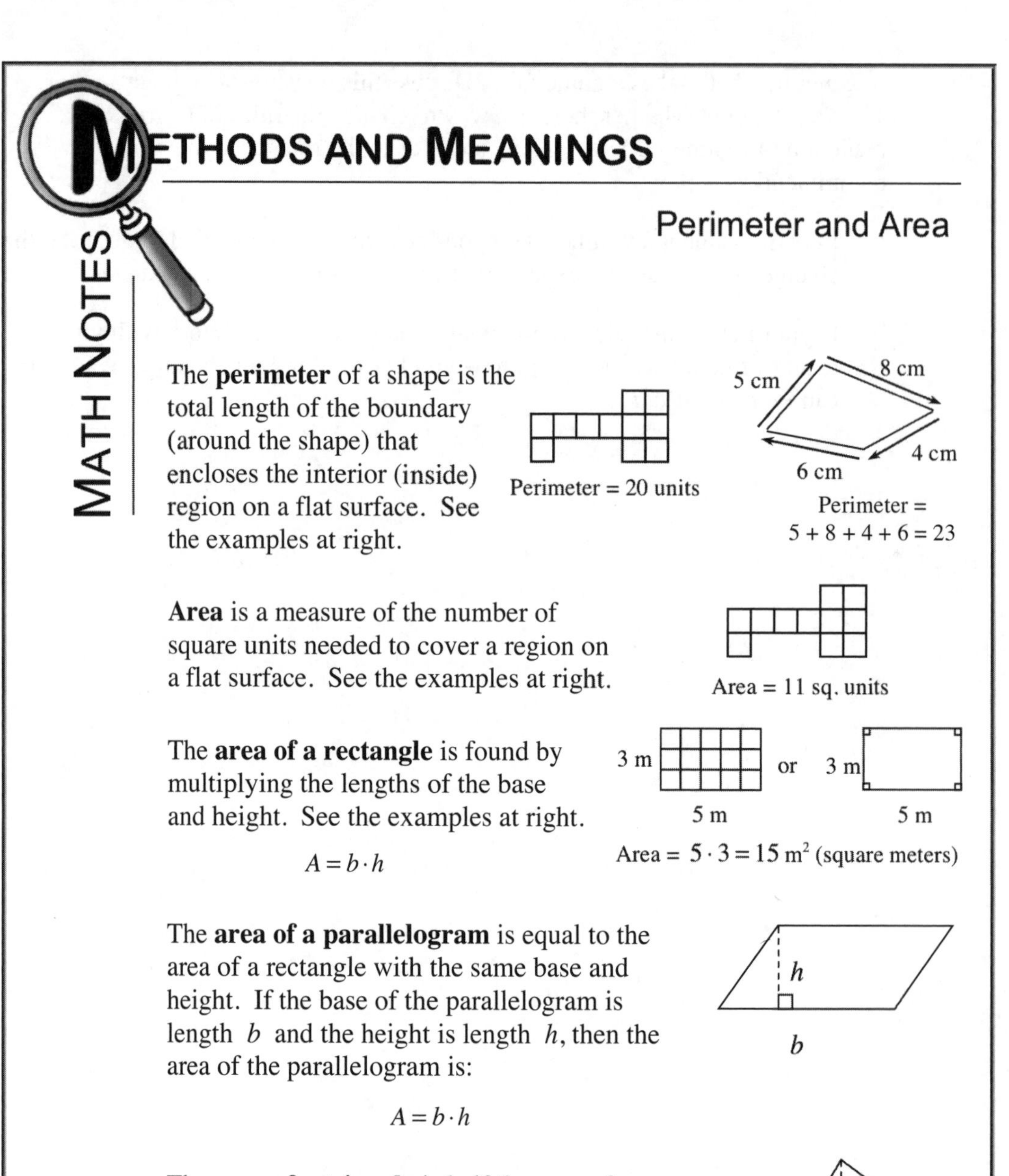

METHODS AND MEANINGS

MATH NOTES

Perimeter and Area

The **perimeter** of a shape is the total length of the boundary (around the shape) that encloses the interior (inside) region on a flat surface. See the examples at right.

Perimeter = 20 units

Perimeter = 5 + 8 + 4 + 6 = 23

Area is a measure of the number of square units needed to cover a region on a flat surface. See the examples at right.

Area = 11 sq. units

The **area of a rectangle** is found by multiplying the lengths of the base and height. See the examples at right.

$$A = b \cdot h$$

Area = $5 \cdot 3 = 15$ m^2 (square meters)

The **area of a parallelogram** is equal to the area of a rectangle with the same base and height. If the base of the parallelogram is length b and the height is length h, then the area of the parallelogram is:

$$A = b \cdot h$$

The **area of a triangle** is half the area of a parallelogram with the same base and height. If the base of the triangle is length b and the height length h, then the area of the triangle is:

$$A = \frac{1}{2} b \cdot h$$

Finally, the **area of a trapezoid** is found by averaging the two bases and multiplying by the height. If the trapezoid has bases b_1 and b_2 and height h, then the area is:

$$A = \frac{1}{2}(b_1 + b_2)h$$

1-11. Find the perimeter and area of each figure below. Review the Math Notes box in this lesson for help. Be sure to include the correct units in your answers.

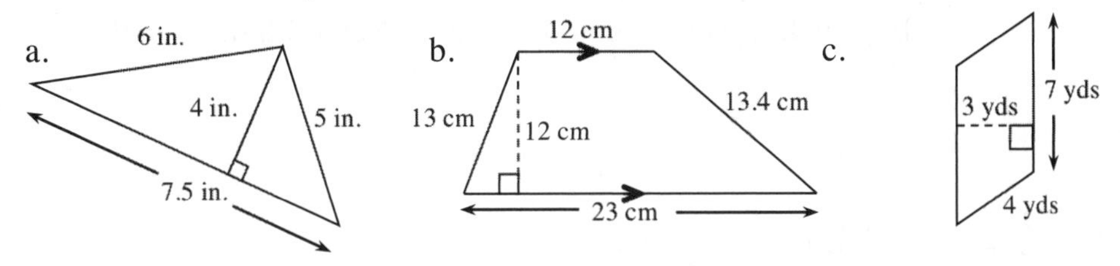

1-12. Think about games that you can remember playing with your friends or family.

a. Talk with your family and/or friends and list as many games as you can think of.

b. Label each game on your list as "fair," "unfair," or "I'm not sure." For any game that you think is unfair, write down your reasons.

1-13. For each of the following pairs of events, predict which is more likely to happen and explain your reasoning.

a. Event 1: You will win more than $1,000,000 in a lottery sometime in your life.
Event 2: You will learn to speak a language that you do not already know.

b. Event 1: Your classmates will all wear the same kind of shoes on the same day.
Event 2: Your classmates will all eat the same thing for lunch on the same day.

1-14. Copy the number line below onto your paper. Place a point on the number line and label the point for each of the following numbers: -4, 3, 0.5, -3.5, 0, 1, -2, 5.

−5 −4 −3 −2 −1 0 1 2 3 4 5

1-15. Maria was playing a game with her brother. She said, *"I'm thinking of a number. When you multiply my number by six and add seven, you get twenty-five. What is my number?"*

a. Find Maria's number.

b. Explain how you figured out your answer to Maria's number puzzle.

1.1.3 What is my number?

Finding Unknowns

Today you will think about how to find a mystery number based on information given to you as part of a game. In the game, you will practice mental-math computations and will investigate ways to represent different situations. When you solve the number-game puzzles, you also might use a skill called *reversing* your thinking. Reversing is an important way of thinking mathematically. It means solving problems both backward and forward. As you work with your team, ask each other these questions:

How can we represent it?

What is the best approach for this problem?

Have we found all of the answers?

1-16. GUESS MY NUMBER

Today you will play the "Guess My Number" game. A pencil and a piece of paper may come in handy as you play the game. Each game below gives clues to a mystery number. Your task has two parts. First, figure out what the number is. Second, explain why you think it is the mystery number.

Game #1: *When I triple my number and add five, I get eleven. What is my number?*

Game #2: *When I add two to my number and then multiply it by five, I get thirty. What is my number?*

Game #3: *When I take half of my number and add two, I get twenty-four. What is my number?*

Game #4: *When I double my number and add eight, I get my number plus twelve. What is my number?*

Game #5: *When I double my number, add four, and then subtract my number and subtract three, I get my number plus one. What is my number?*

1-17. Make up your own "Guess My Number" games with your team and be ready to share them with the class. Make at least one game that has only one answer. Also make one that works for all numbers. Can you create a game that does not work for any number?

MATH NOTES

METHODS AND MEANINGS

Mean

To understand a set of data, you often need to be able to describe the approximate "center" of that data. One way to do this is to find the **mean** of the data set, which is also called the **arithmetic average**.

To find the mean of a set of data, add the values of the data elements (numbers) and then divide by the number of items of data. The mean is a useful way to describe the data when the set of data does not contain **outliers**. Outliers are numbers that are much smaller or much larger than most of the other data in the set.

Suppose the following data set represents the number of home runs hit by the best seven players on a Major League Baseball team during one season:

16, 26, 21, 9, 13, 15, and 9.

The mean is $\frac{16+26+21+9+13+15+9}{7} = \frac{109}{7} \approx 15.57$.

This number shows that a typical player among the best seven home-run hitters on the team hits about 15 or 16 home runs each season.

1-18. Thu wants to play "Guess My Number." She states, "*When I triple my number and add five, I get twenty-six. What is my number?*" What is her number? Show how you know.

1-19. One of the ideas that you have explored in previous courses is how to describe a set of data. One of the ways that you may have seen before is finding an **average** (also called a **mean**). Read the Math Notes box for this lesson to review what a mean is and how to find it. Then find the mean for each set of data below.

a. Jane's quiz scores: 82, 64, 73, 91, 85

b. The number of cats your teammates have as pets: 0, 1, 3, 2

c. The number of minutes Pam talked on the phone: 35, 40, 12, 16, 25, 10

1-20. Julio is an architect who designs skyscrapers. Assume that each story (also called a "floor" or "layer") of a new building is 15 feet high as you help Julio answer the following questions.

a. How high would a two-story building be? What about a 10-story building? What about a 30-story building?

b. If Julio had to design the building to be 750 feet tall, how many stories should the building have?

1-21. Which is greater, $\frac{3}{4}$ or $\frac{11}{16}$? How can you be sure?

1-22. Find the perimeter and area of each figure below.

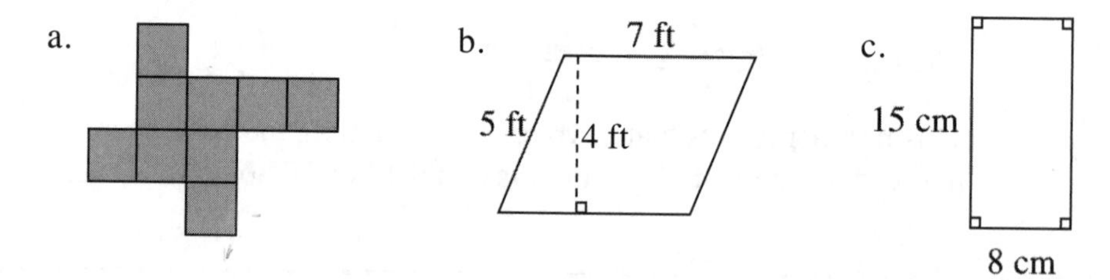

1.1.4 How big is a million?

Investigating a Proportional Relationship

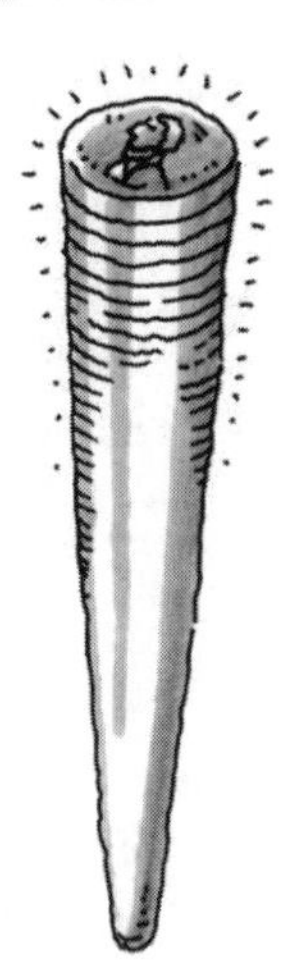

Can you imagine a tower built out of one million pennies? How tall would it be? In this lesson, you will work with your team to predict just how tall such a tower would be. To make sense of this question, you will measure some pennies and investigate the relationship between the height of a tower of pennies and the number of pennies in that tower. This is an example of a special relationship called a **proportional relationship**, which you will learn more about later in this course.

1-23. How tall would a tower of a million pennies be? Would it be taller than your school building? Would it be taller than Mount Everest? (Mount Everest is approximately 8848 meters or 29,029 feet high.)

Discuss these questions with your team and make a prediction. Record your prediction on the table provided by your teacher.

1-24. When you are working with your team to answer the "Penny Tower" questions, as well as other problems in this course, it is important to work effectively with other people. Effective math conversations are a valuable part of the learning process throughout this course. Choose a member of your team to read the "Collaborative Learning Expectations" below out loud.

COLLABORATIVE LEARNING EXPECTATIONS

Working with other students allows you to:

- Develop new ways of thinking about mathematics,
- Learn to communicate about math, and
- Understand ideas better by having to explain your thinking to others.

The following expectations will help you get the most out of working together.

T Together, work to answer questions.
E Explain and give reasons.
A Ask questions and share ideas.
M Members of your team are your first resource.
S Smarter together than apart.

1-25. TINY TOWERS

To begin to investigate this question, start by collecting data. Parts (a) and (b) will lead you through the data-collection process.

a. How many pennies does it take to build a tower that is one centimeter tall? Use the tools provided by your teacher to answer this question.

b. On your own paper, create a table like the one at right. Work with your team to complete the missing information. Be prepared to explain your reasoning to the class.

Height of Tower (cm)	# of Pennies
1	
2	
3	
4	
5	
…	
10	
…	
20	
…	
30	
…	
100	

1-26. THE HUNDRED-PENNY TOWER

"I have an idea!" Carol said. *"If I know how tall a tower of one hundred pennies would be, maybe that can help me figure out how tall a tower of one million pennies would be."*

a. Discuss this idea with your team. How could Carol's idea work?

b. Work with your team to figure out how tall a tower of one hundred pennies would be. Can you find more than one way to figure this out? Be sure that each member of your team is prepared to explain your team's reasoning to the class.

Height of Tower (cm)	# of Pennies
1	
2	
3	
4	
5	
…	…
	100

1-27. THE MILLION-PENNY TOWER

Now it is time to answer the big question: How tall would a tower of one million pennies be?

Your Task: Work with your team to calculate the height of a tower of one million pennies as accurately as you can. Can you find the height more than one way? Be prepared to explain your ideas to the class.

Discussion Points

Where would one million pennies belong in our table?

How can the height of the hundred-penny tower help us?

What is the relationship between the number of pennies and the height of the tower?

Further Guidance

1-28. Carol said, *"To use my hundred-penny height to find the height of one million pennies, I have to know how many hundreds are in one million."*

a. How many groups of 100 pennies are in 1000 pennies?

b. How many 1000s are in 1,000,000? How do you know?

c. Now work with your team to figure out how many towers of 100 pennies it would take to build a tower of 1,000,000 pennies. Be prepared to explain your reasoning to the class.

d. Use this result along with the height of a hundred-penny tower that you found in problem 1-27 to find the height of a tower of one million pennies.

1-29. Anouk was working with Carol. *"I have another way,"* she said. *"I can see in the table that the number of pennies is always seven times the number of centimeters. How can we reverse that to find the number of centimeters if we know the number of pennies?"*

a. Discuss Anouk's question with your team. How can you find the height of the tower if you know the number of pennies in it?

b. Find the height of a tower of 1,000,000 pennies using this method. Does it agree with the result you got in problem 1-28?

Further Guidance section ends here.

1-30. Anouk wants to compare the million-penny tower to the height of Mount Everest. She read on the Internet that Mount Everest is approximately 8848 meters tall. Her calculation for the height of the million-penny tower is in centimeters.

a. How can she change the units so that she can compare them? Discuss this with your team.

b. Compare your own calculation for the million-penny tower to the height of Mount Everest.

c. Look at the predictions made by your class at the beginning of this lesson and decide which team came closest to predicting the actual height.

1-31. How accurate is your result? Is there any reason to believe that there may be some amount of error in your calculation? How much do you think this error would matter? Be prepared to share your ideas with the class.

1-32. **Additional Challenge:** How many pennies would be in a tower that is 10 miles high?

1-33. **Additional Challenge:** The Taipei-101 is the second-tallest building in the world. There is a staircase up to the 91st floor with an average of 22 steps from one floor to the next.

a. How many steps would you have to climb to get from the 1st floor to the 91st floor?

b. When you are standing on the 91st floor, you are 1285 feet above the ground. How many stories are below you? About how many feet tall is each story of the building?

c. About how high is each step?

1-34. LEARNING LOG

Throughout this course, you will be asked to reflect about your understanding of mathematical concepts in a Learning Log. Your Learning Log will contain explanations and examples to help you remember what you have learned throughout the course. It is important to write each entry of the Learning Log in your own words so that later you can use your Learning Log as a resource to refresh your memory. Your teacher will tell you where to write your Learning Log entries. Remember to label each entry with a title and a date so that it can be referred to later.

For your first entry, consider what you know about proportional relationships. The relationship between the number of pennies in a stack and the height of that stack is an example of a proportional relationship. Talk with your team about how you can describe this relationship.

Then record your ideas in your Learning Log, using numbers, words, and tables to help show your thinking. Title this entry "Beginning to Think About Proportional Relationships" and label it with today's date.

METHODS AND MEANINGS

MATH NOTES

Median

The mean is a useful way to find the center when data values are close together or are evenly spaced. Another tool, the **median**, also locates the approximate "center" of a set of data in a different way.

The **median** is the middle number in a set of data *arranged numerically*. If there is an even number of values, the median is the mean of the two middle numbers. The median is more accurate than the mean as a way to find the center when there are outliers in the data set.

Suppose the following data set represents the number of home runs hit by the best seven players on a Major League Baseball team:

16, 26, 21, 9, 13, 15, and 9.

In this example, the median is 15. This is because when the data are arranged in order (9, 9, 13, 15, 16, 21, 26), the middle number is 15.

Mean and median are called **measures of central tendency** because they each describe the "center" of a set of data, but in different ways.

1-35. Read the Math Notes box for this lesson and review the information about how to find the median of a data set. Then find the median for Andy's test scores: 76, 84, 93, 67, 82, 87, and 76.

1-36. Use the fact that there are 12 inches in a foot to answer the questions below.

a. How many inches tall is a 7-foot basketball player?

b. If a yard is 3 feet long, how many inches are in a yard?

1-37. As you can tell from the examples of the number lines below, not all number lines change by one unit from mark to mark. Copy these number lines onto your paper and fill in the missing numbers.

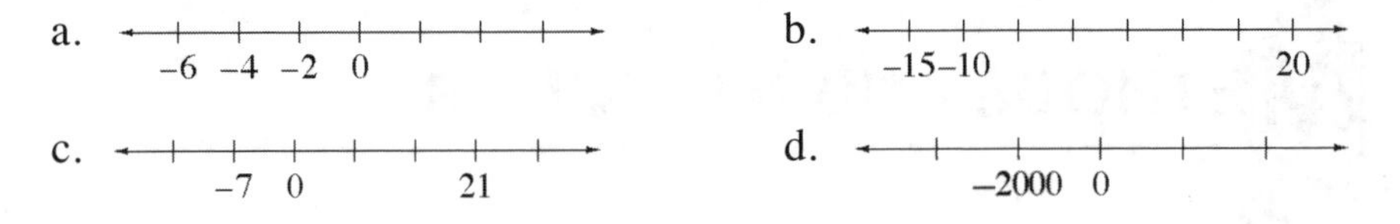

1-38. At the farmers' market, two pounds of peaches cost $4.20. How much will five pounds cost? Show all of your work or explain your reasoning.

1-39. Janice's mother gave her a ten-dollar bill to buy five pounds each of bananas and apples at the grocery store. When she got there, she found that bananas were 80¢ per pound and apples were $1.40 per pound.

Did Janice's mother give her enough money? If so, should she receive any change? If not, how much more money does she need? Show all of your work.

1.1.5 How can I rewrite it?

Investigating Number Patterns

In the past, you may have looked at number patterns to answer questions or to find the next part of a sequence. Have you ever taken a moment to consider how amazing the mathematics is in those patterns? Today you will investigate number patterns and learn about equivalent ways to write the same number. As a team, you will work to justify why two representations are the same and share your reasoning. In this course, you will often be asked to explain your reasons and justify your answers. When you are reasoning and justifying, you will focus on what makes a statement convincing or how you can explain your ideas. As you look at patterns today, ask your team these questions to help guide your conversations:

What can we predict about the next number in the pattern?

How can we justify our answer?

1-40. In this course, you will transition to using "x" as a variable, so this course will avoid using "x" as a multiplication sign. Instead, the symbol "$\cdot$" will be used to represent multiplication. Use a calculator to calculate the value of each expression below.

a. $1\cdot 8+1$

b. $12\cdot 8+2$

c. $123\cdot 8+3$

d. $1234\cdot 8+4$

e. What patterns do you see in parts (a) through (d) above? Discuss the patterns with your team. Be sure that when your team agrees on something, it is recorded on each person's paper.

f. Use the patterns you found to *predict* the next three expressions and their values. Do not calculate the answers yet. Instead, what do you *think* they will be?

g. Use your calculator to check the solution for each expression you wrote in part (f). Were your predictions correct? If not, look at the pattern again and figure out how it is changing.

1-41. Sometimes patterns are not created with addition and multiplication, but with the numbers themselves. For example, when the fractions in the sequence below are changed to decimals, an interesting pattern develops.

$$\frac{1}{9}, \frac{2}{9}, \frac{3}{9}, \text{ and } \frac{4}{9}$$

a. Use your calculator to change each of the fractions above to a decimal. Write each fraction and its equivalent decimal on your paper.

b. Decimals like 0.3333... and the others you found in part (a) are called **repeating decimals** because the digits continue infinitely. Instead of using "..." to show that the numbers repeat, mathematicians write a bar over the digits that repeat, like this: $0.\overline{3}$. It is standard to write the repeating digits just once. For example, $0.2222... = 0.\overline{2}$.

List the next five fractions in the sequence $\frac{1}{9}$, $\frac{2}{9}$, $\frac{3}{9}$, and $\frac{4}{9}$. Predict how they will look if they are rewritten as decimals.

c. Find the decimal equivalents of the five fractions you wrote in part (b) using your calculator. Do they match your predictions? Are there any that are different or that do not follow the pattern?

1-42. Are 0.999..., $0.\overline{9}$, and 1 equal? How do you know? Discuss this with the class and justify your response. Help others understand what you mean as you explain your thinking.

1-43. Decimal numbers that have only a finite number of digits such as 2.173 and 0.04 are called **terminating decimals**. Some fractions can be written as terminating decimals, such as the examples below.

$$\frac{1}{2} = 0.5 \qquad \frac{3}{4} = 0.75$$

Do the decimal equivalents of the numbers below terminate or repeat? Be ready to justify your answer.

a. 0.125 b. $0.\overline{6}$ c. $\frac{5}{6}$

d. 4 e. $\frac{2}{5}$ f. -0.33

1-44. Representing numbers in multiple ways can help to show what those numbers mean. In problem 1-41, you saw that the fraction $\frac{9}{9}$ (or 1) can be represented as the decimal $0.\overline{9}$, and it can also be represented geometrically with a diagram. Portions can also be represented in words, such as "nine ninths," and as **percents**, which are portions of 100. The diagram at right is called a "portions web."

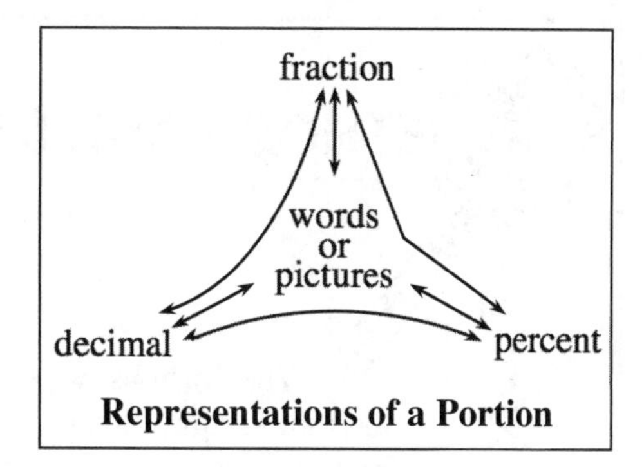

Representations of a Portion

Draw each of the portions webs below on your paper and complete them for the given fractions. In each part, determine if the decimal representation is terminating or repeating.

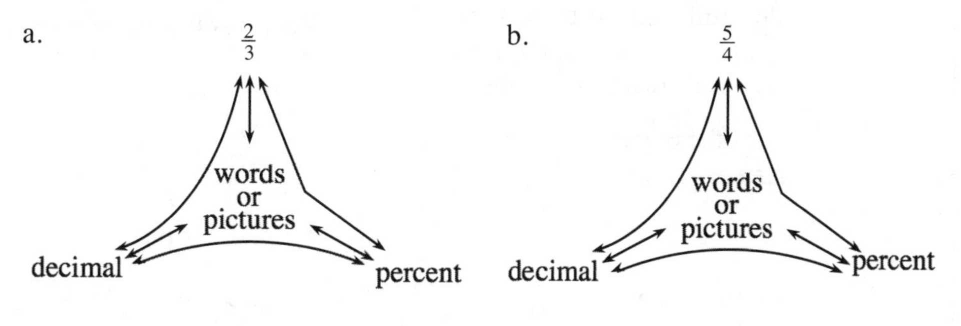

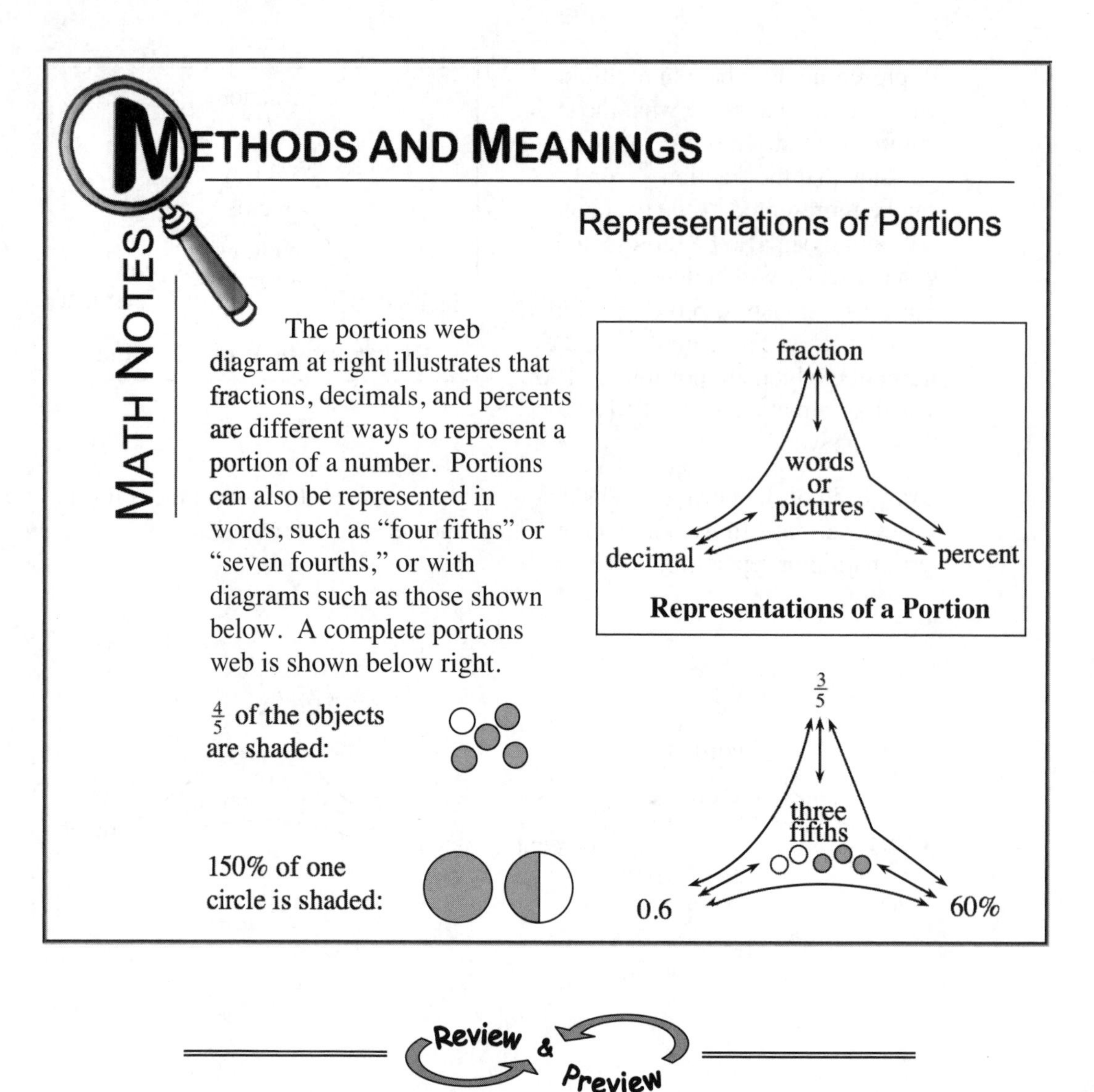

Methods and Meanings

MATH NOTES

Representations of Portions

The portions web diagram at right illustrates that fractions, decimals, and percents are different ways to represent a portion of a number. Portions can also be represented in words, such as "four fifths" or "seven fourths," or with diagrams such as those shown below. A complete portions web is shown below right.

Review & Preview

1-45. Copy the rows of equations below and write what you predict will be the next five rows in the sequence.

$1 \cdot 9 + 2 = 11$

$12 \cdot 9 + 3 = 111$

$123 \cdot 9 + 4 = 1111$

$1234 \cdot 9 + 5 = 11111$

a. What patterns do you see?
Write your answer in complete sentences.

b. Use a calculator to discover whether your predictions were correct. If they were not correct, look at the pattern again and figure out how it is changing.

1-46. Look at the representations shown in the Math Notes box for this lesson ("Representations of Portions"). Copy the diagrams below and write a fraction and a percent for the shaded portion of each one.

1-47. Represent each of the fractions below both with a diagram and with words.

a. $\frac{2}{3}$ b. $1\frac{1}{8}$ c. $\frac{6}{9}$

1-48. If five notebooks cost \$5.25, how much would three notebooks cost?

1-49. Find the perimeter and area of each figure below.

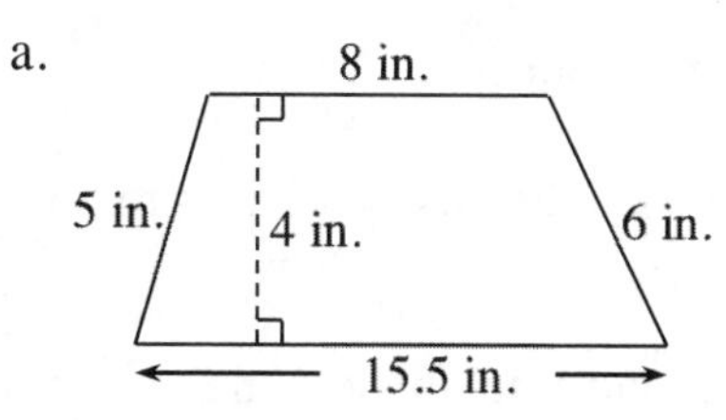

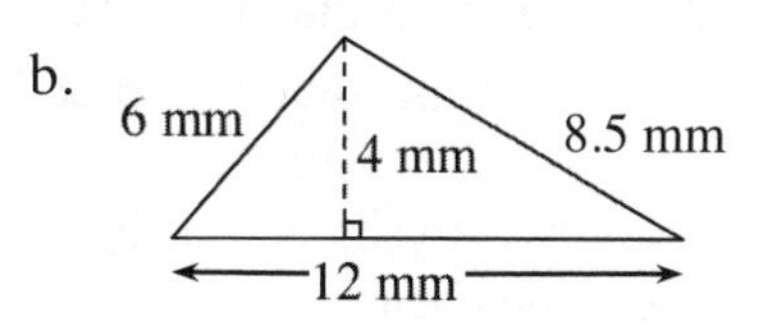

1.2.1 What are the chances?

Introduction to Probability

You have probably heard a weather forecaster say that the chance of rain tomorrow is 40%. Have you thought about what that means? Does it mean that it will rain tomorrow for sure? What is the chance that it will not rain? In today's lesson, you will investigate the chance, or the **probability**, of something happening or not happening. As you do the activities, ask your team these questions:

What is the probability that the event will occur?

How can we record that probability?

1-50. POSSIBLE OR IMPOSSIBLE?

With your team, make lists of three different types of events:

1. Events that you think are possible but not certain to happen.
2. Events that are certain to happen.
3. Events that would be impossible to happen.

Be ready to share your lists with the class. Then use your lists to complete the activities below.

a. Draw a line segment on your paper and label the left end "Impossible" and the right end "Certain."

b. At the "Impossible" end, write the events that your team decided could not happen. How could you label the possibility of these events occurring with a percentage?

c. At the "Certain" end, write the events your team has decided are certain to happen. How could you label the possibility of these events occurring with a percentage?

d. Along the line, write the events that you thought were possible. Place them along the line in order from closer to impossible, somewhere in the middle, or closer to certain.

1-51. GO FISH

Mike wants to win a giant stuffed animal at the carnival. He decided to play the "Go Fish" game, which has three prizes: a giant stuffed animal, a smaller stuffed animal, and a plastic kazoo.

The game is set up with a tank containing 1 green fish, 3 blue fish, and 6 yellow fish. To play, Mike must go fishing. The game is set up so that every time a player goes fishing, he or she will catch a fish.

To win the giant stuffed animal, Mike needs to catch a green fish.

a. If *all* of the fish in the tank are green, how would you describe the probability of Mike's winning a giant stuffed animal?

b. The way the tank is set up (with 1 green, 3 blue, and 6 yellow fish), what are the chances that Mike will catch a black fish?

c. Given the information in the problem, what percent of the time would you expect Mike to catch a green fish and win the giant stuffed animal? Be ready to explain your thinking.

1-52. In the game described in problem 1-51, you could expect Mike to win a giant stuffed animal 10% of the time. A percentage is one way to express the probability that a specific event will happen. You might also have said you expected Mike to win 1 out of every 10 attempts. So the **probability** that Mike will win is $\frac{1}{10}$, because the 1 represents the number of **desired outcomes** (*green* fish that Mike can catch) and the 10 represents the number of **possible outcomes** (*all* the fish that Mike could catch).

a. What is the probability that Mike will catch a blue fish? A yellow fish? Write each of these probabilities as a fraction and a percent.

b. Probabilities such as the ones you found in part (a) are called **theoretical probabilities** because they are calculated mathematically based on what is expected.

   What is the theoretical probability of getting a fish that is green, blue, *or* yellow (that is, a fish that is *any* of those three colors)? How do your answers for this problem compare to the probabilities you considered in problem 1-50?

1-53. BUILDING A FISH TANK

The managers of the carnival company have hired your team to help them redesign the "Go Fish" game. They want to control the probability for winning to be sure they make a profit. You can make decisions about the total number of fish in the tank and the colors of those fish to meet the carnival company's requirements.

Work with your team to decide how many fish of each color you could put in the tank so that the probability of catching a green fish will be each of the following numbers. Be ready to explain your thinking to the class.

a. $\frac{2}{7}$

b. $\frac{5}{7}$

c. $\frac{8}{7}$

d. $\frac{7}{7}$

1-54. SPINNERS – THEORY vs. REALITY, Part One

Your teacher will give your team a spinner. You will need to decide how to color the spinner so that it meets the following criteria.

40% should be red.

$\frac{1}{10}$ should be yellow.

30% should be blue.

The rest should be green.

a. Which color is the most likely result of a spin? How do you know?

b. Which color is the least likely result of a spin? How do you know?

c. Work with your team to determine the theoretical probability of the spinner landing on each of the four colors (red, yellow, blue, and green). Express your answers as fractions and percents.

d. What is the probability of the spinner landing on purple? Explain.

e. What is the probability of the spinner landing on either red or blue?

1-55. SPINNERS – THEORY vs. REALITY, Part Two

Now you will use your new spinner to do an investigation.

a. Each person in your team should spin the spinner 10 times while the other team members record the color resulting from each spin.

b. Write the number of times the spinner landed on each color as the numerator of a fraction with the total number of spins as the denominator.

c. Now combine your team's data with the results from the rest of your classmates. Use the class data to write similar fractions as you did in part (b) for each color.

d. Recall that the numbers you calculated in part (c) of problem 1-54 are theoretical probabilities, because you calculated these numbers (before actually spinning the spinner) to predict what you expected to happen. The numbers you found in your investigation (when you actually spun the spinner) are called **experimental probabilities**, because they are based on the results from an actual experiment or event. Both theoretical and experimental probabilities can be written as a percent, a fraction, or a decimal.

i. Does it make sense that the theoretical probabilities and the experimental probabilities you calculated for the spinner might be different? Explain.

ii. Does it make sense that the experimental probabilities that you found for the class are different from those found for just your team?

1-56. LEARNING LOG

Write a Learning Log entry that explains how to find the probability of an event. Describe the difference between experimental and theoretical probability. Be sure to use examples to make your points clear. Title this entry "Probability" and label it with today's date.

1-57. Joyce's dad packs her lunch and always packs a yogurt. Joyce knows that there are five yogurts in the refrigerator: one raspberry, two strawberry, one blueberry, and one vanilla. Her dad usually reaches into the refrigerator and randomly grabs a yogurt.

a. Which flavor is she most likely to have in her lunch today?

b. What are her chances of finding a vanilla yogurt in her lunch bag?

1-58. Copy the number line below and place the following probabilities on it.

a. A $\frac{1}{4}$ chance that you will be the team member who gets supplies tomorrow.

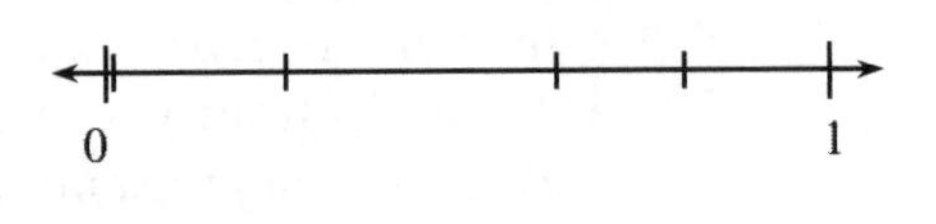

b. A 25% chance of snow tomorrow.

c. A 0.8 probability of eating vegetables with dinner.

d. $P(\text{blue marble}) = \frac{5}{8}$.

e. A 0.01 probability that it will be 85° on Saturday.

1-59. Write "theoretical" or "experimental" to describe the probabilities for each of the following situations.

a. The chance of getting tails when flipping a coin is $\frac{1}{2}$.

b. I flipped a coin eight times and got heads six times, so the probability is $\frac{6}{8}$.

c. My mom packed my lunch three of the past five days, so the probability that my mom will pack my lunch is $\frac{3}{5}$.

d. The chance of winning the state lottery is 1 in 98,000,000.

e. Based on mathematical models, the chance of rain today is 60%.

f. Lena got three hits in her last seven times at bat, so her chance of getting a hit is $\frac{3}{7}$.

1-60. FRACTIONS AND PERCENTS

Marianna represented several percents as portions of 100 in the pictures below.

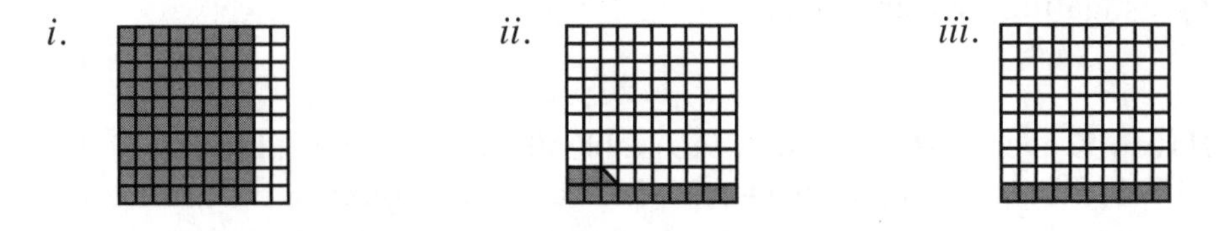

a. Write the percent represented in each picture.

b. Write the portion represented in each picture as a fraction in at least two different ways.

1-61. Find the mean and median for the lengths of the jumping frogs' bodies shown below (the length are in centimeters).

20.3, 12.5, 7.6, 13.9, 9.2, 21.7, 7.6, 17.5, 15.6, 14.1

1-62. Craig is practicing his baseball pitching. He kept track of the speed of each of his throws yesterday, and made the histogram at right.

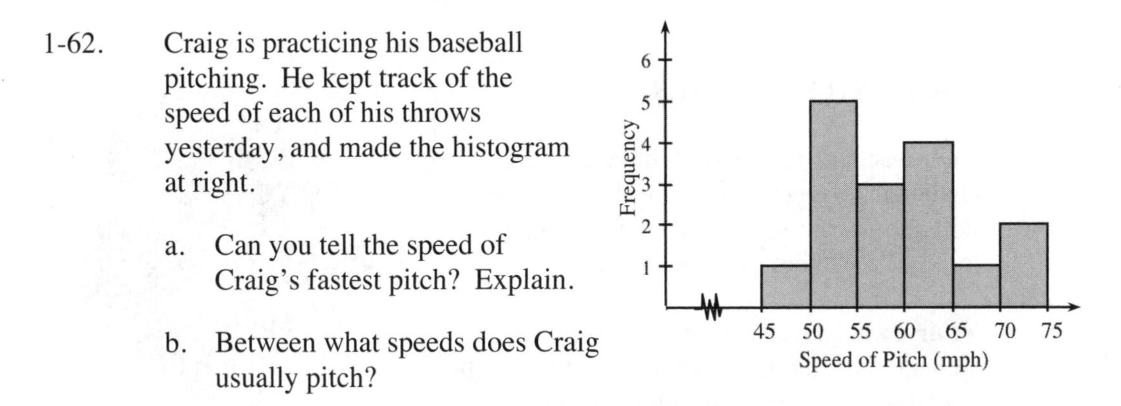

a. Can you tell the speed of Craig's fastest pitch? Explain.

b. Between what speeds does Craig usually pitch?

c. Based on this data, what is the probability that Craig will pitch the ball between 70 and 75 miles per hour?

1.2.2 How can I use probability to make predictions?

Investigating Probability

Have you ever tried to predict which football team will win a big game? If so, you probably did not just pick the team with the coolest colors or the neatest mascot. You may have based your pick on statistics about win-loss records, player injuries, and other data. Knowing what has happened in the past can sometimes help you predict what will happen in the future. In this lesson, you will use data to make predictions.

As you work with your team to uncover a mystery spinner, keep the questions below in mind.

What is the probability or likelihood?

What do we expect to happen?

How does the actual event compare to our prediction?

What can we know for sure?

1-63. THE MYSTERY SPINNER

Your teacher has a hidden spinner. Your challenge is to perform an experiment that will allow you to predict what the spinner looks like without ever seeing it.

Your Task: Your teacher will spin the spinner and announce each result. During the experiment, you will consider several questions about the results and about the hidden spinner. However, you will not be allowed to see it. Using the information you get, work with your team to figure out what the spinner looks like. When you think you know what it looks like, draw a diagram of the spinner.

1-64. Use the data you collected in problem 1-63 to answer the following questions.

a. Based on your data, how can you describe the likelihood of landing on each part of the spinner? How does the spinner that your team drew represent these likelihoods? Be prepared to share your ideas with the class.

b. Use your data to write the experimental probability of each of the following results as a fraction, a decimal, and a percent.

   i. The spinner lands on purple.

   ii. The spinner lands on green or orange.

c. If your teacher were to spin the spinner 15 more times, how might this change your answers for part (b)?

d. Do you know for sure that the spinner you drew in problem 1-63 looks exactly like your teacher's? Are you certain that the portions that you drew for each color are the same size as the portions on your teacher's spinner? Why or why not?

1-65. Now your teacher will reveal the mystery spinner.

a. How does your team's spinner compare to the actual spinner? Discuss the similarities and differences.

b. Do your spinner and your teacher's spinner show the same likelihood for each section being spun? Explain why or why not.

1-66. One way to compare your spinner and your teacher's spinner is to calculate the theoretical probability for each colored section of your teacher's spinner.

a. What are some reasons the experimental probability and the theoretical probability for any section of the spinner could be different?

b. Estimate the theoretical probability for getting each color on your teacher's spinner.

c. How do the experimental probabilities (based on your class data) and the theoretical probabilities (based on the actual spinner) compare? How do you think they would compare if there were twice as many spins made? What about three times as many spins?

Problem continues on next page. →

1-66. *Problem continued from previous page.*

d. If you were to spin the spinner the number of times listed below, how many times would you expect it to land on orange? Explain how you found your answers.

i. 6 times

ii. 48 times

e. Approximately how many times would you expect to land on orange if you were to spin 100 times?

1-67. Rachel and her little sister Christie often argue about who should wash the dishes at their house. Rachel suggests that they flip coins to solve their argument.

"Flipping a coin is fair, since heads and tails each have an equal chance of happening. Each one has a probability of $\frac{1}{2}$*,"* Rachel says. *"If the coin shows heads, then I do the dishes. If it shows tails, then you do them."*

a. Is this system fair? That is, does each girl have an equal likelihood of washing the dishes each day? What is the theoretical probability for heads? For tails?

b. Rachel and Christie flip a coin every evening for the first week. Christie has washed the dishes four times, and Rachel has washed the dishes three times. Christie tells Rachel that the system is not fair, because Christie has done the dishes more often than Rachel. Is Christie right?

c. After the second week of coin flipping, Christie has washed the dishes ten times and Rachel has washed the dishes four times. Now Christie is really upset at Rachel because she has washed the dishes so many times.

In light of this new information, do you think the system is fair or not fair? What would you recommend to Christie? Discuss your ideas with your team and be prepared to discuss this with the class.

1-68. Flipping a coin has a theoretical probability of $\frac{1}{2}$ for heads and $\frac{1}{2}$ for tails, unless the coin is "rigged." Over the course of a large number of flips, each of the two outcomes will be closer to the theoretical probability ($\frac{1}{2}$) than they will for a few flips. But is it possible to determine the theoretical probability in other situations?

You will think about theoretical probability more in parts (a) through (e) below. It will help you to know that a standard deck of 52 playing cards has four suits: spades and clubs, which are black, and hearts and diamonds, which are red. Each suit has 13 cards: cards numbered 2 through 10, three "face" cards (a jack, a queen, and a king), and an ace. It will also be helpful to know that a standard number cube, also called a die (plural: dice), has six sides. Each side has a different number of dots, 1 through 6.

Look at the situations below and decide with your team if you can find a theoretical probability for each one. If you decide that you can find the theoretical probability, then do so.

a. Picking an ace from a standard 52-card deck.

b. *Not* rolling a 3 on a standard number cube.

c. The chances of a thumbtack landing with its point up or on its side.

d. Getting the one red crayon from a set of eight different-color crayons.

e. The likelihood that you will run out of gas on a long car trip.

1-69. **Additional Challenge:** Three friends join together and form a club. They want to select one of themselves randomly to be the club's leader. Describe how they can do this fairly using only a coin.

MATH NOTES

METHODS AND MEANINGS

Scaling Axes

The numbers on each axis of a graph or a number line show the **scaling** of the axes. The difference between consecutive markings tells the size of the **interval**. When you scale each axis, you must use equal intervals to represent the data accurately. For example, an interval of 5 creates a scale numbered $-15, -10, -5, 0, 5, 10, 15$, etc. Unequal intervals distort the relationship in the data.

Notice on the graph at right that 80 marks the end of the *fourth* interval from zero on the horizontal axis. If you divide 80 years by 4 you can see that the length of an interval on this graph is 20.

$$80 \div 4 = 20$$

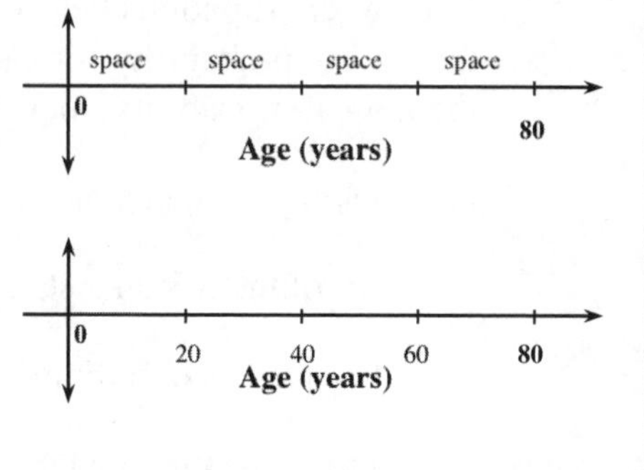

The second graph at right has each interval labeled. Labeling the graph this way is called "scaling the axis."

1-70. Imagine that you have a bag containing 10 marbles of different colors. You have drawn a marble, recorded its color, and replaced it fifty times, with the following results: 9 purple, 16 orange, 6 yellow, and 19 green marbles. Make a prediction for how many marbles of each color are in the bag. Show all of your work or explain your reasoning.

1-71. A fair number cube with the numbers 1, 2, 3, 4, 5, and 6 is rolled.

a. What is the probability of getting an even number?

b. What is the probability of getting a factor of 6?

1-72. Ramon is saving $7.75 per week to buy a new cell phone. The phone he wants costs $125.00. For how many weeks will he need to save his money? First, estimate your answer. Then figure out the actual number of weeks.

1-73. If 18 inches is equal to $1\frac{1}{2}$ feet, how many feet long is a 36-inch board? A 72-inch board? A 144-inch board?

1-74. Read this lesson's Math Notes box about scaling axes. Then, on your paper, copy the incomplete axes below and write the missing numbers on each one.

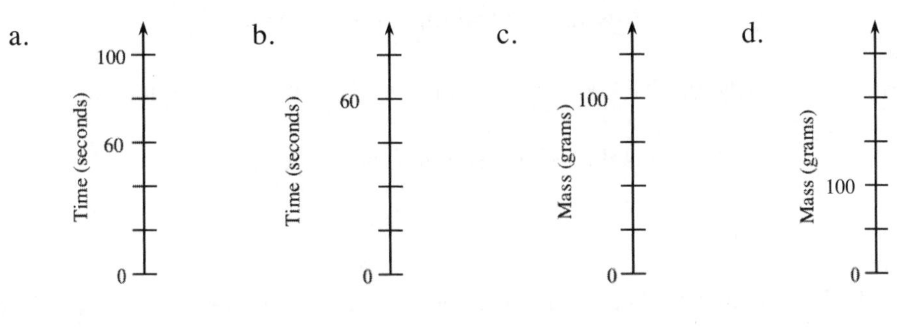

1.2.3 How can I change the chances?

Modifying the Sample Space

If you want to have the best chances of getting a red gumball from a gumball machine, is it better if the machine is full of gumballs or half empty? How do the chances of getting an ace in a deck of playing cards change if you have three or four decks of cards to choose from instead of only one deck? In this lesson, you will think about the size of the **sample space** (the collection of all possible outcomes of an event). Think about these questions as you work today:

How has the "whole" or total changed?

How has the "portion" or part we are interested in changed?

Has the event become more or less likely?

1-75. Your team will be given a bag containing a set of colored blocks or counters. Each team will receive a bag that is identical to yours.

a. Look at the blocks in your bag. If you were to reach into the bag and select one block without looking, what is the likelihood that it would be:

i. Red? *ii.* Green?

iii. Blue? *iv.* Orange?

b. Do your answers for part (a) represent theoretical or experimental probabilities? Justify your response.

1-76. If you were to select one block from the bag 12 times, replacing the block you drew between each selection, how many of those times would you expect to have selected a blue block? What if you drew 24 times? Discuss both situations with your team and explain your answers.

1-77. DOUBLING BAGS

Now imagine that you and another team have combined the blocks from both of your bags into one bag.

a. Do you think the larger sample space will change the likelihood of drawing blocks of different colors? Discuss this with your team and be ready to explain your ideas to the class.

b. Get a second bag of blocks from your teacher and combine the contents of both bags. How many total blocks are there in the bag now? How many are there of each color?

c. Work with your team to find the theoretical probability for selecting each color of block in the combined bags.

d. Has the probability for drawing each different-colored block changed? How do your answers for part (c) above compare to the theoretical probabilities that you calculated for the original bag in problem 1-75? With your team, make sense of how the probability for drawing a blue block compares before and after combining the bags.

e. If you were to make 12 draws from the combined bag, replacing the block between draws, how many times would you expect to draw a blue block? Explain why your answer makes sense.

1-78. In problems 1-75 through 1-77, even though you combined bags or changed the number of selections you made, the probability of drawing a blue block remained the same.

a. Do you think the probabilities would change if you combined three bags? Why or why not?

b. What change do you think you could make to increase the chances of choosing a blue block? Explain your reasoning.

1-79. **Additional Challenge:** Use the spinner from the Lesson 1.2.2 Resource Page (available from your teacher or www.cpm.org). Play a game with the spinner while keeping score as follows:

- Every time you spin purple, you lose two points.
- Every time you spin green, you get one point.
- Every time you spin orange, you get three points.

If you play this game for a long time, do you think it is more likely that you will end up with a positive score or a negative score? Make a prediction and then try it out. You may want to keep score with counters.

MATH NOTES

METHODS AND MEANINGS

Probability Vocabulary and Definitions

Outcome: Any possible or actual result of the action considered, such as rolling a 5 on a standard number cube or getting tails when flipping a coin.

Event: A desired (or successful) outcome or group of outcomes from an experiment, such as rolling an even number on a standard number cube.

Sample space: All possible outcomes of a situation. For example, the sample space for flipping a coin is heads and tails; rolling a standard number cube has six possible outcomes (1, 2, 3, 4, 5, and 6).

Probability: The likelihood that an event will occur. Probabilities may be written as fractions, decimals, or percents. An event that is guaranteed to happen has a probability of 1, or 100%. An event that has no chance of happening has a probability of 0, or 0%. Events that "might happen" have probabilities between 0 and 1 or between 0% and 100%. In general, the more likely an event is to happen, the greater its probability.

Experimental probability: The probability based on data collected in experiments.

$$\text{Experimental probability} = \frac{\text{number of successful outcomes in the experiment}}{\text{total number of outcomes in the experiment}}$$

Theoretical probability is a calculated probability based on the possible outcomes when they all have the same chance of occurring.

$$\text{Theoretical probability} = \frac{\text{number of successful outcomes (events)}}{\text{total number of possible outcomes}}$$

In the context of probability, "successful" usually means a desired or specified outcome (event), such as rolling a 2 on a number cube (probability of $\frac{1}{6}$). To calculate the probability of rolling a 2, first figure out how many possible outcomes there are. Since there are six faces on the number cube, the number of possible outcomes is 6. Of the six faces, only one of the faces has a 2 on it. Thus, to find the probability of rolling a 2, you would write:

$$P(2) = \frac{\text{number of ways to roll 2}}{\text{number of possible outcomes}} = \frac{1}{6}. \text{ or } 0.1\overline{6} \text{ .or approximately } 16.7\%$$

1-80. Tom keeps all of his favorite marbles in a special leather bag. Right now, five red marbles, four blue marbles, and three yellow marbles are in the bag.

a. If he randomly chooses one marble to give to a friend, what is the probability that it is blue?

b. Tom does not really want to give away blue marbles and would like to change the probability that he chooses a blue marble to $\frac{1}{10}$. How many marbles that are not blue could he add to the bag so that the probability of choosing a blue marble becomes $\frac{1}{10}$?

1-81. Your team is in charge of games at the CPM Amusement Park. One of the games involves a robotic arm that randomly grabs a stuffed animal out of a large bin. You need to set up the game so that the probability of a customer's grabbing a teddy bear is exactly $\frac{1}{2}$.

a. How would you set up the bin? Explain.

b. What if you returned to check on the bin and found that there were 4 teddy bears left and 12 other animals? What could you add to or remove from the bin to return the probability of selecting a teddy bear to $\frac{1}{2}$?

1-82. Write four different fractions that are equal to 1. Use your calculator to check that you are correct.

1-83. A rectangular park is 150 yards on one side and 125 yards on the other.

a. If Debbie walks around the park two times, how far does she walk? Sketch a figure and show your work.

b. If Debbie wanted to walk 1,000,000 yards, how many times would she have to walk around the park?

1-84. Find the perimeter and area of each figure below.

a.

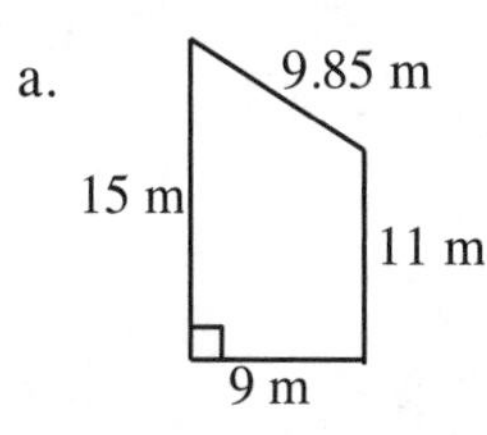

b.

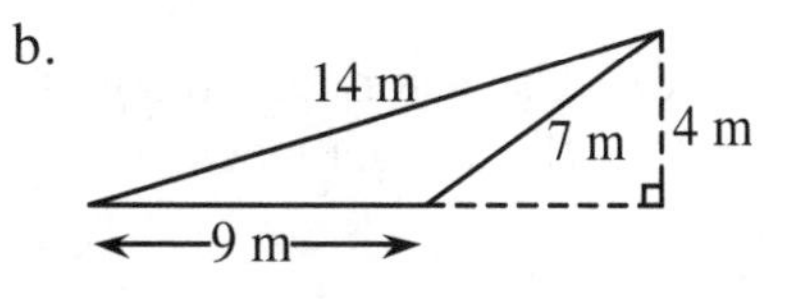

1.2.4 How can I change fractions to percents?

Expressing Fractions as Percents

In the last few lessons, you have been working with fractions and percents to represent probabilities. In this lesson, you will use geometric strategies to further your understanding of how to convert fractions to percents and to model the conversion. Learning the geometric strategies will give you a deeper conceptual knowledge of the connections between these different representations of portions.

1-85. After 25 flips of a fair coin, Lorraine and her partner recorded 14 heads ($\frac{14}{25}$ heads).

a. Is this more than, less than, or equal to 50%, the theoretical probability of flipping heads? Talk with your partner about how you know.

b. Percentages are one way to compare different portions of the total. If you have not already done so, work with your partner to calculate what percentage of Lorraine's flips were heads. Be prepared to share your strategy for finding the percentage with the class.

1-86. DaMarr also kept track of the number of heads he flipped. He wrote his experimental probability of flipping heads as the fraction $\frac{7}{20}$. He wants to rewrite $\frac{7}{20}$ as a percent. To do so, he knows that he needs to rewrite it as a portion of 100. He started by drawing the picture at right to represent $\frac{7}{20}$.

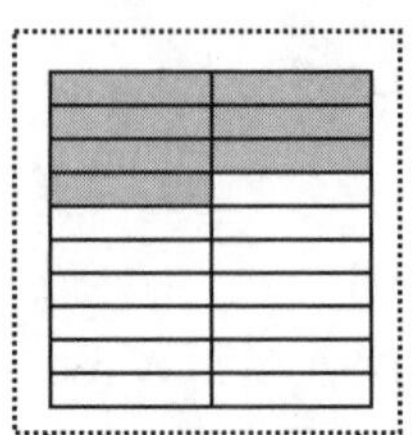

a. As he looked at his picture, DaMarr realized that he could adjust his drawing to show 100 parts instead of 20. DaMarr then drew a new diagram below his original picture. How many of the 100 parts are shaded? Explain your reasoning.

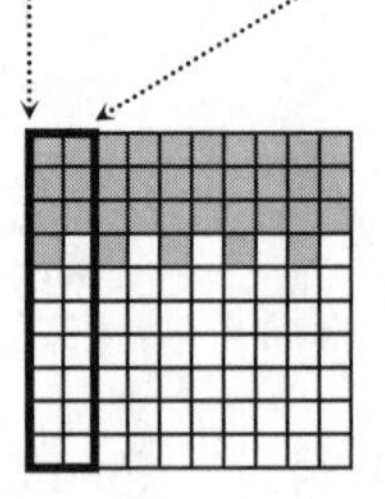

New diagram

b. Explain how DaMarr can use his new picture to write $\frac{7}{20}$ as a percent.

c. Use a similar strategy to rewrite $\frac{3}{10}$ as a percent. Show your steps.

1-87. Randy was playing "Double Heads," a game in which he would flip two coins at a time. He recorded the number of times he flipped two heads at the same time. He flipped the coins 50 times, and there were 20 times when both coins landed heads up, which he recorded as $\frac{20}{50}$.

a. How does $\frac{20}{50}$ compare to 50%?

b. Randy claims, "$\frac{20}{50}$ is equivalent to $\frac{70}{100}$ *because if I add 50 to the denominator to get 100 and add 50 to the numerator to get 70, the fraction becomes* $\frac{70}{100}$." Explain to Randy why $\frac{20}{50}$ and $\frac{70}{100}$ are not equivalent portions.

Note: This stoplight icon will appear periodically throughout the text. Problems with this icon display common errors that can be made. Be sure not to make the same mistakes yourself!

1-88. Three students invented a game in which they flip coins for one minute and then determine who flipped the highest percentage of heads. After their first round, each of them thinks that he or she was the winner of the game. Here is what they reported:

- *"I think I won,"* said Maria, *"Of my flips,* $\frac{12}{25}$ *were heads."*
- Autymn said, *"I flipped my coin 40 times and had a total of 18 heads. Since both of my numbers are larger than yours, I must have won."*
- Kumar reported, *"I recorded 44% of my flips as heads."*

Help the students determine their percentage of heads. Justify your answer.

1-89. Change the fractions to percents using a strategy of your choice.

a. $\frac{13}{20}$ b. $\frac{7}{10}$ c. $\frac{12}{25}$ d. $\frac{9}{30}$

1-90. Rewrite each fraction as a percent and each percent as a fraction. Show your thinking with pictures or labeled calculations.

a. $\frac{2}{5}$ b. 45% c. 120% d. $\frac{21}{40}$

1-91. Marissa is drawing coins from a bag that contains 5 pennies, 4 nickels, 5 dimes, and 2 quarters.

a. What is the probability that she will draw a nickel? Write your answer as a fraction, as a decimal, and as a percent.

b. If one penny, two dimes, and one quarter are added to the bag, what is the new probability that Marissa will draw a nickel? Write your answer as a fraction, as a decimal, and as a percent.

c. In which situation is it more likely that Marissa will draw a nickel?

1-92. Calculate the mean of each data set below. Can you find any shortcuts that allow you to find the mean without having to do much calculation?

a. 6, 10, 6, 10

b. 11, 12, 12, 13, 12

c. 0, 5, 4, 8, 0, 7

1-93. If five slices of pizza cost $5.50, how much do two slices cost? Ten slices? Half a slice?

1-94. Rewrite each expression as a single fraction.

a. $\frac{3}{8}-\frac{1}{6}$ b. $\frac{4}{5}+\frac{3}{5}$ c. $\frac{5}{9}-\frac{1}{5}$

1.2.5 How can I represent it?

Rewriting Fractions

When probabilities and portions are expressed as fractions, they can sometimes be difficult to compare. For example, is a $\frac{2}{5}$ probability of winning a game greater than a $\frac{3}{7}$ probability?

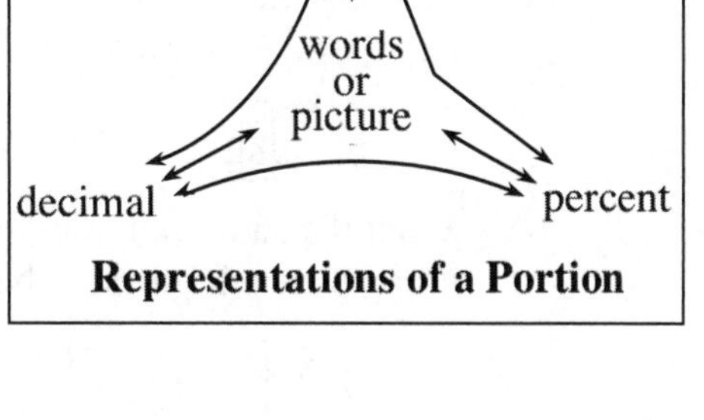

Representations of a Portion

In Lesson 1.1.5, you used different ways to represent a portion to help figure out whether $0.\overline{9}$ is equal to 1. In this lesson, you will develop strategies for rewriting fractions so you can compare different portions.

1-95. FRACTION TO PERCENT

Lila wants to rewrite $\frac{10}{25}$ as a percent. She decided to represent $\frac{10}{25}$ first in a picture.

a. How many sets of 25 will she need to make 100?

b. How many sets of shaded squares will she need? How many shaded squares is that in total?

c. Lila drew the picture below, and then she wrote the equation on the right to represent her work with the shapes.

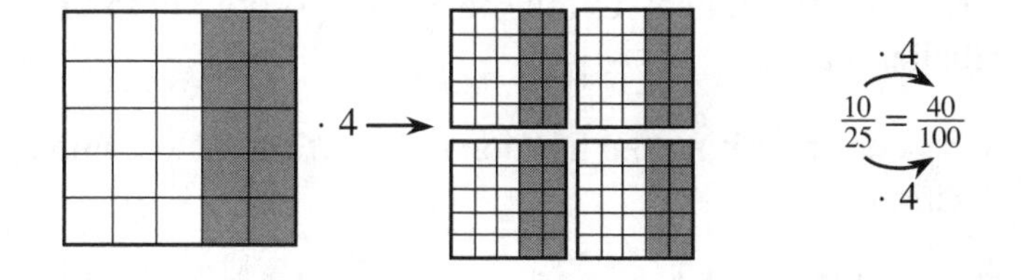

When Lila multiplies the number of shaded squares by 4 and the number of total squares by 4, does the amount of shading compared to the total squares change? Explain how you know.

1-96. Multiplying any number by 1 does not change the value of the number. This is called the **Identity Property of Multiplication**. When the numerator (top number) and denominator (bottom number) of a fraction are multiplied by the same number, some people like to say that the fraction is multiplied by a **Giant One**. For example:

$$\frac{10}{25} \cdot \frac{4}{4} = \frac{40}{100}$$

a. Why is the fraction $\frac{4}{4}$ called a Giant One?

b. Each fraction below is shown next to a Giant One. Multiply the expressions to rewrite each fraction.

i. $\frac{9}{25} \cdot \frac{6}{6}$ *ii.* $\frac{6}{15} \cdot \frac{3}{3}$

c. What if you do not know which numbers to use in a Giant One? Copy and complete each problem below on your paper.

i. $\frac{5}{7} \cdot \frac{\square}{\square} = \frac{40}{\square}$ *ii.* $\frac{5}{7} \cdot \frac{\square}{\square} = \frac{\square}{70}$

1-97. Deanna is trying to compare $\frac{3}{7}$ to $\frac{2}{5}$. She started by representing $\frac{3}{7}$ in a picture. Then she divided the picture into five horizontal rows to rewrite the portion as $\frac{15}{35}$. Here is her work so far:

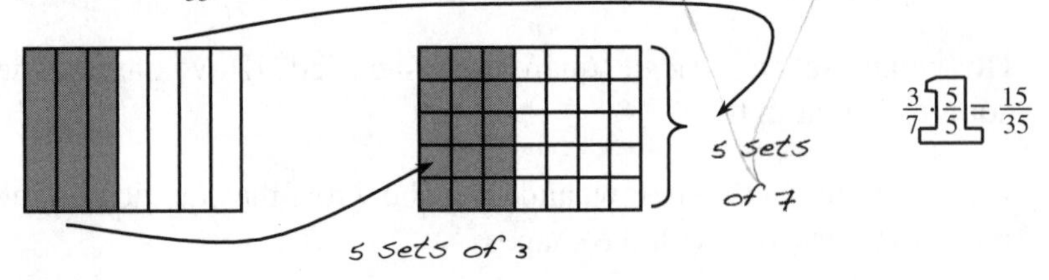

a. Use a similar strategy to rewrite $\frac{2}{5}$ as a portion of 35. Is $\frac{2}{5}$ bigger or smaller than $\frac{3}{7}$?

b. Why does rewriting the fractions make it easier to compare the two fractions?

c. Why did Deanna choose 35 for her new denominator? Could she have chosen a different number?

1-98. FAMILIES OF FRACTIONS

Using a Giant One, you can rewrite any fraction as a different fraction that represents the same portion of a whole. Fractions that are equal but that are written in different ways are called **equivalent fractions**.

For each fraction below, make three new fractions that are equivalent.

a. $\frac{7}{12}$ b. $\frac{3}{10}$ c. $\frac{9}{27}$

1-99. Adele, Karla, and Lisa are reading the same book. Each has read a different number of pages, as described below.

Adele has read $\frac{5}{8}$ of the book.

Karla has read $\frac{12}{16}$ of the book.

Lisa has read $\frac{13}{24}$ of the book.

Help them decide who has the most left to read.

a. What denominator could they use to compare the portions they have read?

b. Which girl has the largest part left to read? Justify your ideas.

c. How many pages could the book have? Be ready to explain your answer.

1-100. Use the Giant One to rewrite each fraction as a part of 100. Then write the equivalent percent.

a. $\frac{3}{4} \cdot \frac{\square}{\square} = \frac{\quad}{100}$ b. $\frac{42}{200} \cdot \frac{\square}{\square} = \frac{\quad}{100}$ c. $\frac{7}{16} \cdot \frac{\square}{\square} = \frac{\quad}{100}$

d. How do you decide which number to use in the Giant One?

1-101. Which of the events below is most likely to happen? Justify your answer by rewriting the portion in a different form. In each case, show your thinking with pictures or with labeled calculations.

a. A $\frac{4}{5}$ chance that the teacher will assign homework today.

b. A 78% chance of a thunderstorm tomorrow.

c. A $\frac{7}{10}$ probability of picking a green marble.

1-102. LEARNING LOG

Think about the methods you have for comparing two probabilities to decide which is greater. In your Learning Log, create an example and explain two different strategies for comparing probabilities. Title this entry "Comparing Probabilities" and label it with today's date.

MATH NOTES

METHODS AND MEANINGS

Multiplicative Identity

If any number or expression is multiplied by the number 1, the number or expression does not change. The number 1 is called the **multiplicative identity**. So, for any number x:

$$1 \cdot x = x \cdot 1 = x$$

One way the multiplicative identity is used is to create equivalent fractions using a Giant One.

$$\frac{2}{3} \cdot \frac{2}{2} = \frac{4}{6}$$

By multiplying a fraction by a fraction equivalent to 1, a new, equivalent fraction is created.

1-103. In problem 1-95, Lila rewrote $\frac{10}{25}$ as $\frac{40}{100}$ and represented it with the picture at right. Tony thinks this fraction is also equal to $\frac{2}{5}$.

a. Is Tony correct? Use the picture or calculations to explain your reasoning. Write your answer in complete sentences.

b. How could Tony write an equivalent (equal) fraction using tenths? That is, what fraction in the form $\frac{?}{10}$ can represent the diagram above?

1-104. Zaria wants you to solve this puzzle: *"I am thinking of a number. If you divide my number by 2 and subtract 4, you will get 2. What is my number?"* Show how you know your answer is correct.

1-105. Rewrite each fraction below as an equivalent fraction and as a percent.

a. $\frac{5}{20}$ b. $\frac{9}{25}$ c. $\frac{9}{6}$

1-106. Rewrite each expression as a single fraction.

a. $\frac{3}{8}+\frac{1}{8}$ b. $\frac{4}{5}+\frac{3}{4}$ c. $\frac{6}{7}-\frac{2}{5}$

1-107. What is the length of the marked portion of each line segment? Copy the segment onto your paper before finding the missing length. Assume that the entire line segment is subdivided into equal sections.

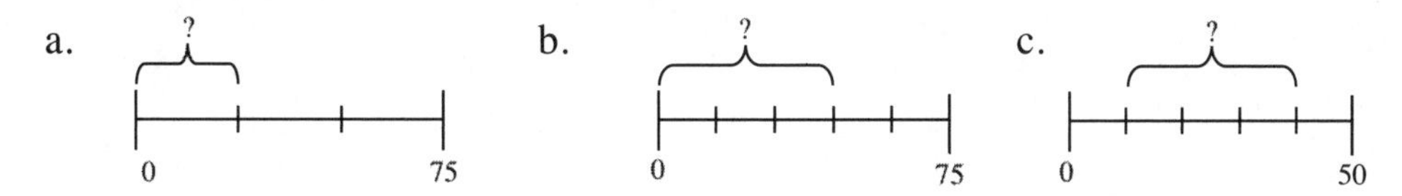

1.2.6 How do I add outcomes?

Fraction Addition

When finding probabilities, you often need to add fractions. Today you will investigate fraction addition.

1-108. Justin is working on a new problem: $\frac{1}{3}+\frac{1}{2}$. He drew the picture below to represent the problem.

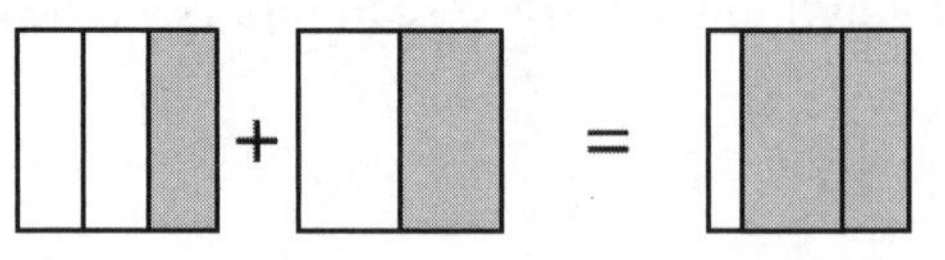

a. Could you name Justin's sum as a single fraction? Would he be correct to name it $\frac{2}{3}$?

b. Kermit sees Justin's work and says, *"You need to make all of the pieces the same size before you try to write the sum. You can use a Giant One to rewrite $\frac{1}{3}$ and $\frac{1}{2}$ each as sixths."* He writes:

$$\frac{1}{3} \cdot \boxed{\frac{}{}} = \frac{}{6} \qquad \frac{1}{2} \cdot \boxed{\frac{}{}} = \frac{}{6}$$

Finish Kermit's work to rewrite each fraction so that its denominator is 6.

c. What is the sum of the new fractions? Fix Justin's picture or draw a new diagram to explain why your answer makes sense.

d. Discuss with your team why Kermit might have chosen to rewrite each fraction as sixths. Could he have used a different number? Be ready to share your thinking.

1-109. Before you can write the sum of two fractions, they must be rewritten so that both wholes have an equal number of parts. In other words, they must be rewritten to have a **common denominator**.

Three students were adding the fractions $\frac{1}{4}+\frac{5}{12}$ below. They each found a different common denominator:

Lily:	Armando:	Josue:
$\frac{1}{4}+\frac{5}{12}$	$\frac{1}{4}+\frac{5}{12}$	$\frac{1}{4}+\frac{5}{12}$
$\frac{12}{48}+\frac{20}{48}$	$\frac{3}{12}+\frac{5}{12}$	$\frac{6}{24}+\frac{10}{24}$
$\frac{32}{48}$	$\frac{8}{12}$	$\frac{16}{24}$

a. Who is correct? Can any number be a common denominator? Explain your reasoning.

b. Which of their common denominators is easiest to work with? Why?

c. Find at least three different common denominators you could use to add $\frac{3}{10}+\frac{1}{5}$.

1-110. Vu needs to add $\frac{3}{8}+\frac{5}{6}$. He knows that he can rewrite each fraction as a portion of 48 because 6 and 8 are each factors of 48 in his multiplication table. *"Is there a smaller number that could work as a common denominator?"* he wonders.

a. Where can you look in the multiplication table to see if 6 and 8 are each factors of a number less than 48?

b. Use the multiplication table on the Lesson 1.2.6 Resource Page to find other number(s) you could use as a common denominator to add $\frac{3}{8}$ and $\frac{5}{6}$.

c. Vu's next problem is to add $\frac{5}{4}+\frac{7}{10}$. Use the multiplication table to find the smallest number you could use as a common denominator. This number is called the **lowest common denominator**. After you find the lowest common denominator for Vu's problem, find the sum.

	1	2	3	4	5	6	7	8	9	10
1	1	2	3	4	5	6	7	8	9	10
2	2	4	6	8	10	12	14	16	18	20
3	3	6	9	12	15	18	21	24	27	30
4	4	8	12	16	20	24	28	32	36	40
5	5	10	15	20	25	30	35	40	45	50
6	**6**	**12**	**18**	**24**	**30**	**36**	**42**	**(48)**	**54**	**60**
7	7	14	21	28	35	42	49	56	63	70
8	**8**	**16**	**24**	**32**	**40**	**(48)**	**56**	**64**	**72**	**80**
9	9	18	27	36	45	54	63	72	81	90
10	10	20	30	40	50	60	70	80	90	100

1-111. One study team is trying to find the sum $\frac{5}{6}+\frac{3}{4}+\frac{1}{5}$.

a. They first tried to use 24 as a common denominator. Why does 24 not work as a common denominator?

b. Find a common denominator for this problem and explain how you found it.

c. With your study team, describe how factors and multiples can help you find a common denominator.

1-112. With your team, find each sum. You may want to use the multiplication table to help you find common denominators.

a. $\frac{1}{4}+\frac{5}{6}$ b. $\frac{2}{7}+\frac{2}{3}$ c. $\frac{5}{12}+\frac{1}{2}$ d. $\frac{3}{4}+\frac{1}{2}+\frac{1}{5}$

1-113. THE POWER OF PRIME NUMBERS

Additional Challenge: A **prime number** is a number that has exactly two factors, namely, 1 and itself. Another way to explain this is that prime numbers can only be divided by themselves and by 1 without a remainder. (The only exception to this rule is the number 1, which is not prime.) Every number that is not prime can be rewritten as a product of **prime factors**. For example, $20=2\cdot2\cdot5$ or $36=2\cdot2\cdot3\cdot3$. Prime factors can also be used to build common denominators for fractions.

a. What are the prime factors of each denominator in the sum $\frac{5}{6}+\frac{3}{4}+\frac{1}{5}$ (from problem 1-111)?

b. What are the prime factors of the common denominator you found in part (b) of problem 1-111?

c. What do the lists of factors you made in parts (a) and (b) have in common?

d. How could the prime factors of each denominator in a pair of fractions help you find a common denominator for those fractions? Explain your thinking.

1-114. For each part below, find a Giant One that will multiply the fraction on the left side of the equation to create the equivalent fraction on the right side of the equation. Then complete any other missing information.

a. $\frac{5}{6} \cdot \frac{\ }{\ } = \frac{15}{\ }$

b. $\frac{\ }{3} \cdot \frac{\ }{\ } = \frac{4}{6}$

c. $\frac{\ }{2} \cdot \frac{\ }{\ } = \frac{8}{16}$

d. $\frac{\ }{4} \cdot \frac{\ }{\ } = \frac{6}{24}$

1-115. Fareed wants to add $\frac{1}{4} + \frac{5}{8}$.

a. Add the fractions by using a Giant One to create a common denominator.

b. How can factors help you find a common denominator?

1-116. Mario was visiting the carnival when he noticed a few number relationships. He made them into brainteasers for you.

a. If three tenths of the visitors were adults and there were 100 visitors, how many visitors were adults?

b. Five eighths of the prizes at the Giant Spin were dolls. If there were 64 prizes, how many prizes were *not* dolls?

1-117. Order these numbers from least to greatest:

$$\frac{1}{2} \quad 1.1 \quad \frac{5}{3} \quad 2 \quad 0 \quad 0.4 \quad -2 \quad \frac{5}{8}$$

1-118. Find each sum.

a. $\frac{3}{5} + \frac{1}{3}$

b. $\frac{5}{7} + \frac{1}{2}$

c. $\frac{1}{6} + \frac{2}{8}$

1.2.7 What if there are multiple outcomes?

Compound Probability

So far in this section, you have worked with probabilities involving one specific desired outcome. Now you will investigate probabilities of **compound events**. Compound events are events with combinations of outcomes. In today's lesson, you will find the probability that *either* one of the events *or* the other event occurs. (In Chapter 5, you will consider the probability that *both* one event *and* another event occur.)

Think about these questions as you work with your study team:

How is this probability related to the probability of a single event?

Either what event *or* what other event are we interested in?

Does our answer make sense?

1-119. Thomas helps around the house by doing one chore after school. Each day, Thomas and his aunt use the spinner at right to decide which chore he will do. Here is what Thomas knows:

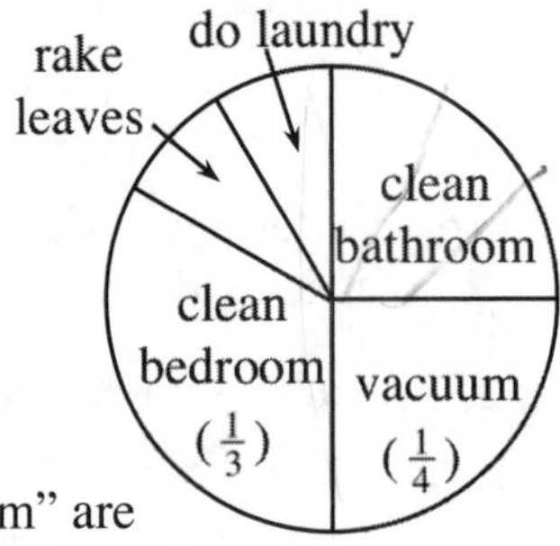

- The sections on the spinner for "rake leaves" and "do laundry" are the same size.
- The sections for "clean bathroom" and "vacuum" are equal in size and together make up half the spinner.

a. What is the probability that Thomas will spin "do laundry"?

b. Thomas hates to clean the bathroom. When he spins the spinner, what is the probability that it will not point to "clean bathroom"? Explain how you found your answer.

1-120. Thomas's aunt hopes that he will *either* spin "clean bedroom" *or* "rake leaves" today.

a. What is P(clean bedroom)? What is P(rake leaves)?

b. Spinning either chore in part (a) would make Thomas's aunt happy. With your study team, discuss the questions below and record your team's answers. Be sure to justify your conclusions.

- What is the probability that he will spin either one of the chores?
- How can you write the two outcomes as a single probability?

1-121. Ms. Nguyen lets her students borrow pens and pencils on days when they have a quiz. She has a paper bag containing hundreds of wooden pencils, mechanical pencils, and blue pens.

Stuart forgot his pencil, and it is quiz day! Ms. Nguyen tells him that one out of every three students who reaches into the bag pulls out a wooden pencil. Two out of every five students pull out a mechanical pencil. The rest of the students pull out a blue pen.

a. If Stuart reaches into the bag without looking, is it more likely that he will choose a wooden pencil or a mechanical pencil? Justify your thinking.

b. How can you describe the probability that Stuart will pull out some kind of pencil—*either* a wooden pencil *or* a mechanical pencil—by using the probabilities that you already know? Consider what you know about adding and subtracting fractions and see if you already have a strategy to write this probability as a single number.

1-122. Felicia was trying to find the probability that she would pull *either* a wooden pencil *or* a mechanical pencil out of Ms. Nguyen's bag from problem 1-121. *"I think I need to combine the probability that I will get a wooden pencil with the probability that I will get a mechanical pencil,"* she said. She set up this expression and drew a picture:

$\frac{1}{3}+\frac{2}{5}$

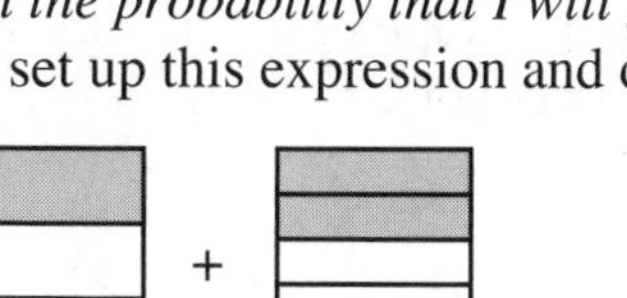

a. Felicia wondered if she could add the parts. Is the sum $\frac{3}{8}$? Why or why not?

b. Discuss with your team how Felicia could change the way she writes each fraction so that she can add them easily. Be ready to explain your reasoning. Then, find the sum.

1-123. Steve shuffles a standard deck of 52 playing cards and starts to turn them over one at a time. The first three cards he turns over are an ace, a 4, and a jack.

a. How many cards are left in the deck?

b. How many of the remaining cards are aces?

c. What is the probability that the fourth card will be an ace?

d. Instead of getting an ace, he gets a 2 as the fourth card. The fifth card is a 5. What is the probability that the next card will be a king?

1-124. What is the probability of getting either blue or green on a spinner that is $\frac{3}{10}$ green and $\frac{1}{5}$ blue? Show your work.

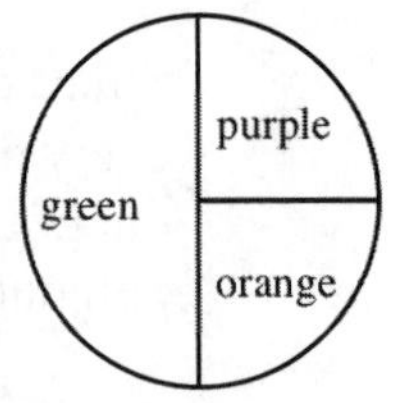

1-125. If you were to spin the spinner at right, what would be the probability of landing on green or purple? Explain how you know.

1-126. Find a value for x that will make each of the following equations true.

a. $x+8=21$ b. $x-32=55$ c. $3x=54$ d. $\frac{x}{5}=10$

1-127. Locate the coordinates of the three highlighted points on the graph of the triangle at right and write them as ordered pairs (x, y).

1-128. Draw an example of each of the following shapes. Refer to the glossary in the back of the book if you need help.

a. rectangle b. square c. parallelogram

d. trapezoid e. scalene triangle f. right triangle

1-129. Find the area and perimeter of each figure below.

a. 41 in., 36 in., 57 in.

b. 73 cm, 92 cm, 56 cm

1.2.8 What part is missing?

Subtracting Probabilities

In Lesson 1.2.7, you calculated probabilities for single events and combinations of events when *either* one outcome *or* the other is desirable. You have also compared those probabilities to decide which outcomes are most likely. In this lesson, you will work with your study team to apply your knowledge of fractions to represent and calculate the probabilities of a variety of events. As you work today, ask each other these questions to focus your discussion:

How can probabilities be combined?

How can the answer be rewritten in a different form?

1-130. Eustice is adding fractions. Here is his work:

$$\frac{1}{2}+\frac{2}{4}=\frac{3}{6}$$

a. How do you think Eustice got his answer? Does his answer make sense? Discuss Eustice's work with your team. Then explain your reasoning on your paper with diagrams and words.

b. Help Eustice find the correct answer.

1-131. Lindsay has a paper bag full of Fruiti Tutti Chews in three different fruit flavors. She says, *"If you reach into the bag, you have a $\frac{1}{3}$ chance of pulling out a Killer Kiwi. There is a $\frac{3}{5}$ chance that you will get Crazy Coconut."*

a. If you reach into the bag, what is P(coconut or kiwi)?

b. Does there have to be another flavor in the bag? How can you tell? If so, assuming that there is only one other flavor, what is the probability of getting that flavor?

c. How many candies might Lindsay have in the bag? Is there more than one possibility? Assume that all candies in the bag are whole candies.

1-132. Lyle asked for a challenge problem, and his teacher gave him this one:

There is a $\frac{2}{7}$ chance of drawing a red marble out of a bag of marbles. If the probability of drawing a red or a blue marble is $\frac{2}{3}$, what is the probability of drawing a blue marble?

When Lyle's teammates saw the challenge he was working on, they each had a different idea for how he should start.

- Mayra suggested that he start by rewriting $\frac{2}{3}$ and $\frac{2}{7}$ so that they have a common denominator.
- Kenessa disagreed. *"You want to set up a subtraction problem,"* she said. She wrote the expression $\frac{2}{3}-\frac{2}{7}$ to show the number Lyle needs to find.
- Darren had a different idea. *"The probability that you would draw either red or blue is the same as the probability of drawing red added to the probability of drawing blue,"* he said. He wrote this equation:

$$\frac{2}{7}+?=\frac{2}{3}$$

a. Which way would you suggest to Lyle as he starts working to find P(blue)?

- Discuss your ideas with your study team.
- Write a clear explanation of which method you recommend and why.
- Include your ideas about whether the other strategies will solve the problem and why you did not choose them.

b. What is the probability of drawing a blue marble? Explain your reasoning.

1-133. Louise is playing a game, but the spinner is incomplete. Each section of the spinner is labeled with the probability of spinning it. What fraction is missing?

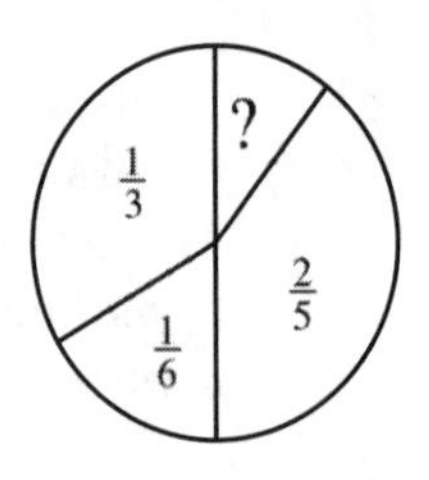

1-134. Charles found a spinner his teacher was making. He knew that if he put his problem-solving skills to use, he would be able to figure out the missing piece and finish the spinner for his teacher.

a. Write an expression for the problem Charles needs to solve. Is there more than one way to do this?

b. Find the solution.

1-135. Work with your study team to invent two new spinners with missing parts, like the spinners in problems 1-133 and 1-134. Then:

- Find the missing piece on your own paper.
- On a new sheet of paper, draw and label your spinner.
- Trade problems with another study team and find the missing parts of their spinners while they find yours.

1-136. LEARNING LOG

In your Learning Log, describe the process you use to add or subtract fractions when the probabilities have different denominators. Create an example and show your solution with pictures and number expressions. Then answer these questions:

- How do you rewrite the fractions to represent pieces that are the same size?
- How do you identify what common denominator to use?

Label these notes "Adding Probabilities with Unlike Denominators" and include today's date.

METHODS AND MEANINGS

MATH NOTES

Equivalent Fractions

Fractions that are equal, but written in different forms, are called **equivalent fractions**. Rewriting a fraction in an equivalent form is useful when you want to compare two fractions or when you want to combine portions that are divided into pieces of different sizes.

A Giant One is a useful tool to create an equivalent fraction. To rewrite a fraction in a different form, multiply the original fraction by a fraction equivalent to 1. For example:

$$\frac{2}{3} \cdot \frac{4}{4} = \frac{2 \cdot 4}{3 \cdot 4} = \frac{8}{12}$$

A picture can also demonstrate that these two fractions are equivalent:

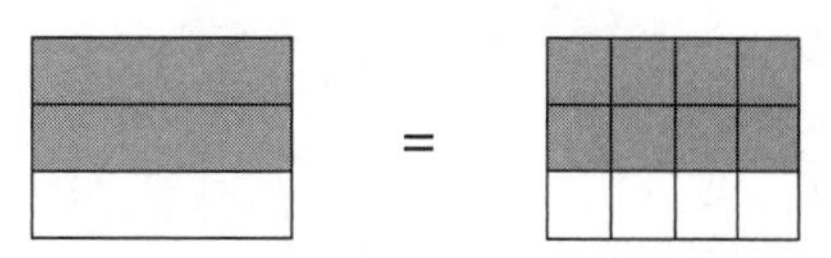

Review & Preview

1-137. Rewrite each fraction below in at least two different ways.

a. $\frac{6}{9}$ b. $\frac{11}{12}$ c. $\frac{3}{8}$ d. $\frac{10}{7}$

1-138. Jonathan measured 2 cups of flour into a bowl on the counter. Then he spilled part of it, and now there is only $\frac{3}{8}$ cup left. How much did he spill?

1-139. Maggie is making muffins with a recipe that yields 18 muffins.

a. There are 12 people in Maggie's book club. If the muffins are divided evenly among each person, how much will each person get? Explain your thinking.

b. If Maggie wanted to divide the muffins evenly between the 36 students in her class, how much muffin would each person get? Explain your thinking.

1-140. **Multiple Choice:** If the probability of getting a particular result in an experiment is 75.3%, what is the probability of *not* getting that result? Explain your choice.

A. $75.3\% + 100\%$ B. $75.3\% - 100\%$

C. $100\% - 75.3\%$ D. $\frac{1}{75.3\%}$

1-141. Throughout this book, key problems have been selected as "checkpoints." Each checkpoint problem is marked with an icon like the one at left. These checkpoint problems are provided so that you can check to be sure you are building skills at the expected level. When you have trouble with checkpoint problems, refer to the review materials and practice problems that are available in the "Checkpoint Materials" section at the back of your book.

This problem is a checkpoint for area and perimeter of polygons. It will be referred to as Checkpoint 1.

For each figure below, find the area and the perimeter.

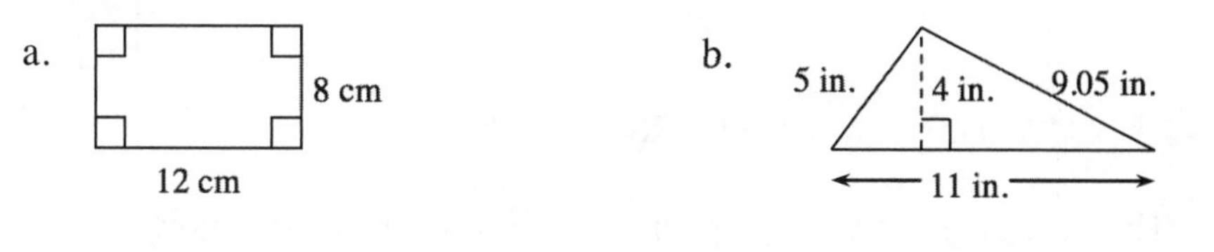

c. Parallelogram

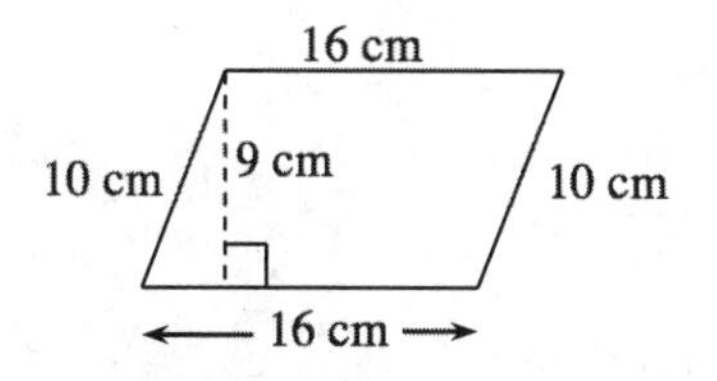

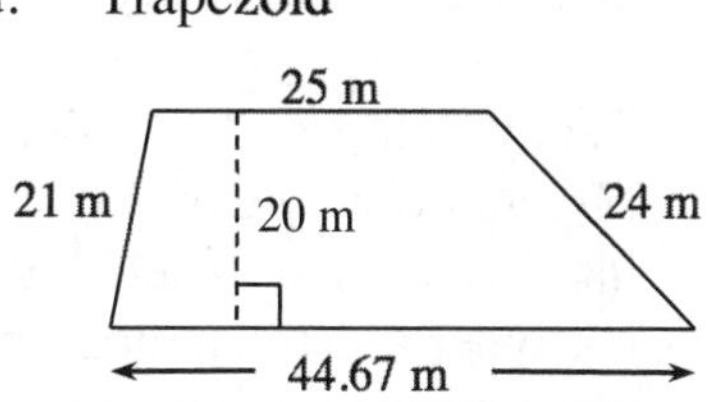

Check your answers by referring to the Checkpoint 1 materials located at the back of your book.

Ideally, at this point you are comfortable working with these types of problems and can solve them correctly. If you feel that you need more confidence when solving these types of problems, then review the Checkpoint 1 materials and try the practice problems provided. From this point on, you will be expected to do problems like these correctly and with confidence.

Chapter 1 Closure What have I learned?

Reflection and Synthesis

The activities below offer you a chance to reflect about what you have learned during this chapter. As you work, look for concepts that you feel very comfortable with, ideas that you would like to learn more about, and topics you need more help with.

① SUMMARIZING MY UNDERSTANDING

This section gives you an opportunity to show what you know about the main math ideas in this chapter.

Candy Callipso, the CEO of the Moon & Mercury Candy Company, has a crisis! She has hired your team to help her solve a problem. A customer ordered a thousand bubblegum machines and specified that each one should have a probability of exactly $\frac{1}{3}$ for getting a blue gumball. The bubblegum machines were created and sent out, but the customer has called, claiming that the machines were filled incorrectly. Candy's records show that each machine was filled with 4 yellow gumballs, 8 red gumballs, 16 green gumballs, and 20 blue gumballs.

Your Task: Work with your team to:

- Figure out whether the machines meet the customer's requirements.
    - If they do, find *at least two* other combinations of gumballs that would satisfy the picky customer.
    - If they do not, find *at least two* ways to adjust the contents of the machines so that the probability of getting a blue gumball is exactly $\frac{1}{3}$.
- Prepare a poster to report to Candy each of your proposed solutions. Be sure to explain how you know each solution will work.

② WHAT HAVE I LEARNED?

Doing the problems in this section will help you to evaluate which types of problems you feel comfortable with and which ones you need more help with.

Solve each problem as completely as you can. The table at the end of this closure section provides answers to these problems. It also tells you where you can find additional help and where to find practice problems like them.

CL 1-142. Vanson has a bunch of boxes that are all the same. He stacked four boxes, measured the stack, and found that it was three feet high.

a. How high will a stack of 20 of these boxes be?

b. The ceiling in the room where Vanson is working is just a little more than 9 feet high. He wants to stack boxes from the floor to the ceiling. How many boxes will fit in one stack?

CL 1-143. Find the perimeter and area of Jacob's swimming pool shown in the diagram below. Be sure to show all of your work.

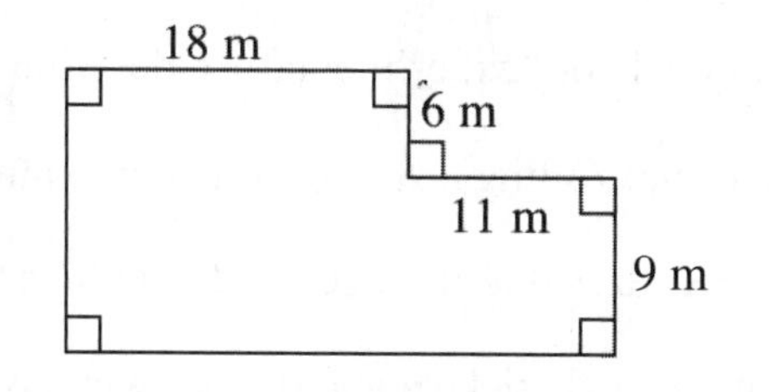

CL 1-144. Tuan is playing a game, but the spinner is incomplete. If the numbers in the sections of the spinner represent the probabilities of spinning each section, help him figure out the fraction for the missing section of the spinner.

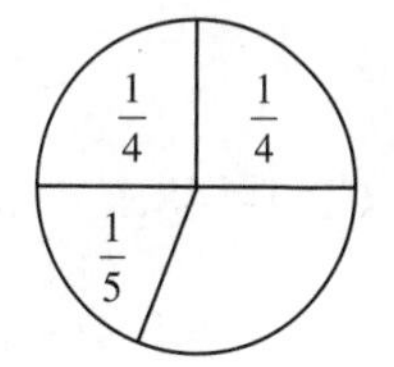

CL 1-145. Complete each portions web.

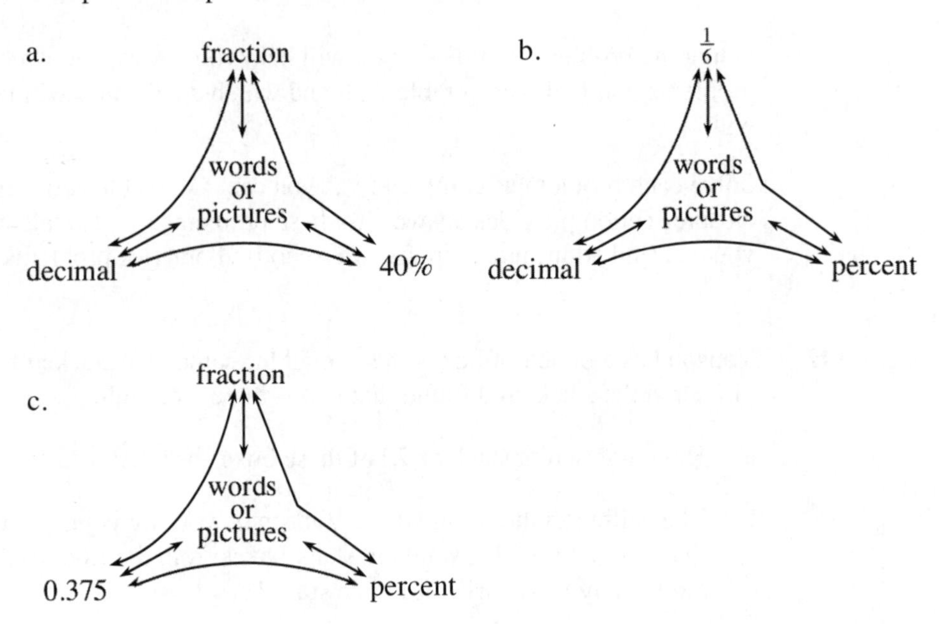

CL 1-146. Add $\frac{1}{6} + \frac{1}{2}$. Show all of your steps.

CL 1-147. Write "theoretical" or "experimental" to describe the following situations.

a. The chance of rolling a sum of 3 with two number cubes is $\frac{1}{18}$.

b. I drew five cards out of a deck and got clubs three times.

c. I bought six raffle tickets and did not win anything.

d. Based on a mathematical model, the chance of a flood next year is 1.2%.

CL 1-148. The county-fair prize wheel has equally spaced sections with the following colors: one is golden, two are silver, three are green, four are blue, six are red, and nine are yellow.

a. What is the probability of landing on gold? Give your answer as a fraction and as a percent.

b. If the probability of landing on yellow is 36%, what is the probability of not landing on yellow?

c. If the wheel is spun 100 times, how many times would you expect to land on silver?

CL 1-149. Kimberly is playing "Guess My Number." Her clue is, "*When I triple my number and subtract 7, I get 83.*" Find Kimberly's number and explain how you know your answer is correct.

CL 1-150. For each of the problems above, do the following:

- Draw a bar or number line that represents 0 to 10.

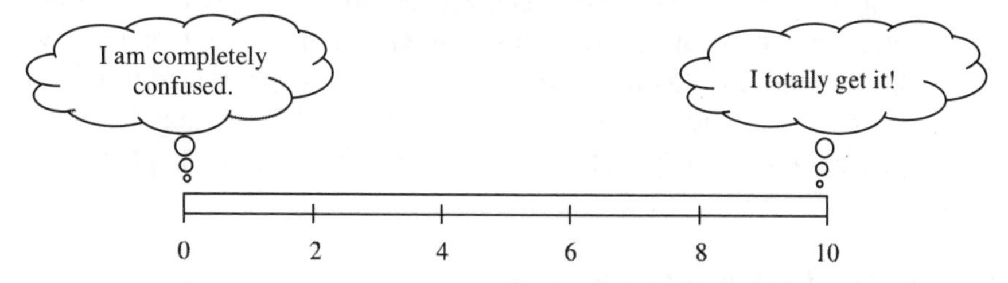

- Color or shade in a portion of the bar that represents your level of understanding and comfort with completing that problem on your own.

If any of your bars are less than a 5, choose *one* of those problems and complete one of the following tasks:

- Write two questions that you would like to ask about that problem.
- Brainstorm two things that you DO know about that type of problem.

If all of your bars are a 5 or above, choose *one* of those problems and do one of these tasks:

- Write two questions you might ask or hints you might give to a student who was stuck on the problem.
- Make a new problem that is similar and more challenging than that problem and solve it.

③ WHAT TOOLS CAN I USE?

You have several tools and references available to help support your learning: your teacher, your study team, your math book, and your Toolkit, to name only a few. At the end of each chapter, you will have an opportunity to review your Toolkit for completeness. You will also revise or update it to reflect your current understanding of big ideas.

The main elements of your Toolkit should be your Learning Logs, Math Notes, and the vocabulary used in this chapter. Math words that are new appear in bold in the text. Refer to the lists provided below and follow your teacher's instructions to revise your Toolkit, which will help make it useful for you as you complete this chapter and as you work in future chapters.

Learning Log Entries

- Lesson 1.1.4 – Beginning to Think About Proportional Relationships
- Lesson 1.2.1 – Probability
- Lesson 1.2.5 – Comparing Probabilities
- Lesson 1.2.8 – Adding Probabilities with Unlike Denominators

Math Notes

- Lesson 1.1.2 – Perimeter and Area
- Lesson 1.1.3 – Mean
- Lesson 1.1.4 – Median
- Lesson 1.1.5 – Representations of Portions
- Lesson 1.2.2 – Scaling Axes
- Lesson 1.2.3 – Probability Vocabulary and Definitions
- Lesson 1.2.5 – Multiplicative Identity
- Lesson 1.2.8 – Equivalent Fractions

Mathematical Vocabulary

The following is a list of vocabulary found in this chapter. Make sure that you are familiar with the terms below and know what they mean. For the words you do not know, refer to the glossary or index. You might also add these words to your Toolkit so that you can reference them in the future.

area	compound events	desired outcomes
equivalent fractions	experimental probability	lowest common denominator
interval	mean	measure of central tendency
median	multiplicative identity	outcome
outliers	parallelogram	percent
perimeter	possible outcomes	probability
proportional relationship	rectangle	repeating decimal
sample space	scaling	terminating decimal
theoretical probability	trapezoid	triangle

Answers and Support for Closure Problems
What Have I Learned?

Note: MN = Math Note, LL = Learning Log

Problem	Solution	Need Help?	More Practice
CL 1-142.	a. 15 feet b. 12 boxes will fit in one stack.	Lesson 1.1.4	Problems 1-36 and 1-83
CL 1-143.	$P = 88$ m, $A = 369$ sq. m	MN: 1.1.2	Problems 1-11, 1-22, 1-49, 1-84, 1-129, and 1-141
CL 1-144.	$\frac{3}{10}$	Lessons 1.2.2 and 1.2.8 MN: 1.2.3	Problems 1-133 and 1-134
CL 1-145.	a. Two fifths, $\frac{2}{5}$, 0.4, 40% b. One sixth, $\frac{1}{6}$, $0.1\overline{6}$, 16.67% c. Three eighths, $\frac{3}{8}$, 0.375, 37.5%	MN: 1.1.5	Problems 1-44, 1-46, and 1-47
CL 1-146.	+ + $\frac{8}{12}$, $\frac{4}{6}$, or $\frac{2}{3}$	Lesson 1.2.6 LL: 1.2.8	Problems 1-94, 1-106, 1-115, and 1-118
CL 1-147.	a. Theoretical b. Experimental c. Experimental d. Theoretical	Lessons 1.2.1 and 1.2.2 MN: 1.2.3 LL: 1.2.1	Problems 1-59 and 1-75
CL 1-148.	a. $\frac{1}{25} = 4\%$ b. 64% c. 8	Lessons 1.2.1 and 1.2.2 MN: 1.2.3 LL: 1.2.1	Problems 1-57, 1-71, 1-80, 1-124, and 1-125
CL 1-149.	Kimberly's number is 30. $30 \cdot 3 - 7 = 83$	Lesson 1.1.3	Problems 1-16, 1-17, 1-18, and 1-104

2
Fractions and
Integer Addition

CHAPTER 2 Fractions and Integer Addition

In Chapter 2 you will work to deepen your understanding about various types of numbers. In Section 2.1, you will look carefully at relationships between fractions, decimals, and percents to rewrite numbers in different forms and to compare them to each other.

In Section 2.2, you will direct an acrobat to move back and forth on a tightrope as you learn about adding and multiplying **integers** (positive and negative whole numbers, and zero). You will also learn how to add and multiply numbers containing fractions and decimals (called **rational numbers**). Then you will represent and combine positive and negative values using pictures. Finally, you will learn ways to make calculations without having to write anything down or use a calculator.

Guiding Questions

Think about these questions throughout this chapter:

How can the number be rewritten?

Are the numbers equal?

How can I visualize it?

How can I describe the motion?

In Section 2.3, you will look at coordinate graphs and learn how to scale axes to make the graphs the most useful for different purposes.

In this chapter, you will learn how to:

- Rewrite numbers in different forms in order to compare them.
- Determine whether a fraction can be rewritten as a repeating or terminating decimal.
- Build (compose) and take apart (decompose) numbers and lengths.
- Add and multiply positive and negative integers and rational numbers.
- Choose appropriate scales and set up useful graphs for data.

Chapter Outline

Section 2.1	In this section, you will look at numbers represented as fractions and as decimals. You will investigate the question, "What makes some decimals repeat?"
Section 2.2	In Section 2.2, you will extend your understanding of length to help you add and multiply positive and negative integers and rational numbers.
Section 2.3	This section reviews your work with coordinate graphs from previous courses. You will plot and read points on graphs and learn how to scale them so that they are useful for showing the relationship that they represent.

2.1.1 When do decimals repeat?

Fraction-to-Decimal Conversions

In previous lessons, you explored different representations of portions (parts) of wholes. You looked at portions represented as fractions and as decimals, and you went back and forth between the representations. While fractions are written in a common format, that is, as the quotient $\frac{a}{b}$ where a and b are integers, their decimal representations have two types, terminating and repeating. Why does this happen? In this lesson, you will work with your team to determine what makes some decimals terminate (end) and some repeat.

2-1. Compare the portions in each picture below.

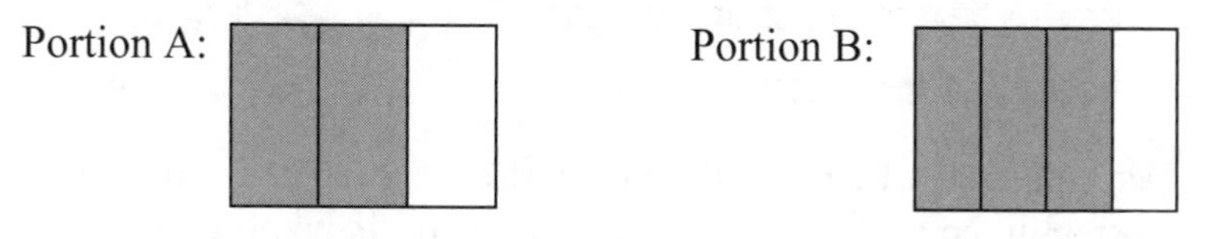

a. Represent each portion as a fraction and as a decimal.

b. The pictures and fractions for each representation are similar, but the decimals look very different. With your team, discuss how the two decimals look different and why they might look this way. Be ready to share your ideas.

2-2. In Lesson 1.1.5, you rewrote fractions like $\frac{1}{9}$ as decimals by dividing on your calculator. Looking at how division works can help explain why fractions can look so different when written as decimals.

$$\frac{1}{9} = 1 \div 9 = 0.111... = 0.\overline{1}$$

Imagine that you have 13 cheese sticks that you need to divide evenly among 5 people. You can write this relationship as 13 cheese sticks $\div$ 5 people or $\frac{13}{5}$ or $5\overline{)13}$. The problem is represented with the pictures and symbols below.

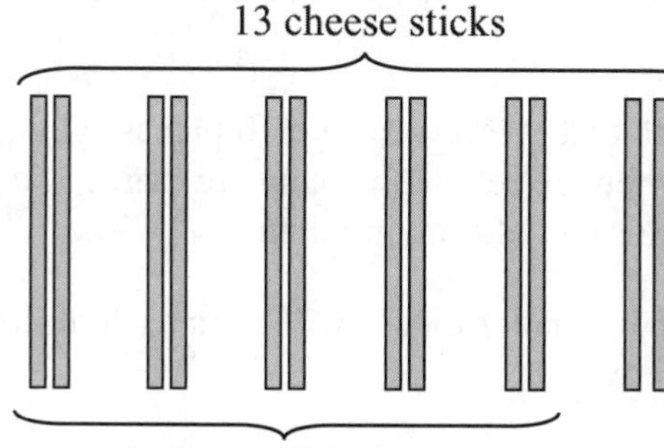

$$\begin{array}{r} 2 \\ 5\overline{)13} \\ \underline{10} \\ 3 \end{array}$$

Problem continues on next page. →

2-2. *Problem continued from previous page.*

a. Talk with your team about how this diagram represents dividing 13 by 5, or $\frac{13}{5}$. Why are there five groups of two pieces?

b. What does the 2 above the division symbol represent? What does the 10 represent?

c. Where are the three leftover pieces shown in the symbols?

d. Our number system is based on powers of ten, so to share the three leftover pieces between the 5 people, we would divide the pieces into tenths. Add a decimal point in the dividend to show that the three wholes are being rewritten as thirty tenths (3.0), as shown below.

3 pieces = $\frac{30}{10}$ pieces

$$\begin{array}{r} 2. \\ 5\overline{)13.0} \\ \underline{10}\downarrow \\ 30 \end{array}$$

Determine how many tenths each person gets. Then show where this is written in the problem, and complete the division process.

e. How much cheese will each person receive? Write your answer as a fraction and as a decimal.

2-3. You know that $\frac{3}{4}$ can be written decimally as 0.75. To see why this is so, set up your own division problem to rewrite $\frac{3}{4}$ as a decimal. Use the Lesson 2.1.1 Resource Page, but *do not use a calculator*. Show your work on the diagram and in symbols.

a. Each bold line in the diagram represents one piece. Are there enough whole pieces to put some in each of four groups? Explain.

b. Divide each of the whole pieces into tenths and then divide these into four groups. How many tenths are in each group? How many tenths are left over?

c. If you divide each tenth that is left over into 10 pieces again, what fraction of the original is each new piece? How many are there? You may need to visualize these pieces instead of drawing them.

d. How many of these new, smaller pieces will be in each of the four groups? How many will be left over?

e. How can you tell that the decimal has terminated (ended) ?

2-4. To see why $\frac{2}{3}$ does not terminate, use the Lesson 2.1.1 Resource Page to rewrite it as a decimal. Follow the same procedure used in problem 2-3, and be sure not to use a calculator.

a. As you continue to divide the pieces into three groups, what happens?

b. How is the process of dividing $\frac{2}{3}$ the same as dividing $\frac{3}{4}$, and how is it different? Why does one decimal terminate, but the other does not?

2-5. Katrina works at the Fraction Factory. Her job is to sort all of the customer orders into two groups: terminating decimals and repeating decimals.

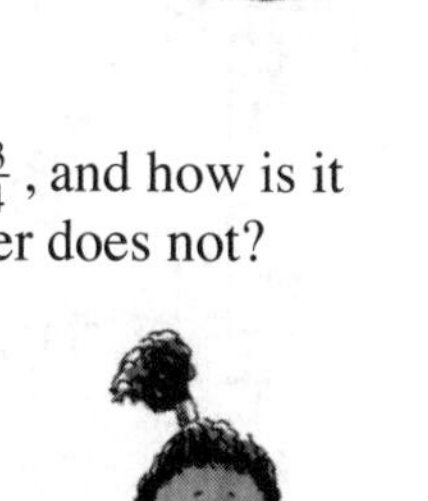

a. Katrina's boss wants her to write $\frac{20}{33}$ as a decimal without using a calculator. Katrina's work so far is shown at right. What results did she get each time she subtracted?

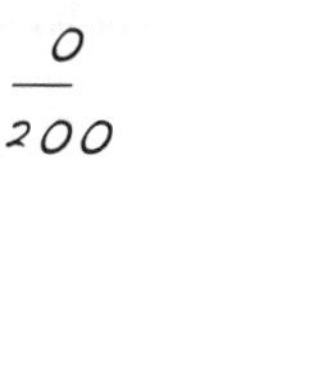

b. Will the decimal for $\frac{20}{33}$ terminate or repeat? How do you know? To be sure, how far should Katrina continue with her division?

2-6. **Additional Challenge:** Represent $\frac{1}{7}$ as a decimal without using your calculator. When does it repeat? How do you know?

2-7. THE ROLE OF THE DENOMINATOR

Additional Challenge: Both $\frac{1}{3}$ and $\frac{2}{3}$ can be rewritten as repeating decimals, $0.\overline{3}$ and $0.\overline{6}$, respectively. Does the number in the denominator cause the fraction to repeat? For example, will every fraction with a denominator of 15 be equivalent to a repeating decimal? (Ignore fractions that are equal to whole numbers, like $\frac{15}{15} = 1$ or $\frac{45}{15} = 3$.)

a. With your team, investigate fractions with a denominator of 15, including $\frac{5}{15}$ and $\frac{10}{15}$. Can you find a fraction with 15 in the denominator that does not repeat and that is not equal to a whole number? Are you able to find one? More than one?

b. Why do some numbers with a denominator of 15 repeat and others do not? Discuss this with your team. Write down an idea and test it.

METHODS AND MEANINGS

MATH NOTES

Mixed Numbers and Fractions Greater Than One

The number $4\frac{1}{3}$ is called a **mixed number** because it is composed of a whole number, 4, and a fraction, $\frac{1}{3}$.

The number $\frac{13}{3}$ is a called a **fraction greater than one** because the numerator is larger than the denominator and its value is therefore greater than one. It is equal to the mixed number $4\frac{1}{3}$. Sometimes fractions greater than one are called *improper fractions*, but this is just a historical term. There is nothing actually wrong with the fraction.

Whether to write a number as a mixed number or a fraction greater than one depends on what arithmetic operation(s) you are performing. For some arithmetic operations, especially multiplication and division, you will usually want to write mixed numbers as fractions greater than one.

2-8. How many tenths are in one whole? How many hundredths?

2-9. Convert the following fractions to decimals. Show your work.

a. $\frac{2}{5}$

b. $\frac{3}{8}$

c. $\frac{30}{20}$

2-10. Mario ordered a pizza for dinner. When it arrived, Mario quickly ate $\frac{1}{8}$ of the pizza. While Mario was getting napkins, his pet poodle ate $\frac{1}{3}$ of the pizza.

a. Draw a model of the pizza that shows the portion that has been eaten.

b. Write a numerical expression to show the fraction of the pizza that is left.

c. About what percent of the pizza is left?

2-11. Nicole has a machine that will produce a number from 1 through 50 when she pushes a button. If she pushes the button, what is:

a. P(multiple of 10)?

b. P(not 100)?

c. P(not a multiple of 4)?

d. P(one-digit number)?

2-12. Lyle and his study team are designing spinners.

a. If one half of the sections on a spinner are green and there are 14 sections, how many are green?

b. If three fourths of the sections on a different spinner have stripes and there are 24 sections, how many sections have stripes?

2-13. Which of the fractions listed below will have repeating decimals and which will have terminating decimals? Explain how you know.

a. $\frac{2}{5}$

b. $\frac{7}{45}$

c. $\frac{5}{99}$

d. $\frac{27}{250}$

2-14. Here are the lengths (in inches) of snakes in a reptile display at the zoo: 10, 31, 36, 36, 38, 42, 47, 48, 49, and 52. Find the mean and median of the lengths.

2-15. Thomas has a bag with 7 green marbles, 5 blue marbles, and 4 red marbles. For each part below, if the marble selected is replaced before the next marble is drawn, find the probability for the given draw. Write your answer as a fraction, as a decimal, and as a percent.

a. A red marble?

b. A red or a green marble?

c. An orange marble?

2-16. Finding patterns is an important problem-solving skill used in mathematics. You will use the patterns in Diamond Problems to solve other problems later in the course. Can you discover a pattern for the numbers in each of the four diamonds below?

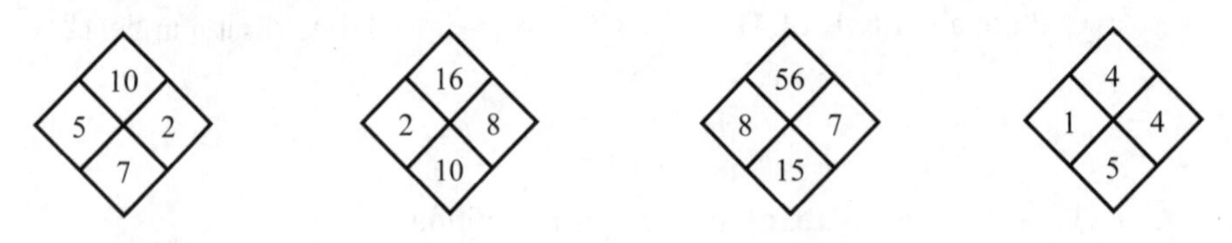

Copy the Diamond Problems below and use the pattern you discovered to complete each of them.

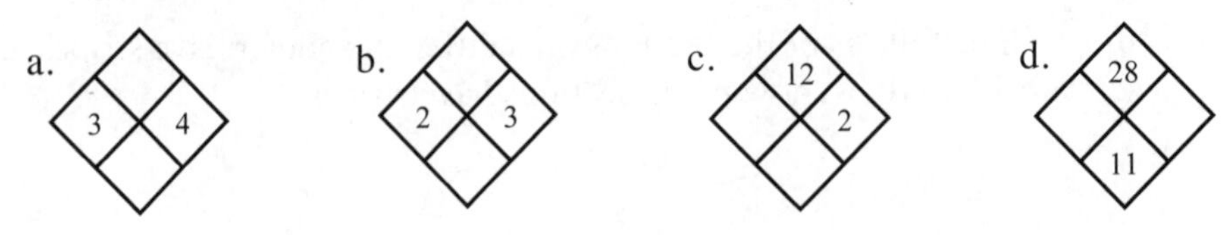

2-17. Read the Math Notes box for this lesson. Then rewrite each number below as a single fraction greater than one.

a. $1\frac{1}{11}$ b. $3\frac{2}{5}$ c. $2\frac{4}{15}$

2.1.2 How can I rewrite a decimal?

Rewriting Decimals as Fractions

In Lesson 2.1.1, you worked with different fractions and found ways to rewrite those fractions as repeating and terminating decimals. In this lesson, you will reverse your thinking and will instead represent decimals as fractions.

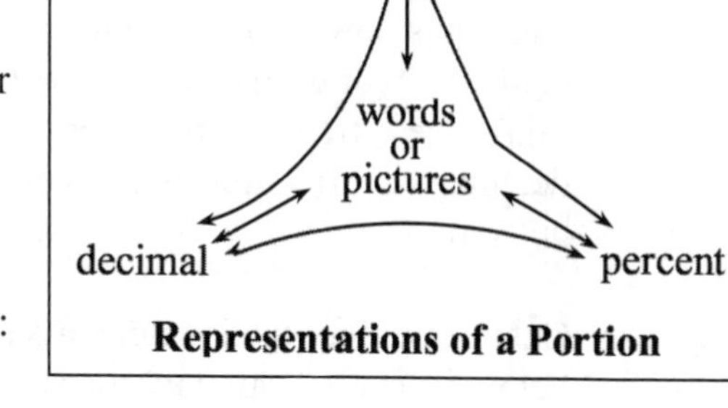

Representations of a Portion

As you work with your team today, ask each other these questions to focus your discussion:

How else can I describe the portion?

How many pieces are in the whole?

2-18. Complete the Representations of a Portion web for each number below. An example for $\frac{2}{3}$ is shown at right.

a. $\frac{7}{10}$

b. 0.75

c. Three fifths

d. $\frac{5}{8}$

$\frac{2}{3}$

two thirds

$0.\overline{6}$ $66\frac{2}{3}\%$

Representations of a Portion

e. With your team, explain how you rewrote 0.75 as a fraction in part (b). Is there more than one way? Be as specific as possible.

2-19. Since 0.7 is described in words as "seven tenths," it is not a surprise that the equivalent fraction is $\frac{7}{10}$. Obtain a set of decimal cards from your teacher or use the list below to complete the following tasks:

- Use the names of fractions (like "twenty-three hundredths") to rewrite each terminating decimal as a fraction. First try to use what you know about place value to write the fraction.
- With your calculator, check to be sure the fraction is equal to the decimal.

a. 0.19 b. 0.391 c. 0.001

d. 0.019 e. 0.3 f. 0.524

2-20. Jerome works at the Fraction Factory in the department that changes decimals into fractions. He has just received an order to rewrite $0.\overline{73}$ as a fraction. He started to rewrite it as $\frac{73}{100}$, but he is not sure that he is correct. Is $\frac{73}{100}$ equal to $0.\overline{73}$? Be ready to justify your answer.

2-21. Katrina is now responsible for finding the decimal equivalent for each of the numbers below. She thinks these fractions have something to do with the decimals and fractions in problem 2-19, but she is not sure.

Get a set of the fractions in parts (a) through (f) below on cards from your teacher, and use your calculator to change each fraction into a decimal. Add the decimal information to the card. Can you find a pattern?

a. $\frac{19}{99}$

b. $\frac{391}{999}$

c. $\frac{3}{9}$

d. $\frac{1}{999}$

e. $\frac{524}{999}$

f. $\frac{19}{999}$

g. What connections do these fractions have with those you found in problem 2-19? Be ready to share your observations with the class.

h. Use your pattern to predict the fraction equivalent for $0.\overline{24}$. Then test your guess with a calculator.

i. Use your pattern to predict the decimal equivalent for $\frac{65}{99}$. Check your answer with your calculator.

2-22. REWRITING REPEATING DECIMALS AS FRACTIONS

Jerome wants to figure out why his pattern from problem 2-21 works. He noticed that he could eliminate the repeating digits by subtracting, as he did in the work at right. This gave him an idea. *"What if I multiply by something before I subtract, so that I'm left with more than zero?"* he wondered. He wrote:

$$\begin{aligned} 0.\overline{73} &= 0.737373.... \\ \underline{-0.\overline{73}} &= \underline{-0.737373....} \\ 0 &= 0 \end{aligned}$$

$$\begin{aligned} 10(0.\overline{73}) &= 7.373737... \\ \underline{-(0.\overline{73})} &= \underline{-0.737373...} \end{aligned}$$

"The repeating decimals do not make zero in this problem. But if I multiply by 100 instead, I think it will work!" He tried again:

$$\begin{aligned} 100(0.\overline{73}) &= 73.737373... \\ \underline{-(0.\overline{73})} &= -\underline{0.737373....} \\ 99(0.\overline{73}) &= 73.0 \end{aligned}$$

a. Discuss Jerome's work with your team. Why did he multiply by 100? How did he get 99 sets of $0.\overline{73}$? What happened to the repeating decimals when he subtracted?

b. *"I know that 99 sets of* $0.\overline{73}$ *are equal to 73 from my equation,"* Jerome said. *"So to find what just one set of* $0.\overline{73}$ *is equal to, I will need to divide 73 into 99 equal parts."* Represent Jerome's idea as a fraction.

c. Use Jerome's strategy to rewrite $0.\overline{85}$ as a fraction. Be prepared to explain your reasoning.

2-23. DESIGN A DECIMAL DEPARTMENT

Congratulations! Because of your new skills with rewriting fractions and decimals, you have been put in charge of the Designer Decimals Department of the Fraction Factory. People write to your department and order their favorite fractions rewritten as beautiful decimals.

Recently, your department has received some strange orders. Review each order below and decide if you can complete it. If possible, find the new fraction or decimal. If it is not possible to complete the order, write to the customer and explain why the order cannot be completed.

Order 1: "I'd like a terminating decimal to represent $\frac{44}{99}$."

Order 2: "Could you send me 0.208 as two different fractions, one with 3000 in the denominator and one with 125 in the denominator?"

Order 3: "Please send me $0.\overline{43}$ written as a fraction."

2-24. **Additional Challenge:**
A strange order has arrived in the Designer Decimals Department. The order requests a new kind of decimal to be written as a fraction.

Please send me the decimal
0.010010001000001. . . .
rewritten as a fraction.

The order is reprinted at right. With your team, rewrite the decimal as an equivalent fraction or explain why you cannot rewrite it.

2-25. LEARNING LOG

Make an entry in your Learning Log that summarizes what you have learned in the past two lessons. For example, how can you tell if a decimal is repeating or terminating? How can you change a decimal to a fraction, especially if it is repeating? Can every fraction be represented as a decimal, and can every decimal be represented as a fraction?

Title your entry "Repeating and Terminating Decimals" and include today's date.

METHODS AND MEANINGS

MATH NOTES

Fraction⇔Decimal⇔Percent

The **Representations of a Portion web** diagram at right illustrates that fractions, decimals, and percents are different ways to represent a portion of a number. Portions can also be represented in words, such as "four fifths" or "twelve fifteenths," or with diagrams.

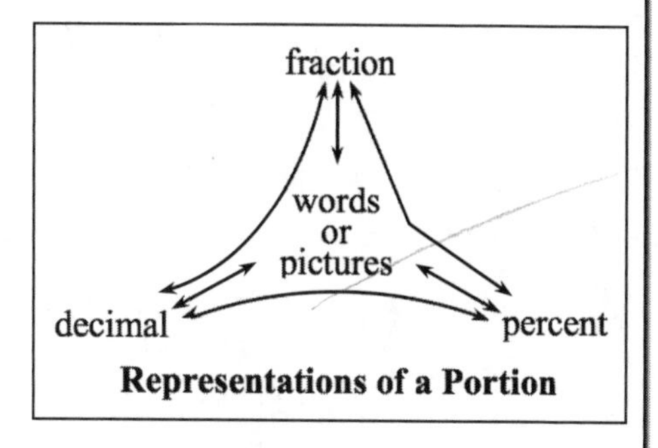

Representations of a Portion

The examples below show how to convert from one form to another.

Decimal to percent:
Multiply the decimal by 100.

$$(0.34)(100) = 34\%$$

Fraction to percent:
Set up an equivalent fraction using 100 as the denominator. The numerator is the percent.

$$\frac{4}{5} \cdot \frac{20}{20} = \frac{80}{100} = 80\%$$

Terminating decimal to fraction:
Make the digits the numerator. Use the decimal place value as the denominator. Simplify as needed.

$$0.2 = \frac{2}{10} = \frac{1}{5}$$

Repeating decimal to fraction:
Count the number of decimal places in the repeating block. Write the repeating block as the numerator. Then, write the power of 10 for the number of places in the block, less 1, as the denominator. Below, the repeating block (713) has 3 decimal places so 713 is the numerator and 1000 – 1 is the denominator.

$$0.\overline{713} = \frac{713}{1000-1} = \frac{713}{999}$$

Percent to decimal:
Divide the percent by 100.

$$78.6\% = 78.6 \div 100 = 0.786$$

Percent to fraction:
Use 100 as the denominator. Use the digits in the percent as the numerator. Simplify as needed.

$$22\% = \frac{22}{100} \cdot \frac{1/2}{1/2} = \frac{11}{50}$$

Fraction to decimal:
Divide the numerator by the denominator. If sets of digits repeat, then write just one of the repeating sets and place a "bar" over it.

$$\frac{3}{8} = 3 \div 8 = 0.375$$

$$\frac{70}{99} = 70 \div 99 = 0.70707... = 0.\overline{70}$$

Review & Preview

2-26. Which of the following fractions are repeating decimals and which are terminating? Show how you made your decisions.

a. $\frac{2}{15}$ b. $\frac{11}{20}$ c. $\frac{17}{40}$ d. $\frac{1}{12}$

2-27. Copy the portions webs below and fill in the missing parts.

a.

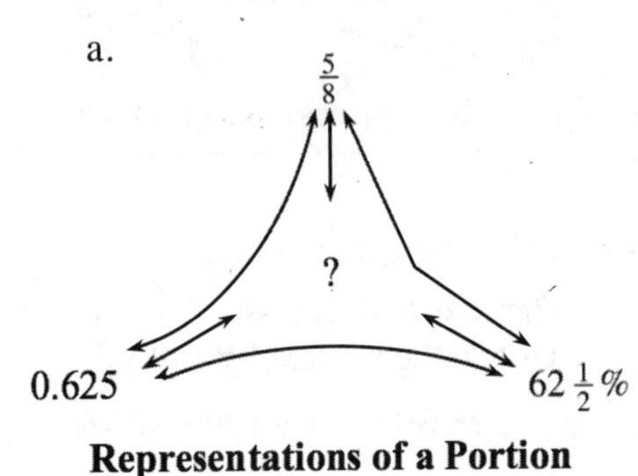

Representations of a Portion

b.

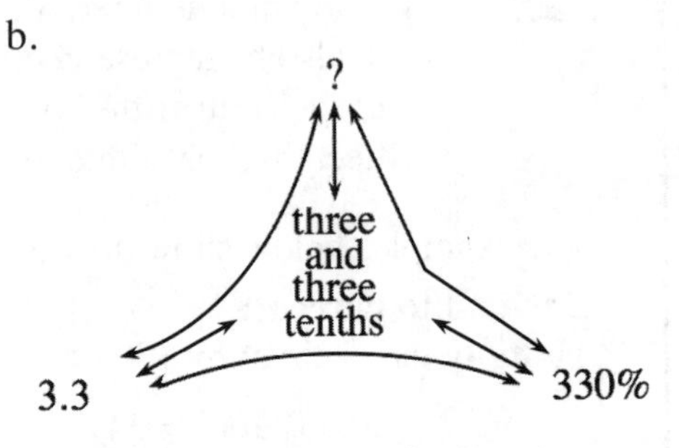

Representations of a Portion

2-28. Lila is making a spinner game for her cousins to play. She has divided it into 8 equal sections and has labeled each section with a symbol. When the spinner lands on a flower (✿), her cousins will win a prize.

a. What is P(★)? Express your answer as a fraction, as a decimal, and as a percent.

b. What is the probability of not getting ♦? Write your answer as a fraction, as a decimal, and as a percent.

c. What is P(✿)? Write your answer as a fraction, as a decimal, and as a percent.

d. If Lila's cousins spin 100 times, about how many times would you expect them to spin a heart (♥)?

2-29. Copy the graphs below onto your paper. Then complete the scale by labeling the remaining tick marks.

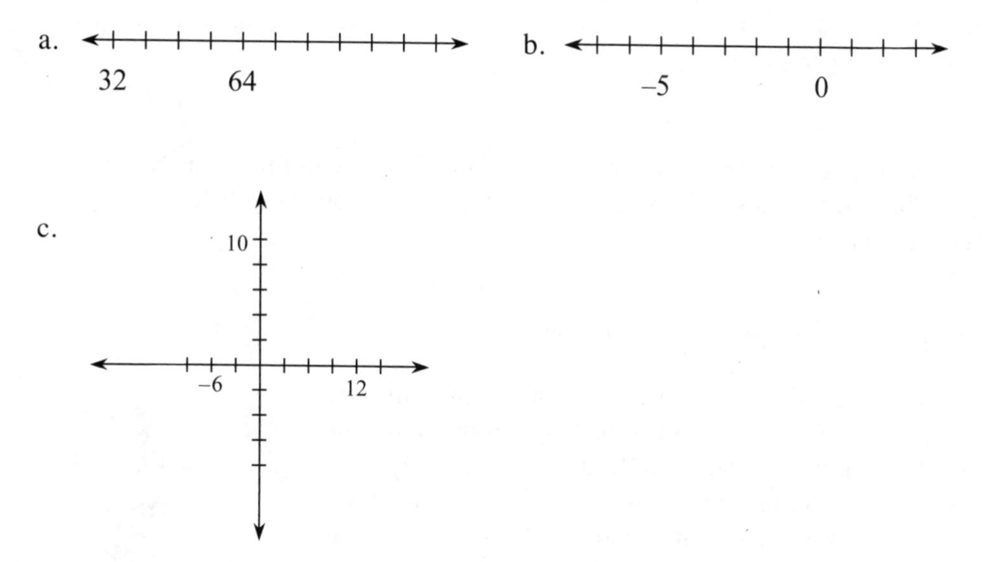

2-30. Approximately 3 out of every 25 Americans live in California. About 3 out of every 50 Americans live in New York, and about 2 out of every 25 Americans live in Texas.

a. Which state has the largest population?

b. Which state has the smallest population?

c. About what percentage of Americans do *not* live in California, New York, or Texas?

2.2.1 How can I build it?

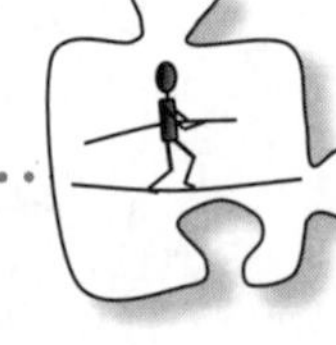

Composing Integers

Units of length can be placed one after another in a line to find a measure of an object's length. Today you will look at how to compose (put together) different lengths to create a new total length.

2-31. CROSSING THE TIGHTROPE

Cecil is an acrobat in a local circus. His job is to move across a tightrope from point A to point B while blindfolded! He can only move using the distances that you tell him to move in your instructions. He needs to reach the end of the tightrope (point B) to take his bow and go down a ladder. Assume the platforms on both sides of the tightrope extend infinitely (have no end). Cecil may go past the ladder. However, if he does, make sure he turns around and goes back toward the ladder.

Your Task: Work with your team to find different combinations of the lengths given in parts (a) through (e) below that will allow Cecil to move from point A and end at point B (the end of the tightrope). You may use each length as many times as you like.

For each crossing, look for at least three different ways to get the acrobat across. For each solution, draw a diagram on your paper that shows how the available lengths were combined to get Cecil across the tightrope.

You can find a digital version of this activity at cpm.org. The length strips from the Lesson 2.2.1A Resource Page might also be helpful.

a. Span of tightrope: 24 feet — Given lengths: 2, 4, 8, 10 feet

b. Span of tightrope: 17 feet — Given lengths: 2, 3, 10 feet

c. Span of tightrope: 15 feet — Given lengths: 3, 4, 6, 11 feet

d. Span of tightrope: 27 feet — Given lengths: 4, 8, 12, 19 feet

e. Span of tightrope: 23 feet — Given lengths: 7, 11, 13 feet

2-32. To represent the way that the acrobat could move across a span of 17 feet, Mara wrote the expressions shown below. If each number represents a length in feet, check that each expression would get Cecil exactly to point B. Be prepared to defend each conclusion with a diagram.

a. $7+3+7$

b. $7+10$

c. $10+7$

d. $10+10+(-3)$

e. What does the -3 in part (d) represent as a movement for Cecil?

2-33. Write numerical expressions (similar to those in problem 2-32) for each of your solutions to part (c) of problem 2-31.

2-34. When combining lengths to make a new length (like you did to get the acrobat across the rope), does the order of the numbers (or lengths) matter? Discuss this with your team or partner and decide whether it matters or not. Be ready to explain why your answer makes sense.

2-35. DESIGNING A TIGHTROPE

In problem 2-31, you found multiple ways to combine lengths to get an acrobat to the end of the tightrope.

a. This time, you are given lengths of 2, 5, and 9 feet. With your team, decide if the acrobat could cross a tightrope of length 1, 2, 3, 4, 5, 6, 7, 8, 9, or 10 feet. For each length that you think is possible, write an expression to represent the acrobat's movements. Remember that you can combine rope lengths going forward (in the positive direction) or backward (in the negative direction). For each length that you think is not possible, explain why it is not possible.

b. Could you combine lengths of 2, 6, and 8 feet to cross a tightrope 15 feet long? Explain why or why not.

MATH NOTES

METHODS AND MEANINGS

Multiplication Using Generic Rectangles

To prepare for later topics in this course and for topics you will encounter in future courses, it is helpful to use an area model and generic rectangle to represent multiplication.

For the problem $67 \cdot 46$, you can think of 67 as 60 + 7 and can think of 46 as 40 + 6. Use these numbers as the dimensions of a large rectangle, as shown at right. Determine the area of each of the smaller rectangles and then find the sum of the four smaller areas. This sum is the answer to the original problem.

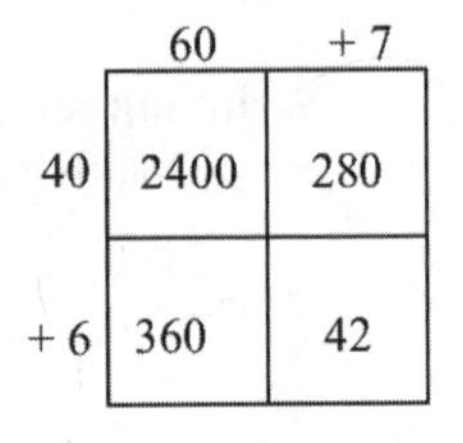

$$67 \cdot 46 = (60+7)(40+6) = 2400 + 280 + 360 + 42 = 3082$$

2-36. Read the Math Notes box in this lesson. Then use generic rectangles to complete the following multiplication problems.

a. $54 \cdot 32$

b. $91 \cdot 78$

2-37. Below are some new distances with given lengths to help Cecil cross the tightrope. Find at least two ways to get Cecil across. Write your solutions as numerical expressions.

a. Span of tightrope: 6 feet Given lengths: 1, 3, 4 feet

b. Span of tightrope: 8 feet Given lengths: 2, 5, 7 feet

2-38. Simplify each of the following expressions to find the length of the tightrope.

a. $5+2+8$

b. $4+9+3$

c. $7+3+2+(-4)$

d. $8+6+2+(-5)$

2-39. Copy these incomplete number lines. Label the missing numbers on each of them.

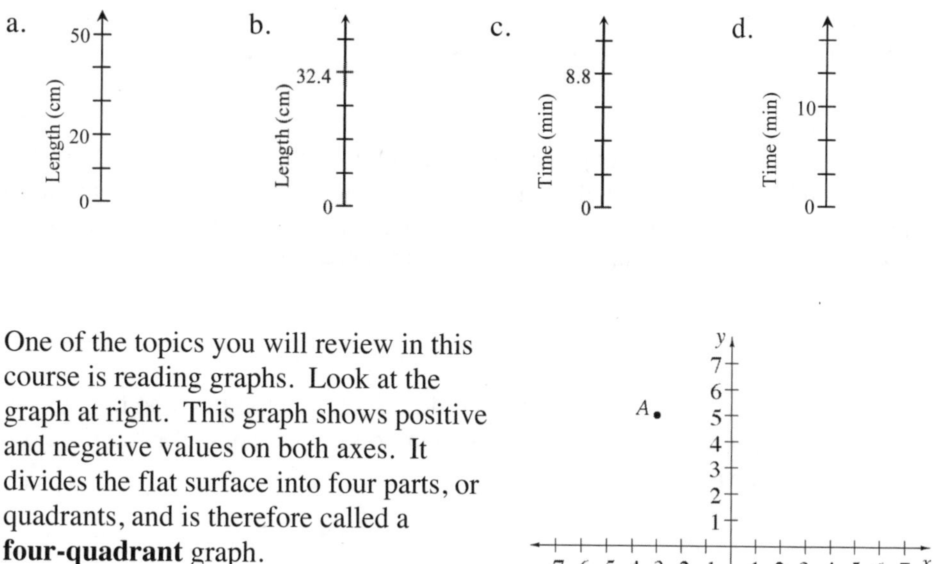

2-40. One of the topics you will review in this course is reading graphs. Look at the graph at right. This graph shows positive and negative values on both axes. It divides the flat surface into four parts, or quadrants, and is therefore called a **four-quadrant** graph.

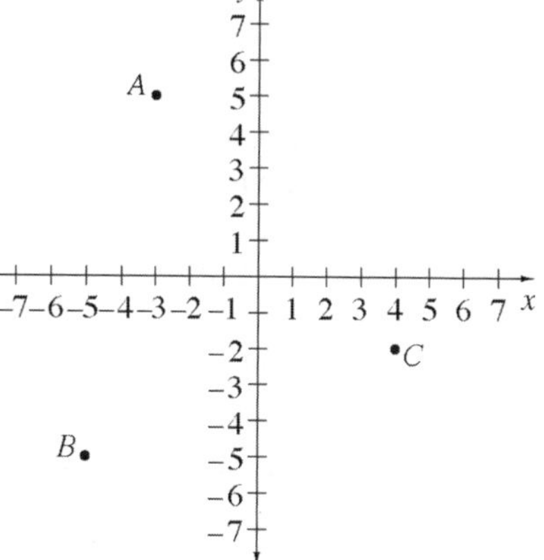

a. The coordinates (the x- and y-values) for point A are $(-3, 5)$. Explain how these numbers tell you the position of point A using the graph.

b. Name the coordinates (x, y) for points B and C.

c. If Samantha moved point A 9 units down and 6 units to the right, at what point would she end up?

2-41. Gracie loves to talk on the phone, but her parents try to limit the amount of time she talks. They decided to keep a record of the number of minutes that she spends on the phone each day. Here are the data for the past nine days: 120, 60, 0, 30, 15, 0, 0, 10, and 20.

a. Find the mean and median for the information.

b. Which of the two measures in part (a) would give Gracie's parents the most accurate information about her phone use? Why do you think so?

2.2.2 How can I find the length?

Adding Integers and Rational Numbers

Today you will continue to explore how to combine integer (positive and negative whole numbers and zero) and rational number (fraction and decimal) lengths in multiple ways to find a new length. You will also continue to learn how different combinations can be written with numerical expressions, such as $3+3+(-2)+11$.

2-42. Find the length of the tightrope if each expression for rope lengths below starts Cecil at point A and has him end at point B. Assume the numbers represent lengths in feet.

a. $8+(-3)+2$

b. $12.25+7.5+(-1.75)$

c. $6.1+(-3.05)+(-2.05)$

d. $-1\frac{1}{4}+8\frac{1}{2}$

e. $14.14+10.325+(-13.6)$

f. $26\frac{1}{3}+(-12\frac{1}{2})+3\frac{1}{6}$

2-43. For Cecil's new act, his tightrope is 5 feet long.

a. If he begins at point A, write two expressions that will make him end at point B. What do these expressions have in common?

b. Explain why $5+2+(-2)$ is **equivalent** to (the same as) telling Cecil to move 5 feet to the right.

c. Will $5+2+(-2)+2+(-2)$ get Cecil to point B? Will $5+2+(-2)+3+(-3)$? How would you describe his movements in these cases?

2-44. What if Cecil's tightrope was a number line like the one shown below?

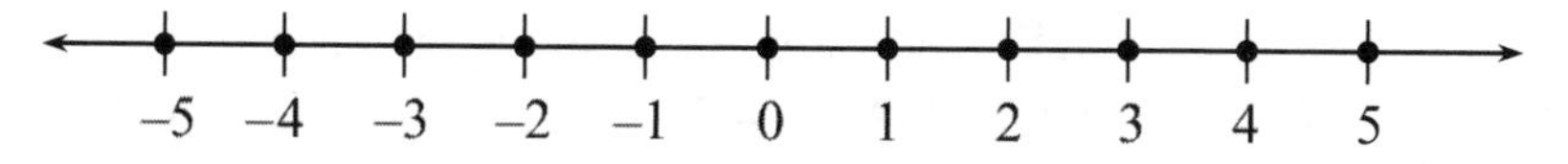

a. On your paper, sketch the number line above.

b. How can you represent $-2+3$ using the number line? Discuss your ideas with your team and use the number line to represent Cecil's movements and your answer.

c. On the same number line, start at 3 and represent $3+2$ and $3+(-2)$. How are these two computations similar and how are they different?

d. Describe how the two computations $8+(-5)$ and $8+5$ would be related if you represented them on a number line.

2-45. In parts (c) and (d) of problem 2-44, you may have discovered that for each of the pairs of computations, the distance that you moved on the number line from each starting value was the same. This was true even though in one case the number added was positive and in the other case it was negative. The *sign* of the number added told you in which *direction* to move, while the *size* of the number told you how *far* to move.

The amount that you moved is one way to describe the absolute value of the number. In a previous course, you may have learned that **absolute value** is the value of a number without regard to its sign, or the distance a number is from 0 on a number line (in either direction) and that the symbol $|x|$ is used to indicate the absolute value of any number x.

Evaluate each absolute value expression below.

a. $|-20-5.3|$ b. $|45+7.7|$ c. $-|8+81|$ d. $-|0-3|$

2-46. MAKING ZEROS

For Cecil's newest act, he starts at point A on the left end of his tightrope, walks on the tightrope, turns around, sometimes many times, and then ends up back at point A on the left end of his tightrope.

a. Work with your team to write at least three expressions that show how Cecil could move and still start and end at point A.

b. Build three more expressions similar to the expressions you wrote in part (a). For your three expressions, do one with two numbers, one with three numbers, and one with eight numbers. What do all of your expressions have in common?

2-47. Sally lives in North Dakota, where the winter temperature is often below zero. One day, the thermometer read 10 degrees below zero, but it rapidly rose 15 degrees in one hour as a warm front moved in. Then it dropped 15 degrees as night fell. What is the resulting temperature? Draw a diagram to represent this scenario.

2-48. Gina was working on the previous problems when she had a new idea.

"Look," she boasted, *"I can use these ideas to add large integers quickly without even picking up a pencil."*

She wrote down each of the following expressions and calculated each answer in less than 5 seconds. Talk with your team about how she could have done this.

a. $583.6 + 212.72 + (-583.6)$

b. $313\frac{6}{11} + (-300)$

c. $212 + (-150.75)$

2-49. Consider Cecil's movements on the tightrope as you answer the questions below.

a. What happens when Cecil goes forward 5 feet and then goes back 5 feet? Where does he end up?

b. Chad decided to record Cecil's moves with the diagram at right. Explain what you think his drawing means.

+ + + + +
− − − − −

c. Using the same strategy, Chad recorded a different set of instructions for Cecil with the diagram shown at right. What could this diagram represent? How long is the tightrope if these moves end at point B?

+ + + + + + + + +
− − −

2-50. LEARNING LOG

How can you describe two numbers that add to zero? Discuss this question with your team and then write your ideas in your Learning Log. Use as many real-world contexts as you can to provide examples. Label this entry "Making Zeros" and label it with today's date.

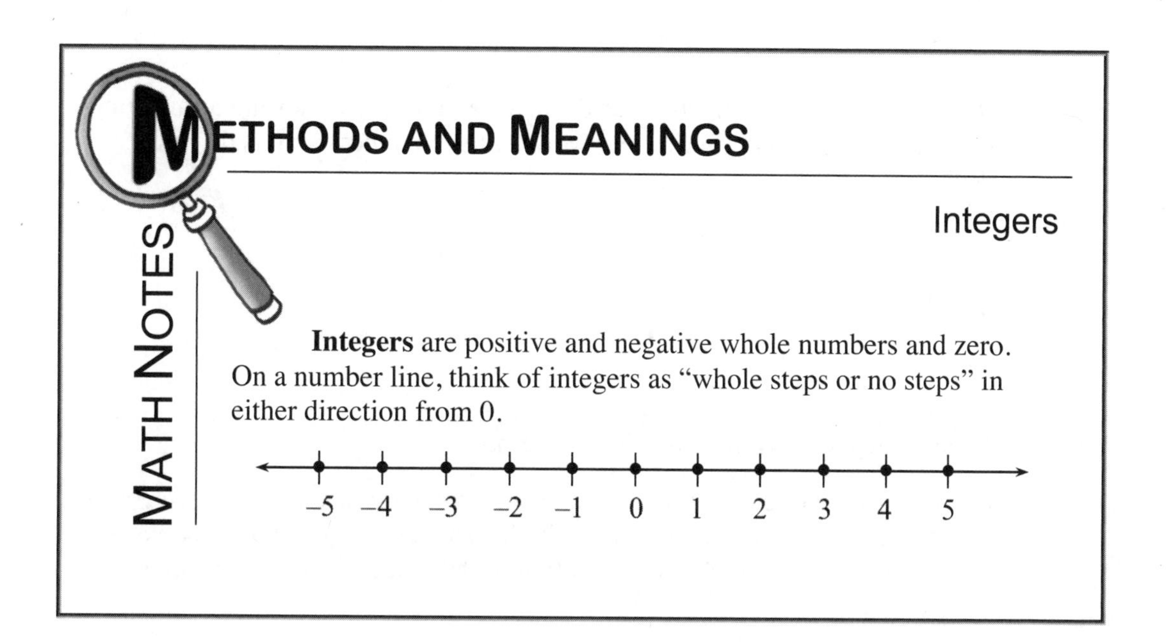

Integers

Integers are positive and negative whole numbers and zero. On a number line, think of integers as "whole steps or no steps" in either direction from 0.

2-51. Write an expression to represent each of the following sketches. Then give the value of each sketch.

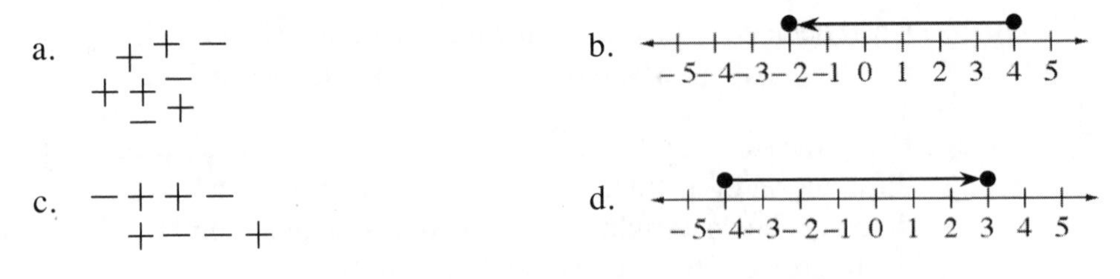

2-52. Use the numbers 5, 6, and 7 and the operations of addition, subtraction, multiplication, and/or division to create three different number expressions with three different values. One of the expressions should have a value of 37.

2-53. Use a number line to show your work as you find the value of each expression.

a. $-5+3.25$

b. $3.18+(-7)$

2-54. Rewrite the following fractions as decimals and decide if they are terminating or repeating decimals. Show your work and explain how you made your decision.

a. $\frac{7}{8}$

b. $\frac{2}{9}$

c. $\frac{4}{7}$

d. $\frac{11}{22}$

2-55. Evan's uncle gave him money for his birthday.

a. Evan plans to put half of the money in his savings account, spend $\frac{1}{5}$ of the money on bubble gum to share with his friends, and buy comic books with the money he has left. What portion of the money will he spend on comic books?

b. Evan uses some of his comic-book money to buy a magazine for $4. If Evan's uncle gave him $30, what fraction of this money did he spend on the magazine?

2.2.3 How can I add signed numbers?

More Addition of Integers and Rational Numbers

In Lesson 2.2.2, you used integers to represent lengths in two directions. You began to think about using "+" and "–" tiles to represent this forward and backward movement. Today, you will use + and – tiles to model expressions with integers, assigning the + tile a value of one (+1) and the – tile a value of negative one (–1). In your teams, think about these questions as you work:

Can we show what an integer represents in more than one way?

What can we do if the numbers are very large?

2-56. WHO HAS MORE?

With a partner, get a bag of + and – tiles from your teacher. Reach into the bag, get a small handful, and put them on your desk. Each person should have his or her own bunch of + and – tiles.

a. Write what you got on your paper.

b. Whose pile has the greatest value? Find the value of each pile to justify your answer.

c. If you took a bigger handful of tiles, would you have a better chance of having a higher value? Discuss this with your partner and decide why or why not.

2-57. WIN-A-ROW

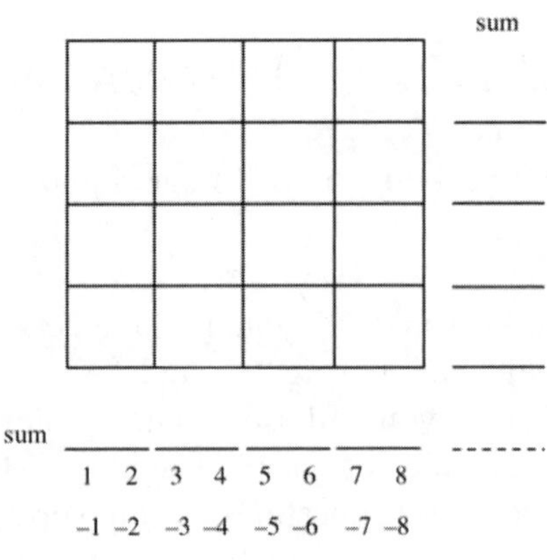

Obtain a Lesson 2.2.3B Resource Page from your teacher. Read the directions for scoring in the game below and play Win-A-Row against a partner.

Scoring: When all the boxes in the table have been filled in, calculate the sum of each row and the sum of each column. Every positive sum means one point for Player 1. Every negative sum means one point for Player 2.

How to Play the Game:

1. Play one round of rock-paper-scissors to determine who plays first.
2. Player 1 places one of the numbers 1, 2, 3, 4, 5, 6, 7, or 8 in the square he or she chooses and then crosses that number from the list.
3. Player 2 places one of the numbers –1, –2, –3, –4, –5, –6, –7, or –8 in another square and then crosses that number from the list.
4. Alternate play until all squares are full and all of the numbers have been crossed off the list.
5. Add the numbers in each row and write each row's sum on the appropriate blank in the "Sum" column. Give the winner of each row one point.
6. Add the numbers in each column and write each column's sum on the appropriate blank in the "Sum" row. Give the winner of each column one point.
7. If the two players tie after adding the rows and columns, find the sum of the diagonal (from top to bottom and left to right) to decide the final winner.
8. If the two players' sums are still tied, find the sum of the other diagonal (from bottom to top and left to right) to decide the final winner.
9. If the game is still tied at this point, both players win!

Ending the Game: The game ends when all squares are full and all sums have been found.

2-58. For each expression below:

- Build each expression with + and – tiles.
- Sketch each collection of + and – tiles and find the value of the expression.
- Write the solution as an equation.

For example, in part (a) below, you might draw the figure at right and record $-8+2=-6$.

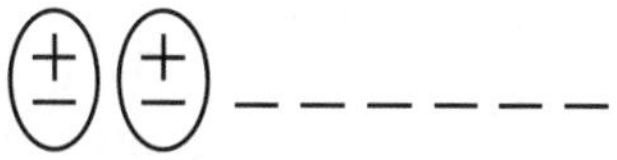

a. $-8+2$
b. $-5+(-3)$
c. $2+(-4)$
d. $-7+(-7)$
e. $-4+3$
f. $-4+8+(-2)$
g. $-3+5+3$
h. $-6+6$

2-59. Think about the problems you have worked on involving positive and negative numbers. How would you find the answer to $-200+14$? Without using your calculator, find the sum. Explain your reasoning to your teammates and be prepared to describe your strategy.

2-60. Using the method you discussed with your teammates, simplify the expressions below.

a. $-100+50$
b. $-30\frac{5}{8}+(-60\frac{1}{4})$
c. $-25.63+(-30.59)$
d. $75+(-30)+160+(-29)$

2-61. **Additional Challenge:** Can you put together any number of + and – tiles to get any value? Consider this question with your team as you answer the following questions.

a. To start, consider the number –3. Can –3 be represented by a pile containing a total of 19 tiles? Of 22 tiles?

b. Write a general description of the total number of + and – tiles that could be in a pile represented by –3.

c. Choose another number and describe the number of + and – tiles in the piles it could represent.

d. Can any number be represented with any number of + and – tiles? Explain.

METHODS AND MEANINGS

MATH NOTES

Additive Inverse and Additive Identity

The **additive identity** is the number zero (0). When you add zero to any number, you get the same number you started with. For example, $3+0=3$. In general, $x+0=x$.

The **additive inverse** of a number is its opposite. For example, the additive inverse of 7 is –7 and the additive inverse of –2 is 2. The additive inverse "undoes" addition. Suppose you have the number 3 and you want to add a number to it to get zero (the additive identity). Then adding –3 gives you $3+(-3)=0$. Thus, –3 is the additive inverse of 3, and 3 is the additive inverse of –3. In general, $x+(-x)=0$.

2-62. Sketch each expression using + and – tiles or draw it on a number line. Then find the simplified value of each expression.

a. $-5+6+4$

b. $7+(-3)+(-4)$

c. $8+|(-2)+(-3)|$

d. $|-5|+3+6$

2-63. What happens if Cecil goes any number of feet in one direction and then goes the same number of feet the other direction? Where does he end up? How do you know?

2-64. John has a bag of marbles that contains 12 red marbles, 20 green marbles, and 17 blue marbles.

a. If John pulls one marble out of the bag, what is the probability that it will not be red? That is, P(not red)?

b. What is the probability that he will draw a purple marble? That is, P(purple)?

2-65. Find the missing lengths in the problems below. Assume each line segment is subdivided into equal segments. Show your work.

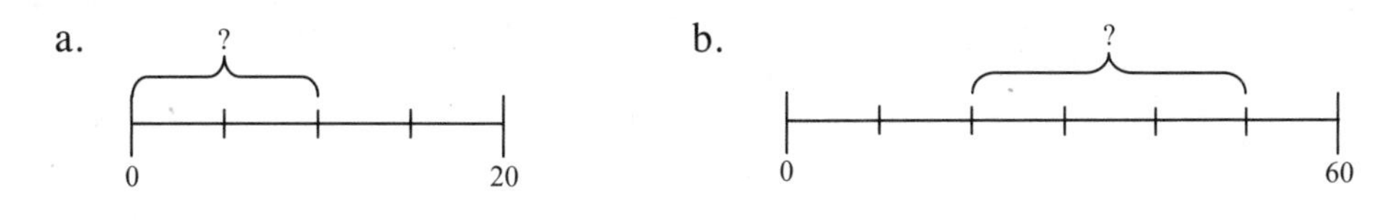

2-66. On Saturday, Stella worked for two hours helping her mother around the house. She spent $\frac{1}{3}$ of her time doing laundry, $\frac{1}{4}$ of her time cleaning, and the rest of her time working in the yard. How much of her time was spent in the yard? Show all of your work. Use a diagram if it helps.

2.2.4 Can I show it another way?

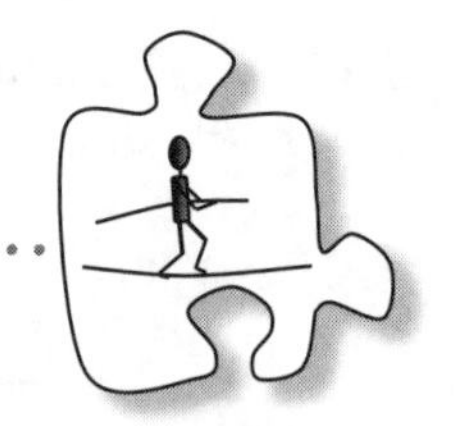

Multiplication as Repeated Addition

In previous lessons, you created expressions to help Cecil cross a tightrope. For example, when the tightrope was 16 feet long, you could have written an expression such as $7+7+7+7+7+7+7+7+(-5)+(-5)+(-5)+(-5)+(-5)+(-5)+(-5)+(-5)$. When a calculation involves adding the same number over and over, as this one does, is there a shorter way to write the expression? Today, you will consider this as you continue to write and simplify expressions.

2-67. Cecil, the tightrope walker introduced in problem 2-31, still needs your help. He wants to cross a rope that is 6 feet long. Using only the lengths of 5 and 8 feet, find *at least two ways* Cecil can move to reach the end of the rope at the ladder. For each solution, draw a diagram and write an expression.

2-68. Cecil moved across the rope as shown at right. Show two ways to represent his moves with number expressions. Do both ways get him to the same endpoint?

6 6 6 6

A B

2-69. Cecil is now so good at crossing the tightrope that he can make a leap of 7 feet at a time. He crossed the rope in these leaps as shown below. Record his moves two ways. Which way is easier to record?

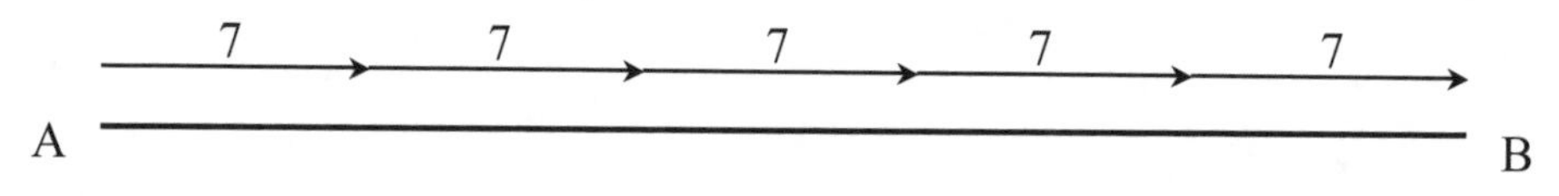

2-70. When adding the same number several times, multiplication can help. For example, if the tightrope walker moved to the right 3 feet, 3 feet, 3 feet, and then 3 feet, it is shorter to write $4(3)$ instead of $3+3+3+3$. Note that parentheses are another way to show multiplication. Use multiplication to write $2+2+2+2+2$.

2-71. How did Cecil, the tightrope walker, move if he started at point A and his moves were recorded as the expression $3(6.2)+2$? Draw a diagram and record how far along his rope he was when he finished.

2-72. Imagine that Cecil, the tightrope walker, starts at point B and walks on the rope toward point A as shown at right.

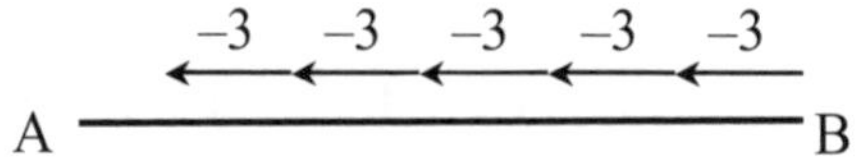

–3 –3 –3 –3 –3

A B

a. How should this be written? Is there more than one way?

b. Where does he end up?

2-73. To represent $2(3)$, Chad drew the diagram at right. How do you predict Chad would draw $5(-3)$? What is the value of this expression?

(+ + +) (+ + +)

2-74. The two equal expressions $2(3)$ and 6 can be represented with the diagram at right. Draw similar diagrams for each of the expressions in parts (a) through (c) below.

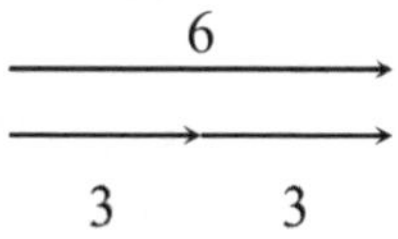

6

3 3

a. What does $2(3+5)$ mean? What is the value of this expression? Describe it with words and a diagram.

b. What does $2(3)+5$ mean? What is the value of this expression? Describe it with words and a diagram.

c. Compare $2(3+5)$ with $2(3)+5$. How are these movements the same or different? Explain your thinking and draw a diagram.

2-75. Draw a diagram to represent the expression $3(-2.5)+(-4)$. Is this the same as $3(-2.5+(-4))$? Use diagrams to justify your decision.

2-76. MENTAL MATH

Work with your team to find strategies for figuring out *mentally* (without using a calculator or writing anything down) how far Cecil moved in parts (a) and (b) below. Then write a number expression for each set of moves along with its result.

a. Cecil traveled 105 feet to the left 7 times. How far did he end up from his starting point?

b. Cecil repeated the following pattern 12 times: He traveled to the right 198 feet and then to the left 198 feet. How far did he end up from his starting point?

2-77. When you need to multiply mentally, it is often useful to use the **Distributive Property**. The Distributive Property states that when you multiply a sum by a number, you must multiply each part of the sum by that number. For example, part (a) of problem 2-76 can be seen as $7(-105) = 7(-100 + (-5))$. The Distributive Property tells us that this is equal to $7(-100) + 7(-5)$ or $-700 + (-35)$. You will explore the Distributive Property further in Chapter 4.

Use the Distributive Property to rewrite and calculate each product shown below.

a. $6(12 + (-4))$

b. $7(300 + (-10))$

c. $4 \cdot 302$

d. $5(871)$

2-78. LEARNING LOG

In your Learning Log, describe what you have learned about adding and multiplying positive and negative integers. Be sure to include examples and diagrams or other representations that explain your thinking. Title this entry "Adding and Multiplying Integers" and label it with today's date.

MATH NOTES

METHODS AND MEANINGS

Addition of Integers

Recall that **integers** are positive and negative whole numbers and zero, that is, $\ldots -3, -2, -1, 0, 1, 2, 3, \ldots$.

You have been introduced to two ways to think about addition. Both of them involve figuring out which, if any, parts of the numbers combine to form zero. One way to think about this concept is to think about the tightrope walker from problem 2-31. If Cecil travels one foot to the right (+1) and one foot to the left (–1), he will end up where he started, so the sum of (+1) and (–1) is zero.

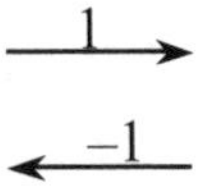

1 →

← –1

Another useful strategy for finding zero is to use + and – tiles. The diagram at right can be represented by the equation $-1+1=0$. You can use this same idea for **adding any two integers**. Use + and – tiles to build the first integer, add the tiles for the second integer, and then eliminate zeros. Study the examples shown in the diagrams below.

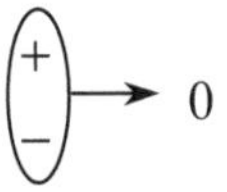

(+ –) → 0

Example 1: $5+(-3)$ 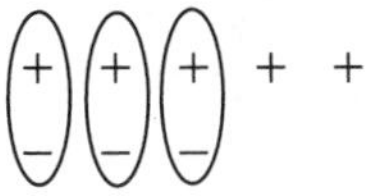 (+ –) (+ –) (+ –) + + $5+(-3)=2$

Example 2: $-5+(2)$ (– +) (– +) – – – $-5+(2)=-3$

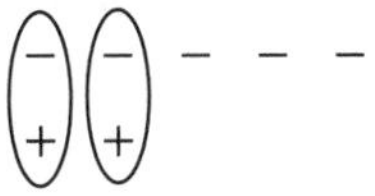

Example 3: $-6+(-2)$ – – – – – – – – $-6+(-2)=-8$

With practice, zeros can be visualized. This helps you determine how many remaining positive or negative tiles show the simplified expression.

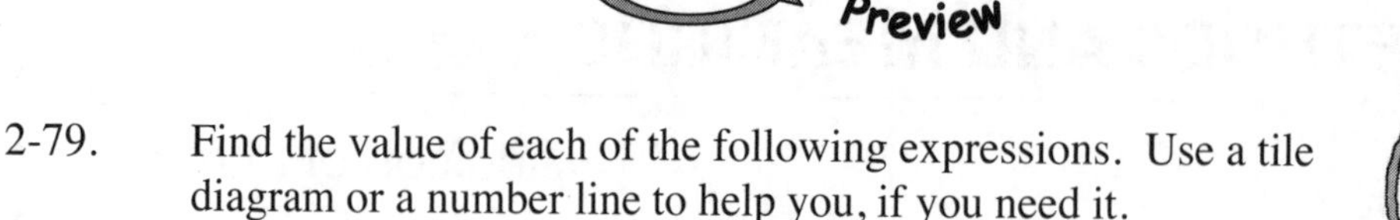

2-79. Find the value of each of the following expressions. Use a tile diagram or a number line to help you, if you need it.

a. $3(4)$

b. $4+11+(-4)$

c. $3.2(2)$

d. $|(-2)+(-2)+(-2)|$

e. $|2(-7.5)|$

f. $\left(10\frac{1}{5}\right)(-5)$

2-80. Use the Distributive Property to rewrite each of the following products as sums, and then calculate the value, as shown in the example below.

Example: $4(307)=4(300)+4(7)=1200+28=1228$

a. $9(410)$

b. $6(592)$

2-81. Copy and complete each of the Diamond Problems below. The pattern used in the Diamond Problems is shown at right.

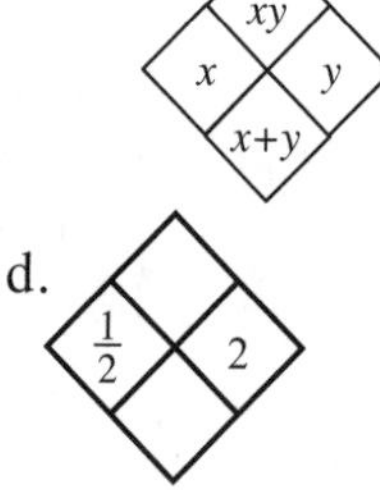

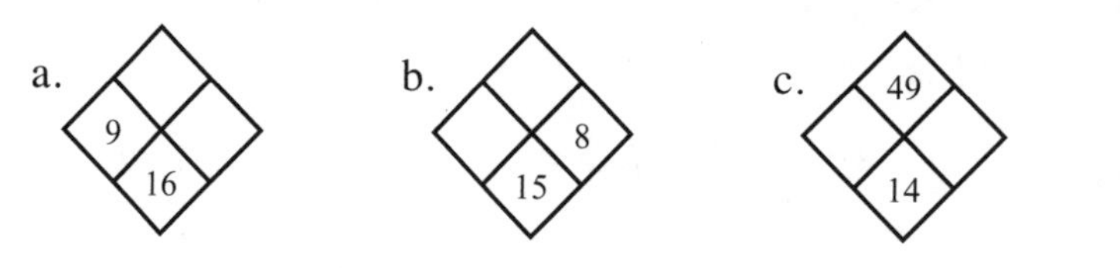

2-82. Copy and complete each of the portions webs below.

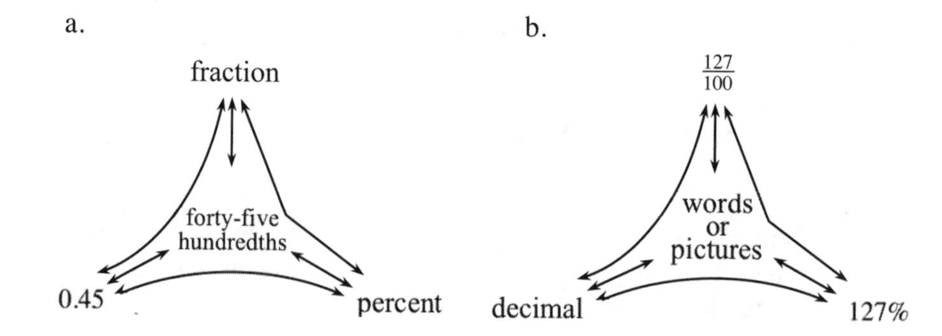

2-83. Camille had a very fun birthday party with lots of friends and family attending. The party lasted for 3 hours. She and her friends played games for $\frac{3}{8}$ of the time, ate pizza and cake for 50% of the time, and spent the remainder of the time opening presents. Draw a diagram and make calculations to show the amount of time spent opening presents.

2-84. Jahna measured the heights of the sunflowers growing in her backyard. Here are the heights that she found (in inches): 34, 48, 52, 61, 76, 76, 61, 84, 61, 39, 83, 61, 79, 81, 56, and 88.

a. Find the mean and median of the heights.

b. Create a histogram to represent this data. Your histogram should have four bins, each with a width of 15.

2.2.5 How big is part of a part?

Multiplication of Portions

You have seen how Cecil's repeated integer-sized moves can be represented with addition or multiplication. But what if you need to calculate part of a whole? For example, if 200 people enter a competition and $\frac{1}{4}$ of them are chosen for the final round, how do you calculate how many were chosen? Sometimes you may even need to calculate a part of a part. For example, if Cameron sprinted $\frac{2}{3}$ of the $\frac{1}{4}$-mile track, how would you calculate how far Cameron sprinted? Today you will use different models to help you answer these kinds of questions.

2-85. Cecil has just created a spectacular routine. (A routine is a sequence of moves to get from start to finish.) His routine has two parts. The first part consists of a series of creative leaps followed by a somersault. The first part ends with Cecil's doing an elaborate bow while balancing on one toe. Then he moves into the second part of the routine, which includes several back flips and spins. When performed perfectly, the routine moves Cecil exactly to the other end of his tightrope. The routine can be represented by the following expressions. First,

Part I: $3(2)+3(3)+(-5)+4$

Then he pauses to take a bow in place. And then,

Part II: $5+3+4(1+-1)+(-3)+(-5)+3(5+(-2))+1$

Work with your team to draw an accurate diagram (drawn to scale) to represent Cecil's routine. Then answer the following questions and be ready to share your reasoning. Assume that the numbers used to describe the routine represent feet.

a. How long is Cecil's tightrope? How far from the starting point is Cecil when he takes his bow after Part I?

b. What portion of the tightrope length does Cecil travel in each part of the routine?

c. Cecil had only completed two thirds of his routine when a rather violent sneeze caused him to fall. How far from the starting point was Cecil when he sneezed and fell?

2-86. Garden Road Middle School is planning a field trip for students to attend a conference about careers in mathematics. Half of the students signed up to go on the field trip, but only three fourths of those students brought back their permission slips to attend the field trip. Explore what fraction of students in the school will be able to go on the field trip.

a. Discuss this problem with your team. Do you have to know how many students go to Garden Road Middle School to be able to answer this question? Why or why not? Once you have reached agreement on this issue, ask your teacher for a Lesson 2.2.5 Resource Page, called "Unit Rectangles," or draw eight identical rectangles on a full sheet of paper. Then follow the steps below to answer the question.

b. The entire school's enrollment—no matter what it is—can be represented with an unshaded unit rectangle, as shown at right.

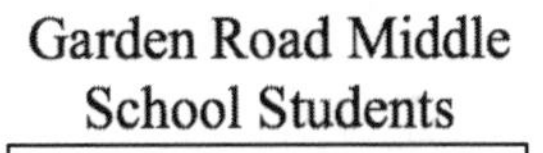

Half of the school plans to attend. To show this, divide your rectangle into two equal pieces, as shown below. Then lightly shade and label one of the halves to show the half of the school that is planning to attend.

Label the other half with an appropriate label.

½ of the school plans to attend

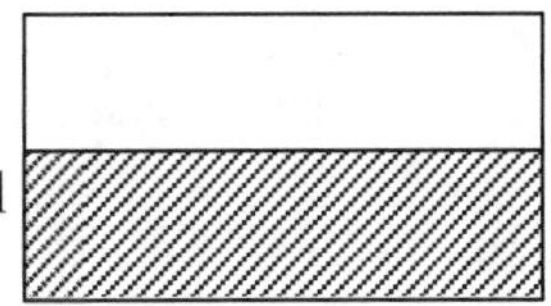

c. Three fourths of the students planning to attend brought back their permission slips to go to the conference. Represent this portion on your rectangle.

d. What fraction of the whole school will attend the conference?

e. If the total school population is 120 students, how many would attend?

f. **Additional Challenge:** How do you know that the total school population cannot be either 125 or 250?

2-87. Howie has $\frac{5}{8}$ of a pizza left over from last night's dinner. He loves pizza and eats half of the remaining pizza the next day for breakfast.

a. Draw your own diagram or use your unit rectangle resource page to determine what portion of the original pizza Howie ate for breakfast.

b. Write an equation to show $\frac{1}{2}$ of $\frac{5}{8}$.

2-88. Joe Dominguez has decided to plant a rectangular flower garden. Joe loves red carnations. He wants 50% of the garden to be planted with carnations, and one third of the carnations must be red.

a. On a unit rectangle, label and shade the fraction of the garden that must be carnations.

b. Now label and shade the fraction of the carnations that must be red.

c. What fraction of the whole garden must be red carnations?

d. What fraction of the garden is not carnations?

e. Express the number of red carnations with a number sentence.

2-89. For each of the four diagrams below, write an equation that represents the darkly shaded portion and a sentence that describes that section.

Example:

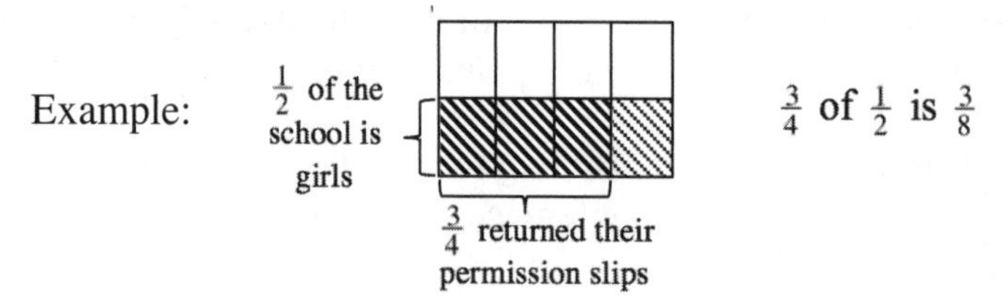

$\frac{3}{8}$ of the students at the school are girls who returned their permission slips.

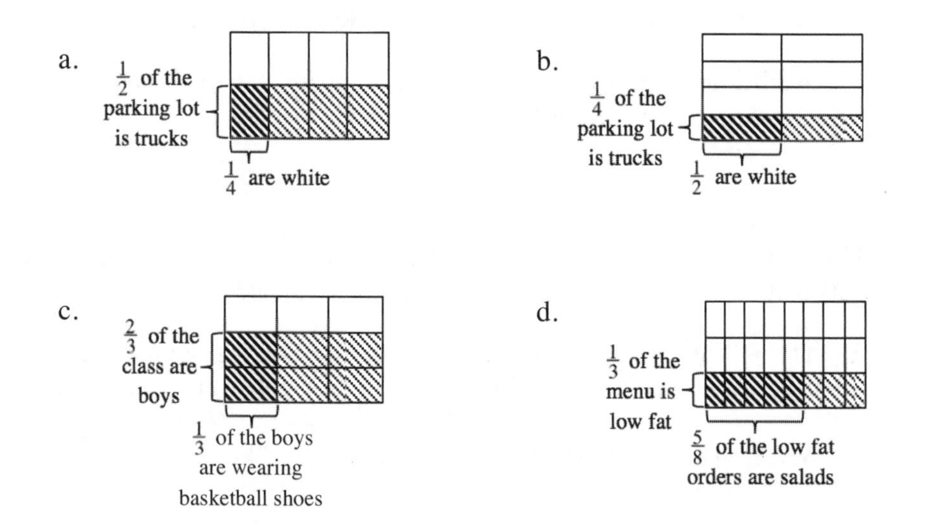

MATH NOTES

METHODS AND MEANINGS

Multiplying Fractions Using a Rectangle

One way to model multiplying fractions is to shade a unit rectangle. Below is an example of shading a unit rectangle to represent $\frac{2}{3}$ of $\frac{2}{5}$ or, written as multiplication, $\frac{2}{3} \cdot \frac{2}{5}$.

Step 1: Divide a rectangle into five sections ("fifths")—the denominator of the second fraction. (Notice that the second number has been drawn first.)

Step 2: Shade horizontal sections to represent how many fifths there are—the numerator of the second fraction.

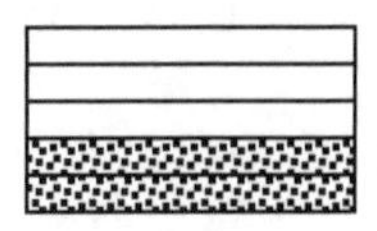

Step 3: Divide the rectangle vertically using the denominator of the other factor ("thirds").

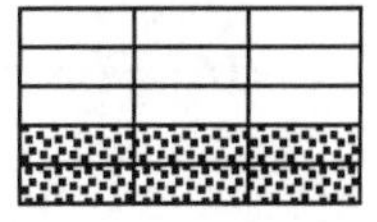

Step 4: Use a darker shading to show how many thirds there are. For this example, shade two thirds of the two fifths.

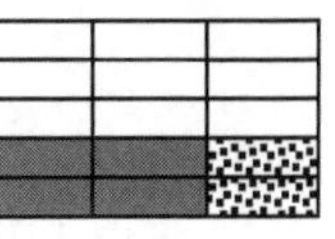

Step 5: The product's numerator is the number of sections that are double-shaded. The product's denominator is the total number of sections in the rectangle. Write an equation to show the product: $\frac{2}{3} \cdot \frac{2}{5} = \frac{4}{15}$. Simplify or reduce the product when possible.

Review & Preview

2-90. Frieda Friendly works for a local car dealership. She noticed that $\frac{3}{4}$ of the cars are sedans and that half of them are white. What fraction of the dealership's cars are white sedans?

a. Use a unit rectangle to represent this situation. Label the parts carefully.

b. Write an equation or a sentence that describes the situation, and answer the question.

c. Write your answer from part (b) as a decimal and as a percent.

2-91. In parts (a) and (b) of problem 2-89, the rectangular models for $\frac{1}{2}$ of $\frac{1}{4}$ and $\frac{1}{4}$ of $\frac{1}{2}$ looked different, but the answers were the same. Read the steps for the example given in the Math Notes box in this lesson for how to calculate $\frac{2}{3}$ of $\frac{2}{5}$. Then follow the steps and draw a similar rectangle to show $\frac{2}{5}$ of $\frac{2}{3}$. Are the answers the same? Why or why not?

2-92. Simplify each expression.

a. $-32+|10+2|$

b. $17\frac{1}{3}+(-50\frac{1}{3})-5\frac{1}{2}$

c. $-5.37+8.14-1.89$

2-93. Do you think it matters what order you follow when performing math operations? Investigate this by doing the following problems.

a. For the problem $9+2(3)$, do you get the same final answer if you add first as you do if you multiply first?

b. For the problem $(2\cdot4)\cdot7$, do you get the same final answer if you start with the first two numbers as you do if you start with the last two numbers?

2-94. **Multiple Choice:** Which of the following numbers could not represent a probability? Write a sentence explaining why they could not.

A. $-\frac{1}{10}$

B. 1

C. 1%

D. 0.1

2.2.6 Is there an easier way?

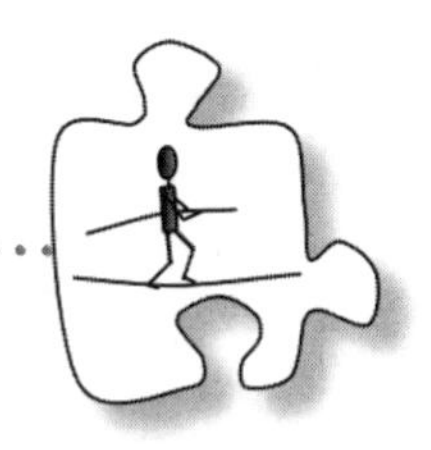

Multiplying Mixed Numbers

Mathematics is a powerful tool for solving many problems you encounter in the real world. But real-world problems worth solving often involve "messy" numbers and many steps. Fortunately, the operations you know (addition, subtraction, multiplication and division) can be applied to all the different kinds of numbers you might encounter. Today you will review multiplication of simple fractions. Then you will extend what you know to working with fractions greater than one, mixed numbers, and decimals. As you work with your team, keep the following question in mind:

Would using a different form of this number make the problem easier?

2-95. While working in class, Stephanie had to do the problem $\frac{3}{5} \cdot \frac{6}{7}$. She started to draw rectangles to solve the problem. Stephanie looked over at Audrey's work and saw that Audrey was way ahead of her.

"How did you get so far ahead of me? Why aren't you drawing rectangles for these problems?" Stephanie asked.

"I remembered a shortcut," Audrey said. *"Didn't you notice that when we drew the rectangles, we got the same thing as if we had multiplied the numerators and then multiplied the denominators? I just did* $3 \cdot 6 = 18$ *and* $5 \cdot 7 = 35$ *and got* $\frac{18}{35}$. *It was a lot faster. So when I saw these problems, I decided I wasn't going to draw the rectangles with all those little pieces."*

a. Check Audrey's method using a rectangle model.

b. What information does multiplying $5 \cdot 7$ tell you about the model?

c. What information does multiplying $3 \cdot 6$ tell you about the model?

2-96. Multiply the following pairs of fractions using rectangles or Audrey's method.

a. $\frac{7}{8} \cdot \frac{5}{6}$

b. $\frac{2}{13} \cdot \frac{4}{5}$

c. $\frac{6}{7} \cdot \frac{6}{7}$

d. $\frac{4}{7} \cdot \frac{3}{8}$

e. $\frac{6}{11} \cdot \frac{1}{2}$

f. $\frac{8}{3} \cdot \frac{9}{14}$

2-97. Ronna is making a small flowerbed that is $3\frac{1}{2}$ feet by $1\frac{1}{2}$ feet. She needs to find the area so she can add the correct amount of fertilizer to the soil.

On your paper, draw the rectangle shown at right. Then complete parts (a) through (c) below.

a. Write the area in each of the four parts of the drawing. Then find the total area.

b. Write an equation that represents the sum of the four areas.

c. What multiplication problem could you use to solve this problem?

2-98. Using the process shown in the previous problem, find the area of Ronna's flowerbed if the dimensions are $1\frac{1}{2}$ feet by $5\frac{1}{3}$ feet. Clearly label all dimensions. Write the multiplication problem that can be used to solve this problem.

2-99. CHANGE CAN BE GOOD

As Jonique was working in class, she had to do the problem $2\frac{1}{2} \cdot 3\frac{1}{4}$. She did not want to draw rectangles. However, she thinks that she has figured out a shortcut for multiplying mixed numbers.

"I know how to change mixed numbers into fractions. That will make the problem much easier," she boasted.

Look at Jonique's work shown at right.

$2\frac{1}{2} \cdot 3\frac{1}{4}$

$\frac{5}{2} \cdot \frac{13}{4}$

$\frac{65}{8}$

$8\frac{1}{8}$

Try Jonique's shortcut on the following problems. Show each step.

a. $3\frac{1}{2} \cdot 1\frac{1}{2}$

b. $1\frac{1}{3} \cdot 2\frac{1}{2}$

c. $1\frac{1}{3} \cdot 3\frac{1}{3}$

d. Compare part (a) with the generic rectangle method in problem 2-97. Which method do you prefer? Why?

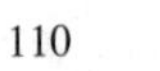

2-100. Have you heard people say, "You can't mix apples and oranges?" Anyone who has made fruit salad might disagree. However, you do have to pay attention to what a number represents when you are using it to solve a problem. To add or multiply two quantities, you may need to convert not only the numbers to some other form (like fractions to decimals), but also the quantities they represent.

For example, to add $\frac{1}{2}$ foot to 3 inches, you need to first convert them to the same units, either feet or inches. You could change $\frac{1}{2}$ foot to 6 inches and then add it to 3 inches to get 9 inches. On the other hand, you could change 3 inches to $\frac{1}{4}$ foot and then add it to $\frac{1}{2}$ foot to get $\frac{3}{4}$ foot.

Complete the specified operations for the following quantities, making sure that you are working with like parts, that is, the same units of measure. Each answer can be expressed with one number, although there are multiple ways to represent each one. Be sure you label your answer.

a. $2\frac{1}{2}$ feet + 8 inches

b. $\frac{3}{8}$ of a day + $\frac{1}{2}$ of a day + 6 hours

c. 12.5 meters + 14 kilometers

d. Cecil performing a routine three times that consists of a 5-foot leap and a 3-yard skip. That is, 3(5 feet + 3 yards).

2-101. Multiply the mixed numbers.

a. $1\frac{1}{3} \cdot 1\frac{1}{2}$

b. $3\frac{1}{3} \cdot 2\frac{1}{2}$

c. $2\frac{1}{2} \cdot 2\frac{1}{2}$

d. $2\frac{1}{2} \cdot 1\frac{1}{4}$

2-102. Below is a fast mental-math technique to find $\frac{5}{6} \cdot 24$. Remember that $\frac{5}{6} \cdot 24 = 5 \cdot \frac{1}{6} \cdot 24$.

a. What is one sixth of 24?

b. What is five times that quantity?

c. What is $\frac{5}{6} \cdot 24$?

2-103. Use the above method to calculate mentally each product below. Write an equation for each problem.

a. $\frac{3}{4} \cdot 24$

b. $\frac{3}{8} \cdot 32$

c. $\frac{4}{7} \cdot 35$

2-104. While going on a field trip, a busload of 54 students will have to be split up into three groups. Two thirds will go to lunch first, and one third will go visit the exhibits. How many will go to lunch first? Write an equation to represent the problem.

2-105. Draw a coordinate grid. Make both the x-axis and y-axis go from –10 to 10. Then plot the following points. Label each point with its letter.

a. $(-2.2, 4.64)$

b. $(8.2, 7.59)$

c. $(-3\frac{4}{7}, -9\frac{3}{10})$

d. $(0.62, -5.1)$

2.3.1 How can I make a useful graph?

Choosing a Scale and Graphing Data

Graphs can be useful tools for finding relationships and making predictions. In this lesson, you will work with your team to make choices about how to set up a graph in the most useful way, depending on its purpose. As you work, use the questions below to help focus your discussion.

Does our data fit? Can we see it clearly?

How can we make it clearer?

How can we make a prediction?

Will a different choice make it easier to predict?

2-106. PAYTON'S BATS

Payton loves bats. She wants to know if she can predict the wingspan of a bat by knowing the length of its body.

Payton looked up measurements for five species of bats. For each species, she found the typical body length (from the head to the tail) and the wingspan (from the tip of one wing to the tip of the other). She organized the information in the table below.

Bats in Tennessee – Typical Body Measurements

Type of Bat	Length (inches)	Wingspan (inches)
Big Brown Bat	5	14
Little Brown Bat	3.5	10
Brazilian Free-Tailed Bat	4.25	12
Evening Bat	4	11
Indiana Bat	3	10

Work with your team to decide how Payton can use the data in the table to predict the wingspan of a bat if she knows its body length. Explain how she would do this.

2-107. Payton has started a graph. Her work is shown at right and on the Lesson 2.3.1A Resource Page.

a. Which axis represents the length of a bat? Which axis represents the wingspan? How can you tell? When you are sure, label each axis.

b. What is the **scale** on the horizontal axis? In other words, what is the length of each single unit on the horizontal axis? What is the scale on the vertical axis? Is this scale appropriate for graphing this data? Discuss this question with your team and write down your ideas.

c. Payton wants her data to be spread out so that she can see relationships clearly. Does this graph allow her to do that? Are there any changes she could make to her graph that might make it clearer? Be prepared to explain your ideas to the class.

2-108. Payton has an idea. *"I will make the numbers on the horizontal axis bigger,"* she says. *"That way, the points will be more spread out and easier to see."*

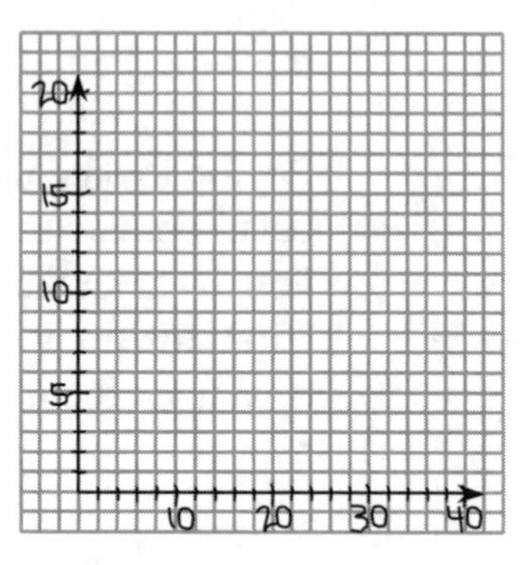

a. Payton's new axes are drawn on the resource page, also shown at right. How has Payton changed the scale? Will all of her data fit on this new graph?

b. Will Payton's new graph be more useful? Discuss this with your team and then test your ideas by plotting Payton's data points on the new set of axes.

2-109. Payton has come to your team for help.

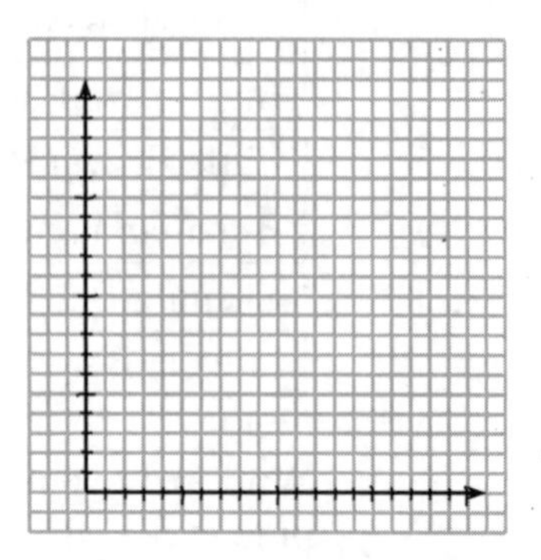

Use the resource page with a set of axes such as the ones at right to complete the following problems.

- Work with your team to decide on a scale for each axis that will make Payton's data (from problem 2-106) easy to see.
- Then, on your own paper, draw axes, mark your scales, and plot Payton's data points.

2-110. Payton found more information about bats. In parts (a) and (b) below, you will use the information she found to make predictions about the bats.

a. The common vampire bat is native to northern Mexico and Central and South America. It feeds on the blood of sleeping cows by making very small cuts into their skin and then licking the wounds.

   Use your graph of bat length and wingspan to predict the wingspan of the common vampire bat if it typically has a length of about 2.75 inches.

b. The Kitti's hog-nosed bat, also called the bumblebee bat, is the world's smallest bat and also the world's smallest mammal! It lives in Thailand and Myanmar. It weighs less than a tenth of an ounce (less than a penny) and is only about one inch long!

   Make a prediction for the wingspan of the Kitti's hog-nosed bat. Be prepared to explain your thinking to the class.

2-111. Paul's movie studio is advertising *Invasion of the Bats*. He is designing a cardboard cutout of a giant bat (four feet long) in flight.

Work with your team to quickly sketch a graph of Payton's data (from problem 2-106) that will also fit the data for Paul's giant bat. Estimate the wingspan Paul should use for his cutout.

2-112. Now compare the graphs that you made in problems 2-106 through 2-111.

a. Which graph would be most useful for making predictions about bats in Tennessee?

b. Which graph would be most useful for making predictions about bats around the world?

2-113. Look at the graphs that your team made in this lesson and compare them to those made by other teams. Work with your team to brainstorm a complete list of information that should go on a graph to make it useful. Be sure to consider each of the questions below.

- What information tells you what is shown on each axis?
- What information tells you the exact coordinates of a point on the graph?
- What information tells you what the graph is about?

Be ready to contribute your team's ideas to a class discussion.

2-114. LEARNING LOG

In your Learning Log, describe the elements needed for a complete graph. Include a sketch of a graph that shows where each of these elements should be located. Title this entry "Making Complete Graphs" and label it with today's date.

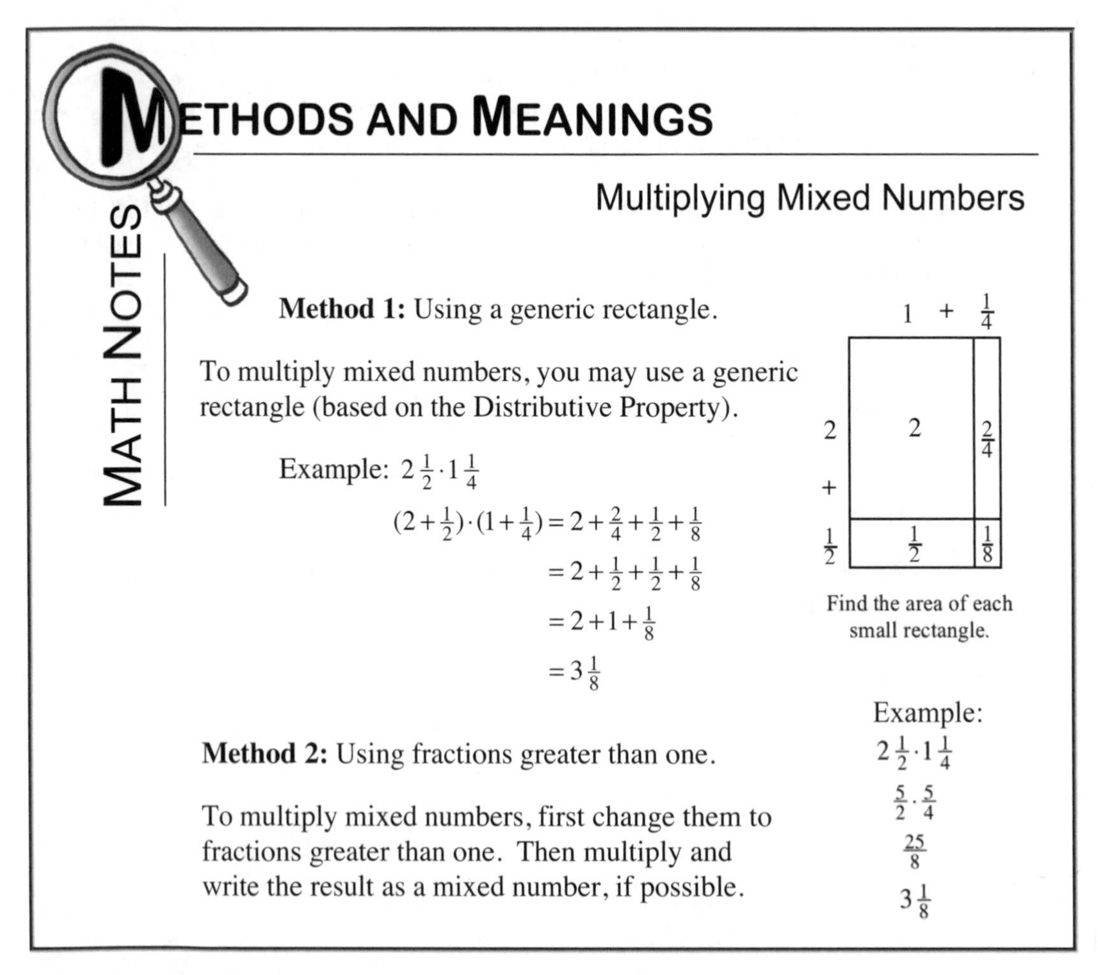

MATH NOTES

METHODS AND MEANINGS

Multiplying Mixed Numbers

Method 1: Using a generic rectangle.

To multiply mixed numbers, you may use a generic rectangle (based on the Distributive Property).

Example: $2\frac{1}{2}\cdot 1\frac{1}{4}$

$$(2+\tfrac{1}{2})\cdot(1+\tfrac{1}{4}) = 2+\tfrac{2}{4}+\tfrac{1}{2}+\tfrac{1}{8}$$
$$= 2+\tfrac{1}{2}+\tfrac{1}{2}+\tfrac{1}{8}$$
$$= 2+1+\tfrac{1}{8}$$
$$= 3\tfrac{1}{8}$$

Find the area of each small rectangle.

Method 2: Using fractions greater than one.

To multiply mixed numbers, first change them to fractions greater than one. Then multiply and write the result as a mixed number, if possible.

Example:
$2\frac{1}{2}\cdot 1\frac{1}{4}$
$\frac{5}{2}\cdot\frac{5}{4}$
$\frac{25}{8}$
$3\frac{1}{8}$

2-115. Complete the scaling for each number line or set of axes.

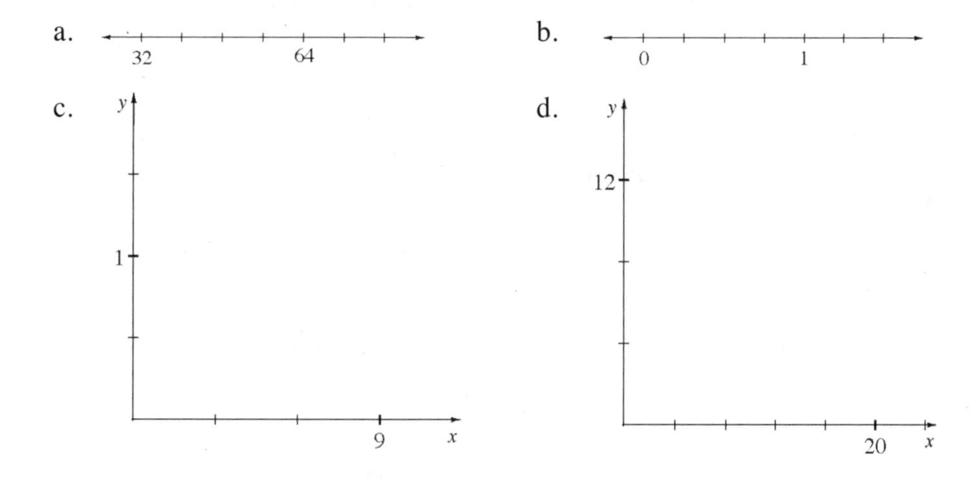

2-116. Copy and complete each of the Diamond Problems below. The pattern used in the Diamond Problems is shown at right.

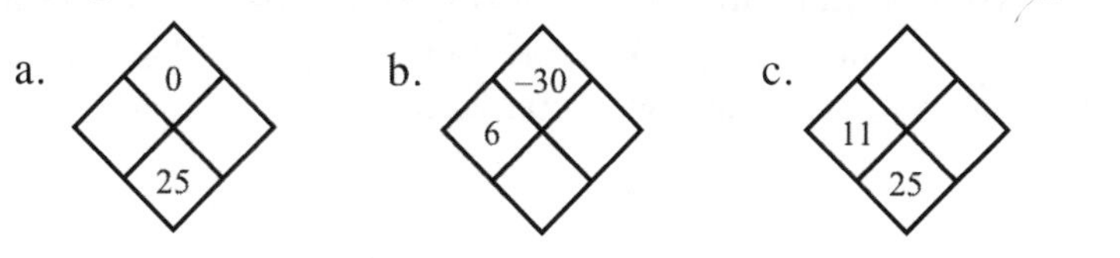

2-117. Copy each expression and then simplify it without using a calculator. Be sure to show all steps.

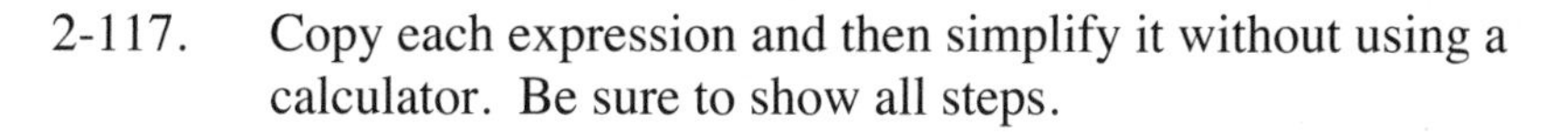

a. $7\frac{5}{8}+2\frac{9}{16}$

b. $2\frac{7}{8}+6\frac{1}{6}$

c. $8-6\frac{2}{5}$

2-118. Carmen is drawing a card from a standard deck of playing cards. Find each probability below. If you need a reminder, you may reread the information about a standard deck of cards in problem 1-68.

a. What is the probability that she will draw a heart?

b. What is the probability that she will *not* draw a club?

2-119. Christina collected information about the ages of the players on her softball team. The ages were 10, 12, 14, 13, 12, 11, 13, 12, 11, 12, 12, and 13. Christina wants to describe the players' ages in an article for the school newspaper. She does not want to list all of the ages, so should she use the range (difference between the highest and lowest values) or a measure of central tendency (mean, median) to describe them? Justify your choice.

2-120. This problem is a checkpoint for multiple representations of portions. It will be referred to as Checkpoint 2.

For each portion of a whole, write it as a percent, as a fraction, and as a decimal.

a. 0.43

b. nine tenths

c. 39%

d. $\frac{16}{25}$

Check your answers by referring to the Checkpoint 2 materials located at the back of your book.

Ideally, at this point you are comfortable working with these types of problems and can solve them correctly. If you feel that you need more confidence when solving these types of problems, then review the Checkpoint 2 materials and try the practice problems provided. From this point on, you will be expected to do problems like these correctly and with confidence.

2.3.2 How can I make the data fit?

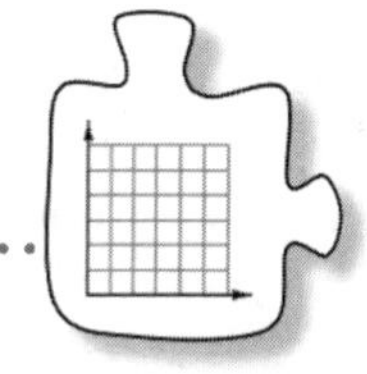

More Graph Scaling

In this lesson, you will use all that you know about graphs to solve challenging graphing problems. Each of the situations in this lesson will require you to think hard about what a graph tells you and what the best way is to show it. As you work together to solve these problems, think about what makes the task challenging. Focus with your team on how you can get yourselves "unstuck" if your teacher is not immediately available.

2-121. Andre works in his family's juice shop. He has invented the new Mathberry Madness smoothie, and word is getting around. He wants a graph showing how many new smoothies have been sold throughout the first month. He has gone through the cash-register records and gathered the data for some of the first 12 days, shown in the table at right.

Day	Smoothies Sold
3	3
4	5
6	10
9	20
10	28
12	38

He wants to graph his data and use it to predict approximately how many Mathberry Madness smoothies he can expect to sell by Day 20. He has started the graph below right.

Your Task:

- Examine Andre's graph. Can you use it to predict how many smoothies would be sold by Day 20? Why or why not?
- Contribute your ideas to a team discussion and then work with your team to decide how to scale the axes so that you can graph Andre's data accurately and make a prediction.
- Then, on your own paper, graph Andre's data.
- Show where on the graph you would expect to place a data point for Day 20 and explain how many smoothies are likely to be sold by then.

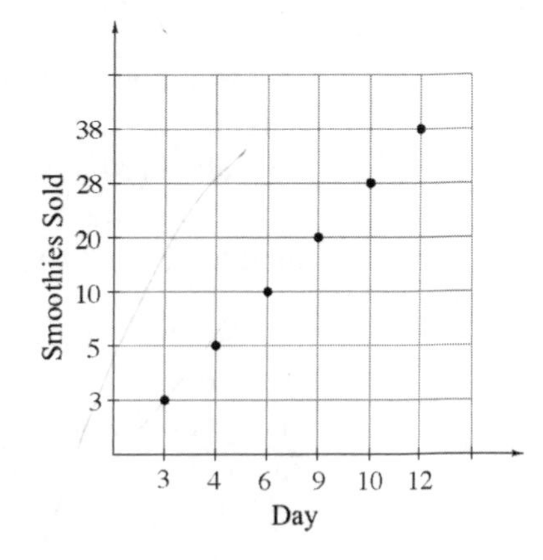

2-122. GRAPHING CHALLENGES

Your teacher will assign your team one of the graphing challenges shown below. Work with your team to plan an appropriate scale for each axis. Then create a graph and place the data on the graph. Be prepared to explain to the class how you created your graph and why it is accurate and easy to read.

Challenge A: The table at right shows the time it took five different students to get to the mall and how far they traveled to get there.

Distance (miles)	Travel Time (minutes)
4.1	13
1.7	7
3.0	10
2.2	20
0.5	9

Challenge B: To use the pool at the Columbus Recreation Center, guests must pay one annual membership fee and then another small fee each time they swim. Jeff and his five friends kept track of how many times they visited the pool in one year and how much money they each spent.

Number of Visits	Cost (dollars)
18	$53
29	$65
100	$135
84	$119
62	$97
114	$149

2-123. Jackson heard that baseball pitchers are getting taller and taller. He found the data shown in the table at right.

Average Heights of Pitchers

Year	Height (in.)
1870	69.3
1900	71.4
1930	72.5
1960	73.5
1970	73.9
1990	74.3
2000	74.4

a. Jackson thought a graph might help him see how the heights are changing, but he thinks that this data will be really hard to graph. Discuss this with your team. Do you agree? What, if anything, makes this data hard to graph? Explain.

b. Jackson has an idea! He decided to change the way he wrote the data and started the table shown on the next page. How did Jackson figure out what numbers to put in the table? Discuss this with your team and then copy and complete the table on your own paper.

Problem continues on next page. →

2-123. *Problem continued from previous page.*

c. On your paper, graph Jackson's data. Be sure to choose an appropriate scale and label the axes so that it is a complete graph.

d. Help Jackson predict how tall pitchers might be on average in the year 2020.

Average Heights of Pitchers

Years after 1870	Height above 60 inches (in.)
0	9.3
30	11.4

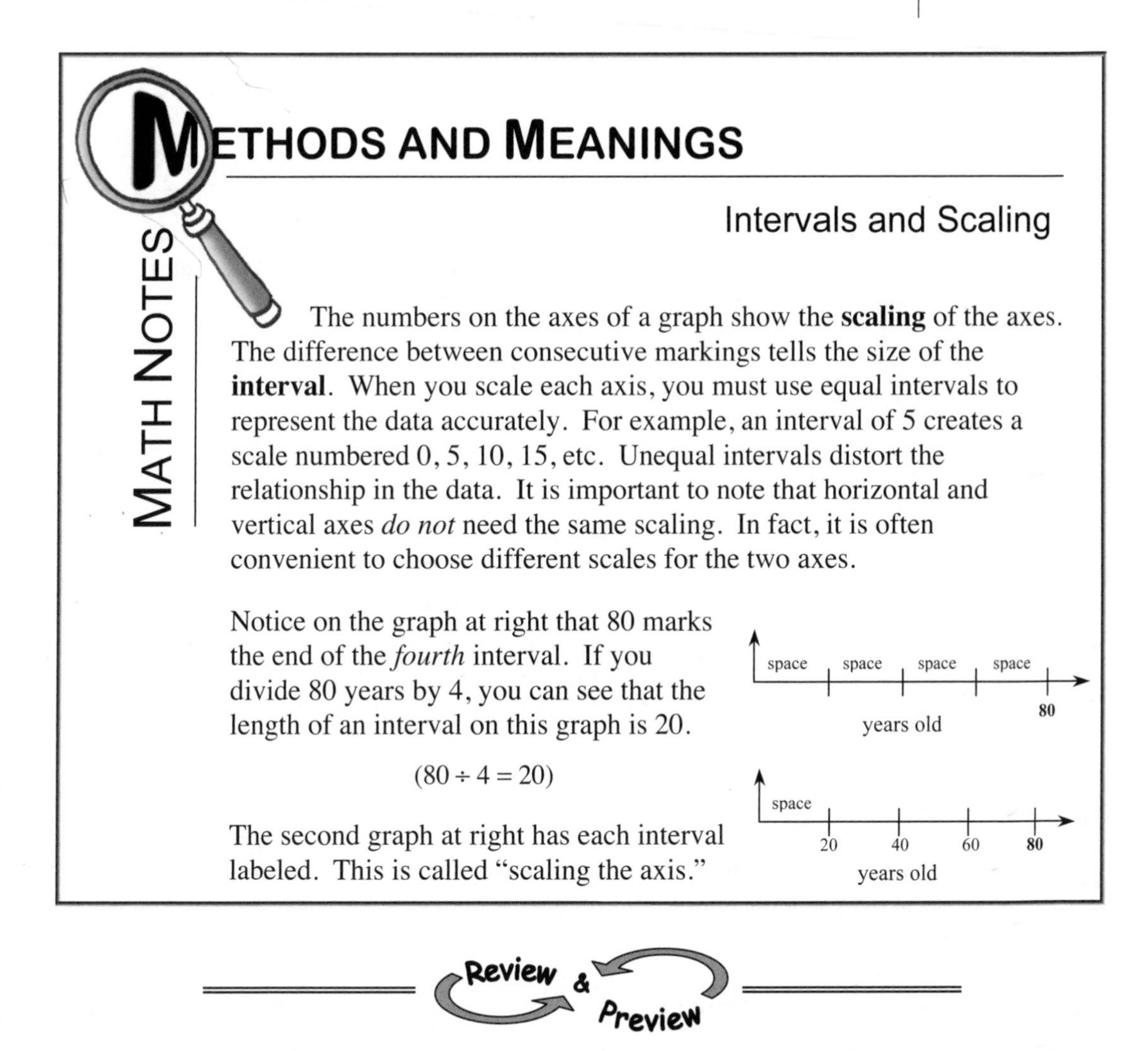

METHODS AND MEANINGS

MATH NOTES

Intervals and Scaling

The numbers on the axes of a graph show the **scaling** of the axes. The difference between consecutive markings tells the size of the **interval**. When you scale each axis, you must use equal intervals to represent the data accurately. For example, an interval of 5 creates a scale numbered 0, 5, 10, 15, etc. Unequal intervals distort the relationship in the data. It is important to note that horizontal and vertical axes *do not* need the same scaling. In fact, it is often convenient to choose different scales for the two axes.

Notice on the graph at right that 80 marks the end of the *fourth* interval. If you divide 80 years by 4, you can see that the length of an interval on this graph is 20.

$$(80 \div 4 = 20)$$

The second graph at right has each interval labeled. This is called "scaling the axis."

Review & Preview

2-124. Troy is a fan of baseball, and his favorite player is Moe Jauer of the Minnesota Triplets. Troy made a table displaying how many home runs Jauer hit during his first five seasons. Graph Troy's data.

Season	Home Runs
1	6
2	9
3	13
4	7
5	9

2-125. Sara turned in the two graphs below for homework, but her teacher marked them wrong. Explain to Sara what mistakes she made. Then choose one of her graphs to correct, copy it on your paper, and correct it.

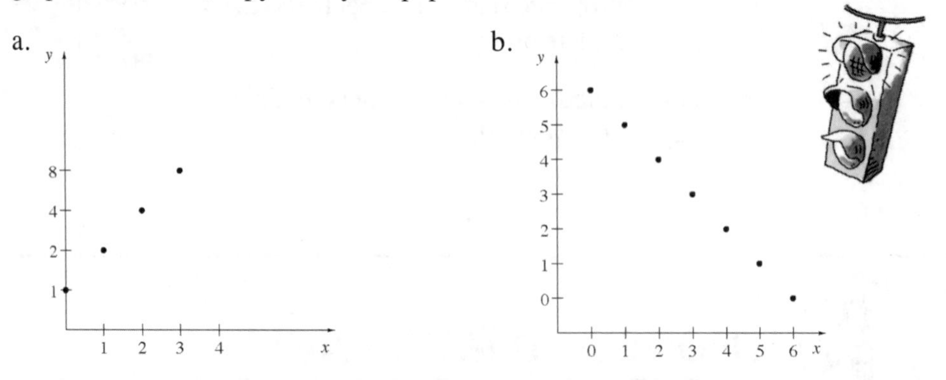

2-126. If a set of xy-axes has 20 grid units in each direction and the greatest value of the data to be placed on the horizontal axis is 132, what would be an appropriate and convenient scale to use for this axis? Explain.

2-127. Simplify each expression.

a. $\frac{2}{3}(0.8)$ b. $\frac{4}{3}\cdot\frac{3}{7}$ c. $-\frac{5}{6}\cdot\frac{4}{7}$ d. $-\frac{4}{5}\cdot(-1\frac{1}{3})$

2-128. For each of the experimental results described, write the indicated probability.

a. A coin is flipped 80 times. It lands tails 47 times. What is the P(heads)?

b. A bag contains purple and orange marbles. Sam randomly takes out one marble and then returns it to the bag. He does this 18 times, and 12 of those times an orange marble is pulled out. What is P(green)?

c. Sarah pulls a card from a standard deck and then replaces it. She does this 30 times, and 40% of the time it is hearts. What is the probability that she does *not* get hearts? (Note: For more information on standard card decks, refer to problem 1-68.)

2-129. Use your reasoning about numbers to answer the following questions.

a. If multiplying by $\frac{1}{4}$ makes a positive number smaller, then what does dividing by $\frac{1}{4}$ do to the value of the number? Explain your reasoning.

b. If multiplying by 1 does not change the value of a number, then what effect does multiplying by $\frac{2}{2}$ have? Explain your reasoning.

c. If you find 80% of a number, do you expect the answer to be greater or less than the number? What if you find 120%? Explain your reasoning.

Chapter 2 Closure What have I learned?

Reflection and Synthesis

The activities below offer you a chance to reflect about what you have learned during this chapter. As you work, look for concepts that you feel very comfortable with, ideas that you would like to learn more about, and topics you need more help with.

① SUMMARIZING MY UNDERSTANDING

This section gives you an opportunity to show what you know the main math ideas in this chapter.

Cecil Steps Up to the Challenge

Cecil has entered the World Tightrope Championships and needs your help to design a winning routine for the competition. After reading the rules handbook, he has learned that the competition will involve a 23-foot long tightrope and that there are four requirements for his routine:

- All moves must be 3 feet, 4 feet, or 5 feet in length.
- Acrobats must cross the center of the rope at least 5 times.
- The routine must include a move of traveling 3 feet six times in a row, a dazzling move known as the Tres Por Seis.
- The routine must include a series of moves that result in traveling backward 11 feet, also referred to as the Gyara.
- Cecil will also get extra points for other creative movements that he adds to his routine, but his total routine must be able to be performed within the 3-minute time limit.

There are ladders at both ends of the tightrope. Cecil must begin his routine at the left side of the tightrope, but he may finish his routine at either end of the tightrope and then climb down the ladder.

Your Task: With your team, design a routine for Cecil. Then create a poster that shows Cecil's movements both as a diagram and as a numerical expression. Lastly, color-code the parts of the routine to show how the diagram and expression are connected.

② WHAT HAVE I LEARNED?

Doing the problems in this section will help you to evaluate which types of problems you feel comfortable with and which ones you need more help with.

Solve each problem as completely as you can. The table at the end of this closure section provides answers to these problems. It also tells you where you can find additional help and where to find practice problems like them.

CL 2-130. Convert the following fractions to decimals and the decimals to fractions.

a. $\frac{13}{9}$ b. $\frac{7}{8}$ c. 0.204 d. 0.47

CL 2-131. Suppose that Cecil, the tightrope walker, can only travel lengths of 5 feet, 6 feet, and 8 feet. He can travel forward or backward and can go farther than his ladder and come back. Show two number expressions that represent a way for Cecil to cross a tightrope of the following lengths. Make at least one of your expressions for each length include a backward movement.

a. 16 feet b. 19 feet c. 13 feet d. 3 feet

CL 2-132. Cecil started from Point A and moved according to the expression $8+(-5)+7+6+(-7)+5+(-8)$. What one additional step does Cecil need in order to return to the starting point?

CL 2-133. Rewrite each of these products as an addition problem and then state the number that the expression represents.

a. 5(3) b. 3(−2)

CL 2-134. George is playing a game, but the spinner is incomplete. Help him figure out what fraction is missing.

$\frac{2}{5}$ $\frac{1}{3}$

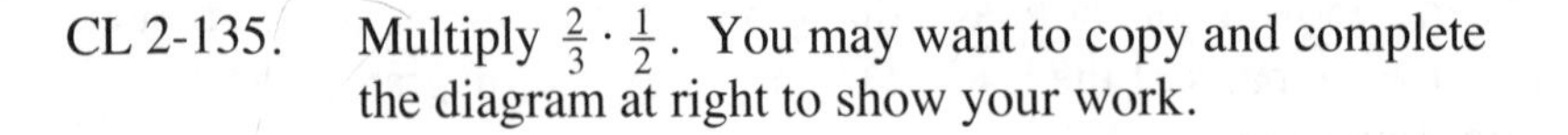

CL 2-135. Multiply $\frac{2}{3} \cdot \frac{1}{2}$. You may want to copy and complete the diagram at right to show your work.

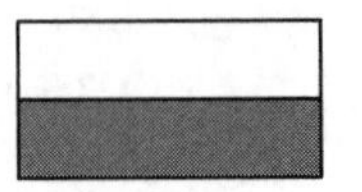

CL 2-136. Mary has a bag of colored tiles. There are 8 red tiles, 7 blue tiles, 9 yellow tiles, and 12 green tiles. If she reaches into the bag, what is the probability of picking a:

a. Yellow tile? b. Green tile? c. Purple tile?

CL 2-137. Copy the incomplete axes and fill in the missing numbers so that the scaling is consistent.

a. 0 16

b. 0 50

CL 2-138. Use the numbers 0, 1, 2, $2\frac{1}{2}$, 3, 7, $7\frac{1}{2}$, 9, and 10 to answer each of the following questions. Note that you may use each number as many times as you like.

a. List five numbers with a mean of 5.

b. List five numbers with a mean of 5 and a median of $2\frac{1}{2}$.

c. If a list of five numbers has a mean of 5, what is the largest median that this set of data can have?

CL 2-139. For each of the problems above, do the following:

- Draw a bar or number line that represents 0 to 10.

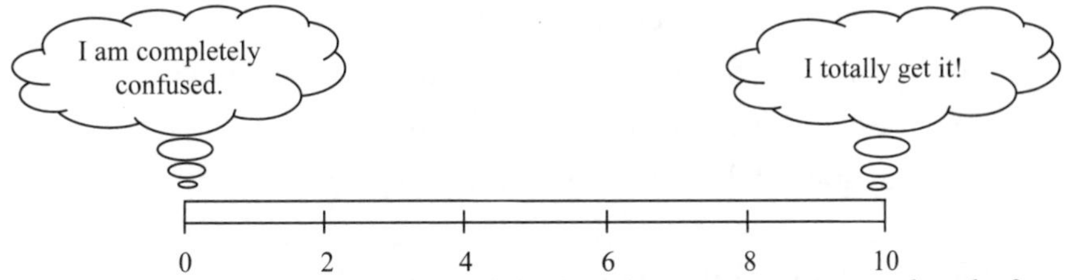

- Color or shade in a portion of the bar that represents your level of understanding and comfort with completing that problem on your own.

If any of your bars show than a 5, choose *one* of those problems and do one of the following tasks:

- Write two questions that you would like to ask about that problem.
- Brainstorm two things that you DO know about that type of problem.

If all of your bars are at 5 or above, choose one problem and do one of these tasks:

- Write two questions you might ask or hints you might give to a student who was stuck on the problem.
- Make a new problem that is similar and more challenging than that problem and solve it.

③ WHAT TOOLS CAN I USE?

You have several tools and references available to help support your learning: your teacher, your study team, your math book, and your Toolkit, to name only a few. At the end of each chapter, you will have an opportunity to review your Toolkit for completeness. You will also revise or update it to reflect your current understanding of big ideas.

The main elements of your Toolkit should be your Learning Logs, Math Notes, and the vocabulary used in this chapter. Math words that are new appear in bold in the text. Refer to the lists provided below and follow your teacher's instructions to revise your Toolkit, which will help make it useful for you as you complete this chapter and as you work in future chapters.

Learning Log Entries

- Lesson 2.1.2 – Repeating and Terminating Decimals
- Lesson 2.2.2 – Making Zeros
- Lesson 2.2.4 – Adding and Multiplying Integers
- Lesson 2.3.1 – Making Complete Graphs

Math Notes

- Lesson 2.1.1 – Mixed Numbers and Fractions Greater Than One
- Lesson 2.1.2 – Fraction ⇔ Decimal ⇔ Percent
- Lesson 2.2.1 – Multiplication Using Generic Rectangles
- Lesson 2.2.2 – Integers
- Lesson 2.2.3 – Additive Inverse and Additive Identity
- Lesson 2.2.4 – Addition of Integers
- Lesson 2.2.5 – Multiplying Fractions Using a Rectangle
- Lesson 2.3.1 – Multiplying Mixed Numbers
- Lesson 2.3.2 – Intervals and Scaling

Mathematical Vocabulary

The following is a list of vocabulary found in this chapter. Some of the words have been seen in the previous chapter. The words in bold are words that are new to this chapter. Make sure that you are familiar with the terms below and know what they mean. For the words you do not know, refer to the glossary or index. You might also add these words to your Toolkit so that you can reference them in the future.

absolute value	**additive identity**	**additive inverse**
Distributive Property	**equivalent**	fraction greater than one
four-quadrant graph	**integers**	interval
mixed number	**rational numbers**	repeating decimal
scaling	terminating decimal	

Answers and Support for Closure Activity #2
What Have I Learned?

Note: MN = Math Note, LL = Learning Log

Problem	Solution	Need Help?	More Practice
CL 2-130.	a. $1.\overline{4}$ b. 0.875 c. $\frac{51}{250}$ d. $\frac{47}{100}$	Lessons 2.1.1 and 2.1.2 MN: 2.1.1 and 2.1.2	Problems 2-9, 2-54, 2-82, and 2-120
CL 2-131.	Answers vary. Sample answers: a. $5+5+6$, $8+8$, $3(8)+(-8)$ b. $5+6+8$, $5(5)+(-6)$ c. $6+6+6+(-5)$, $3(5)+6+(-8)$ d. $5+6+(-8)$, $8+(-5)$	Lessons 2.2.1 and 2.2.2 MN: 2.2.2 and 2.2.4 LL: 2.2.4	Problems 2-37, 2-38, 2-52, 2-58, and 2-62
CL 2-132.	The total is 6, so -6 will return to start.	Lessons 2.2.1 and 2.2.2 MN: 2.2.2 and 2.2.3 LL: 2.2.2 and 2.2.4	Problems 2-48, 2-49, and 2-58
CL 2-133.	a. $3+3+3+3+3=15$ b. $(-2)+(-2)+(-2)=-6$	Lesson 2.2.4 MN: 2.2.4 LL: 2.2.4	Problems 2-67, 2-68, 2-69, 2-70, 2-71, 2-72, 2-75, and 2-79
CL 2-134.	$\frac{4}{15}$	Lessons 1.2.2 and 1.2.8 MN: 1.2.3	Problems CL 1-144, 2-10, 2-55, and 2-66
CL 2-135.	$\frac{2}{6}$ or $\frac{1}{3}$	Lesson 2.2.5 MN: 2.2.5	Problems 2-90 and 2-127
CL 2-136.	a. $\frac{9}{36}$ or $\frac{1}{4}$ b. $\frac{12}{36}$ or $\frac{1}{3}$ c. 0: There are no purple tiles; impossible	Lessons 1.2.1 and 1.2.2 MN: 1.2.3 LL: 1.2.1	Problems CL 1-148, 2-15, 2-28, 2-64, and 2-118

Problem	Solution	Need Help?	More Practice
CL 2-137.	Only the missing numbers are listed. a. 4, 8, 12, 20 b. 25, 75, 100, 125, 150	Lessons 2.3.1 and 2.3.2 MN: 1.2.2 and 2.3.2	Problems 2-29, 2-39, 2-65, 2-115, and 2-126
CL 2-138.	a. Possible responses include: $0, 2\frac{1}{2}, 2\frac{1}{2}, 10, 10$ or $1, 2, 2, 10, 10$ or $1, 3, 7, 7, 7$ b. Possible responses include: $0, 2\frac{1}{2}, 2\frac{1}{2}, 10, 10$ or $1, 2\frac{1}{2}, 2\frac{1}{2}, 9, 10$ c. The sum of the numbers should be 25; the largest median to achieve that with is $7\frac{1}{2}$, using the list $0, 2\frac{1}{2}, 7\frac{1}{2}, 7\frac{1}{2}, 7\frac{1}{2}$.	MN: 1.1.3 and 1.1.4	Problems 2-14, 2-41, 2-84, and 2-119

3
Arithmetic
Properties
(7+5) + 9
=
7 + (5+9)
(a+b) + c
=
a + (b+c)

CHAPTER 3 Arithmetic Properties

The acrobat from Chapter 2 has somersaulted into Chapter 3, where you will continue to use the acrobat's routines as you work with integers. Specifically, you will learn about grouping mathematical operations so that you can simplify expressions accurately. In the first section of this chapter, you will also begin to think about how to figure out unknown amounts, a skill that is essential for algebraic thinking.

In the second section of this chapter, you will revisit integers as you investigate subtraction of positive and negative numbers and think more deeply about multiplication.

Guiding Questions

Think about these questions throughout this chapter:

What strategy can I use?

How can I calculate it?

What is another way to show it?

Section 3.3 extends your previous understanding of operating with portions to include division with fractions, mixed numbers, and decimals.

In this chapter, you will learn how to:

- Simplify expressions with multiple operations by identifying and evaluating groups.
- Subtract and multiply positive and negative numbers.
- Divide with fractions, mixed numbers, and decimals.

Chapter Outline

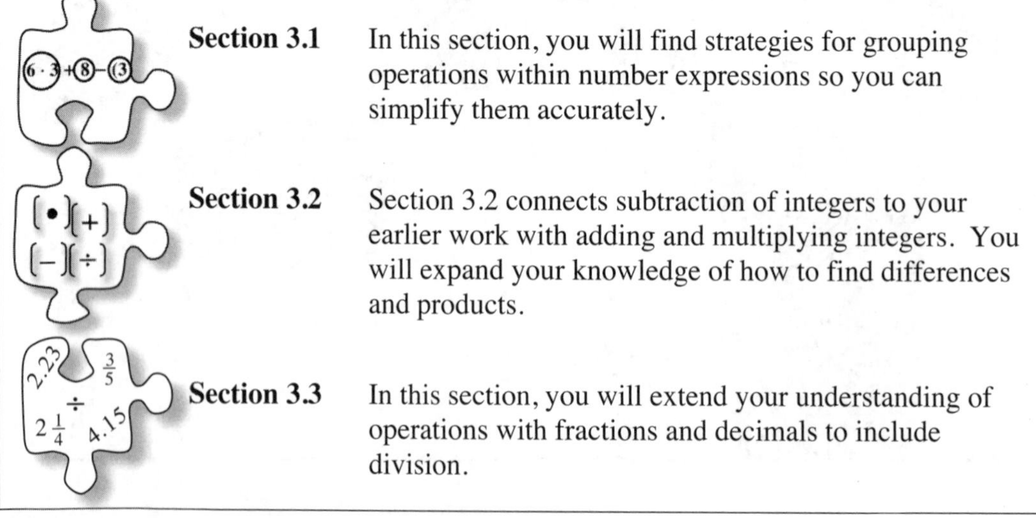

Section 3.1 In this section, you will find strategies for grouping operations within number expressions so you can simplify them accurately.

Section 3.2 Section 3.2 connects subtraction of integers to your earlier work with adding and multiplying integers. You will expand your knowledge of how to find differences and products.

Section 3.3 In this section, you will extend your understanding of operations with fractions and decimals to include division.

3.1.1 How can I simplify it?

Grouping Expressions

In previous lessons you have worked with expressions, combinations of numbers, variables, and operation symbols, that involve either adding integers or multiplying integers. Today you will examine expressions that involve *both* operations. By the end of this lesson, you will be expected to be able to answer these target questions:

How can expressions with the same numbers and operations have different meanings?

Does the order in which we do each operation matter?

3-1. Katrina wrote the following set of instructions for Cecil: $4 \cdot 2.5 + 1$.

a. If Cecil the acrobat follows Katrina's instructions, how far will he go? Draw a diagram of Cecil's movements and show how far he will move.

b. Katrina drew the diagram at right. How was she thinking about Cecil's moves? Write an expression to represent Katrina's diagram.

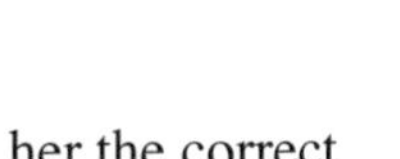

c. Explain why Katrina's diagram in part (b) will not give her the correct length for $4 \cdot 2.5 + 1$.

d. Cecil changed Katrina's set of instructions so that the length of 1 foot came first, as shown in the diagram at right. Write an expression to represent this new diagram. How far does Cecil move here? Does this give the same length as $4 \cdot 2.5 + 1$?

1 → 2.5 → 2.5 → 2.5 → 2.5 →

3-2. Cecil's trainers proposed each of the following movements. Which one requires the longest rope? Draw diagrams to justify your answer.

a. $8+2(6.48)$ feet

b. $2+8(6.48)$ feet

c. $(8+2)6.48$ feet

3-3. The expression $5+3\cdot4+2$ can be used to represent the group of + tiles shown at right.

+ + + +

+ + +　　+ + + +　　+

+ +　　　　　　　　+

+ + + +

a. Work with your team to explain how each part of the expression connects with the groups of + tiles. How many tiles are there?

b. Each group of + tiles is represented by a different part of the expression, also called a **numerical term**. Numerical terms are single numbers or products of numbers. It is often useful to circle terms in an expression to keep track of separate calculations. For example, each term circled in the expression below represents a separate part of the collection of + tiles above.

$$\textcircled{5}+\textcircled{3\cdot4}+\textcircled{2}$$

Circle the terms in the expression shown below. Then explain what each term could describe about collections of + or – tiles.

$$4\cdot5+1+3(-2)+6$$

3-4. Circle the terms and simplify each expression shown below. **Simplify** means to write an expression in its simplest form. In the case of numerical expressions, the simplest form is a single number.

a. $7.08+2.51+(-3.84)$

b. $7.8+2.1(-3)$

c. $5(-\frac{3}{5})+2\cdot1.5$

d. $4.35\cdot2+5+\left(3\frac{1}{4}\right)(-1)+(-10)$

3-5. GROUPING CHALLENGE

Work with your team to add parentheses to $1+3\cdot2+8+(-4)$ so that the resulting expression has the smallest possible value. Then find a different way to add parentheses to the same expression so that it has the largest possible value. For each expression, draw a diagram of how Cecil would move.

3-6. LEARNING LOG

In your Learning Log, answer the target questions for this lesson, which are reprinted below. Be sure to include examples to support your ideas. Title this entry "Grouping Integers" and label it with today's date.

How can expressions with the same numbers and operations have different meanings?

Does it matter in which order we do each operation?

3-7. Consider the expression $7+3\cdot4+2$.

a. What movements does this represent for Cecil walking on his tightrope? Draw a diagram to show his movements and the length of his walk.

b. How many different answers can you get by grouping differently? Add parentheses to the expression $7+3\cdot4+2$ to create new expressions with as many different values as possible.

3-8. Find the distance between each pair of points if they were graphed on a number line. Represent your work using absolute value symbols.

a. –27.1 and 53.2 b. 71.54 and –28.3 c. –38.9 and –7.3

3-9. Find the missing information from the following relationships.

a. Mark has downloaded four times as many songs on his music player as Chloe. If Mark has 440 songs, how many songs does Chloe have?

b. Cici likes to collect shoes, but she only has half the number of pairs of shoes that her friend Aubree has. If Cici has 42 pairs of shoes, how many pairs of shoes does Aubree have?

c. Tito walked three more miles than Danielle. If Danielle walked 2 miles, how far did Tito walk?

3-10. After a pizza party, Julia has parts of five pizzas left over, as shown below. Each pizza was originally cut into 12 pieces, and the shaded areas represent the slices that were not eaten.

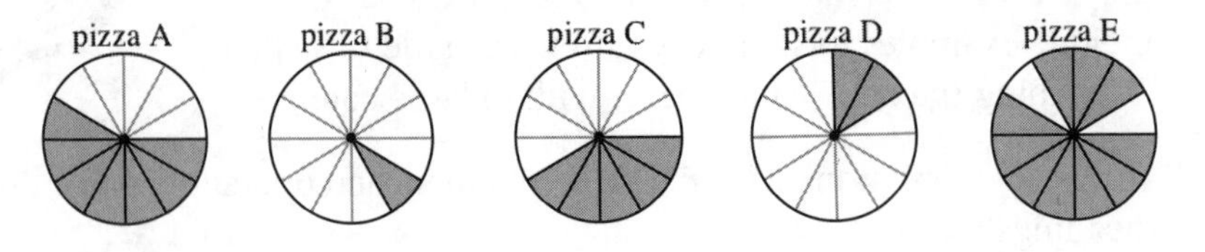

a. What fraction of pizza A is left?

b. If all of the pieces were put together, how many whole pizzas could Julia make? How many extra pieces would she have?

c. Julia wants to write the amount of leftover pizza as a single fraction. How could she do this?

3-11. Copy and complete the generic rectangle below. What multiplication problem does it represent and what is the product?

	—	+ 5
—	200	100
+ 7	—	—

3.1.2 What if they are complicated?

Identifying Terms in Expressions

In today's lesson, you will continue to simplify expressions using the correct Order of Operations. You will also learn how to identify terms in expressions that are more complicated.

3-12. For each of the following expressions:

- Draw a diagram that could represent the expression.
- Simplify the expression.

a. $-3+4(-2)^3+5$

b. $-3^2+4(-2+5)$

3-13. Katrina and Madeline were working on problem 3-12 when Madeline noticed, *"These two expressions look almost the same, except that one has two terms, while the other has three!"*

Discuss Madeline's observation with your team. Explain which expression has two terms and which has three. **Terms** in expressions are separated by addition (+) and subtraction (–) signs unless the sum or difference is inside parentheses.

3-14. Consider the expression $3(5+2\cdot 4)+2(-3)$.

a. Work with your team to draw a diagram representing this expression. Your diagram could show Cecil's movements, for example, or it could show + and – tiles that could be represented by this expression.

b. Simplify the expression.

c. Discuss with your team how you might circle terms in this expression. Be ready to explain your ideas to the class.

3-15. For each of the following expressions, visualize them as Cecil's movements on a tightrope or as groups of + and – tiles. Then:

- Describe to your team members how you see each expression.
- Circle the terms and simplify each expression.

a. $3(8.63)+1$

b. $1+3(8.63)$

c. $4\frac{1}{3}+2\left(3\frac{2}{5}\right)+5$

d. $4\frac{1}{3}+2(3\frac{2}{5}+5)$

e. $4+(-2)+3(5)$

f. $2(-4+3+5)$

g. $2.68(20)+4+3(-5)$

h. $4(-7.6)+3\frac{1}{2}(100+5)$

3-16. AIM FOR 16

In this game, you and the other players will create expressions that contain the same four numbers. Then you will compare the numbers that your expressions represent to see whose number is closest to 16.

Your teacher will roll four number cubes to determine the four numbers you can use in your expression. You may use each number as either a positive or negative integer, and each number must appear exactly once in your expression. For example, if a number cube lands on 5, you can use either 5 or –5 in your expression. Try to make an expression that represents a number that is as close to 16 as possible.

Your score is how far your expression's value is from 16. For example, for an expression that represents 20, the score would be 4, and for an expression that represents 13, the score would be 3. Compare your expression with your opponent's. Whoever has the lowest score wins that round. As you continue playing more rounds, keep track of your total score and try to keep it as low as you can.

3-17. **Additional Challenge:** Simplify each of the expressions below. For each one, be sure to show your work or explain your reasoning.

a. $(4+2(-5)+3(2+(-3))+2)6+(-2)$

b. $(9+3(-2+4))+(6+2(5+(-7))+1)$

3-18. LEARNING LOG

In your Learning Log, summarize what you have learned in this section about simplifying expressions with multiplication and addition. Be sure to include examples to demonstrate your thinking. Title this entry "Simplifying Expressions with Multiplication and Addition" and label it with today's date.

METHODS AND MEANINGS

MATH NOTES

Expressions, Terms, and Order of Operations

A mathematical **expression** is a combination of numbers, variables, and operation symbols. Addition and subtraction separate expressions into parts called **terms**. For example, $4x^2 - 3x + 6$ is an expression. It has three terms: $4x^2$, $3x$, and 6.

A more complex expression is $2x + 3(5 - 2x) + 8$, which also has three terms: $2x$, $3(5 - 2x)$, and 8. But the term $3(5 - 2x)$ has another expression, $5 - 2x$, inside the parentheses. The terms of this expression are 5 and $2x$.

Mathematicians have agreed on an **Order of Operations** for simplifying expressions.

Original expression: $(10 - 3 \cdot 2) \cdot 2^2 - \frac{13 - 3^2}{2} + 6$

Circle expressions that are grouped within parentheses or by a fraction bar: $(10 - 3 \cdot 2) \cdot 2^2 - \frac{(13 - 3^2)}{2} + 6$

Simplify *within* circled terms using the Order of Operations:

$(10 - 3 \cdot 2) \cdot 2^2 - \frac{(13 - 3 \cdot 3)}{2} + 6$

- Evaluate exponents.

$(10 - 6) \cdot 2^2 - \frac{(13 - 9)}{2} + 6$

- Multiply and divide from left to right.

$(4) \cdot 2^2 - \frac{4}{2} + 6$

- Combine terms by adding and subtracting from left to right.

Circle the remaining terms: $(4 \cdot 2^2) - \left(\frac{4}{2}\right) + (6)$

Simplify *within* circled terms using the Order of Operations as described above: $(4 \cdot 2 \cdot 2) - \left(\frac{4}{2}\right) + (6)$

$16 - 2 + 6$

20

3-19. Show the numbers of + and − tiles represented by each expression below. Sketch each model and state the number that it represents.

a. $(-2)+(-6)$ b. $(-2)+4+(-2)$ c. $5+(-8)$

3-20. Copy each expression below and circle each term. Then simplify each expression.

a. $-8+2(-5)$ b. $3(7.5+2)+4.6$

c. $4\frac{1}{2}(-2+1+7)$ d. $5(6+2)+4+2(-5+8)$

3-21. Justin is working with the integer tiles shown in the diagram at right.

+ + + + + +
− − − − − −

a. What is the value of Justin's diagram?

b. If Justin removes three positive tiles, what will the value be?

c. If Justin starts with the original diagram and removes three negative tiles, what will the value be?

d. Justin has a new arrangement of tiles shown at right. If he removes four positive tiles, what will the value be?

+ + + +
− − − − − −

3-22. Linh has a bag of beads that contains 10 glass beads, 7 metal beads, 15 plastic beads, and 3 clay beads. For each part below, if the bead selected is replaced before the next draw, what is the probability that Linh will pull out a:

a. Metal bead? b. Bead that is not plastic? c. Glass or plastic bead?

3-23. Copy each portions web below and fill in the missing parts.

a.

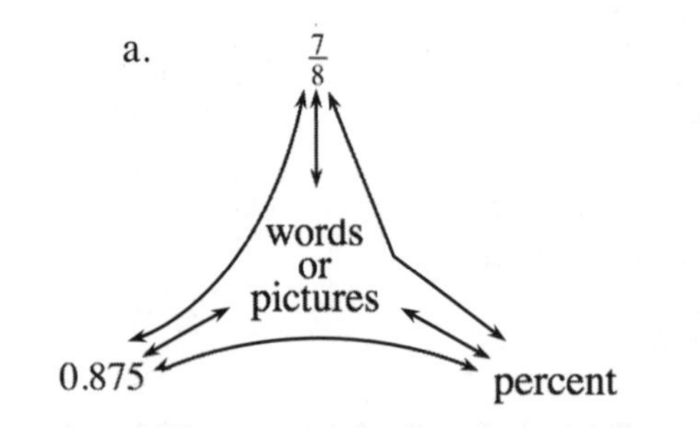

b.

fraction
two and seven tenths
decimal
270%

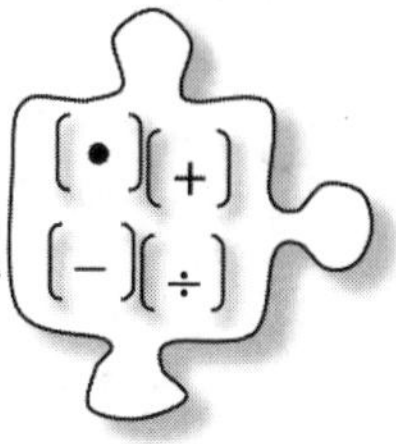

3.2.1 How can I subtract?

Subtraction of Integers

In Chapter 2, you worked with adding and multiplying **integers** (positive and negative whole numbers and zero). In this lesson, you will use + and – tiles to learn about subtraction of integers. Keep the following questions in mind as you work with your team today. At the end of the lesson, you will discuss your conclusions about them.

How can we remove negative tiles when the collection has only positive tiles?

How can we think about subtraction when there are not enough to "take away"?

When does subtracting make the result larger?

3-24. Examine the assortment of positive and negative tiles at right. What integer does this assortment represent?

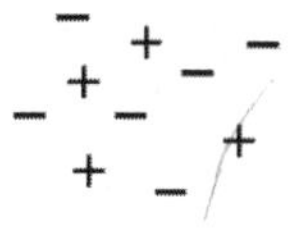

– + – –
+ –
– –
+ – +

a. What happens if three + tiles are removed? How can you use numbers and symbols to represent this action and the resulting value?

b. What happens if three – tiles are removed from the original set of tiles? Again, how can you represent this action and the result using numbers and symbols?

3-25. It is often useful to represent operations and expressions in multiple ways. These ways include:

- A diagram (for example, using + and – tiles or with a number line)
- A numerical expression
- A situation described in words
- The total value

In each part labeled (a) through (c) below, one representation is given. Work with your team to create each of the other representations.

a. Start with: ++++ ++++ ++ –– Then: ++++ ++++ ++ –– →

b. $-8-(-3)$

c. It is cold! The first time I looked at the thermometer today, it said it was 0 degrees Fahrenheit. Then it dropped 5 degrees! How cold is it now?

3-26. Note: Before you start this problem, you may want to review the Math Notes box in Lesson 2.2.4. It will remind you of how to use + and – tiles to represent integer addition.

For each of the expressions below:

- **Build** an assortment of tiles that represents the first integer.
- **Explain** how to subtract using words.
- Find a way to **draw** the process on your paper.
- **Record** the expression and result as a number sentence.

a. $7-5$ b. $0-4$ c. $-6-2$

d. $3-(-4)$ e. $-8-(-5)$ f. $-1-(-9)$

3-27. Subtraction can also be represented on the number line model.

–8 –7 –6 –5 –4 –3 –2 –1 0 1 2 3 4 5 6 7 8

a. Sketch the number line above on your paper.

b. How can you represent $2-7$ using the number line? Discuss your ideas with your team and use the number line to represent your answer.

c. How can you represent $1-(-2)$ using the number line? Again, discuss your ideas with your team and use the number line to represent your answer.

3-28. The Deep Submergence Vehicle, Alvin, can dive to a maximum depth of 14,764 ft. If sea level is 0, then this depth can be written as –14,764 ft. The deepest point in the Pacific Ocean, as well as the world, is a location called Challenger Deep in the Mariana Trench. It has a depth of –35,840 ft. Tory and Nina wanted to know the distance from the bottom of the trench to Alvin when the submarine was at its maximum dive depth.

Tory knew that they needed to subtract to find the difference between the two depths, so she did $-35,840-(-14,764)$. Nina, on the other hand, did $-14,764-(-35,840)$.

a. Complete both computations. What do you notice about the solutions?

b. If you want to find the distance between the two depths, what could you do with the computations to get a positive value? Write both expressions to show this.

c. Use your work from part (b) to find the distance between Alvin at its deepest dive depth and the following points. For each calculation, write an equation and your solution.

i. The Puerto Rico Trench in the Atlantic Ocean, –28,374 ft.

ii. The Eurasia Basin in the Arctic Ocean, –17,881 ft.

iii. The Java Trench in the Indian Ocean, –23,376 ft.

3-29. Absolute value can be thought of as the distance between a number and zero, but it can be thought of as the distance between two non-zero numbers, as well. Use your number line model from problem 3-27 to answer the following questions.

a. Place points at 8.6 and 3.4 on your number line. What is the absolute value (distance) between 8.6 and 3.4? How can you tell?

b. Use the number line to find the absolute value (distance) between –6.72 and 4.13.

3-30. Represent the distance between each pair of points below in two ways using the absolute value symbol. For example, the distance between 8 and 3 can be written $|8-3|=|5|=5$ as well as $|3-8|=|-5|=5$.

a. $-2\frac{1}{6}$ and 1 b. 2.38 and 7.49 c. $9\frac{3}{10}$ and –6.55

3-31. Zariah drew the diagram at right to show Cecil the acrobat's movements on a tightrope.

8 feet

3

2

a. Her expression is $8+(-3)+2$. Discuss with your team how the numbers in her expression are related to the diagram.

b. Zariah decided to change the length of the acrobat's sequence by *removing* the 2-foot arrow. How does this change the length of the sequence? How can this action (removing the 2-foot arrow) be represented in a number sentence?

c. What if Zariah *removed* the 3-foot-long arrow instead, leaving both of the other arrows in the diagram above? How does removing this movement change the overall length of the sequence? How can this action (removing the backwards 3-foot arrow) be represented in her expression? How can it be represented by changing the diagram? Discuss this with your team or the class until the way the expression is written makes sense.

3-32. **Additional Challenge:** Add parentheses to make each subtraction equation true.

a. $1-3-5-7=0$

b. $1-3-5-7=-14$

c. $1-3-5-7=-4$

d. $1-3-5-7=10$

3-33. With your team, discuss the questions that appear at the beginning of this lesson. (They are reprinted below.) Be prepared to explain your ideas to the class.

How can we remove negative tiles when the collection has only positive tiles?

How can we think about subtraction when there are not enough to "take away"?

When does subtracting make the result larger?

METHODS AND MEANINGS

MATH NOTES

Evaluating Algebraic Expressions

An **algebraic expression** consists of one or more variables, or a combination of numbers and variables connected by mathematical operations. Examples of algebraic expressions include $4x$, $3(x-5)$, and $4x-3y+7$.

To **evaluate** an algebraic expression for particular values of the variables, replace the variables in the expression with their known numerical values and simplify. Replacing variables with their known values is called **substitution**. An example is provided below.

Evaluate $4x-3y+7$ for $x=2$ and $y=1$.

Replace x and y with their known values of 2 and 1, respectively, and simplify.

$$4(2)-3(1)+7$$
$$=8-3+7$$
$$=12$$

3-34. The number 6 is represented with + and – tiles at right. For each problem below, start with this diagram and then show how to remove the appropriate number of tiles to represent the problem given. State the final answer for each part.

+ + + + + + + + +
– – –

a. $6-7$

b. $6-(-2)$

c. $6-3$

3-35. Use a number line to show the distance between the two given integers. Plot each integer as a point on the number line, and then find the distance between the two points. Write each situation as a subtraction problem using absolute value symbols.

a. 7 and 4

b. 5 and –2

c. –1 and –3

3-36. Consider the expression $5+4+2(-3)+7+(-5)$.

a. Draw the expression using + and – tiles.

b. Simplify the expression to find the number it represents.

c. Remove the last number from the expression (–5) and find the sum again. Show how this would change your drawing. How much larger or smaller is the answer? Explain how your answer makes sense when compared to the answer in part (b).

3-37. Read the Math Notes box in this lesson. Then use the information to answer the following questions.

Jorge was thinking about using variables to represent lengths of a tightrope walker's many tricks.

a. Jorge wrote the expression $x+x+x+x+3$ to represent the sequence shown in the diagram at right. Does his expression make sense? Explain.

$x \quad x \quad x \quad x \quad 3$

b. Write an expression to represent the sequence shown in the diagram at right.

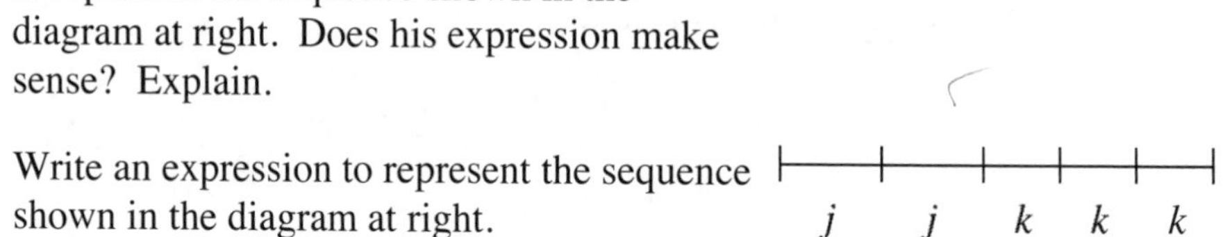

c. In part (a), if $x=5$ feet, how long is the tightrope?

d. In part (b), if $j=3$ feet and $k=2$ feet, how long is the tightrope?

3-38. Simplify the following fraction expressions. Show all of your work.

a. $\frac{3}{4}+\frac{2}{3}$ b. $\frac{7}{8}-\frac{1}{4}$ c. $\frac{3}{5}\cdot\frac{1}{3}$ d. $\frac{4}{7}\cdot\frac{2}{3}$

3.2.2 What patterns can I find?

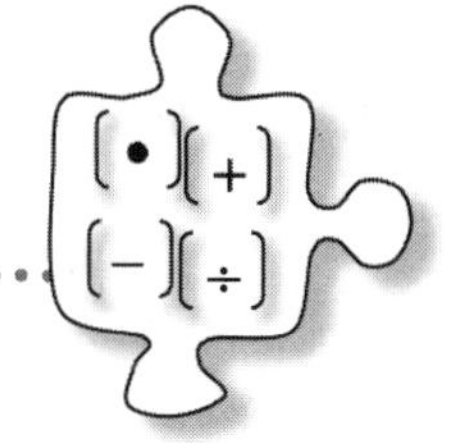

Connecting Addition and Subtraction

You have investigated relationships between addition and multiplication as well as subtraction and multiplication. You also know that multiplication and division are closely related. Are these the only relationships between operations? Today you will investigate this question as you look for relationships between the subtraction and addition.

3-39. Put ten − tiles on your table. With your team, find at least four different sequences of steps (adding or removing any number of + or − tiles in each step) to end up with tiles that represent −4. Represent each of these methods with an expression.

a. Are any of your expressions or methods more efficient than others? Is it possible to combine movements or steps so that you can complete the task in only one step?

b. How many different expressions can you create that accomplish this task in only one step? Be prepared to share your conclusions with the class.

3-40. Now start with five + tiles and find ways to end up with only two + tiles. Use your ideas from problem 3-39 above to find the two most efficient ways to do this with only one step. Describe how the two expressions accomplish the same task.

3-41. Rewrite the expression $7-(-2)$ as an addition expression that gives the same result. Justify your addition expression using the integer tiles.

3-42. HOW CAN WE REWRITE IT?

Do you think that every subtraction problem can be rewritten as an addition problem that gives the same result?

Your Task: Work with your team to develop a convincing argument to answer this question. You may use examples from the list below or make up your own.

$6+(-2)$	$6-2$	$7.85-(-5)$	$7.85+5$
$-\frac{3}{5}-\frac{3}{10}$	$-\frac{3}{5}+(-\frac{3}{10})$	$-8-(-12)$	$-8+12$
$0-5$	$0+(-5)$	$0-(-0.125)$	$0+0.125$

3-43. When would rewriting subtraction problems into addition problems be useful? With your team, decide which of the following expressions you may want to rewrite and why. Be prepared to share your reasons with the class.

a. $-100.86-(-3.86)$

b. $21-(-7)$

c. $-24-6$

d. $-\frac{4}{9}-\frac{3}{9}$

e. $0-1.12$

f. $0-(-37\frac{1}{4})$

3-44. Work with your team to represent the following problem in at least two ways. First, represent it as an expression containing only addition. Second, represent it as an expression containing addition and subtraction. Be prepared to explain to your class the ways that you see it.

While traveling in France, Juno was entertaining himself by riding in an elevator in a very tall building. He started at the ground floor (which in France is considered the 0th floor) and went up 26 floors. Then he rode down 7 floors. Next, he went up another 3 floors and then down again another 16 floors. What floor did Juno end up on?

3-45. LEARNING LOG

In your Learning Log, explain how subtraction and addition are related. Include several examples with diagrams to justify your response. Title this entry "Connecting Addition and Subtraction" and label it with today's date.

MATH NOTES

METHODS AND MEANINGS

Subtracting Integers

One method of adding integers, mentioned in a previous Math Notes box, was to start with a diagram of the first integer, add the second integer to the diagram, eliminate zeros, and then record what is left. One method of subtracting integers is to do the same, except that instead of adding the second integer, you remove the second integer. Sometimes this removal will require adding extra zeros to the diagram. Look at the examples below:

Example 1: $-3-(-2)$

$-\ -\ -$

Remove 2 negatives

$-$ (circled: $-\ -$) →

$-3-(-2)=-1$

Example 2: $-5-(2)$

$-\ -\ -\ -\ -$

Cannot remove 2 positives

$-\ -\ -\ -\ -$ $+\ +$ $-\ -$

Add zeros until you can remove 2 positives

$-\ -\ -\ -\ -$ (circled: $+\ +$) → $-\ -$

$-5-(2)=-7$

Example 3: $3-(-3)$

$+\ +\ +$

Cannot remove 3 negatives

$+\ +\ +$ $+\ +\ +$ $-\ -\ -$

Add zeros until you can remove 3 negatives

$+\ +\ +$ $+\ +\ +$ (circled: $-\ -\ -$) →

$3-(-3)=6$

3-46. Find the value of each expression below. Change any subtraction problem to an equivalent addition problem. Draw a diagram with + and – tiles to justify your answer.

a. $5-7$ b. $-5+(-7)$ c. $-5+7$ d. $-5-(-7)$

3-47. Rewrite each of the following expressions using only addition. Then simplify the expression.

a. $5(-2)-3$

b. $7.69-(-2.5)(-4)$

c. $-7+-3-(-5)$

d. $(-4)(-25)-300$

3-48. Each of the diagrams below represents tightrope moves for an acrobat. For each diagram:

- Describe what the diagram shows about the routine and the length of the tightrope.
- Figure out the length of the acrobat's trick.

a. n | n | n | 10

28

b. x | x

7

3-49. Copy each expression below and simplify it. Be sure to show the steps you use to get the answer.

a. $\frac{11}{12}-\frac{7}{12}$

b. $\frac{1}{2}+\frac{1}{8}+\frac{3}{4}$

c. $\frac{3}{4}-\frac{1}{6}$

3-50. Sketch the rectangle at right on your paper. Calculate the perimeter and area for the given x-values.

3

x

a. $x=5$

b. $x=9$

c. $x=4.6$

3.2.3 How can I multiply integers?

Multiplication as Repeated Subtraction

In this lesson, you will work with your team to continue thinking about what happens when you remove + and – tiles from a collection of tiles representing a number. You will extend your thinking to find ways of making your calculations more efficient when the same number of tiles are removed multiple times. Consider these questions as you work today:

Is there a more efficient way to do this?

How do these ideas compare with what we learned about adding and multiplying integers in Chapter 2?

3-51. For each expression below, predict what you know about the result without actually calculating it. Can you tell if the result will be positive or negative? Can you tell if it will be larger or smaller than the number you started with? Be ready to explain your ideas.

a. $-1-(-6.5)$

b. $2.2-(-2.2)$

c. $12\frac{1}{2}-22\frac{1}{2}$

d. $-100-(-98)$

e. $-10-(-2)-(-2)-(-2)$

3-52. Now draw (or describe) a diagram for each of the expressions in problem 3-51 and calculate the number that each of them represents.

3-53. Troy and Twana are working with the expression $-10-(-2)-(-2)-(-2)$ from part (e) of problem 3-51.

a. Help them find a shorter way to write this expression.

b. Imagine that their expression does not include the -10. How could they write the new expression? What number would this new expression represent? If you were to describe what this expression represents using + and – tiles, what would you say?

3-54. How could you evaluate the product $-7(-11)$? Work with your team to make sense of $-7(-11)$. Prepare a brief presentation explaining why your result must be correct.

3-55. WHAT DOES IT MEAN?

Your Task: Work with your team to create a poster that shows what it means to multiply a negative number by another negative number or to multiply a negative number by a positive number. To demonstrate your ideas, include:

- Examples (from the list below or create your own).
- Pictures or diagrams.
- Any words necessary to explain your thinking.
- Numerical sentences to represent each of your examples.

$4(-3)$	$-4(-3)$	$-4(3)$
$2(-7)$	$-2(-7)$	$-2(7)$

3-56. Marcy asked Dario, "*Why is* $(-1)(-1)=1$*?*" Dario helped her by writing the steps at right. Copy, complete, and give a reason for each of Dario's steps to explain to Marcy why $(-1)(-1)=1$.

$(-1)(0)=0$

$(-1)(-1+1)=0$

$(-1)(-1)+(-1)(1)=0$

$\_\_\_\_\_ + (-1)=0$

3-57. What does $-18 \div 9$ equal? How do you know? Explain why your answer makes sense. Then complete the division problems below.

a. $45 \div (-3)$ b. $-32 \div (-8)$ c. $-54 \div 6$

3-58. LEARNING LOG

In your Learning Log, describe what you understand about the product of two negative numbers and the product of a negative number and a positive number. Also describe how this is related to division with negatives. Give several examples. Title this entry "Multiplying and Dividing With Negative Numbers" and label it with today's date.

MATH NOTES

METHODS AND MEANINGS

Connecting Addition and Subtraction of Integers

Another method for subtracting integers is to notice the relationship between addition problems and subtraction problems, as shown below:

$$-3-(-2)=-1 \quad \text{and} \quad -3+2=-1$$

$$-5-(2)=-7 \quad \text{and} \quad -5+(-2)=-7$$

$$3-(-3)=6 \quad \text{and} \quad 3+3=6$$

$$2-(-8)=10 \quad \text{and} \quad 2+8=10$$

These relationships happen because removing a negative amount gives an identical result to adding the same positive amount and vice versa. The result of subtraction of two integers is the same as the result of the addition of the first integer and the *opposite* (more formally, the **additive inverse**) of the second integer.

Example 1: $-2-(7)=-2+(-7)=-9$

Example 2: $2-(-3)=2+(3)=5$

Example 3: $-8-(-5)=-8+(5)=-3$

Example 4: $2-(9)=2+(-9)=-7$

Review & Preview

3-59. Copy and simplify each expression below.

a. $6+(-18)$

b. $12\frac{1}{2}+(-25)$

c. $-9+(-9)$

d. $-12.2+6.1+15.8$

3-60. Find each of the following products or quotients without using a calculator. Draw a diagram or use words to explain how you know your product makes sense.

a. $6(-3)$

b. $-6(3)$

c. $-8(-3)$

d. $-8(0)$

e. $-20 \div 5$

f. $-36 \div (-9)$

3-61. Simplify each of the following expressions without using a calculator. Draw diagrams or use words to show your thinking.

a. $4(-2\frac{1}{3})+7\frac{1}{6}$

b. $-8+-2(3)$

c. $4+-5(-3)+(-7)$

d. $(-4.25)(2)+(-4.25)(-2)$

3-62. Simplify the following fraction expressions. Show all of your work.

a. $\frac{5}{6}+\frac{1}{4}$

b. $\frac{7}{12}-\frac{2}{5}$

c. $\frac{3}{8}\cdot\frac{2}{3}$

d. $\frac{4}{5}\cdot\frac{7}{8}$

3-63. Nathan wants you to solve this puzzle: *"I am thinking of a number. If you divide my number by 3 and add –3, you will get 4. What is my number?"* Show all of your work.

3.2.4 How does this work with decimals?

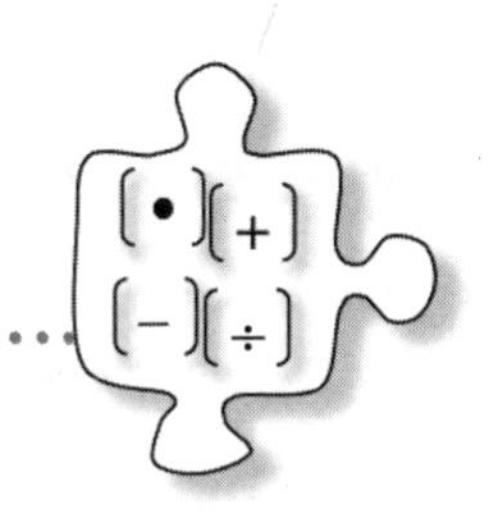

Multiplication of Decimals

Just like "*dec*ade" is another name for *ten* years, a "*dec*imal" number is a number that can be written as a fraction whose denominator is a power of *ten* (10, 100, 1000 etc.). Because our entire number system is based on *ten*, *dec*imals are very important – and they are everywhere! Much of the math you see in science class uses decimals. Of course, you also use them whenever you work with money. Today you will practice working with decimals using what you know about fractions to make sense of the standard algorithm for multiplying decimals. As you work with your team, keep these questions in mind:

How are these decimals like fractions?

What does place value have to do with our answer?

Does our answer make sense?

3-64. Howard went to the mall and saw a banner announcing, "ALL SPORTING GOODS: ONE TENTH OFF!" He saw a pair of roller-blade laces for $0.40 and wanted to find out how much he would save. With your team, follow the steps below to help Howard determine his savings.

Obtain a copy of the Lesson 3.2.4 Resource Page ("Hundredths Grids"). It contains several copies of "hundredths grids," which you will be using throughout this lesson. Hundredths grids are larger versions of unit tiles. Each side measures one unit, divided into ten equal parts.

a. What is the perimeter of each hundredths grid? What is the area?

b. What do each of the small squares in the grid represent? Write your answer in three forms (fraction, decimal, and percent).

c. Why do you think these are called "hundredths grids"?

Problem continues on next page. →

3-64. *Problem continued from previous page.*

d. Forty cents (the cost of Howard's laces) can also be written as 0.40, or simply 0.4. On your resource page of hundredths grids, lightly shade and label 0.4 or $\frac{4}{10}$ vertically, as shown in the diagram at right.

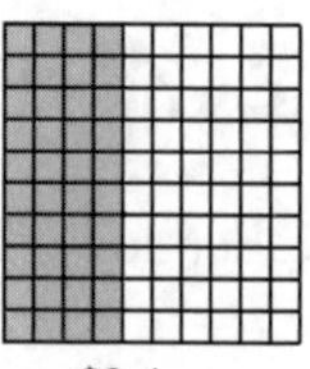

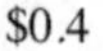

e. Next, in the other direction, lightly shade and label $\frac{1}{10}$ of the grid as shown in the diagram at right. What is the fraction of the grid that is darkly shaded? What is the decimal equivalent of the part of the grid that is darkly shaded?

0.1

$0.4

f. Write two equations that represent this process, one using fractions and one using decimals.

g. How much money will Howard save with the laces on sale?

3-65. While in the sporting-goods store, Howard found some new running shoes advertised to weigh only 70% as much as his old running shoes. His old shoes weighed 0.8 kg. Use the problems below to determine how much these new shoes weigh.

a. Use a hundredths grid to find 70% of 0.8 kg.

b. Write a fraction equation for this problem. Label the answer with correct units.

c. Write a decimal equation for this problem. Label the answer with correct units.

d. Do the new shoes weigh more or less than the old shoes? How much more or less?

3-66. Another way to think about decimal multiplication is with a generic rectangle.

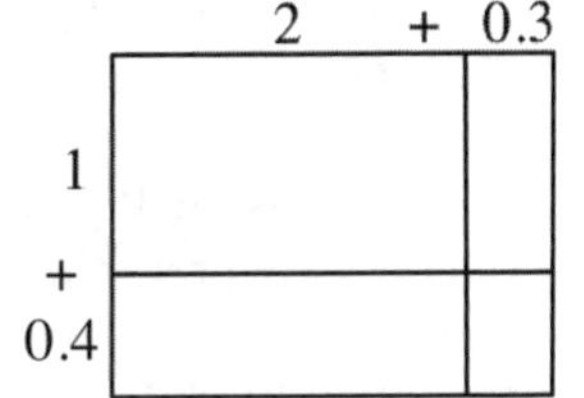

a. What multiplication problem is represented by the generic rectangle shown at right? On your paper, copy this rectangle and write the multiplication problem it represents.

b. Fill in the areas of each of the four sections. What math problem does each smaller section represent?

c. Write the total area as both a sum and a product. Does your answer make sense?

d. Use the standard paper-and-pencil method of multiplying 2.3 by 1.4. Do not use a calculator. Where do you see the numbers from this standard algorithm in the generic rectangle?

3-67. Judy is working on part (d) of problem 3-66 and is trying to make sense of the standard algorithm for decimal multiplication. Her work so far is shown at right.

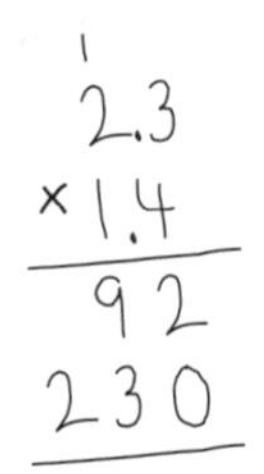

"Wait a minute," Judy said, *"I multiplied 2.3 by 0.4 and then by 1. How in the world could those products be 92 and 230? That just doesn't make sense."*

a. The decimal points are usually left out of a multiplication problem until the last step. You can see that Judy left them out in her work above. If the decimal points were to be put in, where would they go in each line of her work? That is, is 2.3 times 0.4 equal to 92, 9.2, or 0.92? And then in the next line, is 2.3 times 1.0 equal to 230, 23.0, or 2.30?

b. Copy Judy's work on your paper and place the decimal points in the correct locations. Then complete the work. What is 2.3 times 1.4?

3-68. When multiplying decimals, how do you know where to place the decimal point? Think about this as you do parts (a) through (d) below.

a. Write two equations for multiplying 0.3 by 0.16. One equation should express the factors and product using decimals, and one using fractions.

b. In part (a), you multiplied tenths by hundredths to get thousandths. Do you always get thousandths if you multiply tenths by hundredths? Why or why not? What do you get if you multiply tenths by tenths? Hundredths by hundredths? Use several examples to justify your answers.

c. When a multiplication problem is written using decimals, there is a relationship between the number of decimal places in the parts (or factors) of the problem and the number of decimal places in the answer (or product). Describe this relationship.

d. Describe a shortcut for locating the decimal point in the answer to a problem involving decimal multiplication.

3-69. For each of the following problems, use a hundredths grid if needed. Write both a fraction and a decimal equation with your answer.

a. $(0.3)(0.6)$ b. $(0.5)(-0.4)$ c. $-0.2 \cdot -0.7$

3-70. Jerry's teacher gave him the problem $(-2.4)(5.3)$. He decided to use a generic rectangle to find the answer. He used the generic rectangle below and found that $(-2.4)(5.3) = -8.48$.

Jerry's teammate Ron knows that $(2.4)(5.3) = 12.72$, so he thinks that the answer to $(-2.4)(5.3)$ is -12.72.

Who is correct, and what was the mistake that was made by the incorrect student?

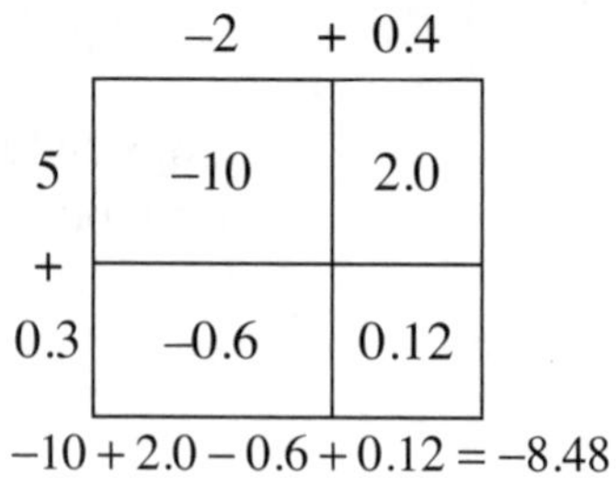

3-71. Draw generic-rectangle diagrams and write equations to find the following products.

a. $(-6.5)(-4.7)$ b. $(-3.8)(4.4)$

3-72. Howard, in his new lightweight running shoes, was able to walk at the rate of 0.83 meters per second. His coach timed his walking at this steady pace for 12.2 seconds. How far did he walk during that time? Use paper and a pencil to show your work, and then check your answer with a calculator.

METHODS AND MEANINGS

MATH NOTES

Multiplication of Integers

Multiplication by a positive integer can be represented by combining groups of the same number:

$(4)(3)=3+3+3+3=12$ and $(4)(-3)=-3+(-3)+(-3)+(-3)=-12$

In both examples, the 4 indicates the number of groups of 3 (first example) and –3 (second example) to combine.

Multiplication by a negative integer can be represented by removing groups of the same number:

$(-4)(3)=-(3)-(3)-(3)-(3)=-12$ means "remove four groups of 3."

$(-4)(-3)=-(-3)-(-3)-(-3)-(-3)=12$ means "remove four groups of –3."

In all cases, if there are an *even* number of negative factors to be multiplied, the product is *positive*; if there are an *odd* number of negative factors to be multiplied, the product is *negative*.

This rule also applies when there are more than two factors. Multiply the first pair of factors, then multiply that result by the next factor, and so on, until all factors have been multiplied.

$(-2)(3)(-3)(-5)=-90$ and $(-1)(-1)(-2)(-6)=12$

3-73. Use what you learned during today's lesson to answer the following questions.

a. Show (2.3)(5.06) as a fraction multiplication problem and explain why the answer is in thousandths (three decimal places).

b. Show (0.004)(3.42) as a fraction multiplication problem and explain why the answer is in hundred-thousandths (five decimal places).

3-74. Mentally calculate the following products. Use the rule for decimal multiplication to write an equation in which the decimal point is written in the correct location.

a. (–0.04)(–0.1) b. (0.03)(–0.02) c. (0.7)(0.4)

d. Stacey said, "*Stephanie, look at my answer to the last problem,* $0.7 \cdot 0.4 = 0.28$. *Usually when I multiply, I get a bigger answer than the numbers I start with. Twenty-eight hundredths, 0.28, is less than either 0.4 or 0.7. I must have made a mistake.*"

Stephanie responded, "*Well, one half times one half is one fourth, and one fourth is less then one half. I think when you multiply by a fraction or decimal less than one, you get less than you started with.*"

Write a sentence or two about who you think is correct and why.

3-75. The highest point in the United States is Mount McKinley, also called Denali, in Alaska. Its summit is 20,335 feet above sea level. Badwater, a basin located in Death Valley, is the lowest point in the United States at 282 feet below sea level. How high is the summit of Denali above the Death Valley location? Show your calculation using absolute value symbols.

3-76. Find the mean, range, and median of these values: 12, 4, –2, 0, 9, –2, 1, 7, 8, 2. Recall that the range is calculated by finding the difference between the largest and smallest data values.

3-77. Simplify each multiplication problem below.

a. $\frac{5}{8} \cdot \frac{2}{3}$ b. $\frac{3}{4} \cdot \frac{2}{5}$

3.2.5 What can I do with integers?

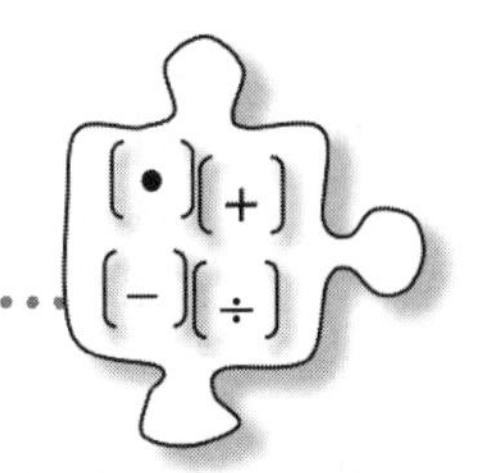

Addition, Subtraction, Multiplication, and Division of Integers

In this lesson, you will have an opportunity to practice adding, subtracting, multiplying, and dividing integers as you play a game against a partner. As you play, consider these questions:

Which operation with these integers will move us farthest?

Which operation with these integers will move us in the direction we want?

Will any operation with these integers allow us to win?

3-78. TUG-O-WAR

Obtain a Lesson 3.2.5 Resource Page from your teacher and play Tug-o-War against your partner. Keep track of any strategies that you use or discover as you are playing. Play until your teacher calls time. The rules are printed below.

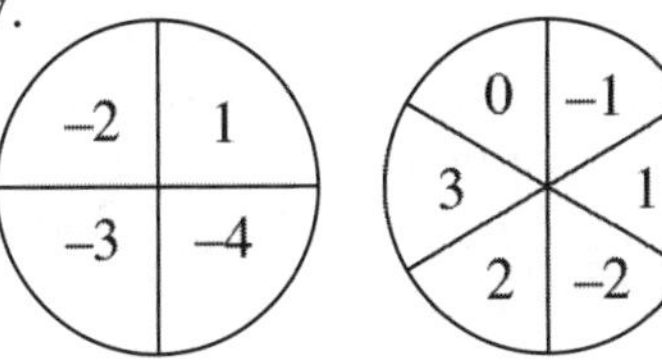

How to Play

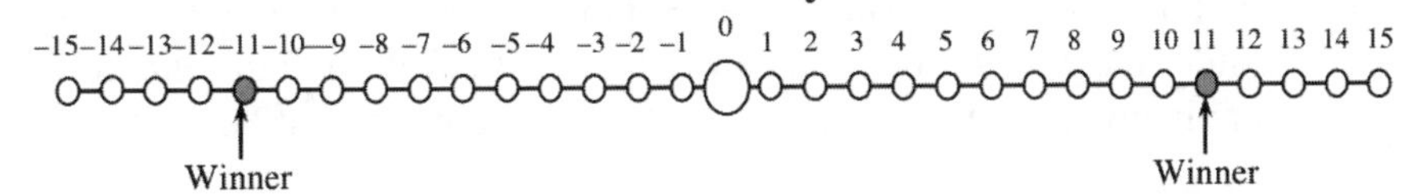

1. Place your marker at zero.
2. Spin both spinners. You may choose to add, subtract, multiply, or divide the two numbers. The result of your calculation determines how many steps you will take and in which direction. For example, if you spin a −2 and a −1, and you choose to add them to get $-2 + (-1) = -3$, you would move three spaces to the left. Note that you always need to land on an integer space (one of the circles), so that may limit your choices.
3. For each move, record on your paper your starting position, the expression and the result for your chosen move, and your ending position.
4. If your move causes your marker to go off the board on any play, you lose your turn.
5. The game ends when one player lands exactly on a "Winner" space.

3-79. With your team and then as a class, discuss any strategies that you used or discovered as you played the Tug-o-War game. Use the focus questions at the beginning of this lesson to guide your discussion.

3-80. Cynthia, Devin, Gavin, and Mark are playing the Tug-o-War game.

a. Cynthia begins her turn with her marker at 15. She spins a 1 and a –3. She thinks that she might be able to get to the winner space at 11 with this spin. Is she correct? Explain why or why not.

b. Devin takes his turn. His marker is on the 1, and he spins a 4 and a –3. Is it possible for Devin to get to one of the winner spaces (at 11 and –11) with these numbers? Explain your answer.

c. Gavin now has his marker at 12, and he spins a –3 and a –2. Gavin is wondering if he can win on this turn. Can he? Explain your answer.

d. Mark is currently at –14 and spins a –3 and a –1. He sees a way to win. How can he do this? Is there more than one way? Explain your answer.

3-81. Roger went home to play the Tug-o-War game with his older brother, Hank. Hank looked at the spinners, thought for a bit, and then told Roger that the game is flawed because you cannot get all of the integers from –10 to +10. Roger wondered if Hank was right.

Are there any integers from –10 to +10 that you cannot get using any of the operations with the results of a spin on each spinner? Do you think that this would make the game unfair or flawed? Work with your team to build a convincing argument that demonstrates whether or not Hank's claim is true.

METHODS AND MEANINGS

MATH NOTES

Multiplicative Inverses and Reciprocals

Two numbers with a product of 1 are called **multiplicative inverses**.

$\frac{8}{5} \cdot \frac{5}{8} = \frac{40}{40} = 1 \qquad 3\frac{1}{4} = \frac{13}{4}$, so $3\frac{1}{4} \cdot \frac{4}{13} = \frac{13}{4} \cdot \frac{4}{13} = \frac{52}{52} = 1 \qquad \frac{1}{7} \cdot 7 = 1$

In general $a \cdot \frac{1}{a} = 1$ and $\frac{a}{b} \cdot \frac{b}{a} = 1$, where neither a nor b equals zero. You can say that $\frac{1}{a}$ is the **reciprocal** of a and $\frac{b}{a}$ is the reciprocal of $\frac{a}{b}$. Note that 0 has no reciprocal.

Review & Preview

3-82. Simplify each expression without using a calculator. For each expression, draw a diagram or use words to explain how you know your answer makes sense.

a. $-8 \div -4$ b. $18 \div -3$ c. $-24 \div 2$ d. $17 \div -1$

3-83. Follow the Order of Operations (use circling the terms if it is helpful) to simplify the following expressions:

a. $-7 + 4 \div (-2)$

b. $17.5 \div (-7) + -8.1(2)$

c. $(8 + -3)(-5\frac{3}{5})$

d. $(4 - (-3)) + (5 \div (-5))$

3-84. Read the Math Notes box in this lesson. Use the information to find the multiplicative inverse, or reciprocal, of each number below.

a. $\frac{7}{13}$ b. $\frac{1}{5}$ c. 2 d. $2\frac{5}{8}$

e. Check your answers by multiplying the given number with your answer and verifying that the product of the numbers is 1.

3-85. Write at least three expressions that use each of the numbers 2, 3, 6, and 8 only once and any operations and grouping symbols (addition, subtraction, multiplication, division, and parentheses). Each expression should have a different value, with one being equal to 28.

3-86. Copy and complete each problem mentally.

a. $\frac{5}{7} \cdot \frac{7}{5} = \square$

b. $\frac{8}{13} \cdot \frac{\square}{\square} = 1$

c. $\frac{\square}{\square} \cdot \frac{31}{27} = 1$

d. $\frac{5}{\square} \cdot \frac{2}{\square} = 1$

e. What do all of the problems have in common?

3.3.1 How can I divide?

Division with Rational Numbers

A fraction is really just a symbolic representation of the quotient (answer to a division problem) of two quantities. The fraction $\frac{3}{4}$ means $3 \div 4 = 0.75$. In this lesson, you will work with dividing fractions, positive and negative mixed numbers, and decimals.

3-87. A **rational number** is any number that can be written as a quotient or fraction of integers, that is, in the form $\frac{a}{b}$, with the denominator not equal to zero.

a. What mathematical operation does a fraction represent?

b. Represent each division problem below as a fraction.

i. $2 \div 8$ *ii.* $72 \div 5$ *iii.* $51 \div 94$

c. Why do you think that the denominator of a fraction cannot equal zero?

d. When would it be most useful to use a fraction to find the answer to a division problem instead of using long division?

3-88. Think about how you rewrote the division problems above as fractions. This can also be done with negative rational numbers (fractions). Is $-\frac{2}{3}$ different from $\frac{-2}{3}$, $\frac{2}{-3}$, and $\frac{-2}{-3}$? Discuss this with your team and decide whether these rational numbers are the same or different. Be prepared to share your answers with the class.

3-89. Huy, Madison, and Ramona were working the following problem and each began her work differently.

$$1\frac{3}{8} \div \frac{3}{4}$$

Ramona's work:

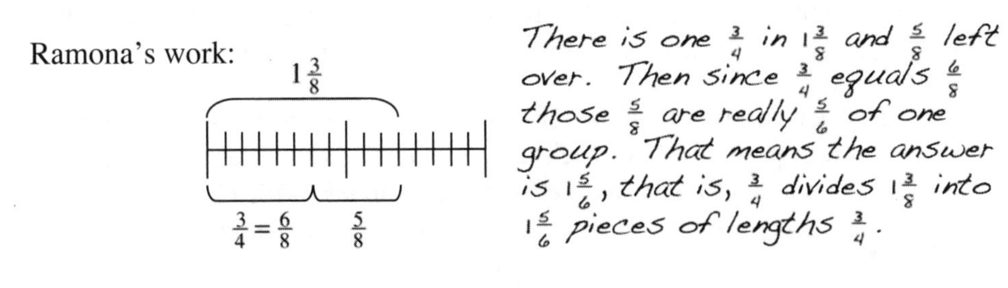

Madison's work:

$1\frac{3}{8} = \frac{11}{8}$ $\quad \frac{3}{4} = \frac{6}{8}$

$11 \div 6 = \frac{11}{6} = 1\frac{5}{6}$

Since $1\frac{3}{8}$ is the same as $\frac{11}{8}$ and $\frac{3}{4}$ is the same as $\frac{6}{8}$, this problem is really the same as $\frac{11}{8} \div \frac{6}{8}$. I can think of this as dividing 11 pieces into groups of 6 or $11 \div 6$.

Huy's work:

$$1\frac{3}{8} \div \frac{3}{4} = \frac{1\frac{3}{8}}{\frac{3}{4}} = \frac{\frac{11}{8}}{\frac{3}{4}}$$

$$\frac{\frac{11}{8}}{\frac{3}{4}} \cdot \frac{\frac{4}{3}}{\frac{4}{3}} = \frac{\frac{44}{24}}{1} = \frac{44}{24} = 1\frac{20}{24} = 1\frac{5}{6}$$

Since a fraction is division, I can write a super fraction and use a Super Giant One to make an equivalent fraction with a denominator of one. Then I just simplify.

Your Task: Work with your team to make sense of each student's approach to the problem. Then use each of the three approaches to do the following two problems.

$\frac{4}{5} \div \frac{1}{2}$ $\quad$ $2\frac{1}{2} \div \frac{3}{4}$

3-90. You have seen three methods for dividing fractions: a diagram, finding a common denominator, and using a Super Giant One. If you need more review of these methods, look at the Math Notes box that follows this lesson. Decide with your team which method you will use for each part (a) and (b) below. Write the problem as a fraction division problem, solve it, and explain what each part of the division problem represents in each story.

a. Gerard loves to cook. His aunt visited Switzerland and brought him back four pounds of Swiss chocolate. Gerard's favorite cookie recipe takes $\frac{3}{4}$ of a pound of chocolate. How many batches of the chocolate cookie recipe can Gerard make using all the chocolate that he has?

b. Lauren was bringing food to a party. She bought a 4-foot sub sandwich and cut it into servings that were each $\frac{3}{5}$ of a foot long. How many servings did she get if she used the whole 4-foot sandwich?

3-91. Use any strategy to solve the following division problems.

a. $-2\frac{1}{8} \div \frac{1}{3}$

b. $\left(-1\frac{3}{4}\right) \div \left(-\frac{2}{5}\right)$

c. How are the sign rules for simplifying expressions with rational numbers similar to the sign rules for simplifying expressions with integers?

3-92. Stella wants to find the **quotient** (answer to a division problem) $0.016 \div 0.25$, but she is not sure how to divide decimals. She decided to rewrite the numbers as fractions.

a. With your team, rewrite $0.016 \div 0.25$ using fractions and use what you know about dividing fractions to find an answer that is *one* fraction.

b. Stella knew that her teacher would want her to write the answer as a decimal, since the original problem was written with decimals. Convert your answer from part (a) to a decimal.

c. Find the quotient $2.38 \div 0.04$.

MATH NOTES

METHODS AND MEANINGS

Fraction Division

Method 1: Using diagrams.

To divide by a fraction using a diagram, create a model of the situation using rectangles, a linear model, or a visual representation of it. Then break that model into the fractional parts named.

For example, to divide $\frac{7}{8} \div \frac{1}{2}$, you can draw the diagram at right to visualize how many $\frac{1}{2}$-sized pieces fit into $\frac{7}{8}$. The diagram shows that one $\frac{1}{2}$ fits, with $\frac{3}{8}$ of a whole left. Since $\frac{3}{8}$ is $\frac{3}{4}$ of $\frac{1}{2}$, you can see that $1\frac{3}{4}$ $\frac{1}{2}$-sized pieces fit into $\frac{7}{8}$, so $\frac{7}{8} \div \frac{1}{2} = 1\frac{3}{4}$.

$\frac{7}{8}$

$\frac{1}{2}$ $\frac{3}{4}$ of $\frac{1}{2}$

Method 2: Using common denominators.

To divide a number by a fraction using common denominators, express both numbers as fractions with the same denominator. Then divide the first numerator by the second. An example is shown at right.

$$\frac{2}{5} \div \frac{3}{10} = \frac{4}{10} \div \frac{3}{10} = \frac{4}{3} = 1\frac{1}{3}$$

Method 3: Using a Super Giant One.

To divide by a fraction using a Super Giant One, write the two numbers (dividend and divisor) as a complex fraction with the dividend as the numerator and the divisor as the denominator. Use the reciprocal of the complex fraction's denominator to create a Super Giant One. Then simplify as shown in the following example.

$$\frac{3}{4} \div \frac{2}{5} = \frac{\frac{3}{4}}{\frac{2}{5}} \cdot \frac{\frac{5}{2}}{\frac{5}{2}} = \frac{\frac{3}{4}\frac{5}{2}}{1} = \frac{3}{4} \cdot \frac{5}{2} = \frac{15}{8} = 1\frac{7}{8}$$

Division with fractions by the Super Giant One method can be generalized and named the **invert and multiply** method. To invert and multiply, multiply the first fraction (dividend) by the reciprocal (or multiplicative inverse) of the second fraction (divisor). If the first number is an integer, write it as a fraction with a denominator of 1. If it is a mixed number, write it as a fraction greater than one. Here is the same problem in the third example above solved using this method:

$$\frac{3}{4} \div \frac{2}{5} = \frac{3}{4} \cdot \frac{5}{2} = \frac{15}{8} = 1\frac{7}{8}$$

Review & Preview

3-93. Complete each of the following division problems by first writing each of them as a fraction.

a. $-6 \div 8$ b. $6 \div (-8)$ c. $0 \div 8$ d. $6 \div 0$

3-94. Use any method to divide.

a. $\frac{3}{4} \div \frac{1}{6}$ b. $\frac{5}{12} \div \left(-\frac{1}{6}\right)$

c. $-\frac{2}{3} \div \frac{1}{2}$ d. $-2\frac{2}{3} \div \left(-\frac{1}{2}\right)$

3-95. One third of a rectangular playground is designed for young children. In that part of the playground, a play structure covers $\frac{2}{5}$ of the children's space.

a. Use a drawing to represent the portion of the playground that is the play structure.

b. Represent the problem with multiplication.

c. What fraction of the total playground is the play structure? Show all of your work.

3-96. Represent each operation below by drawing – tiles. Then simplify each expression.

a. $-6 + (-2)$ b. $-6 - (-2)$

3-97. If the line segment at right is subdivided into equal parts, what is the length of the marked portion of the line?

3.3.2 Why would I use decimals?

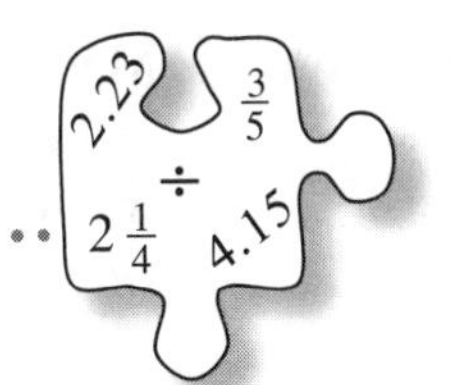

Division with Decimals

Today you will review and practice working with decimals. While you might usually use a calculator when dividing decimals, it is important that you understand how decimal division works. This way, when you encounter problems that involve both decimals and variables, you will be able to simplify expressions and manipulate the symbols correctly and efficiently. Today's problems will help you extend what you know about fraction division to make sense of decimal division.

For today's lesson, you may only use your calculator to check answers that you have first calculated by hand or when you are specifically directed to use it.

3-98. SPACE FOR SPACERS

Mr. Garcia needs to cut short pieces out of a 16-foot-long board to use as spacers in the wall of his new house. The pieces he needs for spacers must be 9 inches long. Without using your calculator, how would you determine how many such spacers could be cut from Mr. Garcia's board?

3-99. Sloan is a fraction wizard and prefers to convert all numbers in any problem to fractions, but her teacher insists that she be able to do Mr. Garcia's problem with decimals as well. Sloan knows that 9 inches is the same as $\frac{3}{4}$ of a foot, so she first wrote Mr. Garcia's problem as $\frac{16}{\frac{3}{4}}$.

"I suppose I could use decimals," Sloan moaned. *"I know the decimal equivalent for $\frac{3}{4}$ is 0.75."* And then she wrote the division as

$$\frac{16}{0.75} = \frac{16}{\frac{75}{100}}.$$

"Oops... I'm just back to fractions. What do I do now?" Sloan asked her teammates.

a. Which Giant One would you have to multiply by to change Sloan's fraction to a fraction with integers? Multiply by that fraction and record your answer.

b. Decide with your team if "1600 divided by 75" is the same problem as "16 divided by 0.75." Why or why not?

c. Write a note to Sloan explaining your answer to part (a). Include the steps to complete Sloan's work using the long division algorithm to divide $75\overline{)1600}$. Show all your work. Write the answer in decimal form.

3-100. Many people have difficulty locating the decimal point in the answer to a problem like $0.5\overline{)16}$. Use your answer to part (b) of problem 3-99 to rewrite $0.5\overline{)16}$ with whole numbers. Then find the answer using long division. Do not use a calculator.

3-101. Use your calculator to do the following problems quickly. As you do them, write an equation for each problem on your paper.

a. 3 divided by 4

b. 1.5 divided by 0.25

c. 15 divided by 2.5

d. 30 divided by 40

e. 0.003 divided by 0.004

f. 0.15 divided by 0.025

g. $\frac{3}{10}$ divided by $\frac{4}{10}$

h. 0.0015 divided by 0.00025

What do you notice about these problems? How can you explain the similarities and differences?

3-102. Eloise wants to divide $0.07 \div 0.4$ and thinks she sees a shortcut. "*Can I just divide* $7 \div 4$ *?*" she wonders.

a. What do you think? Will her shortcut work? Discuss this with your team and be prepared to explain why or why not.

b. Determine the answer to $0.07 \div 0.4$, and show how you found your answer.

3-103. Set up the division problems below with whole numbers, as shown in the previous problem, to help you solve the problems below. Show all of your work.

a. $\frac{2.5}{0.25}$

b. $\frac{-1.12}{0.7}$

c. $\frac{59.1}{0.3}$

3-104. Tom's kitchen is 12.5 feet wide. He wants to tile the floor with 0.75-foot-wide tiles. How many tiles will be needed for one row of tiles that extend across the length of the floor? Write and solve a division problem and explain what each part of the problem represents in the story.

3-105. For each problem below, write and solve a story problem. Be sure to explain what each part of the division problem represents in the story. Be ready to share your stories with the class.

a. $11.25 \div 0.4$

b. $4.3 \div 0.25$

3-106. LEARNING LOG

In your Learning Log, explain how to find the answer to a division problem with rational numbers. Title this entry "Division with Rational Numbers" and label it with today's date.

MATH NOTES

METHODS AND MEANINGS

Multiplying Decimal Numbers

The answer to a multiplication problem is called the product of the factors. One way to place the decimal point correctly in the product is to count the decimal places in each of the factors. Then count that many places to the left from the farthest-right digit in the product.

Examples:

one place	·	two places	=	three places	1 + 2 places = 3 places
2.3	·	5.06	=	11.638	
four places	·	two places	=	six places	4 + 2 places = 6 places
0.0004	·	3.42	=	0.001368	

3-107. Answer the questions below using your work from this lesson.

a. Find $15.75 \div 0.25$ using the standard algorithm for division.

b. Find $15.75 \div 0.25$ using a Giant One.

c. Which method do you prefer?

3-108. Write an equation and find the answer for each of the following problems. Give answers in decimal form.

a. What is the product of three tenths and four hundredths?

b. What is the sum of five and thirteen hundredths plus twelve and six tenths?

c. What is forty-seven and seven tenths minus twenty-three and nineteen hundredths?

d. What is the product of twenty hundredths and sixty-five thousandths?

e. What is the sum of fourteen tenths and fourteen hundredths?

3-109. Each problem below has an error in the answer. Find the error, explain how to correct the mistake, and correct it.

a. $\begin{array}{r} 10 \\ \times\ 0.5 \\ \hline 50 \end{array}$

b. $\begin{array}{r} 467.92 \\ +\ 1.293 \\ \hline 479.85 \end{array}$

c. $\begin{array}{r} 100 \\ -\ 62.837 \\ \hline 38.837 \end{array}$

d. $\begin{array}{r} 1.234 \\ \times\ 0.003 \\ \hline 0.3702 \end{array}$

e. $\begin{array}{r} 4006.3 \\ -\ 34.98 \\ \hline 3971.48 \end{array}$

f. $\begin{array}{r} 45.6 \\ 32.87 \\ +\ 0.003 \\ \hline 374.6 \end{array}$

3-110. This problem is a checkpoint for multiplication of fractions and decimals. It will be referred to as Checkpoint 3.

Multiply each pair of fractions or each pair of decimals. Simplify if possible.

a. $\frac{3}{4} \cdot \frac{3}{5}$

b. $\frac{9}{20} \cdot \frac{4}{9}$

c. $3\frac{1}{6} \cdot 1\frac{1}{3}$

d. $2\frac{1}{4} \cdot 3\frac{1}{5}$

e. $3.62 \cdot 3.4$

f. $0.26 \cdot 0.0008$

Check your answers by referring to the Checkpoint 3 materials located at the back of your book.

Ideally, at this point you are comfortable working with these types of problems and can solve them correctly. If you feel that you need more confidence when solving these types of problems, then review the Checkpoint 3 materials and try the practice problems provided. From this point on, you will be expected to do problems like these correctly and with confidence.

3-111. Complete the following division problems using any method.

a. $\frac{6}{5} \div \left(-\frac{3}{2}\right)$

b. $\frac{7}{4} \div \frac{3}{5}$

c. $-\frac{4}{0} \div 5\frac{11}{14}$

d. $-\frac{2}{3} \div \left(-1\frac{1}{4}\right)$

3.3.3 How can I simplify numerical expressions?

Arithmetic Properties

Remember when operations with numbers were simple? In elementary school, you learned to add, subtract, multiply, and divide whole numbers. As you have seen, there is a lot to consider when operating with different kinds of numbers. In this lesson, you will put together much of your understanding of operations with integers and simplifying numerical expressions to draw conclusions about order and grouping of operations.

3-112. Juno was working on simplifying the expression $24+3+(-4)+7$. *"I know!"* he exclaimed. *"It must be equal to 30, because 20 plus 10 is 30."*

a. Is Juno correct? Is the value of the expression 30?

b. How could Juno have found 20 and 10 in this expression? Discuss this with your team and be prepared to share your ideas with the class.

3-113. In problem 3-112, Juno used his understanding of two different properties: the **Commutative Property of Addition** and the **Associative Property of Addition**. The Commutative Property of Addition allows Juno to rearrange $24+3+(-4)+7$ into a different order, such as $24+(-4)+3+7$. The Associative Property of Addition allows him to group numbers in different ways, so instead of adding from left to right, he can add in two groups and then combine them like this: $(24+(-4))+(3+7)=20+10=30$.

a. Talk with your team about the Commutative Property of Addition. Does it work for other operations? In other words, can multiplication, division, and subtraction be done in any order? Be ready to explain your ideas to the class.

b. Talk with your team about the Associative Property of Addition. Does it work for other operations? In other words, can multiplication, division, and subtraction be done in any grouping? Be ready to explain your ideas to the class.

3-114. Consider expressions involving addition *and* subtraction, such as $7-2+4$.

a. Work with your team to calculate the value of this expression. Be prepared to explain your method to the class.

b. Does the grouping matter? In other words, is $(7-2)+4$ the same as $7-(2+4)$? Explain.

c. Does order matter? In other words, is $7-2+4$ the same as $2-7+4$? Explain.

d. In expressions that involve addition and subtraction, in what order should those operations be calculated? Consider the following expressions to help you think about this.

i. $10-2+4$ *ii.* $3-5-2+6$ *iii.* $7-3-2$

3-115. Juno has another idea. *"Wait!"* he says. *"Can't subtraction be rewritten using addition? Since order doesn't matter when we add, can't we just rewrite the subtraction as addition so we can use any order?"*

Discuss Juno's idea with your team and then rewrite each of the following expressions so that each one involves only addition. Then use the fact that the numbers are all being added and the order can be changed to find a way to simplify each expression efficiently.

a. $17-4-11+15$ b. $2-2\cdot3-4-2(-4)$

3-116. Maria and Jorge were trying to simplify the expression $\left(-\frac{4}{3}\right)\cdot 1\frac{2}{5}\cdot\left(-\frac{3}{4}\right)$. Maria started by rewriting $1\frac{2}{5}$ as $\frac{7}{5}$. Her work is below.

$$\left(-\frac{4}{3}\right)\cdot\frac{7}{5}\cdot\left(-\frac{3}{4}\right)$$

$$\left(-\frac{4}{3}\right)\cdot\left(-\frac{21}{20}\right)$$

$$\frac{84}{60}=1\frac{24}{60}=1\frac{2}{5}$$

Jorge had a different idea. He multiplied $\left(-\frac{4}{3}\right)\cdot\left(-\frac{3}{4}\right)$ first.

a. Simplify the expression $1\frac{2}{5}\cdot\left(-\frac{4}{3}\right)\cdot\left(-\frac{3}{4}\right)$ using Jorge's method. Is your answer equal to Maria's?

b. Jorge used the **Commutative Property of Multiplication**. Why might Jorge have decided to multiply $\left(-\frac{4}{3}\right)\cdot\left(-\frac{3}{4}\right)$ first?

c. In a multiplication problem, the factors can be grouped together in different ways. This is called the **Associative Property of Multiplication**. Use this property and show that $\left(\frac{3}{4}\cdot\frac{2}{5}\right)\cdot(-2)$ and $\frac{3}{4}\cdot\left(\frac{2}{5}\cdot(-2)\right)$ are equivalent.

d. Simplify each expression. First decide if you want to group some factors together.

i. $(-9)\cdot\frac{1}{9}\cdot\frac{3}{8}$ *ii.* $-\frac{5}{12}\cdot\frac{3}{7}\cdot\frac{4}{9}$ *iii.* $-8.1\cdot 5\cdot 2$

3-117. **Additional Challenge:** Use each integer –6, 2, –3, and 1 once with any of the four operations or parentheses to make:

a. The largest possible answer.

b. Zero or the closest number to zero.

c. The smallest possible answer.

3-118. You have learned several methods for solving problems with decimals and fractions. As you solve these problems, clearly show all of your work. Also show the connection between the parts of the word problem and the parts of your math problem. Be sure to explain what your answer represents in the story.

a. Tinaya worked 42.2 hours last week. If she is paid $15.65 an hour, what was her total pay (before taxes) for the week?

b. Joe has a medicine bottle with $6\frac{2}{3}$ oz of liquid medicine in it. If each dose is $\frac{1}{4}$ oz, how many doses does Joe have if he will use all the medicine?

c. If the temperature changes –2.6 degrees each hour for 8.2 hours, how much does the total temperature change?

d. Jack and some friends climbed Long's Peak in Rocky Mountain National Park. Then he and his friends started down the mountain, losing $1515\frac{1}{4}$ feet of elevation each hour. They hiked for $6\frac{1}{5}$ hours to get back down to the parking lot. How many feet of elevation did they lose?

e. Mr. Solomon, the art teacher, has 49.6 pounds of clay. If he gives every student 1.6 pounds of clay and has none left, how many students are in his class?

3-119. Your teacher will assign you one of the situations from problem 3-118 to make a stand-alone poster. A stand-alone poster means explaining all your thoughts in writing because you will not be explaining it orally.

On your poster, be sure to write the original story problem, write the math problem, and show how to solve the problem two different ways. Using drawings or words, show what each part of the math problem and the answer represents.

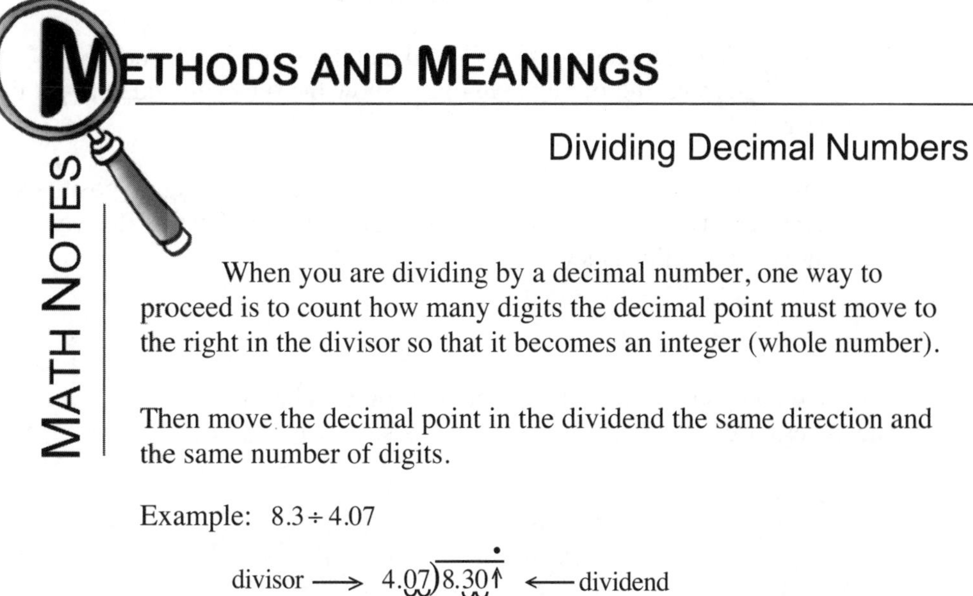

METHODS AND MEANINGS

MATH NOTES

Dividing Decimal Numbers

When you are dividing by a decimal number, one way to proceed is to count how many digits the decimal point must move to the right in the divisor so that it becomes an integer (whole number).

Then move the decimal point in the dividend the same direction and the same number of digits.

Example: $8.3 \div 4.07$

divisor ⟶ $4.07\overline{)8.30}$ ⟵ dividend

Moving the decimal point two places to the right is the same as multiplying both numbers by 100.

The Giant One (Identity Property of Multiplication) illustrates this as shown below.

$$8.3 \div 4.07 = \frac{8.3}{4.07} \cdot \frac{100}{100} = \frac{830}{407}$$

3-120. Hilda was simplifying some numerical expressions and made each of the following sequences of calculations. Name the mathematical property, operation, or idea that justifies how Hilda went from each step to the next step.

a. $5 \cdot \left(-\frac{4}{3}\right) \cdot \left(\frac{2}{5}\right)$
$= \left(-\frac{4}{3}\right) \cdot 5 \cdot \left(\frac{2}{5}\right)$
$= \left(-\frac{4}{3}\right) \cdot \left(5 \cdot \left(\frac{2}{5}\right)\right)$
$= \left(-\frac{4}{3}\right) \cdot \left(\frac{2}{1}\right) = -\frac{8}{3} = -2\frac{2}{3}$

b. $17 + 29 + 3 + 1$
$= 17 + 3 + 29 + 1$
$= (17 + 3) + (29 + 1)$
$= 20 + 30$
$= 50$

3-121. Simplify each of the following expressions.

a. $3 + 4(10 - 8)$

b. $3 + 4 \cdot 10 - 8$

c. $(3 + 4)(10 - 8)$

3-122. Refer to the diagram at right to answer the questions below.

+ + + +
– – – – – –

a. Copy the diagram and add two tiles so that the result is a value of –2. You can add positive and/or negative tiles. Show the tiles you added to get this answer.

b. Copy the diagram again, but this time remove four tiles (again positives and/or negatives) so that the result is a value of 2. Show the tiles you removed to get this answer.

3-123. Copy and complete each of the Diamond Problems below. The pattern used in the Diamond Problems is shown at right.

xy
x y
$x+y$

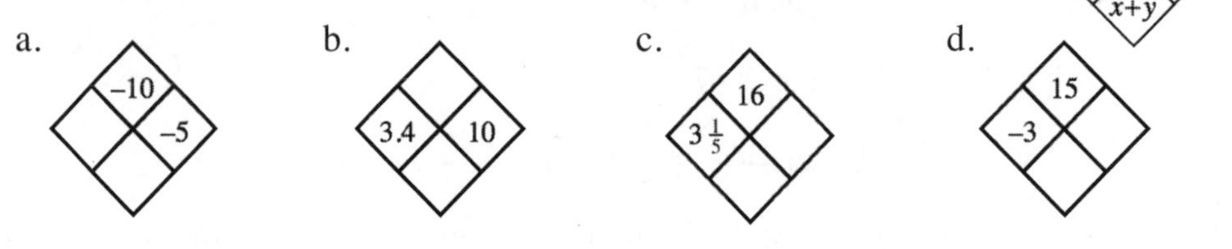

3-124. Greta is trying to determine the portion of green candies in various bags of green and yellow candies. Using the information below, determine the portion of green candies in each bag.

a. Bag A: Two thirds of the candies are yellow. What portion of the candies is green?

b. Bag B: 29% of the candies are yellow. What portion of the candies is green?

c. Bag C: 4 out of every 9 candies are yellow. What portion of the candies is green?

3-125. Solve the following problems without paper or pencil. Just write the answer but be ready to explain your thinking.

a. $2\frac{1}{2} \div \frac{1}{2}$

b. $2\frac{2}{3} \div \frac{1}{3}$

3-126. Simplify each of the following expressions.

a. $3-2\cdot 5$

b. $7(4+3\cdot 2)$

c. $10-6\div 2\cdot 4+2$

3-127. Four friends worked together to wash all of the cars that the Kish family owns. They received $42.36 for doing the work and agreed to divide the earnings evenly. How much money will each friend earn? Show how you know.

3-128. Find each product. Express your answer as both a fraction and a decimal.

a. $1.25 \cdot \left(-\frac{3}{5}\right)$

b. $\left(-3\frac{2}{7}\right) \cdot 0.14$

c. $-4.37 \cdot (-5.2)$

3-129. Cecil the Acrobat walked $3\frac{1}{2}$ feet on his tightrope, backed up 1 foot, then walked $6\frac{1}{2}$ feet to get to the other side.

a. Write an expression to represent Cecil's walk.

b. How far did Cecil walk?

c. Cecil started at the beginning again and walked $6\frac{1}{2}$ feet, backed up 1 foot, then walked $3\frac{1}{2}$ feet. How far did he walk this time? How does this compare to your answer from part (b)? Explain why these answers are the same or different in a sentence or with a drawing.

Chapter 3 Closure What have I learned?

Reflection and Synthesis

The activities below offer you a chance to reflect about what you have learned during this chapter. As you work, look for concepts that you feel very comfortable with, ideas that you would like to learn more about, and topics you need more help with.

① SUMMARIZING MY UNDERSTANDING

This section gives you an opportunity to show what you know about the main math ideas in this chapter.

Writing a Code

You and your team are involved in a very important, top-secret mission! You will work together to create a secret code.

Your Task: Get a secret number and a set of four code-writing numbers from your teacher.

- Work with your team and use your code-writing numbers to write *at least* three expressions that have the value of your secret number and meet the requirements in the list below.
    - Each expression must use all four code-writing numbers *at least* once. You may only use your code-writing numbers, but you may use each one as many times as you wish.
    - Each expression must include *at least* three of the four basic operations (+ , − , · , ÷).
    - When you have finished writing all of your expressions, you must have used all four basic operations and grouping symbols (parentheses).
- Draw diagrams or use words to show how you know each of your expressions has the value of your secret number.
- Explain each of your expressions and diagrams to your teacher.

Cracking the Code

Get a set of three expressions from another team. Simplify each of their expressions to crack their code. Be prepared to explain how you know that you have correctly found their secret number.

② WHAT HAVE I LEARNED?

Doing the problems in this section will help you to evaluate which types of problems you feel comfortable with and which ones you need more help with.

Solve each problem as completely as you can. The table at the end of this closure section provides answers to these problems. It also tells you where you can find additional help and where to find practice problems like them.

CL 3-130. At right is a representation of the number 6. Copy this diagram and use it to illustrate each of the subtraction problems shown below.

+ + + + + + + + +
− − −

a. $6-8$

b. $6-(-1)$

CL 3-131. Simplify each of the following expressions.

a. $(-2)(-5)+7$

b. $4.18+3(-4.6)-2.36$

c. $(3.71+(-5.25))(4+(-9))$

d. $-3(4+(-7))+(-2(5)-17)$

CL 3-132. Robert found a game spinner that was not completely labeled. The spinner is shown at right. Help Robert figure out what fraction of the spinner is missing.

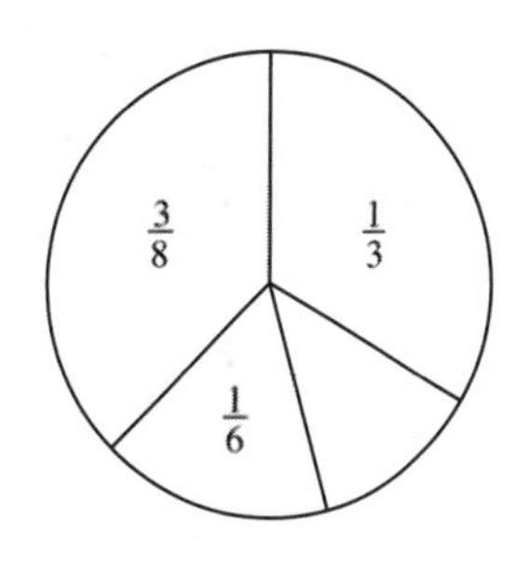

CL 3-133. What number is represented by each of the letters on the number lines below?

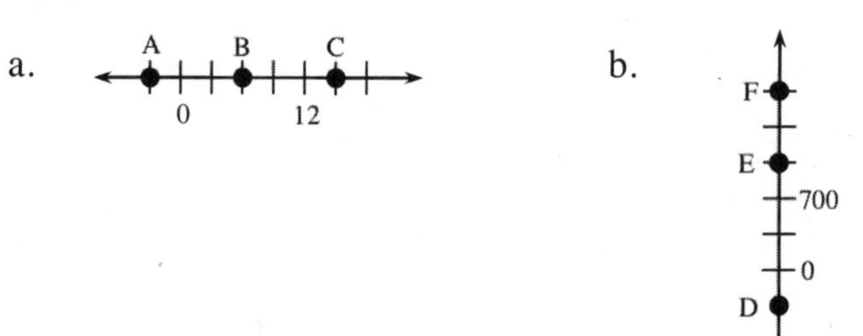

CL 3-134. The diagram at right represents an acrobat's sequence on a tightrope, where m represents the distance in feet that she covers each time she does a leap.

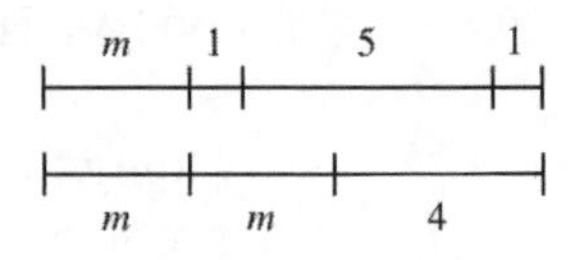

a. How long is each of her leaps? How can you tell?

b. How long is the tightrope?

c. Write expressions to represent each of her two sequences across the tightrope.

CL 3-135. Complete a portions web for each representation of a rational number below.

a. $\frac{70}{100}$

b. 118%

c. 0.085

d.

CL 3-136. Without using a calculator, find the following products.

a. $\frac{11}{4}$ of $\frac{3}{7}$

b. $\frac{5}{12} \cdot 2$

c. 4.16(0.2)

d. $4\frac{2}{5} \cdot 1\frac{1}{3}$

CL 3-137. Without using a calculator, find the following quotients.

a. $\frac{3}{7} \div \frac{2}{3}$

b. $1.2 \div 0.04$

c. $8\frac{2}{3} \div 4\frac{1}{2}$

d. $5.4 \div \frac{3}{5}$

CL 3-138. For each of the problems above, do the following:

- Draw a bar or number line that represents 0 to 10.

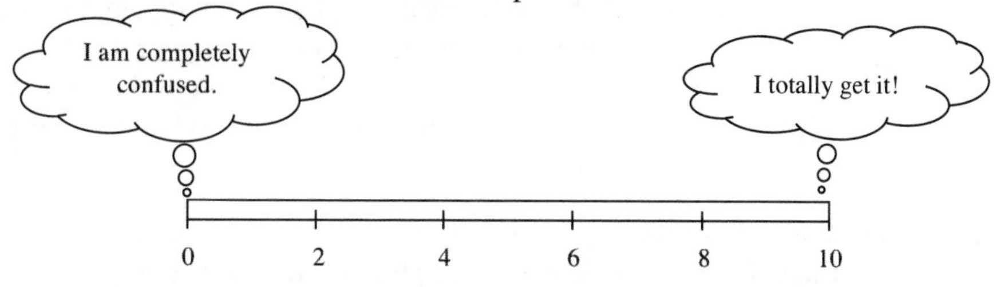

- Color or shade in a portion of the bar that represents your level of understanding and comfort with completing that problem on your own.

If any of your bars are less than a 5, choose *one* of those problems and do one of the following tasks:

- Write two questions that you would like to ask about that problem.
- Brainstorm two things that you DO know about that type of problem.

If all of your bars are at 5 or above, choose one problem and do one of these tasks:

- Write two questions you might ask or hints you might give to a student who was stuck on the problem.
- Make a new problem that is similar and more challenging than that problem and solve it.

③ WHAT TOOLS CAN I USE?

You have several tools and references available to help support your learning: your teacher, your study team, your math book, and your Toolkit, to name only a few. At the end of each chapter, you will have an opportunity to review your Toolkit for completeness. You will also revise or update it to reflect your current understanding of big ideas.

The main elements of your Toolkit should be your Learning Logs, Math Notes, and the vocabulary used in this chapter. Math words that are new appear in bold in the text. Refer to the lists provided below and follow your teacher's instructions to revise your Toolkit, which will help make it useful for you as you complete this chapter and as you work in future chapters.

Learning Log Entries

- Lesson 3.1.1 – Grouping Integers
- Lesson 3.1.2 – Simplifying Expressions with Multiplication and Addition
- Lesson 3.2.2 – Connecting Addition and Subtraction
- Lesson 3.2.3 – Multiplying and Dividing with Negative Numbers
- Lesson 3.3.2 – Division with Rational Numbers

Math Notes

- Lesson 3.1.2 – Expressions, Terms, and Order of Operations
- Lesson 3.2.1 – Evaluating Algebraic Expressions
- Lesson 3.2.2 – Subtracting Integers
- Lesson 3.2.3 – Connecting Addition and Subtraction of Integers
- Lesson 3.2.4 – Multiplication of Integers
- Lesson 3.2.5 – Multiplicative Inverses and Reciprocals
- Lesson 3.3.1 – Division with Fractions
- Lesson 3.3.2 – Multiplying Decimal Numbers
- Lesson 3.3.3 – Dividing Decimal Numbers

Mathematical Vocabulary

The following is a list of vocabulary found in this chapter. Some of the words have been seen in the previous chapter. The words in bold are words that are new to this chapter. Make sure that you are familiar with the terms below and know what they mean. For the words you do not know, refer to the glossary or index. You might also add these words to your Toolkit so that you can reference them in the future.

additive inverse	**algebraic expression**	**Associative Property**
Commutative Property	**evaluate**	integers
multiplicative inverse	**numerical term**	**Order of Operations**
quotient	rational numbers	**reciprocal**
simplify	**substitution**	**terms**

Answers and Support for Closure Problems

What Have I Learned?

Note: MN = Math Note, LL = Learning Log

Problem	Solution	Need Help?	More Practice
CL 3-130.	 a. 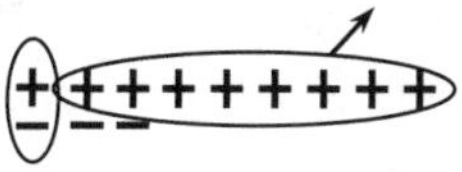 + + + + + + + + + + over − − − (circled zero pairs) = −2 b. + + + + + + + + + + over − − − (circled zero pairs) = 7	Lesson 3.2.1 MN: 3.2.2	Problems 3-34, 3-46, 3-96, and 3-122
CL 3-131.	a. 17 b. −11.98 c. 7.7 d. −18	Sections 3.1 and 3.2 MN: 3.1.2, 3.2.2, and 3.2.4 LL: 3.1.1, 3.1.2, 3.2.2, and 3.2.3	Problems 3-7, 3-20, 3-47, 3-61, 3-83, 3-121, and 3-126

Problem	Solution	Need Help?	More Practice
CL 3-132.	$\frac{3}{24}$ or $\frac{1}{8}$	Lessons 1.2.2 and 1.2.8 MN: 1.2.3	Problems CL 1-144, CL 2-134, and 3-124
CL 3-133.	a. A: –3, B: 6, C: 15 b. D: –350, E: 1050, F: 1750	Lessons 2.3.1 and 2.3.2 MN: 1.2.2 and 2.3.2	Problems CL 2-137 and 3-97
CL 3-134.	a. $m = 3$ feet b. 10 feet c. $m+7$ and $m+m+4$	MN: 3.2.1	Problems 3-37 and 3-48
CL 3-135.	a. $\frac{7}{10}, 0.7, 70\%$, seven tenths b. $\frac{118}{100}$ or $\frac{59}{50}$, 1.18, one and eighteen hundredths c. $\frac{85}{1000}$ or $\frac{17}{200}$, 8.5%, eighty-five thousandths d. $\frac{175}{100}$ or $1\frac{3}{4}$, 1.75, 175%, one and seventy-five hundredths	Lessons 2.1.1 and 2.1.2 MN: 2.1.1 and 2.1.2	Problems 2-27, 2-82, CL 2-130, and 3-23
CL 3-136.	a. $\frac{33}{28}$ b. $\frac{10}{12}$ or $\frac{5}{6}$ c. 0.832 d. $\frac{88}{15}$	Lesson 3.2.4 MN: 3.3.2	Problems 3-77, 3-110, and 3-128
CL 3-137.	a. $\frac{9}{14}$ b. 30 c. $\frac{52}{27} = 1\frac{25}{27}$ d. 9	Lessons 3.3.1 and 3.3.2 MN: 3.2.5, 3.3.1, and 3.3.3 LL: 3.3.2	Problems 3-94, 3-107, and 3-111

4 Proportions and Expressions

CHAPTER 4 Proportions and Expressions

In Section 4.1, you will investigate how to enlarge and reduce figures so that they maintain their same shape. Your work with similar figures and scale drawings, such as maps and blueprints, will lay the foundation for much of the rest of the chapter.

Maps, blueprints, and scale models all have one thing in common: they are proportional to what they represent. This is a concept that you will explore in Section 4.2. You will also study proportional relationships using tables, graphs, and the Giant One.

Section 4.3, you will begin to build expressions using a new tool called "algebra tiles." You will use a variable to help you describe the perimeter and area of shapes built with tiles when one dimension is unknown or represents various possible lengths. You will write expressions and simplify them.

Guiding Questions

Think about these questions throughout this chapter:

What's the relationship?

How can I solve it?

What is being compared?

Which shapes are similar?

Are these representations equivalent?

In this chapter, you will learn how to:

- Find solutions to problems involving proportional relationships.
- Identify proportional relationships in tables, graphs, and equations.
- Calculate unit rates.
- Combine like terms and simplify algebraic expressions.
- Rewrite expressions by combining like terms and using the Distributive Property.
- Simplify and compare two algebraic expressions.

Chapter Outline

Section 4.1 You will examine several similar shapes to determine how those shapes are related. You will use the patterns that you identify to find missing lengths and areas on shapes and to make scale drawings.

Section 4.2 This section introduces the idea of a proportional relationship through tables, graphs, equations, and real-life situations. You will learn strategies for solving proportional situations.

Section 4.3 Here, you will be introduced to algebra tiles. You will use their areas and perimeters to build expressions and combine like terms. You will work with algebraic expressions, simplifying and evaluating them for given values.

4.1.1 Are the figures the same shape?

Similar Figures

Today you will extend your study of ratios by looking at enlargements and reductions of geometric figures. Think of a copy machine and what it does to a picture when the "enlargement" button is selected. The machine makes *every length* of the picture larger or smaller by multiplying it by the same number, called the **multiplier**. That multiplier is also called the **scale factor**.

4-1. Karen is learning how to use the copy machine at her school's main office and decides to scale the figure shown at right by 300%. She wonders what will happen to the figure.

> Note: For all of these problems, the original size dot paper in the enlargement (or reduction) is kept the same so that you may compare the sizes of the figures.

a. Copy the original figure on your dot paper and label the length of each side. Then scale the figure by 300%. That is, make another copy of the figure and multiply each of the side lengths by 3. Label the length of each new side. What do you notice about the two figures? Note the sides and the angles.

b. Refer to the darkened side on the original figure. Then darken the **corresponding** (matching) side on the copy. What is the length of this side on the original figure? What is the length of this side on the copy? Write and simplify the ratio of this pair of sides in the order $\frac{\text{copy}}{\text{original}}$.

c. Choose another pair of corresponding sides in the figures. Write and simplify the ratio of these sides in the order $\frac{\text{copy}}{\text{original}}$.

d. Predict the simplified ratio you would get for another pair of corresponding sides of the two figures. Now test your prediction. Write and simplify the ratio for the remaining pairs of corresponding sides. Was your prediction correct?

e. Compare your simplified ratios from parts (b), (c), and (d). What do you notice? How do your answers relate to the scale factor of 300%?

4-2. Karen wants to try scaling the figure shown at right by 50%. What do you think will happen to the figure?

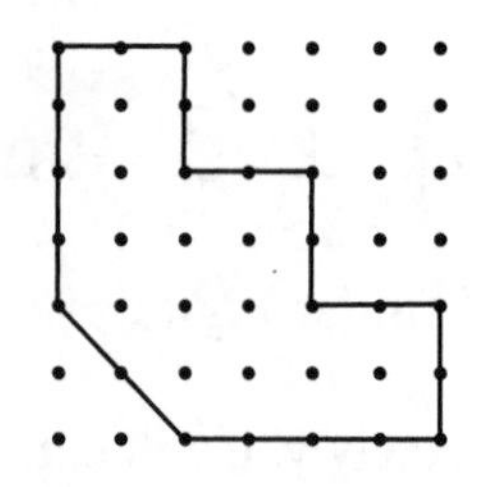

a. Sketch the figure shown at right and make a copy of the figure scaled by 50% on your dot paper. What is the same about the copy and the original? What is different?

b. How is your copy different than the copy you made in problem 4-1?

c. Locate at least three pairs of corresponding sides. There are nine in all. Then write and simplify the ratio of each pair of corresponding sides in the order $\frac{\text{copy}}{\text{original}}$.

d. Compare the ratios from each pair of corresponding sides with the scale factor. What do you notice? How do your ratios compare to the scale factor?

4-3. Examine the figure at right.

a. Use dot paper to sketch the original figure.

b. With your team, choose a scale factor the will make the figure larger. Sketch the copy. What was your scale factor? What is the ratio of the corresponding sides? How do the angles compare?

c. With your team, choose a scale factor that will make the figure smaller. Sketch the copy. What was your scale factor? What is the ratio of the corresponding sides? How do the angles compare?

4-4. **Similar figures** are figures that have the same shape but are not necessarily the same size. One characteristic of similar shapes is that ratios of the sides of one figure to the corresponding sides of the other figure are all the same. Another characteristic is that the corresponding angles of the two figures are the same.

Patti claims she made a similar copy of each of the original figures shown in parts (a) and (b) below. For each pair of figures, write and simplify the ratios for each pair of corresponding sides in the order $\frac{\text{copy}}{\text{original}}$. Compare the ratios. Are the figures similar? That is, did Patti really make a copy?

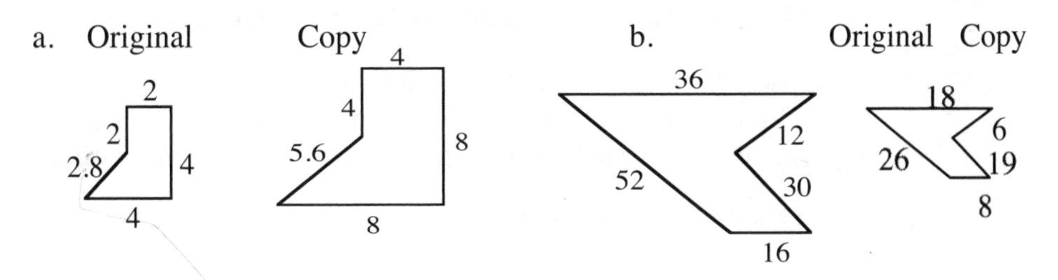

4-5. **Additional Challenge:** Draw a rectangle on dot or graph paper. Then enlarge the sides of the rectangle using a scale factor of 3.

a. Compute the perimeter and area of both the new and enlarged rectangles.

b. Write and reduce each of the following ratios:

$\frac{\text{new perimeter}}{\text{original perimeter}}$ $\frac{\text{new area}}{\text{original area}}$

c. How does each ratio compare with the scale factor?

MATH NOTES

METHODS AND MEANINGS

Mathematical Properties

When two numbers or variables are combined using addition, the order in which they are added does not matter. For example, $7+5=5+7$. This fact is known as the **Commutative Property of Addition**.

Likewise, when two numbers are multiplied together, the order in which they are multiplied does not matter. For example, $5 \cdot 10 = 10 \cdot 5$. This fact is known as the **Commutative Property of Multiplication**.

These results can be generalized using variables:

$$a+b=b+a \text{ and } a \cdot b = b \cdot a$$

Note that subtraction and division do not satisfy the Commutative Property, since $7-5 \neq 5-7$ and $10 \div 5 \neq 5 \div 10$.

When three numbers are added, you usually add the first two of them and then add the third one to that result. However, you could also add the last two together and then add the first one to that result. The **Associative Property of Addition** tells you that the order in which the numbers are added together does not matter. The answer to the problem $(7+5)+9$, for example, is the same as $7+(5+9)$.

Likewise, when three numbers are multiplied together, which pair of numbers are multiplied together first does not matter. For example, $(5 \cdot (-6)) \cdot 10$ is the same as $5 \cdot (-6 \cdot 10)$. This is the **Associative Property of Multiplication**.

These results can be generalized using variables:

$$(a+b)+c=a+(b+c) \text{ and } (a \cdot b) \cdot c = a \cdot (b \cdot c)$$

Note that subtraction and division are *not* associative, since:

$$(7-5)-1 \neq 7-(5-1) \text{ and } (10 \div 2) \div 5 \neq 10 \div (2 \div 5).$$
$$2-1 \neq 7-4 \qquad 5 \div 5 \neq 10 \div 0.4$$

To multiply $8(24)$, written as $8(20+4)$, you can use the generic rectangle model at right.

	20	+4
8	$8 \cdot 20$	$8 \cdot 4$

The product is found by $8(20)+8(4)$. So $8(20+4)=8(20)+8(4)$. This example illustrates the **Distributive Property**.

Symbolically, for any numbers a, b, and c: $a(b+c)=a(b)+a(c)$.

4-6. Simplify the expressions below.

a. $8-13-(-4)$ b. $4-(-7)+(-2)$ c. $-7+3-20$

4-7. Copy each expression and simplify it. Show all of your steps.

a. $1.234+0.58+5.316$ b. $6.1-1.536$ c. $4.8(0.6)$

4-8. Tina's rectangular living-room floor measures 15 feet by 18 feet.

a. How many square feet of carpet will Tina need to cover the entire floor?

b. The carpet Tina likes is sold by the square yard. How many square yards will she need? (1 yard = 3 feet)

4-9. Find the missing parts of each number line. Assume that the lines have been split into equal parts.

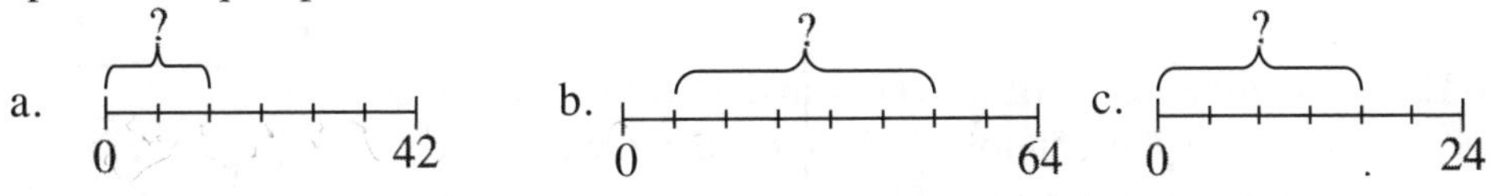

4-10. Copy and simplify each expression.

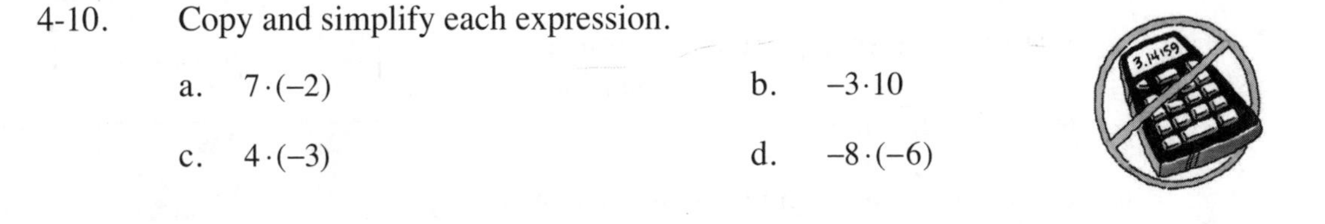

a. $7\cdot(-2)$ b. $-3\cdot 10$

c. $4\cdot(-3)$ d. $-8\cdot(-6)$

4.1.2 How can I use a scale drawing?

Scale Drawings

Maps are examples of **scale drawings**. They are reduced versions of the original regions. A map is **similar** to the original region, because it has the same shape. Because of this, maps conveniently allow users to determine distances between two points.

In a scale drawing, it is important to decide on the unit of measure. Maps made in the United States usually represent distances in miles, but they certainly cannot use actual miles as the unit of measure. Otherwise, a map of Pennsylvania would be over 250 miles long and 450 miles wide! A map includes a **scale**, which shows the units in which the map is drawn. An example is shown at right.

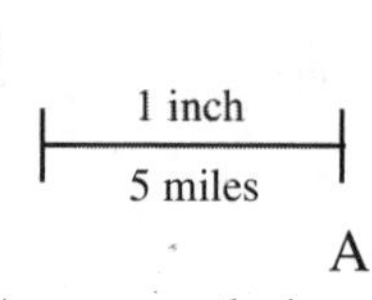

4-11. Suppose Eulalia uses a map of Pennsylvania to determine that Valley Forge is 14 miles from downtown Philadelphia. Did she really measure 14 miles? Explain how she probably determined the distance.

4-12. Guillermo needs a scale drawing of his house placed on its suburban lot. The lot is 56' wide and 100' deep. The garage is 20' back from the street. He has a sketch of his house – *not* drawn to scale – with the measurements shown at right.

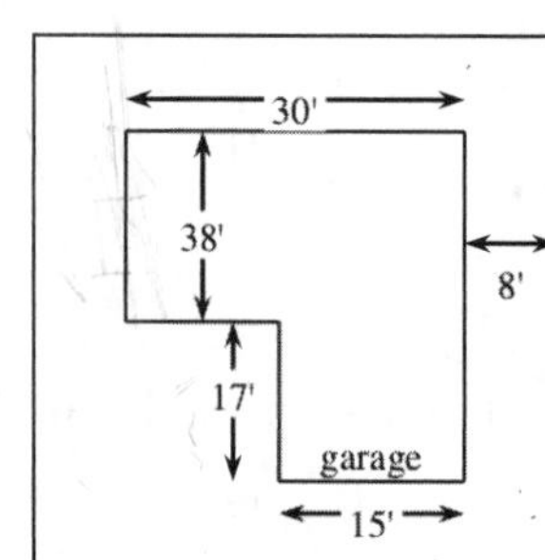

a. Use graph paper and a ruler to create a scale drawing of Guillermo's house on its lot. Be sure to state your scale.

b. Guillermo wants to put a rectangular swimming pool in his backyard. What is the largest pool you would advise him to have installed?

4-13. The scale drawing at right shows the first floor of a house. The actual dimensions of the garage are 20 feet by 25 feet. All angles are right angles.

2 inches
1 inch
Living Room
Garage
1¼ inches
Dining Room
Kitchen
Office

a. How many feet does each inch represent? That is, what is the scale?

b. What are the length and width of the living room on the scale drawing (in inches)?

c. What are the actual length and width of the living room (in feet)?

d. If the family wants to lay carpet in the living room and carpeting costs \$1.25 per square foot, how much will the carpet cost?

4-14. Use your ruler to complete the following problems.

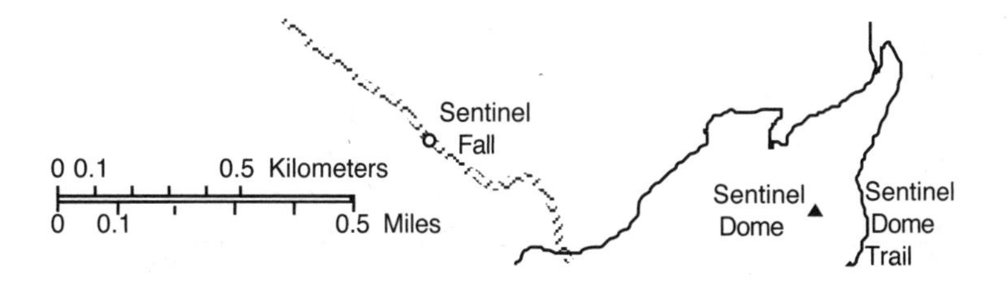

a. Notice that the scale on the map shown above only gives kilometers and miles. Use your ruler to determine how many inches represent 0.5 miles.

b. What is the distance on the map from Sentinel Fall to Sentinel Dome, in inches?

c. What is the distance from Sentinel Fall to Sentinel Dome, in miles?

4-15. Hank is planning his vegetable garden. He has created the scale drawing below. The actual area for the tomatoes will be 12 feet by 9 feet. All angles are right angles.

a. What scale did Hank use?

b. If the horizontal length of the zucchini plot shown in the diagram is $1\frac{5}{8}$ inches, what is the area of the entire vegetable garden in square feet?

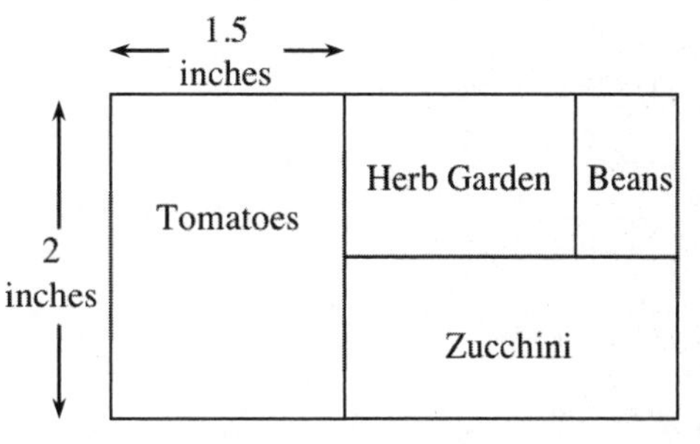

MATH NOTES

METHODS AND MEANINGS

Similarity and Scale Factor

Two figures are **similar** if they have the same shape but not necessarily the same size. In similar figures, the lengths of all corresponding pairs of sides have the same ratio and the measures of corresponding angles are equal.

A **scale factor** compares the sizes of the parts of the scale drawing of an object with the actual sizes of the corresponding parts of the object itself. The scale factor in similar figures is the simplified ratio of any pair of corresponding sides.

Example: ΔABC is the original triangle.

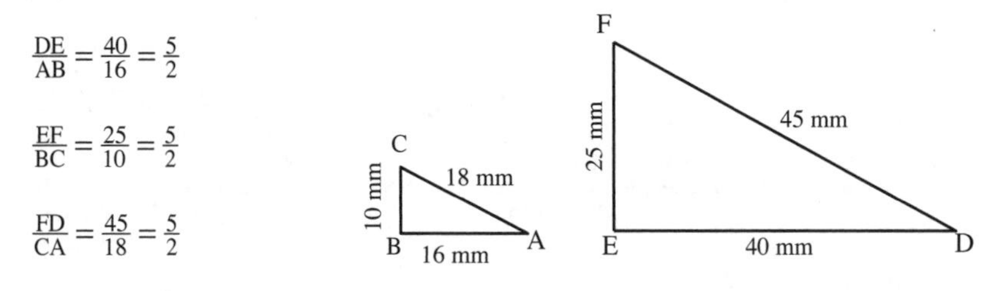

The simplified ratio of every pair of corresponding sides is the same. The scale factor is $\frac{5}{2}$.

4-16. Draw a diagram that could be represented by each of the following number expressions. Then circle the terms and calculate the value of each expression.

a. $4+2(5)+(-3)$

b. $4+2\left(5+(-3)\right)$

4-17. While Mrs. Poppington was visiting the historic battleground at Gettysburg, she talked with the landscapers who were replacing the sod in a park near the visitor center. The part of the lawn being replaced is shown in the diagram at right. Measurements are in yards. The diagram is not drawn to scale, but all corners are right angles.

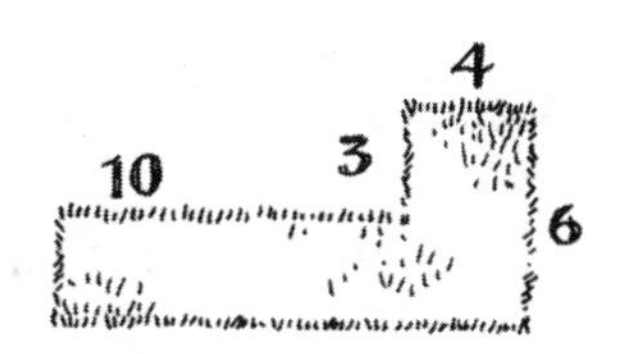

a. Use your ruler to make a scale drawing of the lawn that is being replaced. Let $\frac{1}{4}$ inch equal 1 yard.

b. How many square yards of sod will be needed?

c. At $2.43 a square yard, how much will the sod cost?

d. The area will be surrounded by a temporary fence that costs $0.25 per linear foot to rent. How many feet will be needed, and how much will it cost?

e. What will be the total cost of materials for the sod and fencing?

4-18. Troy has a number cube with the numbers 1 through 6 on it. Assuming each side is equally likely to appear when he rolls the cube, find the following probabilities. Note: When two or more numbers are multiplied, each of the numbers is a factor of the product.

a. P(rolls a 2)

b. P(rolls an odd number)

c. P(rolls a factor of 6)

4-19. Copy and complete each of the Diamond Problems below. The pattern used in the Diamond Problems is shown at right.

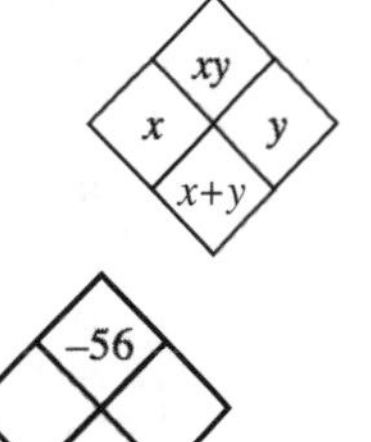

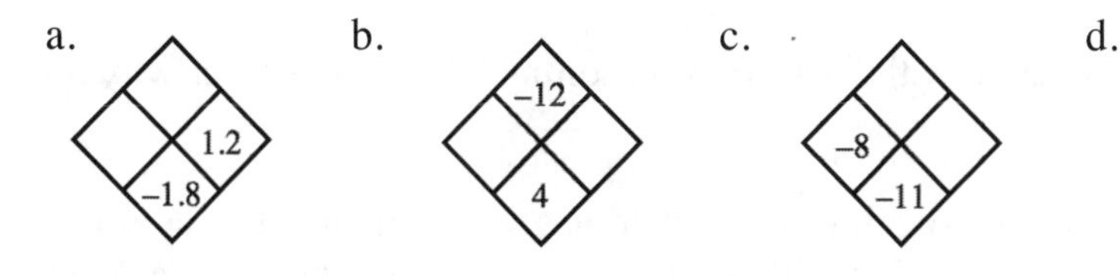

4-20. Simplify each expression below.

a. $(4.76)(12.5)$

b. $45.6 + 23.68$

c. $48 - 12.62$

d. $10(0.034)$

e. $368.9 - 234.78$

f. $13.6 + 23.05 + 0.781$

4.2.1 How does it grow?

Recognizing Proportional Relationships

Grocery stores often advertise special prices for fruits and vegetables that are in season. You might see a sign that says, "Special Today! Buy 2 pounds of apples for $1.29!" How would you use that information to predict how much you need to pay if you want to buy six pounds of apples? Or just 1 pound of apples? The way that the cost of apples grows or shrinks allows you to use a variety of different strategies to predict and estimate prices for different amounts of apples. In this section, you will explore different kinds of growth patterns. You will use those patterns to develop strategies for making predictions and deciding if answers are reasonable.

As you work in this section, ask yourself these questions to help you identify different patterns:

How are the entries in the table related?

Can I double the values?

What patterns can I see in a graph?

4-21. COLLEGE FUND

Five years ago, Gustavo's grandmother put some money in a college savings account for him on his birthday. The account pays simple interest, and now, after five years, the account is worth $500. Gustavo predicts that if he does not deposit or withdraw any money, then the account balance will be $1000 five years from now.

a. How do you think Gustavo made his prediction?

b. Do you agree with Gustavo's reasoning? Explain why or why not.

4-22. Last week, Gustavo got his bank statement in the mail. He was surprised to see a graph that showed that, although his balance was growing at a steady rate, the bank predicted that in five years his account balance would be only $600. *"What is going on?"* he wondered. *"Why isn't my money growing the way I thought it would?"*

With your team, discuss how much Gustavo's account appears to be growing every year. Why might his account be growing in a different way than he expected? Be ready to share your ideas.

4-23. Gustavo decided to look more carefully at his balances for the last few years to see if the bank's prediction might be a mistake. He put together the table below.

Time Since Original Deposit (years)	2	3	4	5
Bank Balance (dollars)	440	460	480	500

a. How has Gustavo's bank balance been growing?

b. Does Gustavo's money seem to be doubling as the number of years doubles? Explain your reasoning.

c. Is the bank's prediction a mistake? Explain your answer.

4-24. Once Gustavo saw the balances written in a table, he decided to take a closer look at the graph from the bank to see if he could figure out where he made the mistake in his prediction. Find the graph at right on the Lesson 4.2.1 Resource Page.

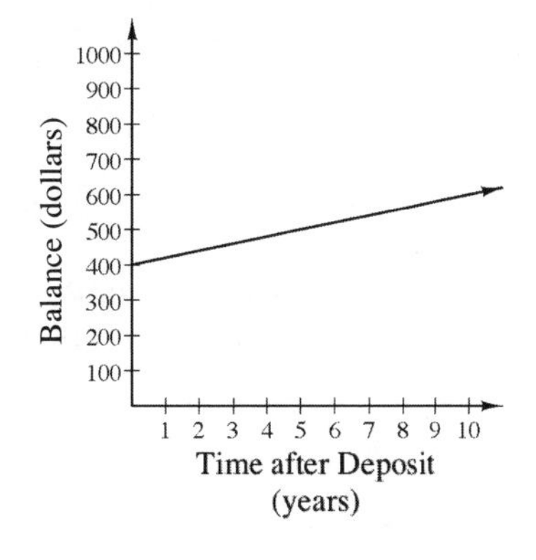

a. There is additional information about Gustavo's account that you can tell from the graph. For example, what was his starting balance? How much does it grow in 5 years?

b. Gustavo had assumed his money would double after 10 years. What would the graph look like if that were true? Using a different color, add a line to the graph that represents what Gustavo was thinking.

c. Is it possible that Gustavo's account could have had $0 in it in Year 0? Why or why not?

4-25. FOR THE BIRDS

When filling her bird feeder, Sonja noticed that she paid \$27 for four pounds of bulk birdseed. "*Next time, I'm going to buy 8 pounds instead so I can make it through the spring. That should cost \$54.*"

a. Does Sonja's assumption that doubling the amount of birdseed would double the price make sense? Why or why not? How much would you predict that 2 pounds of birdseed would cost?

b. To check her assumption, she found a receipt for 1 pound of birdseed. She decided to make a table, which is started below. Copy and complete her table.

Pounds	0	1	2	3	4	5	6	8
Cost		\$6.75			\$27			

c. How do the amounts in the table grow?

d. Does the table confirm Sonja's doubling relationship? Give two examples from the table that show how doubling the pounds will double the cost.

4-26. What makes Sonja's birdseed situation (problem 4-25) different from Gustavo's college fund situation (problem 4-21)? Why does doubling work for one situation but not in the other? Consider this as you examine the graphs below.

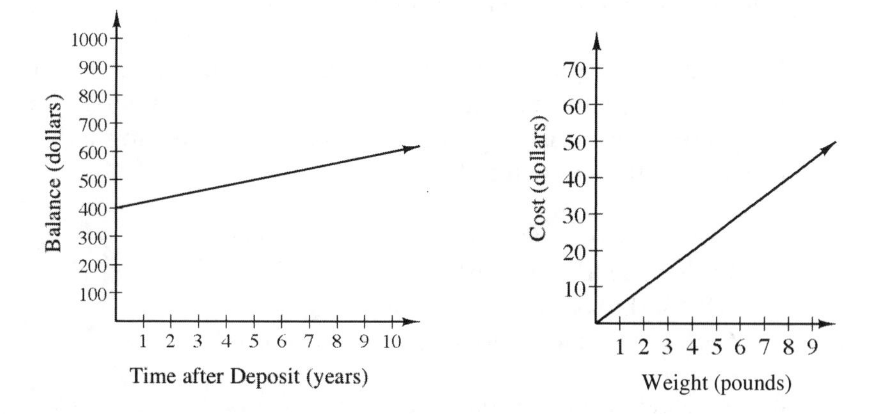

a. With your team:

- Describe how each graph is the same.
- Describe what makes each graph different.

b. How do the differences explain why doubling works in one situation and not in the other? Generalize why doubling works in one situation and not in another.

c. The pattern of growth in Sonja's example of buying birdseed is an example of a **proportional relationship**. In a proportional relationship, if one quantity is multiplied by a scale factor, the other is scaled by the same amount. Gustavo's bank account is *not* proportional, because it grows differently; when the number of years doubled, his balance did not.

Work with your team to list other characteristics of proportional relationships, based on Sonja's and Gustavo's examples. Be as specific as possible.

4-27. IS IT PROPORTIONAL?

When you are making a prediction, it is important to be able to recognize whether a relationship is proportional or not.

Your Task: Work with your team to read each new situation below. Decide whether you think the relationship described is **proportional** or **non-proportional** and justify your reasoning. Be prepared to share your decisions and justifications with the class.

a. Carlos wants to buy some new video games. Each game he buys costs him $36. Is the relationship between the number of games Carlos buys and the total price proportional?

b. A single ticket to a concert costs $56, while buying five tickets costs $250. Is the relationship between the number of tickets bought and the total price proportional?

c. Vu is four years older than his sister. Is the relationship between Vu and his sister's age proportional?

d. Janna runs at a steady pace of 7 minutes per mile. Is the relationship between the number of miles she ran and the distance she covered proportional?

e. Carl just bought a music player and plans to load 50 songs each week. Is the relationship between the number of weeks after Carl bought the music player and the number of songs on his player proportional?

f. Anna has a new video game. It takes her five hours of playing the game to master level one. After so much time, Anna understands the game better and it only takes her three hours of playing the game to master level two. Is the number of hours played and the game level proportional?

4-28. LEARNING LOG

In your Learning Log, explain how you can tell if a relationship is proportional. Give several examples of a proportional relationship and at least one that is not proportional. Label this entry "Recognizing Proportional Relationships" and include today's date.

4-29. The lemonade stand at the county fair sells the lemonade at a price of two cups for \$3.60. Complete the table at right to find what Paula's family will pay to buy lemonade for all eight members of the family.

# of Lemonades	Price (\$)
1	
2	3.60
3	
4	
5	
6	
7	
8	

4-30. Carmen is downloading music for her πPod. Each song costs \$1.75. Is this relationship proportional? Explain your reasoning. What is the cost for five songs?

4-31. Simplify each expression.

a. $-3+7$ b. $7+(-8)$ c. $-6-9$

d. $-3+4(-2)$ e. $4-2(-5)$ f. $(-7+3)(4-5\cdot 2)$

4-32. Copy and complete each of the Diamond Problems below. The pattern used in the Diamond Problems is shown at right.

Pattern: top xy, left x, right y, bottom $x+y$

a. top 6, right −1

b. left 3, bottom −5

c. left 1.2, bottom 11.2

d. top 24, bottom 10

4-33. Lucy keeps track of how long it takes her to do the newspaper's crossword puzzle each day. Her recent times, in minutes, were:

8 22 19 12 18 19 10 35 12 19 16 21

a. What is the median of her data? b. What is the mean?

4.2.2 How can I see a proportion?

Proportional Relationships with Tables and Graphs

In Lesson 4.2.1, you learned that you could identify proportional relationships by looking for a constant multiplier. In fact, you have already seen a relationship with a constant multiplier in this course. Today you will revisit the earlier situation that contains a proportional relationship.

4-34. GRAPHING THE PENNY-TOWER DATA

In Chapter 1, you found a multiplicative (or proportional) relationship between the height of a stack of pennies and the number of pennies in the stack. That is, you could always find one piece of information by multiplying the other by a constant number.

Height of Tower (cm)	# of Pennies
1	
15	
4	28
	63
3	
12	

a. Copy the table at right and work with your team to fill in the missing values. What strategies did you use to determine the missing numbers?

b. How many pennies are in a tower with a height of 0 cm? Add a row to your table with this value.

c. Graph this data. Be sure to scale the axes so that all of the points in your table are visible on your graph.

d. What do you notice about the graph of height and the number of pennies? How does this graph compare to Sonja's graph of birdseed weight and cost that you made in Lesson 4.2.1? What do the graphs have in common? How are they different?

4-35. Kaci loves cheese and buys it whenever she can. Recently, she bought 5 pounds of mozzarella cheese for $15.00 and 3 pounds of havarti for $7.50.

a. Obtain a copy of the Lesson 4.2.2 Resource Page for each member of your team. Then work together to record, plot, and label Kaci's two cheese purchases.

b. With your team, find another point that you could plot on the graph for *each* kind of cheese. Record these points in the tables. That is, find another combination of pounds of cheese and the associated cost for the mozzarella and then another combination of pounds and cost for the havarti.

c. Work with your team to discuss and answer the following questions. Then decide how best to complete the two tables and graphs that you started in parts (a) and (b).

- Can you find any other points that should be in the mozzarella table and graph? Add them.
- Can you find any other points that should be in the havarti table and graph? Add them.
- Should the points on each graph be connected? If so, why does that make sense? If not, why not?

d. How do the graphs for each type of cheese compare? What is the same and what is different?

e. Which cheese is more expensive (costs more per pound)? How can you tell by looking at the graph? How can you tell by looking at the table?

f. What is significant about the point $(1, y)$ for each line on the graph or in your table?

4-36. Look back at the tables and graphs you created for proportional relationships in the previous problems.

a. How can you use a table to decide if a relationship is proportional?

b. How can you use a graph to decide if a relationship is proportional?

4-37. Which of the tables below shows a proportional relationship between x and y? How can you tell?

a.

x	y
1	2
2	4
3	6
4	8

b.

x	y
1	2
2	3
3	4
4	5

4-38. The following graphs show examples of relationships that are *not* proportional. For each graph, explain what makes the relationship different from the proportional relationships you have studied.

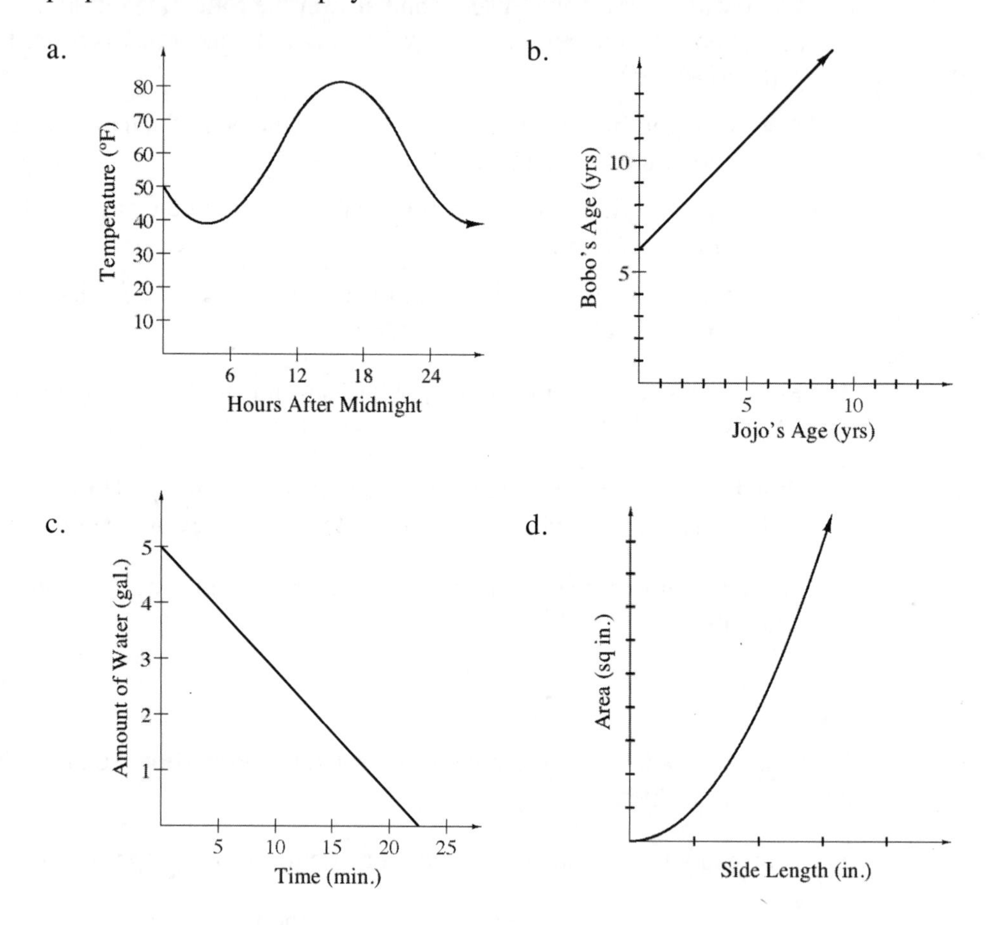

4-39. Use your understanding of proportions to help Kaci find each of the missing quantities below, using the information given in problem 4-35. Be prepared to explain your strategies.

a. How much do 7.5 pounds of mozzarella cheese cost?

b. How much do 1.5 pounds of havarti cheese cost?

c. How much mozzarella cheese can Kaci buy for $12?

d. How much havarti cheese can Kaci buy for $10?

e. **Challenge:** Write an equation relating the amount of cheese to the cost of the cheese. Verify that you get the same answers for parts (a) through (d) above when using your equation.

4-40. LEARNING LOG

In your Learning Log, explain what a proportional relationship is and how you can see it on a graph and in a table. Include diagrams to illustrate your thinking and make an example of your own. Title this entry "Proportional Relationships in Graphs and Tables" and label it with today's date.

4-41. On your own graph paper, draw axes, decide on a scale, and plot points to represent the data in the table at right. Does this data appear to be proportional? Explain why or why not.

Quantity x	Quantity y
2	6.3
6	18.9
9	28.35
5	15.75
1	3.15

4-42. A bag contains 4 brown marbles, 3 green marbles, 2 red marbles, and 1 purple marble. Calculate the probability of drawing each color, and write each answer as a fraction, as a percent, and as a decimal.

4-43. Each of the diagrams below represents a sequence for a tightrope walker. For each one, explain the sequence and find the length of the unknown trick.

4-44. Identify the mathematical property, operation, or idea that justifies each sequence of expressions below. Then find the value of the expression.

a. $7 \cdot 2 + 4 - 2(7+3)$
$7 \cdot 2 + 4 - 2(7) - 2(3)$
$7 \cdot 2 - 7(2) + 4 - 2(3)$

b. $6 \cdot 3 + 3 \cdot 4 - 8$
$18 + 12 - 8$
$18 - 8 + 12$

c. $3^2 + 5(1-3) + 4 \cdot 5 + 1$
$3^2 + 4 \cdot 5 + 1 + 5(-2)$
$9 + 20 + 1 - 10$

d. $(8 + (-12)) + 10 + 2$
$8 + (-12 + 10 + 2)$

4-45. Write three different sentences that could describe the relationship between the quantities below.

$27, $81

4.2.3 How can a graph help?

Unit Rate and Proportional Equations

Proportional relationships can be identified in both tables and graphs. Today you will have an opportunity to take a closer look at how graphs and tables for proportional relationships can help you organize your work to find any missing value quickly and easily.

4-46. Robert's new hybrid car has a gas tank that holds 12 gallons of gas. When the tank is full, he can drive 420 miles. Assume that his car uses gas at a steady rate.

a. Is the relationship between the number of gallons of gas used and the number of miles that can be driven proportional? For example, does it change like Sonja's birdseed prediction, or is it more like Gustavo's college savings? Explain how you know.

b. Show how much gas Robert's car will use at various distances by copying and completing the table below.

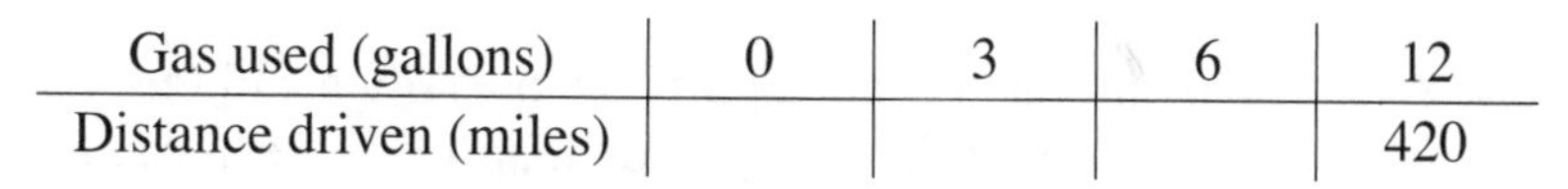

Gas used (gallons)	0	3	6	12
Distance driven (miles)				420

c. Robert decided to graph the situation, as shown at right. The distance Robert can travel using one gallon of gas is called the **unit rate**. Use Robert's graph to predict how far he can drive using one gallon of gas. That is, find his unit rate.

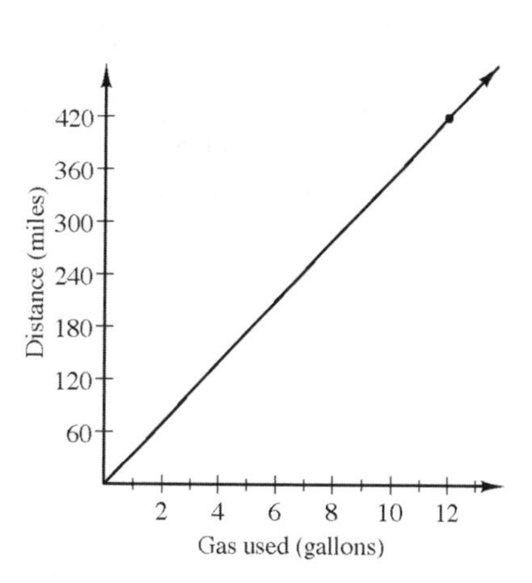

d. While a graph is a useful tool for estimating, it is often difficult to find an exact answer on a graph. What is significant about the point labeled $(1, y)$? How can you calculate y?

e. Use the table in part (b) and your result in part (d) to find Robert's unit rate.

f. Work with your team to write the equation to find the exact number of miles Robert can drive with any number of gallons of gas. Be prepared to share your strategy.

g. Use your equation to find out how many gallons of gas Robert will need to drive 287 miles.

4-47. THE YOGURT SHOP

Jell E. Bean owns the local frozen yogurt shop. At her store, customers serve themselves a bowl of frozen yogurt and top it with chocolate chips, frozen raspberries, and any of the different treats available. Customers must then weigh their creations and are charged by the weight of their bowls.

Jell E. Bean charges \$32 for five pounds of dessert, but not many people buy that much frozen yogurt. She needs you to help her figure out how much to charge her customers. She has customers that are young children who buy only a small amount of yogurt as well as large groups that come in and pay for everyone's yogurt together.

a. Is it reasonable to assume that the weight of the yogurt is proportional to its cost? How can you tell?

b. Assuming it is proportional, make a table that lists the price for at least ten different weights of yogurt. Be sure to include at least three weights that are not whole numbers.

c. What is the unit rate of the yogurt? (Stores often call this the unit price.) Use the unit rate to write an equation that Jell E. Bean can use to calculate the amount any customer will pay.

d. If Jell E. Bean decided to start charging \$0.50 for each cup before her customers started filling it with yogurt and toppings, could you use the same equation to find the new prices? Why or why not?

4-48. Lexie claims that she can send 14 text messages in 22 minutes. Her teammates Kenny and Esther are trying to predict how many text messages Lexie can send in a 55-minute lunch period if she keeps going at the same rate.

a. Is the relationship between the number of text messages and time in minutes proportional? Why or why not?

b. Kenny represented the situation using the table shown below. Explain Kenny's strategy for using the table.

Kenny's work

Messages	Minutes
14	22
7	11
	55

c. Esther wants to solve the problem using an equation. Help her write an equation to determine how many text messages Lexie could send in any number of minutes.

d. Find the missing value in Kenny's table.

e. Solve Esther's equation. Will she get the same answer as Kenny?

f. What is Lexie's unit rate? That is, how many text messages can she send in 1 minute?

4-49. **Additional Challenge:** Use your reasoning skills to compute each unit rate (the price per pound).

a. \$4.20 for $\frac{1}{2}$ pound of cheese

b. \$1.50 for $\frac{2}{3}$ pound of bananas

c. \$6.00 for $\frac{3}{4}$ pound of deli roast beef

d. \$7.50 for $\frac{5}{6}$ pound of sliced turkey

MATH NOTES

METHODS AND MEANINGS

Proportional Relationships

A relationship is **proportional** if one quantity is a multiple of the other. This relationship can be identified in tables, graphs, and equations.

Table: Equivalent ratios of $\frac{y}{x}$ (or $\frac{x}{y}$) can be seen in a table.

Graph: A straight line through the origin.

Equation: An equation of the form $y = kx$ where k is the **constant of proportionality**.

Example: Three pounds of chicken cost \$7.00. What is the cost for x pounds?

Equation: $y = \frac{7}{3}x$

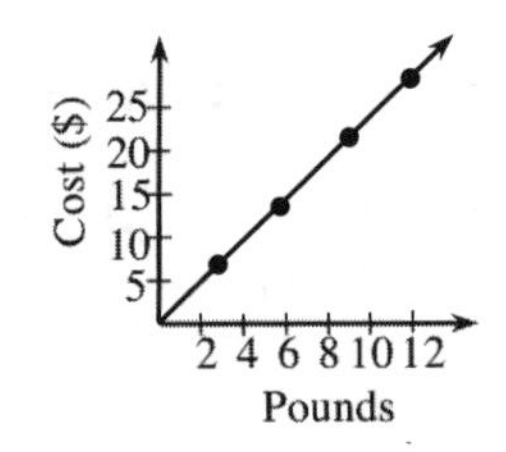

Pounds (x)	0	3	6	9	12
Cost (y)	0	7	14	21	28

The relationship between pounds and cost is proportional. The table has equivalent ratios ($\frac{7}{3} = \frac{14}{6} = \frac{21}{9}$), the graph is a straight line through the origin, and the equation is of the form $y = kx$.

Example: The county fair costs \$5.00 to enter and \$1.00 per ride.

Equation: $y = 1x + 5$

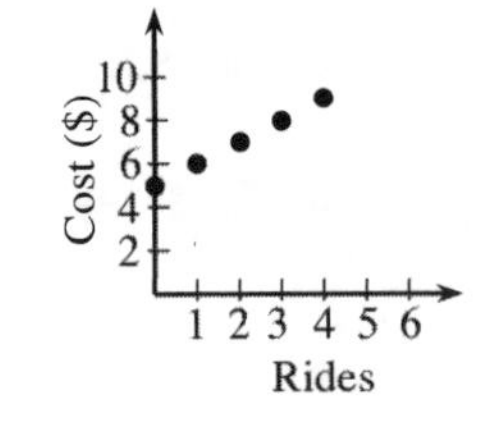

Rides (x)	0	1	2	3	4
Cost (y)	5	6	7	8	9

The relationship between rides and cost is not proportional, because the table does not contain equivalent ratios ($\frac{6}{1} \neq \frac{7}{2} \neq \frac{8}{3}$), the graph does not pass through the origin, and the equation contains addition.

4-50. Complete the proportion table below and graph the results.

Pounds of Nails	2	3		6		10		x
Cost ($)			2.15	2.58	3.44		8.60	

a. What is the unit rate (price) of the graph?

b. What does the unit rate (price) tell you about the cost of the nails?

4-51. The choir is planning a trip to the water park. The cost to use a school bus is $350. Complete the table at right then graph your result. Is this a proportional relationship?

Number of Students on the Trip	Bus Cost per Student ($)
10	
15	
20	
35	

4-52. Paige traveled to Australia and is making her favorite bread recipe. She usually bakes the bread in a 350°F oven. She is surprised to learn that the oven temperatures in Australia are measured in degrees Celsius. In the formula at right, F stands for Fahrenheit and C stands for Celsius. Use the formula and the Order of Operations to help Paige determine how she should set the oven in degrees Celsius.

$$C = \frac{5(F-32)}{9}$$

4-53. Simplify each of the following expressions.

a. $\frac{2}{5} - \frac{1}{6}$

b. $\frac{3}{7} - \frac{7}{14}$

c. $\frac{5}{8} - \frac{2}{3}$

4-54. The probability of getting a white marble from a bag is $\frac{1}{5}$. If there are 37 white marbles in the bag, what is the total number of marbles in the bag?

4.2.4 What are the connections?

Connecting Representations of Proportional Relationships

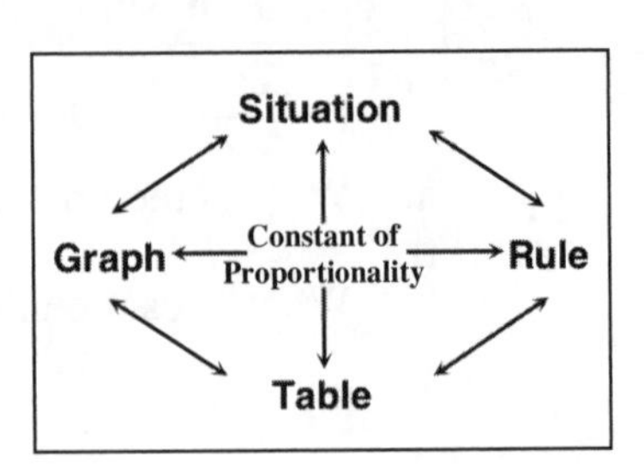

In the previous lessons, you studied different ways to represent proportional relationships. You organized information into tables and graphs. You also wrote equations modeling the proportional relationships. Proportional relationship equations are of the form $y = kx$, where k is the **constant of proportionality**. Today you will find connections between different representations of the same proportional relationship, explore each representation more deeply, and learn shorter ways to go from one representation to another. As you work today, keep these questions in mind:

How can you see growth in the rule?

How do you know your rule is correct?

What does the representation tell you?

What are the connections between the representations?

4-55. Graeme earns \$4.23 for each half-hour that he works. How much money does he earn during a given amount of time?

a. Represent this situation using a table.

b. What is the constant of proportionality (or the unit rate)? How can you find it from a table?

c. How can you use a table to determine if a relationship is proportional?

4-56. Jamie ran 9.3 miles in 1.5 hours. How far can she run in a given amount of time, if she runs at a constant rate?

a. Represent this situation with a graph.

b. What is the constant of proportionality? How can you find it on a graph?

c. How can you use a graph to determine if a relationship is proportional?

4-57. A recipe calls for $2\frac{2}{3}$ cups of flour to make two regular batches of cookies. Shiloh needs to make multiple batches of cookies.

a. Represent this situation with an equation.

b. What is the constant of proportionality? How can you identify it in an equation?

c. How can you use an equation to determine if a relationship is proportional?

4-58. CONNECTIONS WEB FOR PROPORTIONAL RELATIONSHIPS

Your teacher will assign your team a situation from the previous problems. Your team's task is to create a poster showing every way you can represent the proportional relationship and the connections between each representation. Use the web at right to help you get started.

Situation
Graph
Constant of Proportionality
Rule
Table

4-59. LEARNING LOG

In your Learning Log, create a generic connections web for proportional relationships. For each representation, explain how you know the relationship is proportional. Title this entry "Connections Web for Proportional Relationships" and label it with today's date.

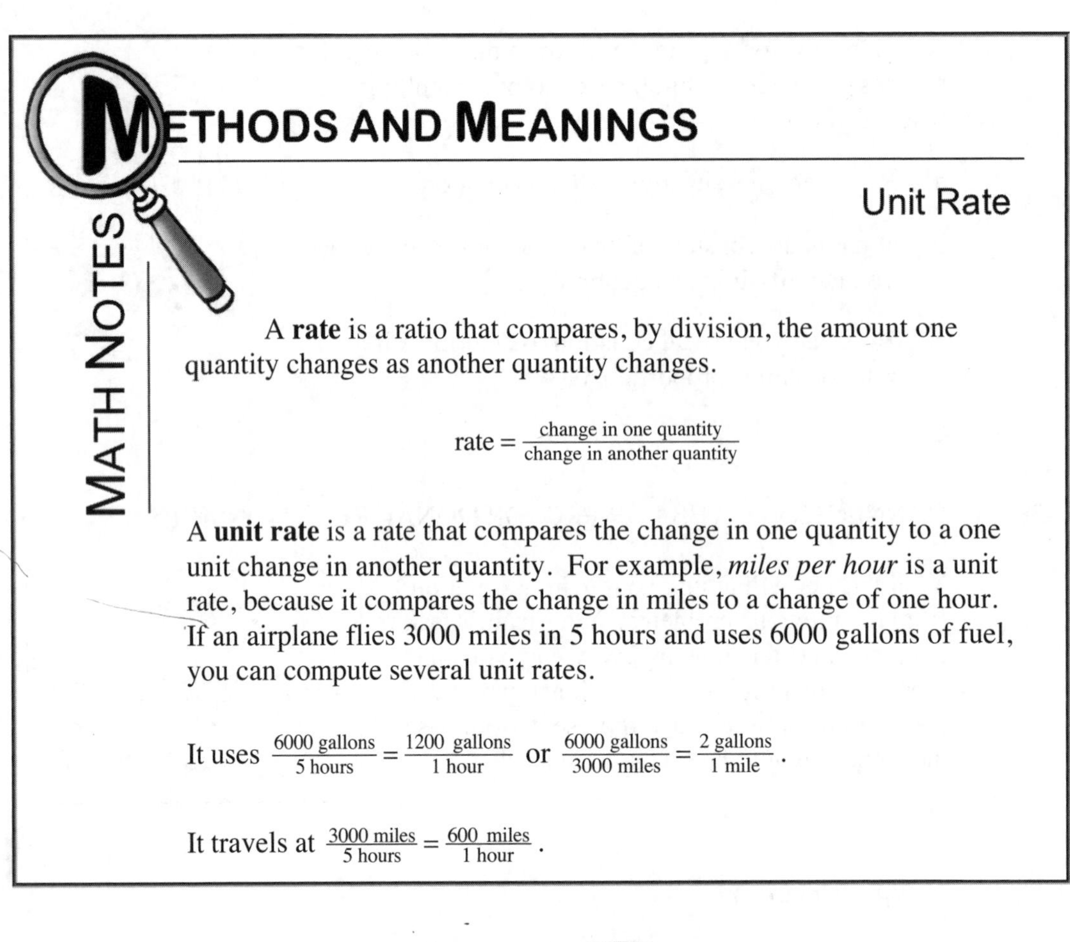

Unit Rate

A **rate** is a ratio that compares, by division, the amount one quantity changes as another quantity changes.

$$\text{rate} = \frac{\text{change in one quantity}}{\text{change in another quantity}}$$

A **unit rate** is a rate that compares the change in one quantity to a one unit change in another quantity. For example, *miles per hour* is a unit rate, because it compares the change in miles to a change of one hour. If an airplane flies 3000 miles in 5 hours and uses 6000 gallons of fuel, you can compute several unit rates.

It uses $\frac{6000 \text{ gallons}}{5 \text{ hours}} = \frac{1200 \text{ gallons}}{1 \text{ hour}}$ or $\frac{6000 \text{ gallons}}{3000 \text{ miles}} = \frac{2 \text{ gallons}}{1 \text{ mile}}$.

It travels at $\frac{3000 \text{ miles}}{5 \text{ hours}} = \frac{600 \text{ miles}}{1 \text{ hour}}$.

4-60. Is the relationship shown in the table at right proportional? If so, use it to complete a Proportions Web. If not, explain why it is not.

Hours Worked	Amount of Dirt Excavated (cubic yards)
3	6.6
4	8.8
8	17.6
9	19.8

4-61. In a recent snail race, the winning snail traveled 5.85 cm in $\frac{3}{4}$ of a minute. How fast was the snail traveling in centimeters per second?

4-62. Find the area and perimeter of the shape at right.

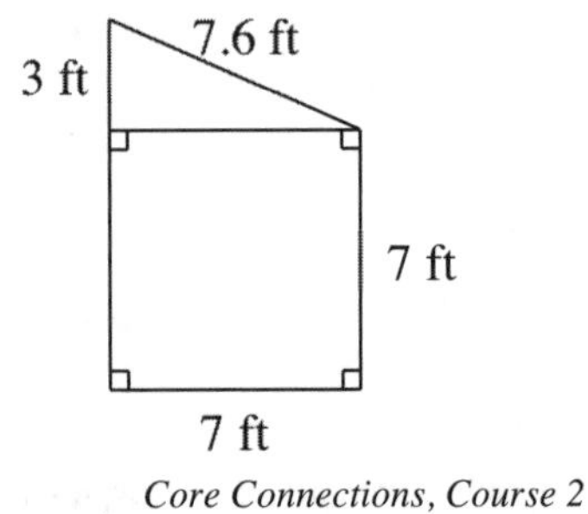

4-63. Circle terms and simplify each of the following expressions.

a. $3+1\cdot4+(-7)$

b. $50+3(-10)+2(-20)$

c. $4+(-50)\cdot2$

d. $(4+(-170))(5+(-4))$

4-64. CECIL'S LATEST TRICK

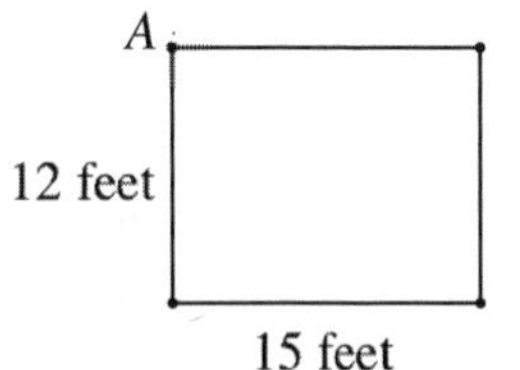

To amaze the audience, Cecil set up four tightropes in a rectangle, each connected at a pole as shown in the diagram at right. A ladder down from the ropes is located at point *A*.

a. If Cecil starts at point *A* and must travel completely around the rectangle, how far must Cecil travel?

b. How can Cecil's distance be represented by an expression?

4-65. State whether each equation below represents a proportional relationship. How can you tell?

a. $y=x+2.3$

b. $y=\frac{6}{13}x$

c. $7-y=2x$

4-66. A stack of six bricks is two feet high. Use that information to answer the questions below.

a. How many bricks are in a stack 20 feet high?

b. How high is a stack of 20 bricks?

4-67. Alexa is looking at the shape at right. She needs to make several different figures that are similar to it.

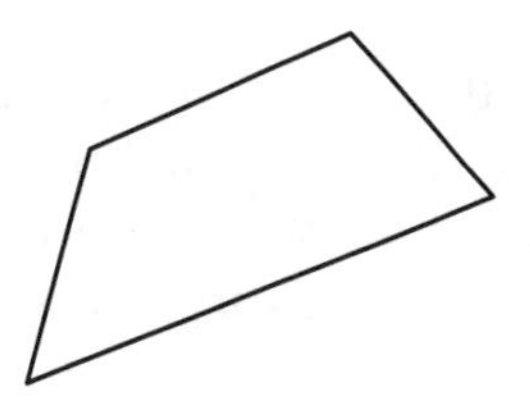

a. If she uses the scale factor $\frac{8}{5}$, will the new shape that she creates be larger or smaller than the original? Justify your answer.

b. List two different scale factors Alexa could use to make a smaller shape.

c. List two different scale factors Alexa could use to make a larger shape.

4-68. Kirk is helping his grandparents set up their new portable music players. His grandmother, Maude, has 1 jazz album, 2 country-western albums, and 5 heavy-metal albums. Kirk's grandfather, Claude, has 3 classical albums, 2 rap albums, and 7 heavy-metal albums.

If Kirk's grandparents' portable music players are on random shuffle mode, who has the greater chance of listening to a heavy-metal album? Explain how you know.

4-69. At your first job, you may be amazed to learn that one fourth of your paycheck will go to pay taxes.

Suppose the amounts listed in parts (a) through (c) below are the earnings for three employees. Determine how much of each paycheck will go to pay taxes.

a. $84 b. $128 c. $210

4.3.1 How can I simplify?

Combining Like Terms

Mathematics can be used to describe patterns in the world. Scientists use math to describe various aspects of life, including how cells multiply, how objects move through space, and how chemicals react. Often, when scientists try to describe these patterns, they need to describe something that changes or varies. Scientists call the quantities that change **variables**, and they represent them using letters and symbols.

In this course, you will spend time learning about variables, what they can represent, and how they serve different purposes. To start, you will use variables to describe the dimensions and areas of different shapes. You will begin to organize the descriptions into **algebraic expressions**.

As you work with your teammates, use these questions to help focus your team's discussion:

How can you organize groups of things?

What is the area?

Which lengths can vary?

4-70. AREA OF ALGEBRA TILES

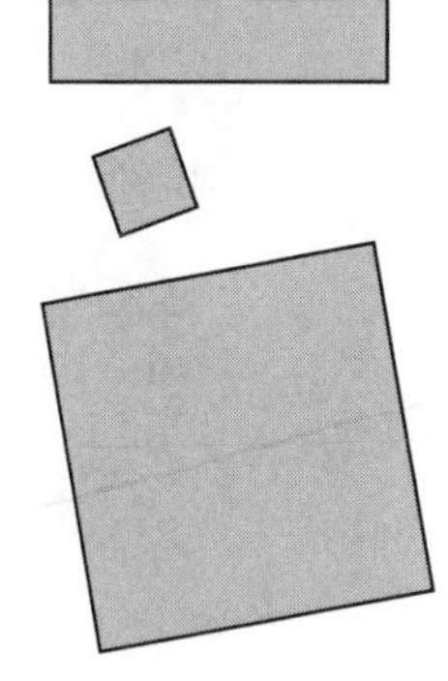

Your teacher will provide your team with a set of algebra tiles. Remove one of each shape from the bag and put it on your desk. Trace around each shape on your paper. Look at the different sides of the shapes.

a. With your team, discuss which shapes have the same side lengths and which ones have different side lengths. Be prepared to share your ideas with the class. On your traced drawings, color-code lengths that are the same.

b. Each type of tile is named for its area. In this course, the smallest square will have a side length of 1 unit, so its area is 1 square unit. This tile will be called "one" or the "unit tile." Can you use the unit tile to find the side lengths of the other rectangles? Why or why not?

c. If the side lengths of a tile can be measured exactly, then the area of the tile can be calculated by multiplying these two lengths together. The area is measured in square units. For example, the tile at right measures 1 unit by 5 units, so it has an area of 5 square units.

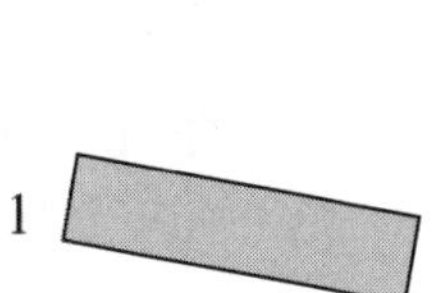

The next tile at right has one side length that is exactly one unit long. If the other side length cannot have a numerical value, what can it be called?

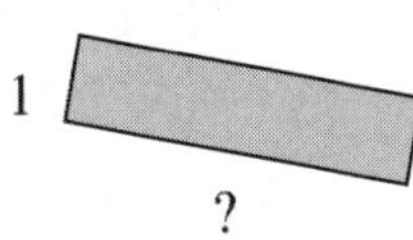

d. If the unknown length is called "x," label the side lengths of each of the four algebra tiles you traced. Find each area and use it to name each tile. Be sure to include the name of the type of units it represents.

4-71. When a collection of algebra tiles is described with mathematical symbols, it is called an **algebraic expression**. Take out the tiles shown in the picture below. Then work with your team to do the following tasks.

- Use mathematical symbols (numbers, variables, and operations) to record the area of this collection of tiles.
- Write at least three different algebraic expressions that represent the area of this tile collection.

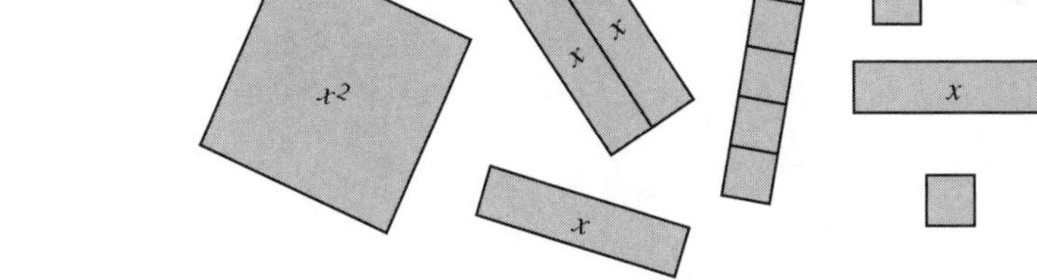

4-72. Put the tiles pictured in each collection below on your table. Then work with your team to find the area as you did in problem 4-71.

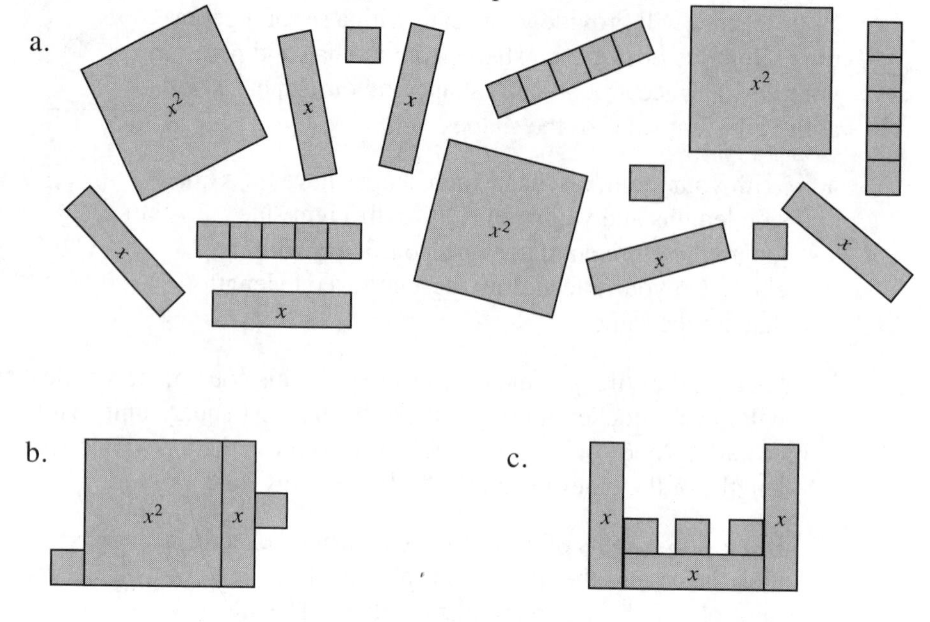

4-73. The perimeter of each algebra tile can be also written as an expression using variables and numbers.

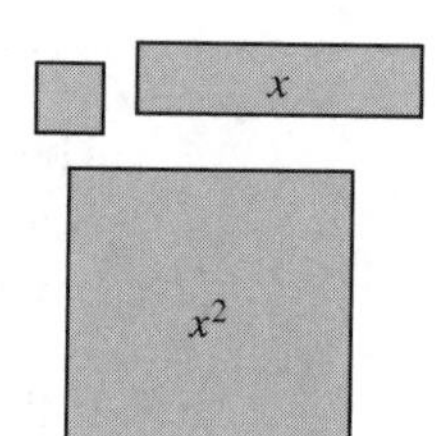

a. Write at least two different expressions for the perimeter of each tile shown at right.

b. Which way of writing the perimeter seems clearest to you? What information can you get from each expression?

c. Lianna wrote the perimeter of the collection of tiles at right as $2x+1+1+1+2x+1$ units, but her teammate Jonah wrote it as $4x+4$. How are their expressions different?

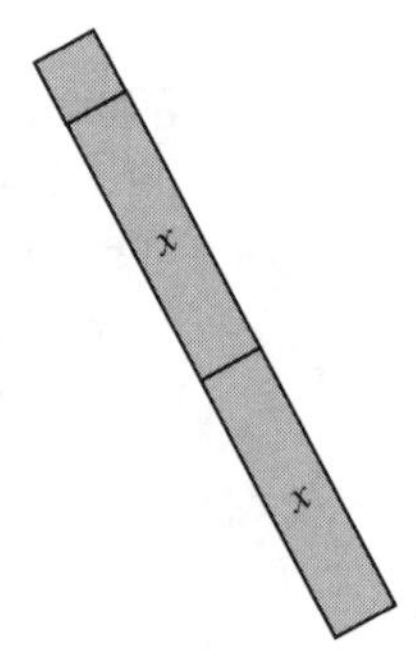

d. Which expression represents the perimeter?

4-74. The expressions that you have written to represent area and perimeter are made up of **terms** that are separated by addition and subtraction.

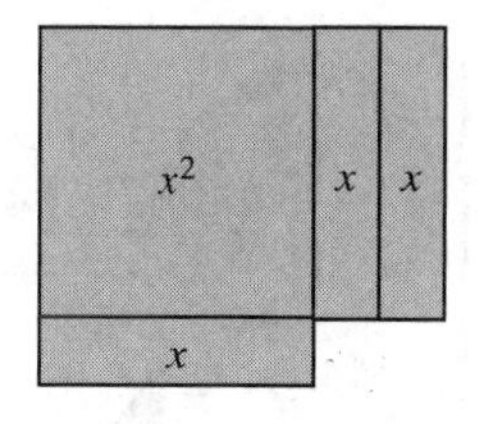

a. Write an expression for the perimeter of the figure at right.

b. How many x lengths are represented in the expression in part (a)? How many unit lengths?

c. **Combining like terms** (like terms contain the same variable raised to the same power) is a way of simplifying an expression. Rewriting the perimeter of the shape above as $P = 4x + 6$ **combines** the separate x-terms as $4x$ and combines the units in the term 6.

If you have not already done so, combine like terms for the perimeter expressions that you wrote in problem 4-73.

Math Notes

Methods and Meanings

Naming Algebra Tiles

Algebra tiles help you represent unknown quantities in a concrete way. For example, in contrast to a 1×5 tile that has a length of 5 units, like the one shown at right, an x-tile has an unknown length. Its length can be represented with a symbol or letter (like x) that represents a number, called a **variable**. Because its length is not considered fixed, the x-tile could be 6 units, or 5 units, or 0.37 units long.

Algebra tiles can be used to build algebraic expressions. The three main algebra tiles are shown at right. The large square has a side of length x units. Its area is x^2 square units, so it is referred to as an x^2-tile.

The rectangle has length of x units and width of 1 unit. Its area is x square units, so it is called an x-tile.

The small square has a side of length 1 unit. Its area is 1 square unit, so is called a one or unit tile. Note that the unit tile in this course will not be labeled with its area.

4-75. Sketch the shape made with algebra tiles at right on your paper. Then answer parts (a) and (b) below.

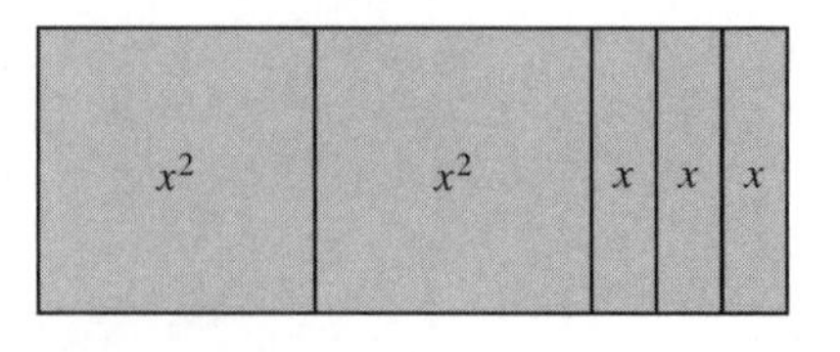

a. Find the area and perimeter of the shape.

b. If the algebra tiles were rearranged into a different shape, how would the area change?

4-76. What is the length of the marked portion of each line segment? Copy the segment onto your paper before finding the missing length. Assume that the entire line segment is subdivided into equal sections.

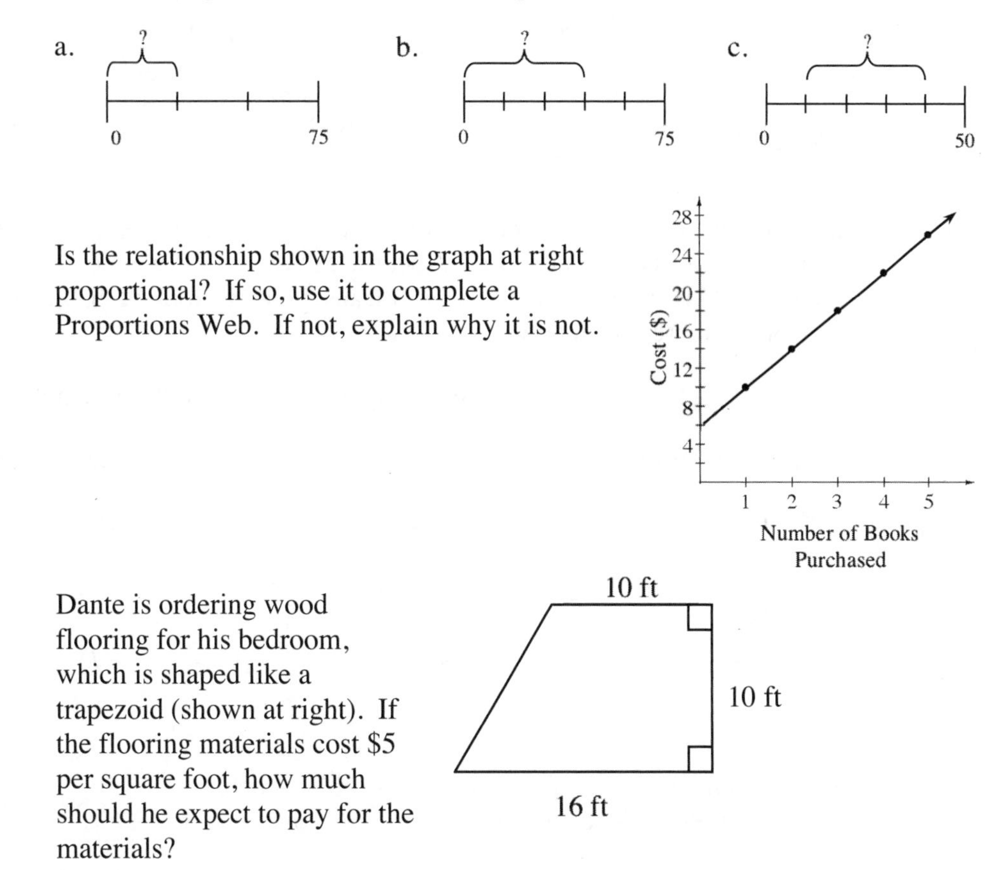

4-77. Is the relationship shown in the graph at right proportional? If so, use it to complete a Proportions Web. If not, explain why it is not.

4-78. Dante is ordering wood flooring for his bedroom, which is shaped like a trapezoid (shown at right). If the flooring materials cost \$5 per square foot, how much should he expect to pay for the materials?

4-79. Sammy is training for a running race. Today he ran $3\frac{3}{5}$ miles in 33 minutes. What is his pace in miles per hour?

4-80. Daisy and Alexandra each have a group of algebra tiles on their desks as described below.

Daisy has these tiles: $x, x, x^2, 1, x^2, x, x^2$, and x.

Alexandra has $x^2, x, 1, 1, 1, x, x^2, x$, and 1.

a. Sketch each girl's tiles.

b. If the girls put their tiles together, how many of each type of tile will they have? Write an expression that represents this sum.

4-81. Copy and complete the portions web at right.

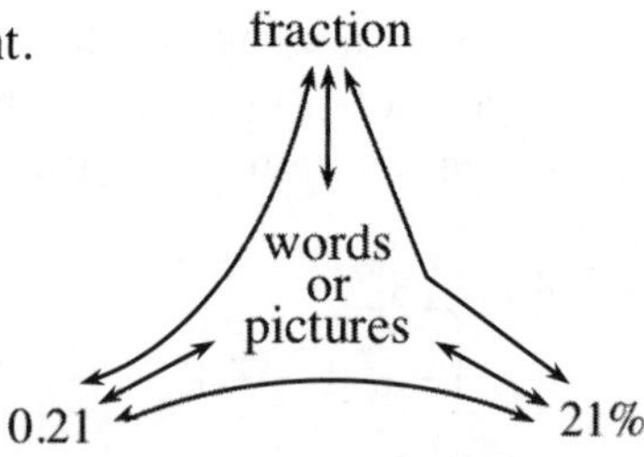

4-82. For each shape drawn below, choose one of the names on the list above them that best describes that shape. Be as specific as you can. If you do not remember what one of the shape names means, you may look in the glossary of this book for more information.

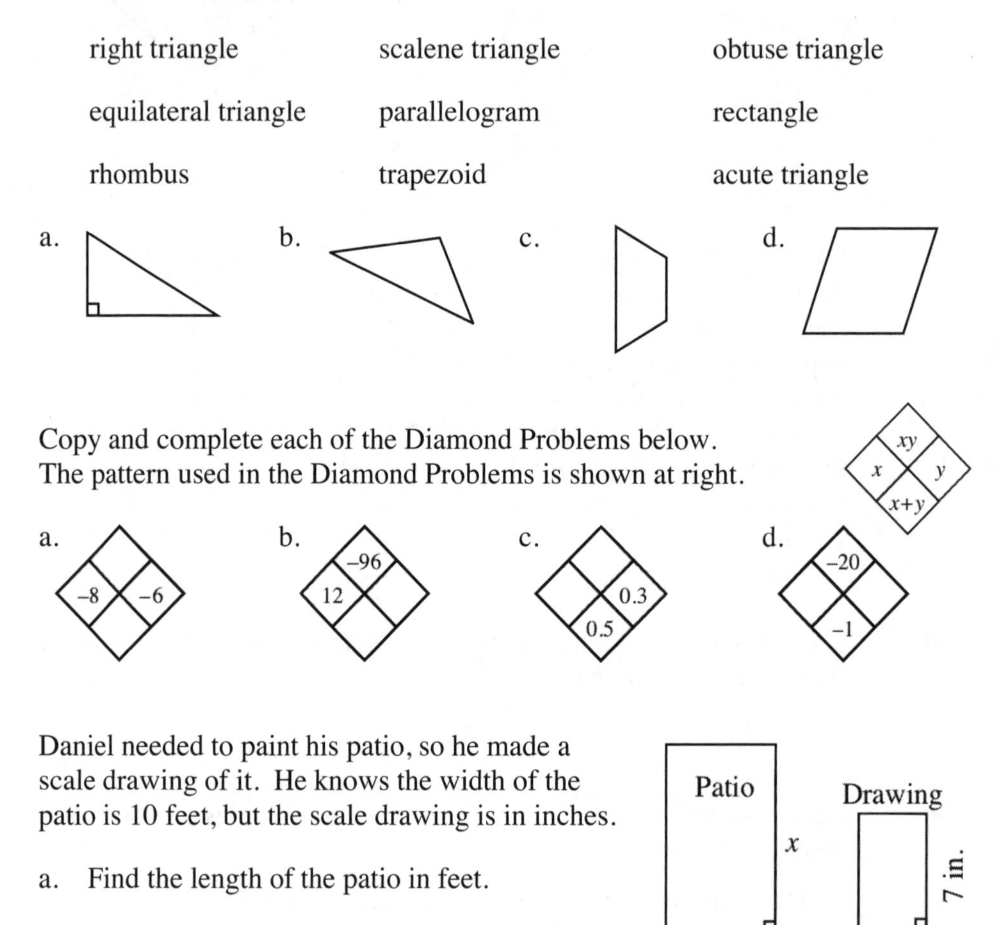

right triangle	scalene triangle	obtuse triangle
equilateral triangle	parallelogram	rectangle
rhombus	trapezoid	acute triangle

a. b. c. d.

4-83. Copy and complete each of the Diamond Problems below. The pattern used in the Diamond Problems is shown at right.

a. b. c. d.

4-84. Daniel needed to paint his patio, so he made a scale drawing of it. He knows the width of the patio is 10 feet, but the scale drawing is in inches.

a. Find the length of the patio in feet.

b. Find the area of the patio so Daniel knows how much paint to buy.

c. One can of paint covers 125 square feet. How many cans of paint will Daniel need to buy?

4.3.2 How can I group them?

Distributive Property

In Lesson 4.3.1, you used variables to name lengths that could not be precisely measured. Using variables allows you to work with lengths that you do not know exactly. Today you will work with your team to write expressions for the perimeters of different shapes using variables. As you work with your teammates, use these questions to help focus your team's discussion:

Which lengths can vary?

How can you see the perimeter?

How can you organize groups of things?

4-85. Using algebra tiles on your desk, make the shapes shown below. Trace each shape and label the length of each side on your drawing. With your team, find and record the total perimeter and area for each shape. If possible, write the perimeter in more than one way.

a.

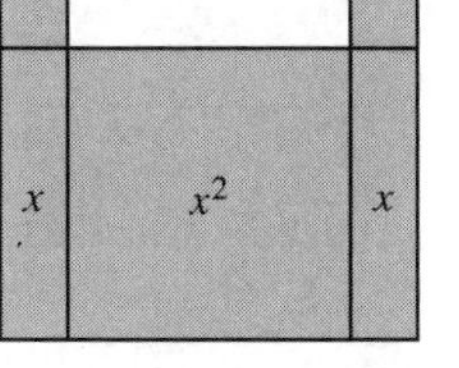

b.

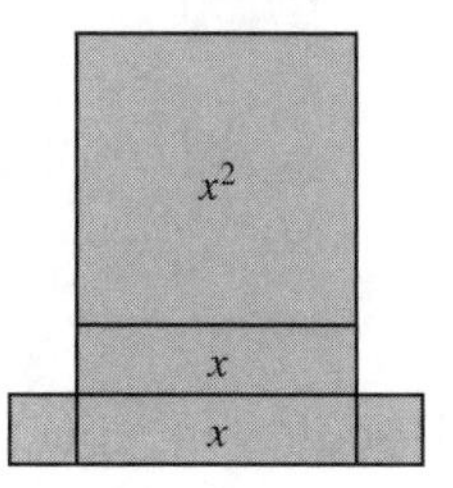

c.

4-86. In problem 4-85, x is a variable that represents a number of units of length. The value of x determines the size of the perimeter and area of the shape.

Using the shapes from problem 4-85, sketch and label each shape with the new lengths given below. Then **evaluate** each expression for the given value of the variable. That is, rewrite the expressions, replacing the variable with the number given, and then simplify them to determine the perimeter and area of each shape.

a. $x = 6$ for all three shapes

b. $x = \frac{1}{2}$ for all three shapes

c. Compare your method for finding perimeter and area with the method your teammates used. Is your method the same as your teammates' methods? If so, is there a different way to find the perimeter and area? Explain the different methods.

4-87. Build each of the shapes below using algebra tiles. Look carefully at the lengths of the right sides.

i.

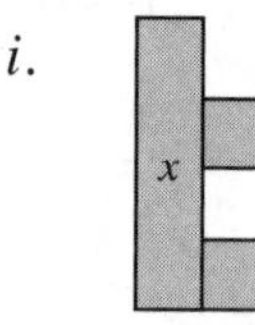

ii.

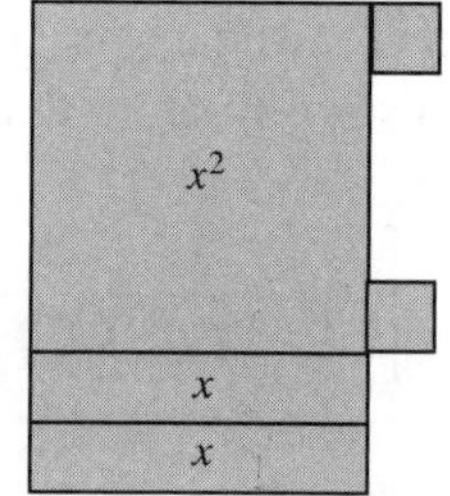

a. Discuss with your team how to label the length of the right side of each figure. Label each length on your paper. Explain your reasoning.

b. Find the perimeter of each figure. Write the perimeter in simplest form by combining the like terms.

4-88. Build the shape at right using algebra tiles. Then, on graph paper, draw the shape when x is equal to each of the lengths below.

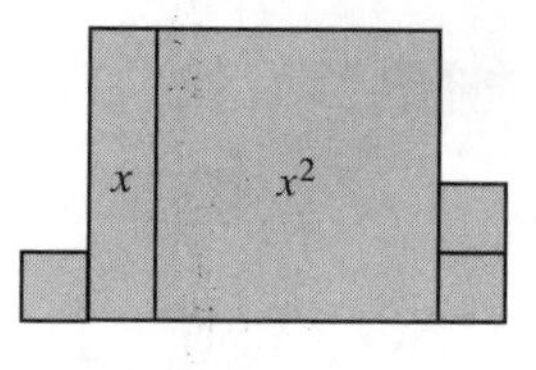

a. $x = 5$ units b. $x = 3$ units c. $x = 2$ units d. $x = 1$ unit

4-89. Parentheses in an algebraic expression allow you to show that tiles are grouped together.

a. Build these steps with algebra tiles. Use an x tile to represent "any number."

1. Think of any number.
2. Triple it.
3. Add 1.
4. Multiply by 2.

b. Look at the algebra tiles you used to build the final step of part (a). Write two different algebraic expressions to represent those tiles.

4-90. Build the following expressions with algebra tiles. Then rewrite the expression a different way. Remember that parentheses in an algebraic expression allow you to show that tiles are grouped together.

a. $4(2x+3)$

b. $12x+18$

c. $10+15x$ (Hint: Divide into as many equally-sized groups as possible)

4-91. You have been writing expressions in different ways to mean the same thing. These expressions depend on whether you see tiles grouped (like four sets of $2x+3$ in part (a) of problem 4-90) or whether you see separate tiles (eight x-tiles and 12 unit tiles). These two expressions are equivalent based on a mathematical property called the **Distributive Property**.

Use the Distributive Property to write an equivalent expression for $21x+7$. See if you can do it by visualizing tiles.

4-92. LEARNING LOG

In your Learning Log, explain what you know now about the Distributive Property and how to use it to write equivalent expressions. Include an example of different ways to write an expression with numbers and with variables, such as $3(x+4)$, by drawing pictures and writing equivalent expressions. Title this entry "Distributive Property" and include today's date.

MATH NOTES

METHODS AND MEANINGS

Combining Like Terms

This course uses tiles to represent variables and single numbers (called **constant terms**). Combining tiles that have the same area to write a simpler expression is called **combining like terms**. See the example shown at right.

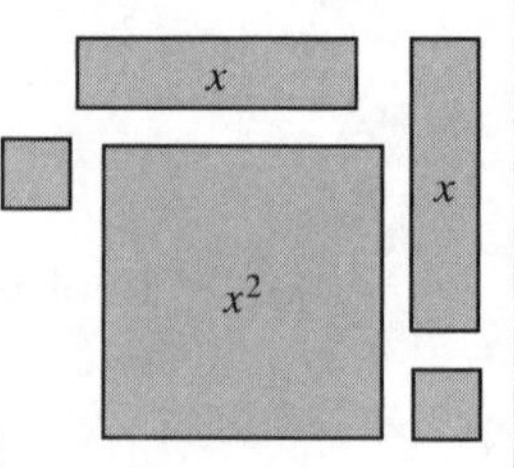

$x^2 + 2x + 2$

More formally, **like terms** are two or more terms that have the same variable(s), with the corresponding variable(s) raised to the same power.

Examples of like terms: $2x^2$ and $-5x^2$, $4ab$ and $3ab$.

Examples that are *not* like terms: 5 and $3x$, $5x$ and $7x^2$, a^2b and ab.

When you are not working with the actual tiles, it helps to visualize them in your mind. You can use these images to combine those terms that are the same. Here are two examples:

Example 1: $2x^2 + x + 3 + x^2 + 5x + 2$ is equivalent to $3x^2 + 6x + 5$.

Example 2: $3x^2 + 2x + 7 - 2x^2 - x + 7$ is equivalent to $x^2 + x + 14$.

When several tiles are pushed together and form a more complicated figure, the area of the new figure is the sum of the areas of the individual pieces, and the perimeter is the sum of the lengths around the outside. Area and perimeter expressions can be **simplified**, or rewritten, by combining like terms.

For the figure at right, the perimeter is:
$x + 1 + x + 1 + 1 + 1 + 1 + 1 + x + x = 4x + 6$ units.

4-93. Copy the diagrams of algebra tiles below on your paper. Then find the perimeter of each shape.

a.

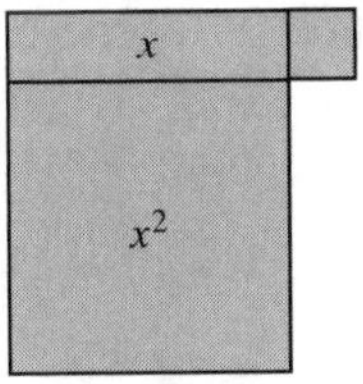

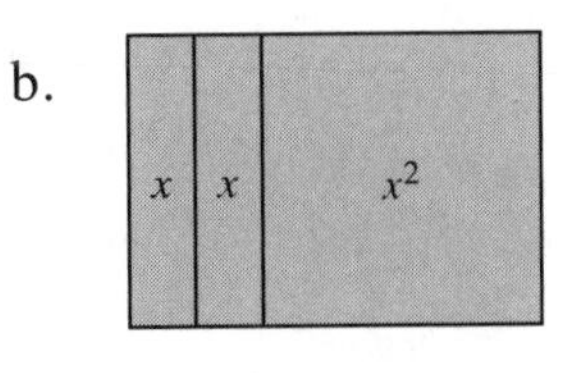

4-94. Figures A and B at right are similar. Assuming that figure A is the original figure, find the scale factor and find the lengths of the missing sides of figure B.

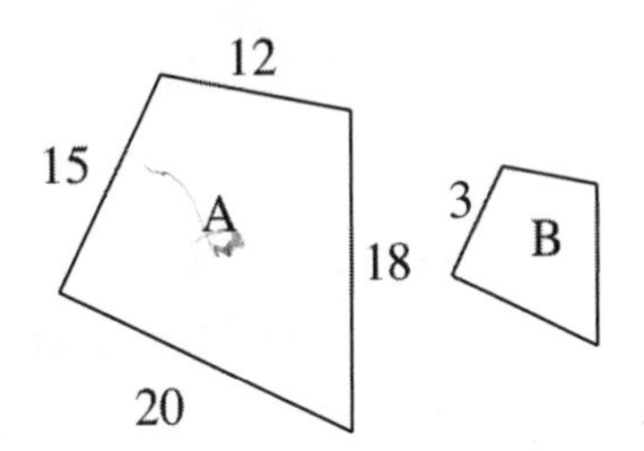

4-95. What fraction of one hour (60 minutes) is represented by the following numbers of minutes? Simplify each fraction whenever possible. A sketch of a clock might help you.

a. 10 minutes b. 15 minutes c. 30 minutes d. 20 minutes

4-96. Rainer bought 1.43 pounds of lunch meat at the store for $10.98. What was the unit rate (price) of the lunch meat?

4-97. Use absolute value to write an expression describing the size of each amount.

a. An elevation of 250 feet.

b. A credit card balance of $23.75.

c. A football player rushed for –5 yards.

d. A bank balance of $198.32.

e. An elevation of Death Valley of –86 m.

4-98. Sketch the algebra tile shape shown at right on your paper. Then:

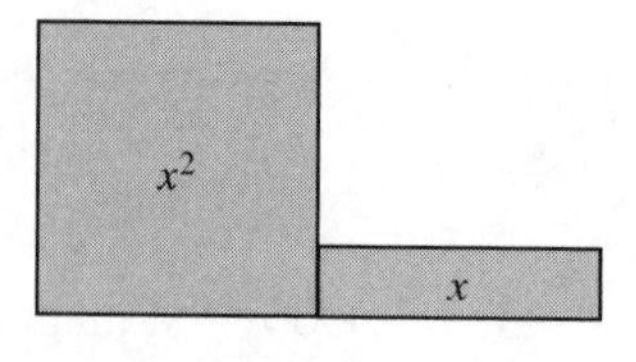

- Write an expression for the area of the shape.
- Write and simplify an expression for the perimeter of the shape.
- Calculate the area and perimeter of the shape for each value of x.

a. $x = 7$ b. $x = 2.5$ c. $x = 15$

4-99. Find the perimeter of the figure at right.

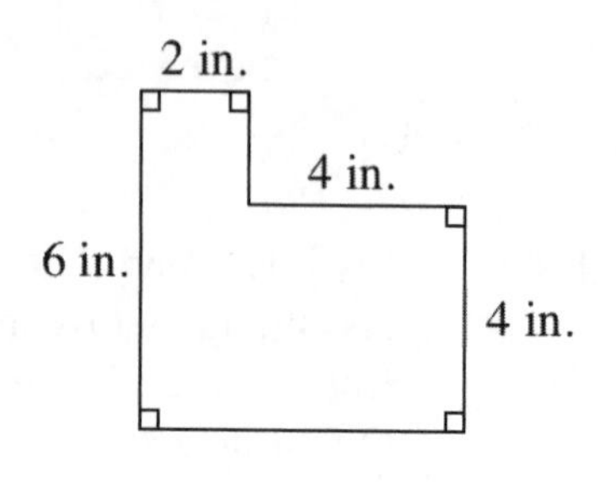

4-100. Multiply $\frac{4}{5} \cdot \frac{1}{3}$. You may want to show your thinking with a diagram.

4-101. Copy and simplify each expression.

a. $-2+5$ b. $(-4)\cdot(6)$ c. $4-(-3)$

d. $10+(-2)-7$ e. $-5-3(2-6)$ f. $(3-3)(10^2-11)$

4-102. Copy and complete the portions web at right by including a picture, a decimal, and a percent representation of $\frac{9}{20}$.

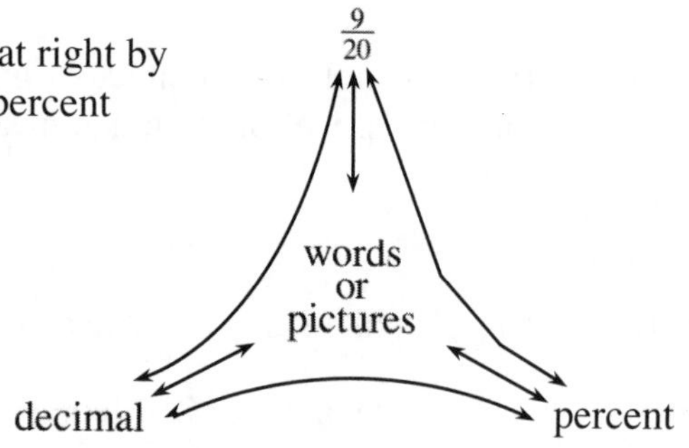

4.3.3 How can I simplify with negatives?

Simplifying With Zero

In the previous lessons, you simplified and rewrote algebraic expressions. In this lesson, you will continue to explore various ways to make expressions simpler by finding parts of them that make zero.

Zero is a relative newcomer to the number system. Its first appearance was as a placeholder around 400 B.C. in Babylon. The Ancient Greeks philosophized about whether zero was even a number: *"How can nothing be something?"* East Indian mathematicians are generally recognized as the first people to represent the quantity zero as a numeral and number in its own right about 600 A.D.

Zero now holds an important place in mathematics both as a numeral representing the absence of quantity and as a placeholder. Did you know there is no year 0 in the Gregorian calendar system (our current calendar system of 365 days in a year)? Until the creation of zero, number systems began at one.

Consider the questions below as you work today.

How can I create a zero?

How can I rewrite this expression in the most efficient way?

4-103. CONCEPTS OF ZERO

Zero is a special and unusual number. As you read above, it has an interesting history. What do you know about zero mathematically? The questions below will test your knowledge of zero.

a. If two quantities are added and the sum is zero, what do you know about the quantities?

b. If you add zero to a number, how does the number change?

c. If you multiply a number by zero, what do you know about the product?

d. What is the opposite of zero?

e. If three numbers have a product of zero, what do you know about at least one of the numbers?

f. Is zero even or odd?

4-104. When you use algebra tiles, +1 is represented with algebra tiles as a shaded small square and is always a positive unit. The opposite of 1, written –1, is an open small square and is always negative. Let's explore the variable x-tiles.

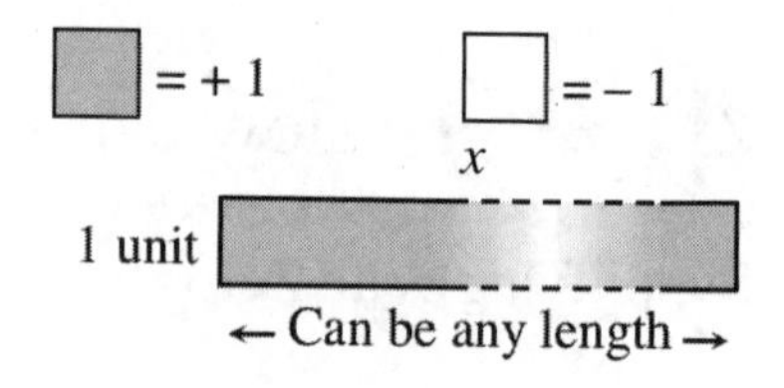

a. The variable x-tile is shaded, but is the number represented by a variable such as x always positive? Why or why not?

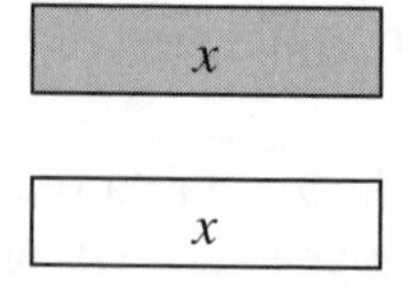

b. The opposite of the variable x, written $-x$, looks like it might be negative, but since the value of a variable can be any number (the opposite of –2 is 2), what can you say about the opposite of the variable x?

c. Is it possible to determine which is greater, x or $-x$? Explain.

d. What is true about $6+(-6)$? What is true about $x+(-x)$ (the sum of a variable and its opposite)?

4-105. Get a Lesson 4.3.3 Resource Page from your teacher, which is called "Expression Mat." The mat will help you so you can tell the difference between the expression you are working on and everything else on your desk.

Expression Mat

From your work in problem 4-104, you can say that situations like $6+(-6)$ and $x+(-x)$ "create zeros." That is, when you add an equal number of tiles and their opposites, the result is zero. The pairs of unit tiles and x-tiles shown in that problem are examples of "zero pairs" of tiles.

Build each collection of tiles represented below on the mat. Name the collection using a simpler algebraic expression (one that has fewer terms). You can do this by finding and removing zero pairs and combining like terms. Note: A zero pair is two of the same kind of tile (for example, unit tiles), one of them positive and the other negative.

a. $2+2x+x+(-3)+(-3x)$

b. $-2+2x+1-x+(-5)+2x$

4-106. An **equivalent expression** refers to the same amount with a different name.

Build the expression mats shown in the pictures below. Write the expression shown on the expression mat, then write its simplified equivalent expression by making zeros (zero pairs) and combining like terms.

a.

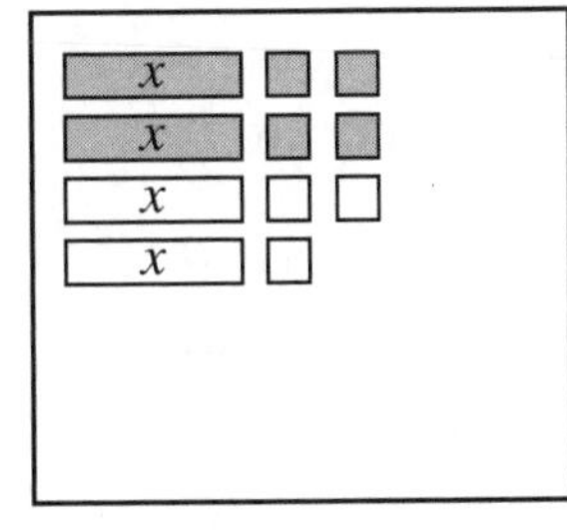

b.

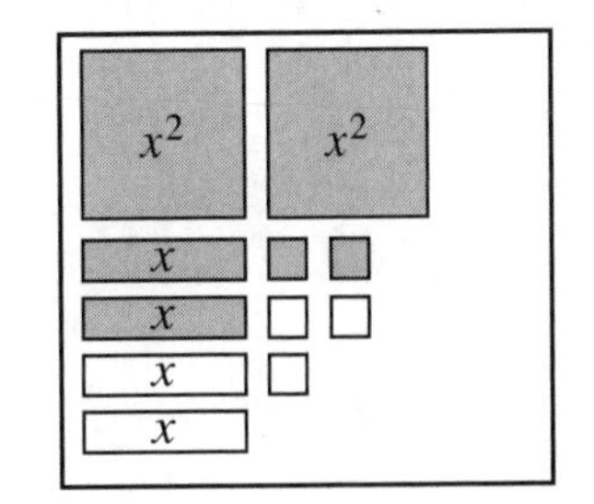

4-107. On your Expression Mat, build what is described below. Then write two different equivalent expressions to describe what is represented. One of the two representations should include parentheses.

a. The area of a rectangle with a width of 3 units and a length of $x+5$.

b. Two equal groups of $3x-2$.

c. Four rows of $2x+1$.

d. A number increased by one, then tripled.

4-108. Copy and rewrite the following expressions by combining like terms and making zeros. Using or visualizing algebra tiles may be helpful.

a. $(-1)+(-4x)+2+2x+x$

b. $2.5x+4+(-3.25)+3x$

c. $3x^2+(-2x^2)+5x+(-4x)$

d. $x-6+4\frac{1}{2}x+5\frac{1}{3}$

4-109. Earlier, you used properties of addition and multiplication to create equivalent expressions with numbers. You can do the same with expressions that have variables. For each pair of expressions below, identify the property used from the list below.

a. $3x+18+(-2x)+2$
$= 3x+(-2x)+18+2$
$= x+20$

b. $3x+2(4x-8)$
$= 3x+(8x-16)$
$= 11x-16$

c. $3x \cdot 4$
$= 4 \cdot 3x$
$= 12x$

d. $(3x+4)-6$
$= 3x+(4-6)$
$= 3x-2$

A. Associative Property of Addition

B. Commutative Property of Addition

C. Commutative Property of Multiplication

D. Distributive Property

4-110. **Additional Challenge:** Division by zero is an interesting concept. Some students believe that when you divide by zero, the result is zero. Consider how the numerical equation $30 \div 6 = 5$ can be reversed to make the multiplication equation $5 \cdot 6 = 30$.

a. Reverse the division equation $24 \div 4 = 6$ into a multiplication equation.

b. Now take the equation $24 \div 0 = x$ and reverse it into a multiplication equation. What value of x can make this equation true? Explain.

c. Why do you think the solution to a number divided by zero is called "undefined?"

d. Is $0 \div 24$ also "undefined"? Why or why not?

4-111. LEARNING LOG

In your Learning Log, explain in your own words how to simplify expressions. Include an example of different ways to write the expression $3x+5-2(x+4)+3$ by drawing pictures and writing equivalent expressions. Title this entry "Simplifying Expressions" and include today's date.

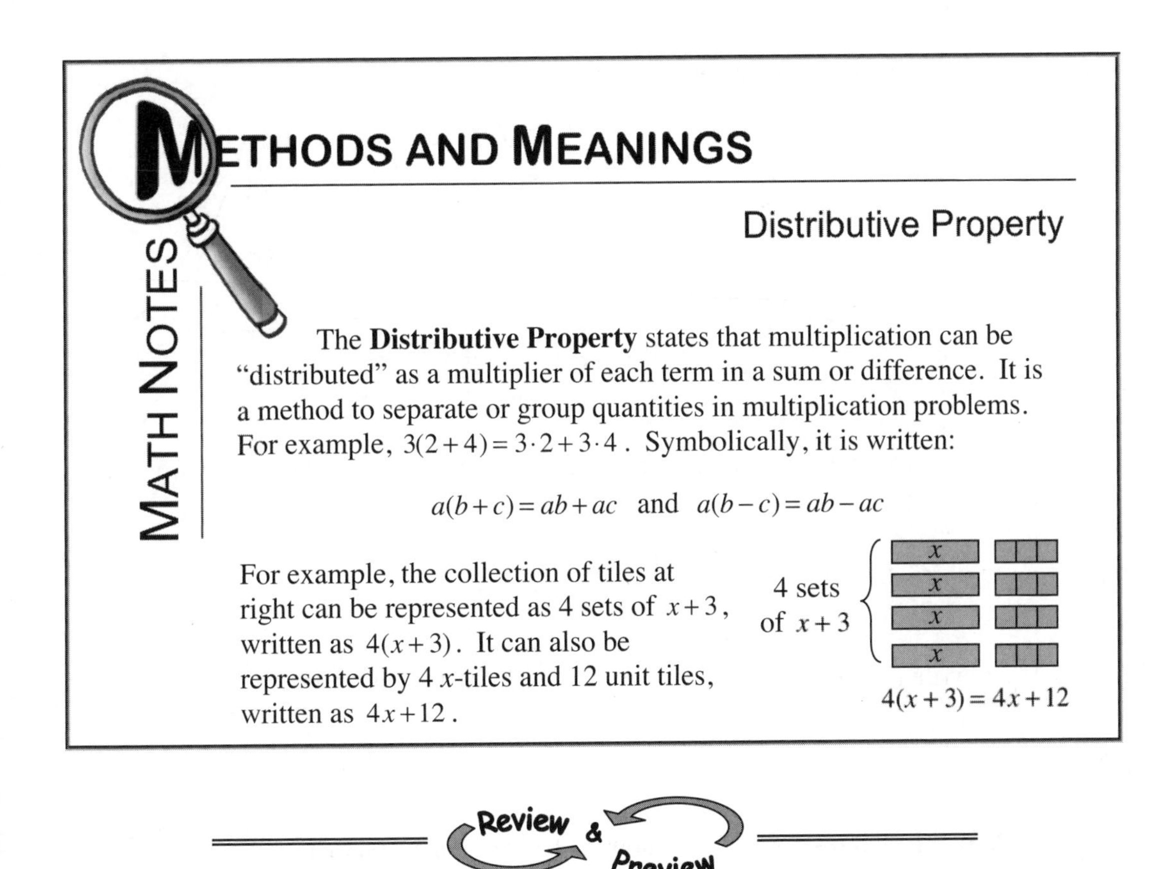

Methods and Meanings

MATH NOTES

Distributive Property

The **Distributive Property** states that multiplication can be "distributed" as a multiplier of each term in a sum or difference. It is a method to separate or group quantities in multiplication problems. For example, $3(2+4)=3\cdot 2+3\cdot 4$. Symbolically, it is written:

$$a(b+c)=ab+ac \quad \text{and} \quad a(b-c)=ab-ac$$

For example, the collection of tiles at right can be represented as 4 sets of $x+3$, written as $4(x+3)$. It can also be represented by 4 x-tiles and 12 unit tiles, written as $4x+12$.

Review & Preview

4-112. Find the perimeter and area of each figure made of algebra tiles below.

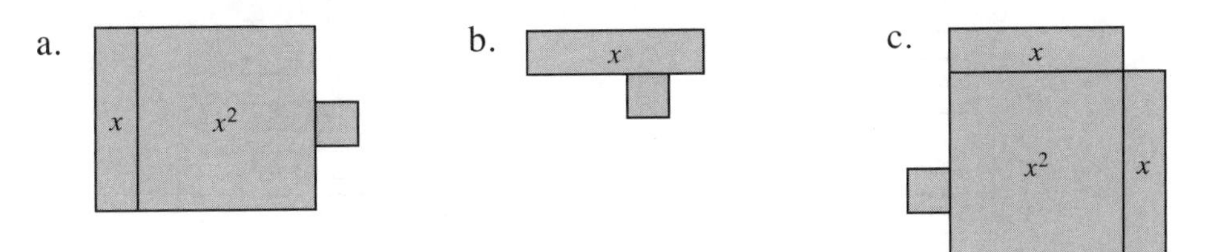

4-113. Sketch each collection of tiles below. Name the collection using a simpler algebraic expression, if possible. If it is not possible to simplify the expression, explain why not.

a. $(-2x)+5+3x-4x+(-1)+(-x)$

b. Six plus four times a number, plus four minus four times the number.

c. Three groups of a number plus two.

d. $5+7x^2+4x$

e. $4x^2-2x^2+(-6)+3$

4-114. Complete the portions webs below.

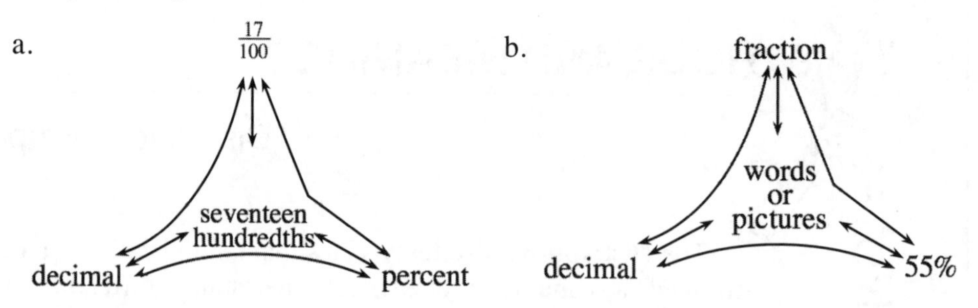

4-115. Copy each expression and simplify it. Be sure to show the steps you use to get the answer.

a. $\frac{19}{20}-\frac{1}{4}$ b. $\frac{22}{25}-\frac{7}{10}$ c. $\frac{9}{32}+\frac{7}{8}$

4-116. Rewrite each percent as a fraction and each fraction as a percent.

a. 20% b. $\frac{2}{5}$ c. 75% d. $\frac{2}{3}$

4-117. Write the expression as shown on the Expression Mats, then simplify by making zeros and combining like terms.

■ = +1
□ = −1

a. b.

4-118. Joan's Candy Emporium is having a sale. Three pounds of gummy bunnies are selling for $4.00.

a. How much will two pounds cost?

b. What is the unit rate for gummy bunnies?

4-119. Evaluate each expression below for the given value. That is, find the value of the expression when the variable is equal to the value given.

a. $2a-7$ when $a=3$ b. $10+4m$ when $m=-2$

c. $9+(-2n)$ when $n=4$ d. $\frac{x}{2}+5$ when $x=6$

4-120. Identify the length of the missing section of each line. Assume that the lines are divided into equal parts.

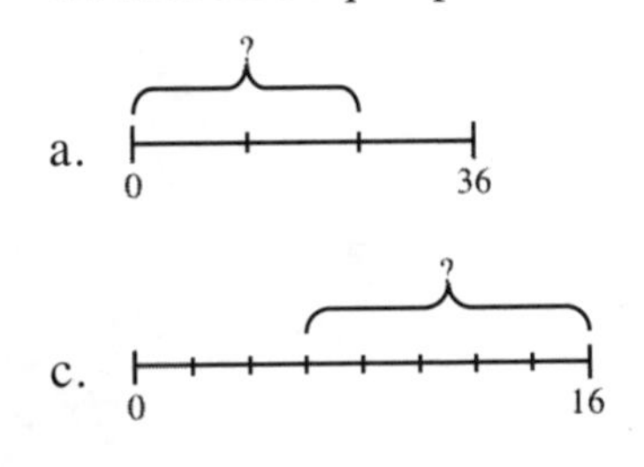

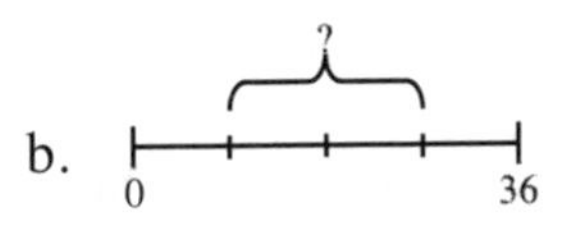

4-121. Kris said, *"The Rawlings Rockets basketball team does not have any really tall players."* These are the player's heights in inches: 70, 77, 75, 68, 88, 70, and 72.

a. Which number does not seem to fit this set of data?

b. Do you agree or disagree with Kris? Explain.

Chapter 4 Closure What have I learned?

Reflection and Synthesis

The activities below offer you a chance to reflect about what you have learned during this chapter. As you work, look for concepts that you feel very comfortable with, ideas that you would like to learn more about, and topics you need more help with.

① SUMMARIZING MY UNDERSTANDING

This section gives you an opportunity to show what you know the main math ideas in this chapter.

SHAPE CHALLENGE – PART ONE

You and your team will choose four algebra tiles and use them to build a shape to challenge your classmates. You may choose whatever tiles you would like to use as long as you use exactly four tiles.

As a team, decide on the shape you want to make. Experiment with different shapes until you find one you think will have a challenging perimeter and area for your classmates to find. Then, to share your challenge with the class:

- Build the shape with algebra tiles in the middle of your team so everyone can see it.
- Get an index card from your teacher. On one side, neatly draw the shape and label each side.
- Write a simplified expression for the perimeter and for the area on the same side of the card. This will be the answer key. Show all of your steps clearly.
- Turn the card face down so the answer is hidden, put the names of your team members on the top of the card, and then put it beside the shape you built with your algebra tiles.

Remember that your work needs to be clear enough for your classmates to understand.

Follow your teacher's directions to complete challenges created by other teams. As you look at their shapes, sketch them on your paper. Work with your team to label the sides and find the perimeter and area of each shape. Be sure to combine like terms to make the expressions as simple as possible.

① SHAPE CHALLENGE – PART TWO

Choose two of the shapes from "Shape Challenge – Part One." Sketch each shape and label it with its perimeter and area. Do not forget the correct units. It is not necessary to draw the figures to scale. Rewrite each expression with the values given below and then evaluate it.

a. $x = 1.5$ units

b. $x = 3\frac{3}{4}$ units

② WHAT HAVE I LEARNED?

Doing the problems in this section will help you to evaluate which types of problems you feel comfortable with and which ones you need more help with.

Solve each problem as completely as you can. The table at the end of this closure section provides answers to these problems. It also tells you where you can find additional help and where to find practice problems like them.

CL 4-122. Hilda was simplifying some numerical expressions and made each of the following sequences of calculations. Name the mathematical property, operation, or idea that justifies how Hilda went from each step to the next step.

a.
$$\begin{aligned} &5 \cdot 412 \\ &= 5(400 + 10 + 2) \\ &= 5 \cdot 400 + 5 \cdot 10 + 5 \cdot 2 \\ &= 2000 + 50 + 10 \\ &= 2060 \end{aligned}$$

b.
$$\begin{aligned} &15 + 32 + 5 - 2 \\ &= 15 + 5 + 32 - 2 \\ &= (15 + 5) + (32 - 2) \\ &= 20 + 30 \\ &= 50 \end{aligned}$$

CL 4-123. Copy and complete each of the Diamond Problems below. The pattern used in the Diamond Problems is shown at right.

xy
x y
x+y

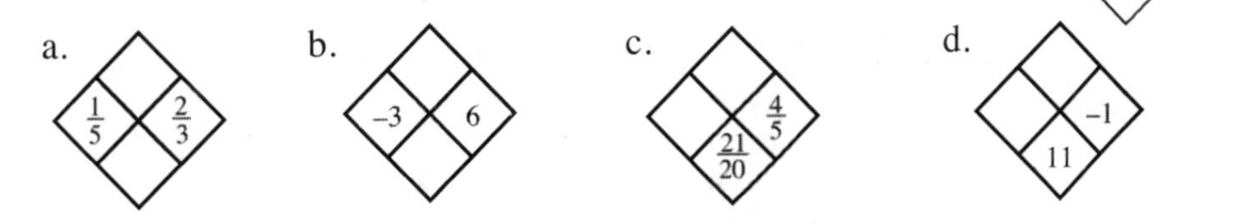

CL 4-124. Copy the following expressions on your paper and simplify them by combining like terms. Using algebra tiles may be helpful.

a. $4x+2+2x+x^2+x$

b. $10x+4-3+8x+2$

c. $4+x^2+3x+2x^2+4$

d. $x+4+(x-1)+3+2x$

CL 4-125. The shapes at right are similar.

a. What is the scale factor?

b. Find the sides labeled x and y.

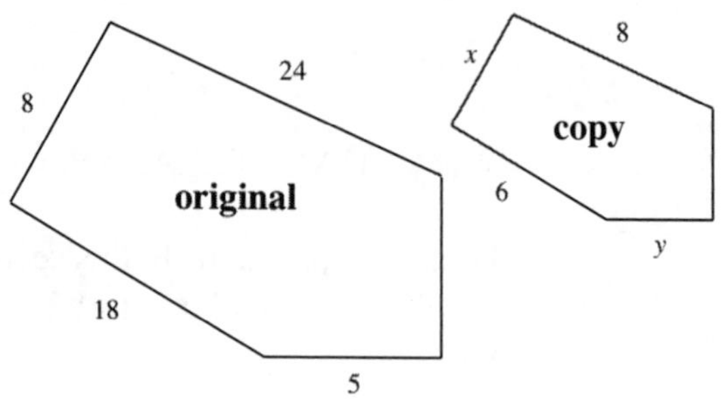

CL 4-126. Simplify each expression.

a. $\frac{3+(-7)}{-2}$

b. $\frac{4-16}{-2(-2)}$

c. $5(2+(-9))+(-25)$

d. $-3(4)+5(4)-2(7)$

CL 4-127. A speed skater covered 1500 meters in 106.43 seconds. Find his unit rate of speed in meters per second.

CL 4-128. Which table or tables below show a proportional relationship? Justify your answers.

a.

x	5	7	9	−8	0	11	15
y	9	13	17	−17	−19	21	29

b.

x	7	14	91	9	−12	−36	81
y	$3\frac{1}{2}$	7	$45\frac{1}{2}$	$4\frac{1}{2}$	−6	−18	$40\frac{1}{2}$

c.

x	−3	−10	0	10	5	4	$\frac{1}{2}$	−3
y	−27	−1000	0	1000	125	48	$\frac{1}{8}$	−27

CL 4-129. A box contains 15 yellow, 15 orange, and 15 green tennis balls. If Izzy draws a tennis ball at random out of the box, what is the probability that she drew either a green or an orange tennis ball? Show your work and express your answer as a percent.

CL 4-130. For each of the problems above, do the following:

- Draw a bar or number line that represents 0 to 10.

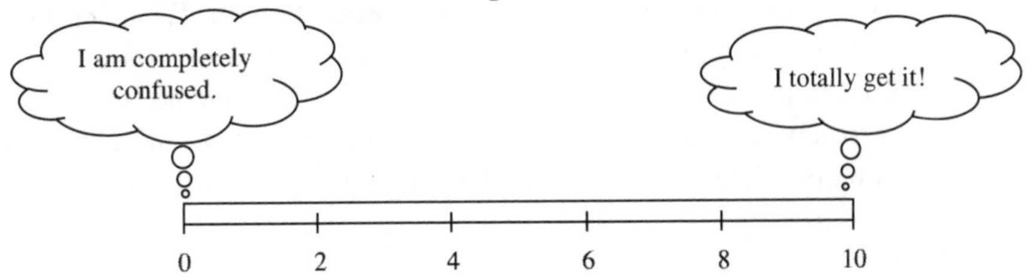

- Color or shade in a portion of the bar that represents your level of understanding and comfort with completing that problem on your own.

If any of your bars are less than a 5, choose *one* of those problems and do one of the following tasks:

- Write two questions that you would like to ask about that problem.
- Brainstorm two things that you DO know about that type of problem.

If all of your bars are a 5 or above, choose one of those problems and do one of these tasks:

- Write two questions you might ask or hints you might give to a student who was stuck on the problem.
- Make a new problem that is similar and more challenging than that problem and solve it.

③ WHAT TOOLS CAN I USE?

You have several tools and references available to help support your learning: your teacher, your study team, your math book, and your Toolkit, to name only a few. At the end of each chapter, you will have an opportunity to review your Toolkit for completeness. You will also revise or update it to reflect your current understanding of big ideas.

The main elements of your Toolkit should be your Learning Logs, Math Notes, and the vocabulary used in this chapter. Math words that are new appear in bold in the text. Refer to the lists provided below and follow your teacher's instructions to revise your Toolkit, which will help make it useful for you as you complete this chapter and as you work in future chapters.

Learning Log Entries

- Lesson 4.2.1 – Recognizing Proportional Relationships
- Lesson 4.2.2 – Proportional Relationships in Graphs and Tables
- Lesson 4.2.4 – Connections Web for Proportional Relationships
- Lesson 4.3.3 – Simplifying Expressions

Math Notes

- Lesson 4.1.1 – Mathematical Properties
- Lesson 4.1.2 – Similarity and Scale Factor
- Lesson 4.2.3 – Proportional Relationships
- Lesson 4.2.4 – Unit Rate
- Lesson 4.3.1 – Naming Algebra Tiles
- Lesson 4.3.2 – Combining Like Terms
- Lesson 4.3.3 – Distributive Property

Mathematical Vocabulary

The following is a list of vocabulary found in this chapter. Some of the words have been seen in the previous chapter. The words in bold are words that are new to this chapter. Make sure that you are familiar with the terms below and know what they mean. For the words you do not know, refer to the glossary or index. You might also add these words to your Toolkit so that you can reference them in the future.

algebraic expression	Associative Property	**combining like terms**
Commutative Property	**constant term**	**constant of proportionality**
corresponding parts	Distributive Property	**equivalent expressions**
evaluate	proportional relationship	**scale drawing**
scale factor	**similar figures**	simplify
terms	**unit rate**	**variable**

Answers and Support for Closure Problems
What Have I Learned?

Note: MN = Math Note, LL = Learning Log

Problem	Solution	Need Help?	More Practice
CL 4-122.	a. Decomposed 412, Distributive Property, multiplied each term, added terms together. b. Commutative Property of Addition, Associative Property of Addition, added as indicated by grouping symbols, added each term.	Lesson 3.3.3 MN: 4.1.1	Problems 4-44 and 4-109
CL 4-123.	a. $\frac{2}{15}$, $\frac{13}{15}$ b. $-18, 3$ c. $\frac{4}{20}$ or $\frac{1}{5}$, $\frac{1}{4}$ d. $12, -12$	Problem 2-16	Problems 2-81, 2-116, 3-123, 4-19, 4-32, and 4-83

Problem	Solution	Need Help?	More Practice
CL 4-124.	a. x^2+7x+2 b. $18x+3$ c. $3x^2+3x+8$ d. $4x+6$	Lessons 4.3.1 and 4.3.3 MN: 4.3.2 LL: 4.3.3	Problems 4-80, 4-108, and 4-113
CL 4-125.	a. $\frac{1}{3}$ b. $x=\frac{8}{3}$ or $2\frac{2}{3}$ $y=\frac{5}{3}$ or $1\frac{2}{3}$	Lesson 4.1.1 MN: 4.1.2	Problems 4-1, 4-2, 4-3, and 4-94
CL 4-126.	a. 2 b. –3 c. –60 d. –6	Sections 3.1 and 3.2 MN: 3.1.2, 3.2.2, and 3.2.4 LL: 3.1.1, 3.1.2, 3.2.2, and 3.2.3	Problems CL 3-131, 4-16, and 4-63
CL 4-127.	$\approx \frac{14.09 \text{ meters}}{1 \text{ second}}$	Lesson 4.2.3 MN: 4.2.4	Problems 4-50, 4-61, 4-79, 4-96, and 4-118
CL 4-128.	Table (b) is proportional because it is the only one that could contain $(0,0)$ and grows using a Giant One.	Section 4.1 MN: 4.2.3 LL: 4.2.1, 4.2.2 and 4.2.4	Problems 4-29, 4-30, 4-41, 4-50, 4-51, 4-60, and 4-77
CL 4-129.	$66\frac{2}{3}\%$	Lessons 1.2.1, 1.2.2, and 1.2.3 MN: 1.2.3 LL: 1.2.1	Problems CL 1-148, CL 2-136, 4-42, 4-54, and 4-68

5 Probability and Solving Word Problems

CHAPTER 5 Probability and Solving Word Problems

How often do you need to compare one thing to another? You probably compare prices when you are buying something, and you may compare heights of basketball players as you watch a game. In mathematics, comparing one thing to another is an important strategy to learn about how they are related.

In Section 5.2, you will continue your study of probability. You will learn how to calculate probabilities of two or more events and how to decide when different games are fair. You will also calculate the probability that more than one event will take place. As you do this, you will learn new ways to organize the possible outcomes and will explore situations where one outcome is more likely than another.

In Section 5.3, you will use variables to represent a single unknown number in different contexts, such as the length of the side of a figure or the number of frogs in a pond. You will learn about the 5-D Process, a strategy to organize your thinking that can help you solve problems.

Think about these questions throughout this chapter:

What is the part?

What is the whole?

Which is more likely?

Is it fair?

How can I represent the relationship?

How can I organize my thinking?

In this chapter, you will learn how to:

- Find and use percentages to solve problems.
- Calculate the probability of compound (multiple) events.
- Use experimental results to make and test conjectures about unknown sample spaces.
- Describe how the relationship between experimental and theoretical probabilities for an experiment changes as the experiment is conducted many times.
- Solve situational problems using the 5-D Process.

Chapter Outline

Section 5.1	This section introduces a linear diagram that you will use to represent relationships between parts and the whole to solve problems.
Section 5.2	You will investigate probability using a deck of cards and a random number generator. You will learn to represent multiple events using a probability tree, a list, and a table. You will also revisit the idea of the fairness of events and compare experimental and theoretical probabilities.
Section 5.3	This section will introduce the 5-D Process as a problem-solving method. You will learn how to understand a problem by drawing, describing, and defining its elements. You will learn strategies that lead to writing and solving equations later in the course.
Mid-Course Reflection	Finally, you will reflect about the content and work you have done in Chapters 1 through 5.

5.1.1 How can I find a percentage?

Part-Whole Relationships

Food labels tell you about what is in the food you eat. The nutrition-facts label lists the percentages of macronutrients (protein, carbohydrates, and fat) as well as vitamins and minerals in each serving. However, it often does not tell you exactly how much of each thing is in the food or how much you should have each day to be healthy.

If you know how much Vitamin C is in a serving, can you figure out how much is needed in a day? To help you answer a question like that, in this section you will develop strategies for finding information about parts and wholes.

Nutrition Facts	
Serving Size 1 cup (228g)	
Serving Per Container 4	
Amount Per Serving	
Calories 250	Calories from Fat 110
	% Daily Value*
Total Fat 12g	**18%**
Saturated Fat 3g	**15%**
Cholesterol 30mg	**10%**
Sodium 470mg	**20%**
Total Carbohydrate 31g	**10%**
Dietary Fiber 0g	**0%**
Sugars 5g	
Protein 5g	
Vitamin A	**4%**
Vitamin C	**2%**
Calcium	**20%**
Iron	**4%**

5-1. WHAT ARE YOU EATING?

The government has created guidelines for how much of various nutrients, vitamins, and minerals a person should eat or drink each day to be healthy. These guidelines are then used to create labels like the one shown above to inform the public about the nutritional content of food.

According to the sample label above, one serving of Cheesy Mac macaroni and cheese contains 15% of the recommended daily amount of saturated fat that a person should eat. Nutritionists recommend that a person should have no more than a certain amount of saturated fat each day. One serving of Cheesy Mac has 3 grams (3g) of saturated fat. How many grams of saturated fat should a person eat in one day?

Your Task: With your team, determine how many grams of saturated fat a person should eat each day. Look for more than one way to solve the problem and be ready to explain your reasoning.

Discussion Points

What information do you have about the part?

What do you know about the whole?

How could you represent this situation with a number line?

Further Guidance

5-2. To help you represent the situation in problem 5-1, copy the number line below on your paper.

Recommended Daily Intake of Saturated Fat

0% ———————————————— 100%

a. With your team, decide how to **partition** the line (divide it into equal parts) so that 15% is shown. Why did you choose to make that number of parts? Is there another way that you could have divided the line?

b. The amount of saturated fat in one serving of Cheesy Mac is 3 grams. Where should 3g be labeled on the number line? Add this number to your diagram and justify your decision.

c. Use your diagram to help you decide how much saturated fat is in the recommended daily serving. Record your thinking.

Further Guidance section ends here.

5-3. One way to write a percentage is as a **ratio** (comparison) of parts out of 100. For example, the ratio $\frac{15}{100}$ represents 15 parts out of 100 total parts.

a. Jill represented the amount of saturated fat in the recommended daily amount with the ratio $\frac{3}{20}$. What does the 3 represent? What does the 20 represent?

b. The ratios $\frac{15}{100}$ and $\frac{3}{20}$ are two different ways to compare the saturated fat in one serving to the recommended daily amount. How can you show that the ratios are equivalent (the same)?

5-4. One granola bar contains 4g of dietary fiber. The label says that 4g is 16% of the daily recommended amount. Louis decided to draw a diagram like the one below to understand this situation.

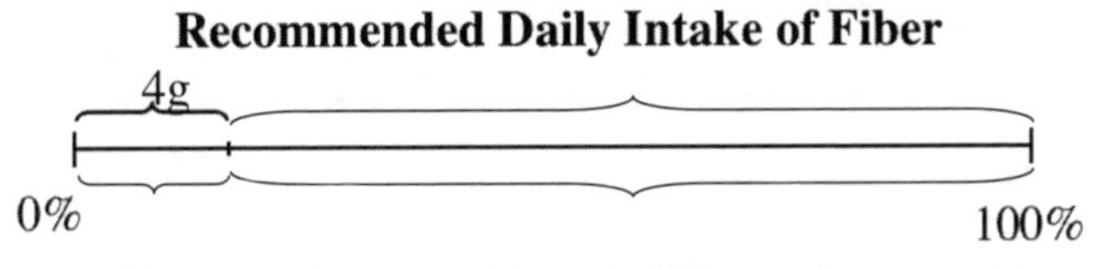

a. Copy the diagram on your paper and add the label for 16%.

b. How many grams of fiber are recommended each day? How can you show this with equal ratios?

c. What percent of fiber should Louis get from other foods? Why is this percent equivalent to the ratio $\frac{21\text{ g}}{25\text{ g}}$?

d. What other amounts are missing on the diagram? Add labels for all parts, percents, and the whole.

e. Chris is eating cookies that contain 12g of dietary fiber, which he says is 48% of the recommended daily amount. How can you use ratios and part (b) above to check that 12g is equivalent to 48%?

5-5. One large carrot contains approximately 6 mg of Vitamin C. The recommended daily intake of Vitamin C is 60 mg. Resa wanted to find out what percentage of her daily Vitamin C she gets from one carrot. She started with a line divided into 10 parts.

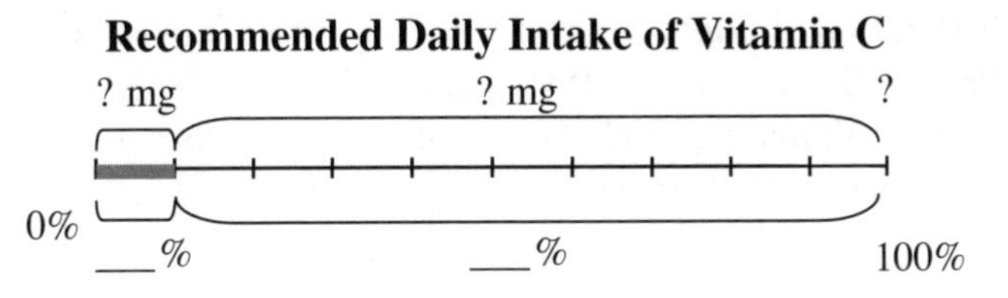

a. Why do you think she divided the line segment into 10 parts?

b. Copy the diagram on your paper and fill in the missing labels.

c. The ratio $\frac{6\text{ mg}}{60\text{ mg}}$ represents the portion of Vitamin C in one large carrot. Work with your team to find this ratio in the diagram. Where do you see each amount? What other ratio could you write that would be equal to this?

d. Use the diagram to help you find and write at least two other ratios on the number line that are equal to each other.

5-6. Resa was mixing blue and red paint to create purple paint. She created the drawing below to show the portions of blue paint to red that she used.

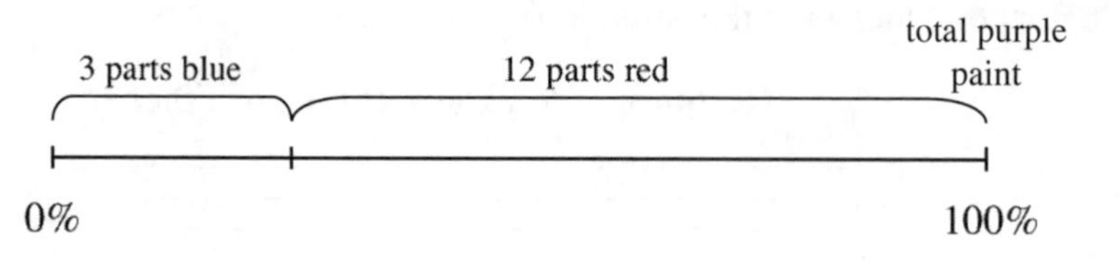

a. What does the picture tell you about the paint mixture? What statements can you make?

b. If you have not stated it yet, what percent of the paint is blue? What percent of the paint is red? Justify your answer.

5-7. **Additional Challenge:** Turner Middle School has 110 boys. Fifty-six percent of the students in the school are girls. How many students go to this school?

a. Create a model like Resa's from problem 5-5. Label the percentage of girls, the percentage of boys, and the number of boys on your drawing, as well as 0% and 100%.

b. How many students go to the school? How do you know?

c. How many girls go to the school? Explain your reasoning.

5-8. **Additional Challenge:** Maria is making paper flowers as decorations for the fall dance. She has made 40 flowers so far, and she is 16% finished. If she plans to finish making 70% of the total flowers needed by tonight, how many more will she need to make by then? Show your work.

MATH NOTES

METHODS AND MEANINGS

Equivalent Ratios

A **ratio** is a comparison of two quantities by division. A ratio can be written in words, as a fraction, or with colon notation. Most often in this course, ratios will be written as fractions or stated in words.

For example, if there are 28 students in a math class and 15 of them are girls, you can write the ratio of the number of girls to the number of students in the class as:

15 girls to 28 students $\qquad \frac{15 \text{ girls}}{28 \text{ students}} \qquad$ 15 girls : 28 students

You used a Giant One to write equivalent fractions in Chapter 1. To rewrite any ratio as an **equivalent ratio**, write it as a fraction and multiply it by a fraction equal to one. For example, you can show that the ratio of raisins to peanuts is the same for a larger mixture using a Giant One like this:

$$\frac{4 \text{ raisins}}{7 \text{ peanuts}} \cdot \frac{20}{20} = \frac{80 \text{ raisins}}{140 \text{ peanuts}}$$

Equivalent fractions (or ratios) can be thought of as families of fractions. There are an infinite number of fractions that are equivalent to a given fraction. You may want to review the basis for using a Giant One — the Multiplicative Identity — in the Math Notes box in Lesson 1.2.5.

5-9. Find the missing values on the diagram below. Assume that each line is evenly divided.

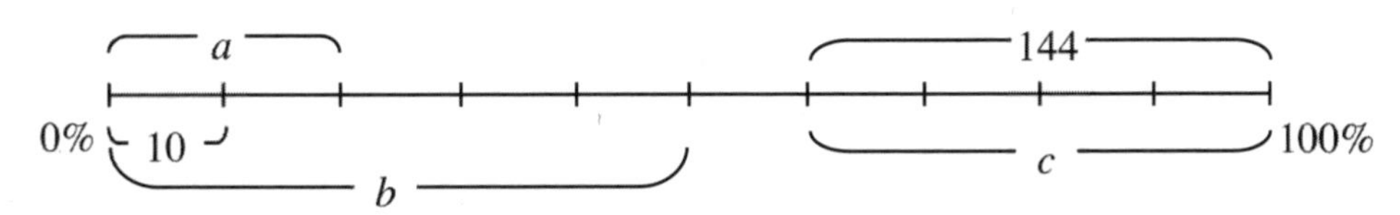

5-10. A fish tank that holds 80 gallons of water is 55% full.

a. Create a drawing like Louis's in problem 5-4 to represent this situation.

b. How many gallons are in the tank now? How many more gallons are needed to fill the tank?

5-11. Fill in the missing numbers in each number sentence.

a. $\frac{5}{8} \cdot \frac{3}{3} = \frac{?}{?}$ b. $\frac{9}{15} \cdot \frac{?}{?} = \frac{?}{60}$ c. $\frac{7}{20} \cdot \frac{?}{?} = \frac{?}{110}$ d. $\frac{44}{100} \cdot \frac{?}{?} = \frac{?}{60}$

e. What strategies did you use to find the numbers in the Giant One in parts (b), (c), and (d)?

5-12. Complete a Proportions Web for the following situation.

Clifford works 40 hours per week while working as a laboratory technician. He earns $453.60 for each week of work.

5-13. Simplify the following expressions.

a. $\frac{2}{3} + \frac{4}{5}$ b. $\left(\frac{4}{5}\right)\left(\frac{2}{3}\right)$ c. $\frac{4}{5} - \left(-\frac{2}{3}\right)$

5.1.2 What is the percentage of the whole?

Finding and Using Percentages

How are sales advertised in different stores? In a clothing store, items are often marked with signs saying, "20% off" or "40% discount." In a grocery store, sale items are usually listed by price. For example, pasta is marked, "Sale price 50¢," or boxes of cereal are marked "$2.33 each." In the clothing store, you are able to see how much the discount is, but the price you will pay is often not stated. On the other hand, sometimes in the grocery store it is not possible to tell the size of the discount. It might only be a small fraction of the original price.

The actual dollar amount of the discount and the percentage comparing it to the whole are important pieces of information that help you decide if you are getting a good deal. Today you will create complete information about a sale situation from the information given in a problem.

By the end of this lesson, you will be expected to answer these target questions:

How can I find a percentage of a whole?

How can I find a percent if I have two parts that make a whole?

How can I find the whole amount if I know the parts?

5-14. Marisa is always looking for a great deal while shopping. She found a sale rack where all of the jeans are marked 40% off. Her favorite jeans regularly cost $65.

a. To figure out if she has enough money to buy a pair of jeans, Marisa decides to estimate. She thinks that the jeans will cost approximately $30. Is her estimate reasonable? Explain your thinking.

b. To find the exact answer, Marisa created the diagram below. How could she add marks to partition the line evenly? Partition the line and calculate the missing values.

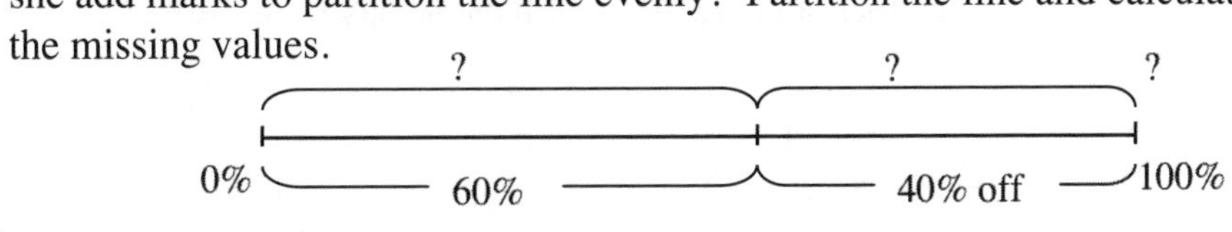

c. How much money will Marisa save? What is the price she will have to pay?

d. Marisa wants to check her answer from part (c). How could she use ratios with the amount she saved and the original price to verify that she received a 40% discount?

5-15. At the same sale, Kirstin sees a shirt on sale for just \$37.50. It originally cost \$50.

a. Estimate the percentage of the discount on the shirt.

b. Draw a diagram to represent this situation. Label all parts.

c. What percent is the discount on Kirstin's shirt?

d. What is the relationship between the discount, the sale price, and the original price? Write a statement that shows the relationship between the sale price, discount, and original price.

5-16. So far in this section, you have used a linear model to represent percent problems in various contexts.

a. Obtain a Lesson 5.1.2 Resource Page and use the linear models to find parts and wholes when different types of information are provided on the diagrams.

b. For each diagram, write at least three statements describing how parts and percentages are related. Some statements are started for you.

5-17. When Kirstin was about to pay for her clothes, she realized that she had forgotten to include an 8% sales tax.

a. The belt Kirstin wants to buy costs \$15. She does not have paper to draw a linear model. To estimate tax, she figured that calculating 10% would be close enough. Explain how Kirstin might find 10% of \$15 without a linear model.

b. Calculate exactly how much the 8% sales tax will cost Kirstin. What will be the total amount she will have to pay to the store?

MATH NOTES

METHODS AND MEANINGS

Part-to-Whole Relationships

Percentages, fractions, and decimals are all different ways to represent a portion of a whole or a number. Portion-whole relationships can also be described in words.

You can represent a part-to-whole relationship with a linear model like the one below. To solve a percentage problem described in words, you must first identify three important quantities: the percent, the whole, and the part of the whole. One of the quantities will be unknown. A diagram can help you organize the information. For example:

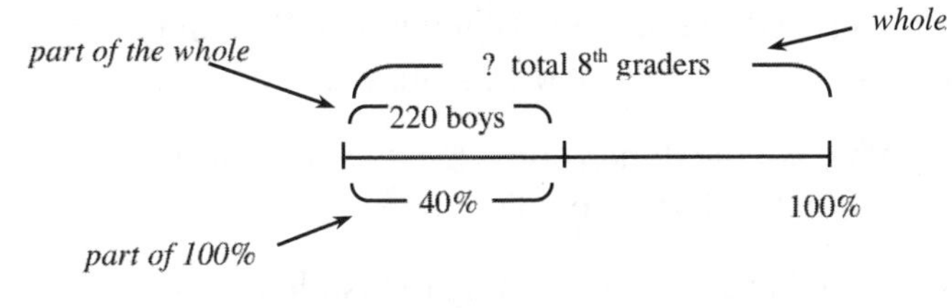

Once the parts have been identified, you can use reasoning to extend the part to the whole. For example, if 220 students are 40% of eighth graders, then 10% must be $220 \div 4 = 55$. Then 100% must be $55 \cdot 10 = 550$ students. Another way to solve the problem is to find the ratio of 220 boys to the whole (all students) and compare that ratio to 40% and 100%. This could be written:

$$\frac{40}{100} \cdot \left[\frac{\ }{\ }\right] = \frac{220}{?}\text{, then } \frac{40}{100} \cdot \left[\frac{5.5}{5.5}\right] = \frac{220}{?}$$

You can see above that the total number of 8th graders is 550.

To remember how to rewrite decimals or fractions as percents, and to rewrite percents as fractions or decimals, refer to the Math Notes box at the end of Lesson 1.3.1.

Review & Preview

5-18. A shade of orange paint is made with 5 parts red paint and 15 parts yellow paint.

a. What percent of the paint is red?

b. What is the simplified ratio of yellow to red paint?

5-19. Janelle earned 90% on a test and got 63 points. How many total points were possible on the test? Draw a diagram to organize your information before solving the problem.

5-20. The diagram at right is the floor plan of Randy's apartment. All measurements are in feet. Use the diagram to answer the following questions.

7	bathroom	kitchen
10	bedroom	living room
	9	15

a. What are the dimensions (length and width) of Randy's living room?

b. Randy's friends are coming to visit him soon. He plans to keep them out of his bedroom. Find the area of each of the other three rooms he will have to clean.

c. What is the total area of the rooms he will have to clean?

5-21. Simplify each expression.

a. $-\frac{4}{5}+\frac{3}{10}$

b. $2\frac{5}{8}-1\frac{1}{3}$

5-22. The trapezoids at right are similar shapes.

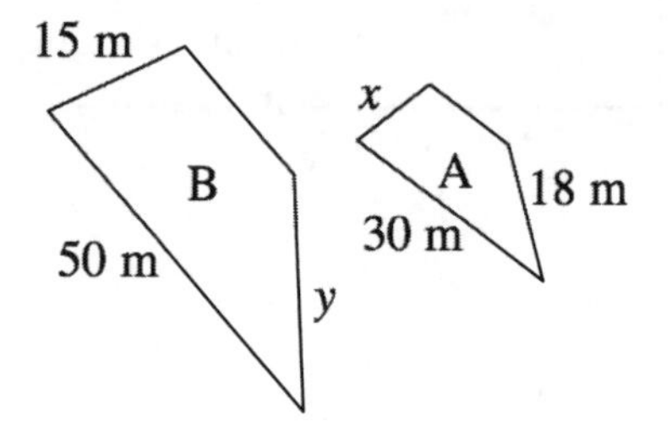

a. What is the scale factor from shape A to shape B?

b. Find the lengths of the missing sides.

5.2.1 Is it a fair game?

Probability Games

Have you ever played a game where everyone should have an equal chance of winning, but one person seems to have all the luck? Did it make you wonder if the game was fair? Sometimes random events just happen to work out in one player's favor, such as flipping a coin that happens to come up heads four times in a row. But it is also possible that games can be set up to give an advantage to one player over another. If there is an equal chance for each player to win a game, then it is considered to be a **fair game**. If it is not equally likely for each player to win, a game is considered to be **unfair**.

In this lesson you will continue to investigate probability. As you work, ask these questions in your study team:

How many outcomes are possible?

How many outcomes are desirable?

5-23. PICK A CARD, ANY CARD

What is the probability of picking the following cards from the deck? Write your response as a fraction, as a decimal, and as a percent.

a. P(black)?

b. P(club)?

c. If you drew a card from the deck and then replaced it, and if you repeated this 100 times, about how many times would you expect to draw a face card (king, queen, or jack)? Explain your reasoning.

5-24. Sometimes it is easier to figure out the probability that something will *not* happen than the probability that it will happen. When finding the probability that something will not happen, you are finding the probability of the **complement**. Everything in the sample space that is not in the event is in the complement.

a. What is the probability you *do not* get a club, written P(not club)?

b. What is P(not face card)?

c. What would happen to the probability of getting an ace on a second draw if you draw an ace on the first draw and do not return it to the deck? Justify your answer.

5-25. Rob decided to play a card game with his friend, Travis. He told Travis that if he picked a black card with a value of nine or greater, Travis would win. (Jacks, queens, and kings are considered to be greater than nine.) If Rob picked a red card with a value of less than nine, Rob would win. (Aces are considered to have the value of one in this case.)

a. What is the probability that Travis will win?

b. What is the probability that Rob will win?

c. According to the definition in the introduction to this lesson, is this a fair game? Why or why not?

5-26. The city has created a new contest to raise funds for a big Fourth of July fireworks celebration. People buy tickets and scratch off a special section on the ticket to reveal whether they have won a prize. One out of every five people who play get a free entry in a raffle. Two out of every fifteen people who play win a small cash prize.

a. If you buy a scratch-off ticket, is it more likely that you will win a free raffle ticket or a cash prize? Explain your answer.

b. What is the probability that you will win something (either a free raffle entry or a cash prize)?

c. What is the probability that you will win nothing at all? To justify your thinking, write an expression to find the complement of winning something.

5-27. Alicia's favorite candies are Fruiti Tutti Chews, which come in three flavors: Killer Kiwi, Crazy Coconut, and Ridiculous Raspberry. This year will be the 50th year that the candy has been made. To celebrate, the company that makes Fruiti Tutti Chews is running new advertisements and introducing a fourth flavor: Perfect Peach.

a. One of the new advertisements states that if you reach into any bag of Fruiti Tutti Chews, you have a $\frac{2}{3}$ probability of pulling out a Killer Kiwi candy. Another advertisment says that $\frac{3}{5}$ of each bag is Ridiculous Raspberry. Are the advertisements telling the truth?

b. Alicia learns that when she opens a new bag of candy, she has a $\frac{2}{5}$ chance of pulling out a piece of Ridiculous Raspberry and a $\frac{1}{3}$ chance of pulling out a piece of Killer Kiwi. Could she have a $\frac{4}{15}$ chance of pulling out a piece of Perfect Peach? Explain your reasoning.

c. When the company introduces the new flavor, it plans to make Perfect Peach $\frac{3}{10}$ of the candy in each bag. If there is an equal amount of the remaining three flavors, what is the probability that the first piece you pull out of the bag will be Crazy Coconut? Justify your answer.

5-28. LEARNING LOG

So far you have calculated probabilities of different events and analyzed a game to see if it was fair. Along the way, you also found the probability of *either* one *or* another event taking place (such as winning *either* a raffle entry *or* a cash prize in part (b) of problem 5-26).

Make an entry in your Learning Log and title it "Probability for 'Either/Or' Events." Create an example and explain how you would calculate the probability when two different outcomes are favorable (such as the example of the raffle ticket and cash). Then, record any questions you have about probability. Your questions might relate to things that you have already worked on or may be about situations you have not yet studied.

5-29. Find the probability of each event. Write your answer as a fraction and as a percent.

a. Drawing a diamond from a standard deck of cards.

b. Rolling a number less than five on a standard number cube.

c. Drawing a blue marble from a bag of 18 marbles, three of which are blue.

5-30. Imagine a standard deck of cards with all of the aces and twos removed. Find each probability below.

a. P(heart) b. P(black) c. P(face card)

d. How is the P(face card) different with this deck from the probability if the deck was not missing any cards? Which probability is greater? Why?

e. P(not heart)

5-31. The Kennedy High School cross-country running team ran the following distances in recent practices:

3.5 miles, 2.5 miles, 4 miles, 3.25 miles, 3 miles, 4 miles, and 6 miles.

Find the mean and median of the team's distances.

5-32. Find the area of each figure below.

a.

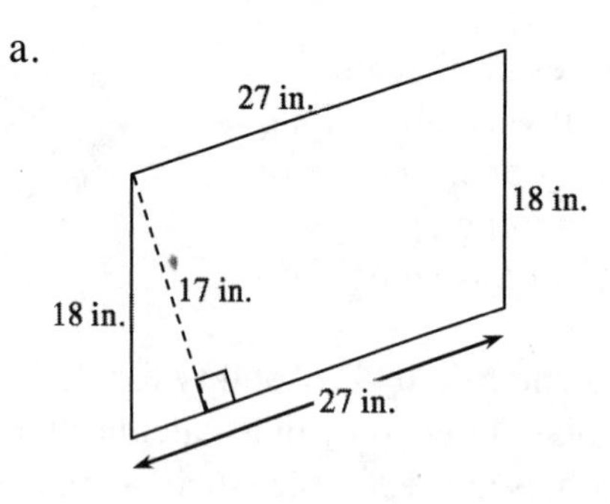

b.

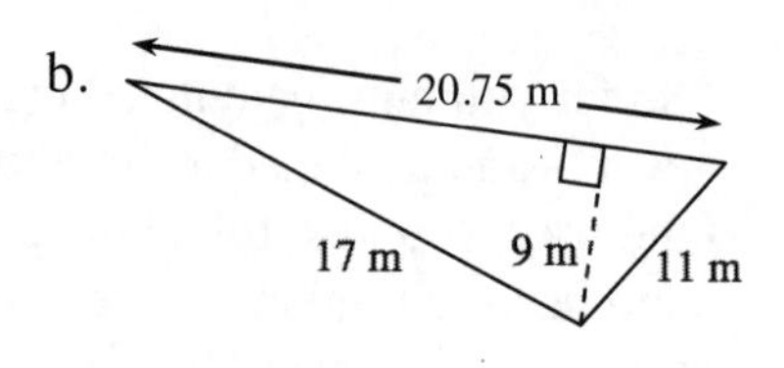

5-33. Evaluate the following expressions using the Order of Operations.

a. $3(8-4)+4^2-(2+3)$

b. $7\cdot4-3\cdot8+2^2-6$

c. $7-(-3)+(-4+3)$

d. $-6-4(3\cdot2)+5^2$

5.2.2 What if it is more complicated?

Computer Simulations of Probability

If you toss a coin ten times, what is the probability of getting three or more "heads" in a row? If an airline overbooks a certain flight, what is the chance more passengers show up than the airplane has seats for? When 67 people get cancer in 250 homes in a small town, could that be due to chance alone, or is polluted well water (or some other cancer-causing source) a more likely explanation of the cluster of cancer cases?

When the mathematics becomes too complicated to figure out the theoretical probability of certain events, statisticians often use computer **simulations** instead.

Many simulations require the use of random numbers. Random numbers have no pattern; they cannot be predicted in any way. Knowing a random number in no way allows you to predict the next random number. An example of a random number generator is a standard number cube, which randomly generates a number from 1 to 6 when you roll it.

Complex simulations like modeling the weather, traffic patterns, cancer radiation therapy, or stock-market swings require tens of billions of random numbers. For those simulations, a large computer running for hours or even days is needed. However, many simple simulations can be done with classroom technology.

5-34. RANDOM NUMBER GENERATOR

Imagine a random number generator that produces numbers from 1 to 20. In each game below, if the stated outcome happens, Player X wins. If it does not, then Player Y wins.

Game 1: A prime number = Player X wins

Game 2: An even number = Player X wins

Game 3: A number not divisible by three = Player X wins

a. In each case, what is the theoretical probability that Player X wins? That Player Y wins? Decide whether each game above is fair.

b. In which of the three games is Player X most likely to win? Why?

c. In Game 1, the prime number game, if you play 40 times, how many times would you expect Player X to win? What if you played 50 times?

Problem continues on next page. →

5-34. *Problem continued from previous page.*

d. Obtain a random number generator from your teacher and set it up to generate integers from 1 to 20. Play the prime number game (Game 1) ten times with a partner. Start by deciding who will be Player X and who will be Player Y. Record who wins each time you play.

e. How did the experimental and theoretical probabilities of Player X's winning from part (a) and part (d) compare?

5-35. Janelle is going to babysit her nephew all day five times this summer. She had the idea that one way to entertain him is to walk to McBurger's for a Kids Meal for lunch each time. The Kids Meal comes packed randomly with one of three possible action figures. Janelle would like to know the probability that they get all three figures in five trips.

a. Call the action figures #1, #2, and #3. Use the random number generator to simulate five trips to McBurger's. Did you get all three action figures?

b. Simulate another five trips to McBurger's. Did you get all three action figures this time? Do the simulation at least 20 times (that is, 20 sets of 5 random numbers), keeping track of how many times you got all three action figures in five tries, and how many times you did not.

c. Use your results to estimate the probability of getting all three action figures in 5 trips. Should Janelle be worried?

d. How could Janelle get an even more accurate estimation of the probability?

5-36. Janelle's aunt and uncle have three children, two of whom are girls. Assuming that girl children and boy children are equally likely, Janelle thought that the chance of having two or more girls out of 3 children must be 50%. Janelle's brother thought the chance of having so many girls had to be less than 50%.

a. What do you think? Make a conjecture about the probability of having two or three girls in a family of three siblings.

b. Do a computer simulation with the random number generator to estimate the probability of having two or three girls in a family of three siblings. Use a 1 to represent a girl and a 0 to represent a boy and simulate a family of three children. Do enough trials to get a good estimate.

5-37. Sophia and her brother are trying to create a fair game in which you roll two number cubes. They cannot agree on the probability that the numbers on both number cubes will be even, so they decide to design a simulation.

a. Make a conjecture. What is the probability both dice are even?

b. Design a simulation with a random number generator. How many random numbers do you need? In what interval should the numbers be? How many times will you do the simulation?

c. Set up and run the simulation that you designed with the random number generator and estimate the probability. How does it compare with your conjecture from part (a)?

5-38. A BETTER CHANCE OF WINNING

Each of the problems below describes two different games you can play with a random number generator. In each case, you will win if the random number generator gives you the indicated kind of number. Find the theoretical probability that you win each game below. Decide and justify whether Game I or Game II in each part, (a) through (c), gives you a better chance of winning.

	Game I	**Game II**
a.	Picking a prime number from the integers between 1 and 20	Picking a prime number from the integers between 21 and 40
b.	Picking a multiple of 5 from the integers between 1 and 20	Picking a multiple of 5 from the integers between 1 and 40
c.	Picking a multiple of 7 from the integers between 1 and 40	Picking a multiple of 6 from the integers between 1 and 25

5-39. If you used a random number generator for the numbers from 1 through 20 to play a game, what is the theoretical probability of getting each of these outcomes?

a. A multiple of 3 *or* a multiple of 7, P(multiple of 3 or multiple of 7)

b. P(even or odd)

c. P(prime or 1)

d. How did you find the probabilities of these events? Be ready to share your ideas with the class.

5-40. The average annual rainfall in Tucson, Arizona is 12 inches. Between January and April, 2.4 inches of rain fell. What percentage of the annual rainfall fell after April (May through December)? You may want to draw a diagram to organize information.

5-41. Evaluate the expression $2x^2 + x + 6$ for the given values of x below.

a. $x = 3$ b. $x = -2$ c. $x = 0$ d. $x = 5$

5-42. Use graph paper to solve the following problem.

a. Draw a four quadrant graph and label each axis. Plot the following ordered pairs: $(-3, 2)$, $(-8, 2)$, $(-10, 8)$, and $(-5, 8)$. Connect the points in the given order as you plot them. Then connect the fourth point to the first one.

b. Describe the shape on your graph. What is its area?

5.2.3 What if there is more than one event?

Compound Independent Events

When you studied probability in earlier lessons, you focused on probabilities of single events (for example, one draw of a card, or picking one cube from a bag). You also examined probabilities of *either* one *or* another of two events occurring (for example, winning either a raffle ticket or cash; drawing either a king or queen). In this lesson, you will begin to investigate when one *and* another event *both* occur, such as flipping two coins or spinning a spinner multiple times. Throughout this lesson, use these questions to help focus your team's discussion:

Does the result of one event affect the other?

How many possibilities are there?

5-43. In Chapter 1, you met Chris and her older sister, Rachel, who made a system for determining which one of them washes the dishes each night. Chris has been washing the dishes much more than she feels is her fair share, so she has come up with a new system. She has proposed to Rachel that they get two coins, and each day she and Rachel will take a coin and flip their coins at the same time. If the coins match, Chris washes the dishes; if they do not match, Rachel washes the dishes.

Rachel thinks that this is a good idea and that her little sister is very silly! She thinks to herself, *"Since there are two ways to match the coins, Heads-**and**-Heads or Tails-**and**-Tails, and only one non-match, Heads-**and**-Tails, then Chris will STILL wash the dishes more often. Ha!"*

a. Do you agree with Rachel? Why or why not?

b. Does it matter if they flip the coins at the same time? That is, does the result of one coin flip depend on the other coin flip?

c. What are all of the possible outcomes when the girls flip their coins? Organize the possibilities. Use the word "and" when you are talking about *both* one thing *and* another occurring.

Problem continues on next page. →

5-43. *Problem continued from previous page.*

d. Look at your list from part (c). Imagine that the coins are a penny and a nickel instead of two of the same coin. Does your list include both the possibilities of getting a heads on the penny and tails on the nickel and vice versa? If not, be sure to add them to your list.

e. Is Rachel right? Does this method give her an advantage, or is this a fair game? What is the theoretical probability for each girl's washing the dishes?

5-44. ROCK-PAPER-SCISSORS

Read the rules for the rock-paper-scissors game below. Is this a fair game? Discuss this question with your team.

How to Play

- At the same time as your partner, shake your fist three times and then display either a closed fist for "rock," a flat hand for "paper," or a partly closed fist with two extended fingers for "scissors."
- Rock beats scissors (because rock blunts scissors), scissors beats paper (because scissors cut paper), and paper beats rock (because paper can wrap up a rock). If you both show the same symbol, repeat the round.

a. While both players are making their choice at the same time, this game has *two events* in every turn. What are the two events?

b. If you and a partner are playing this game and you both "go" at the same time, does your choice affect your partner's choice? Explain.

c. Are the two events in this game **dependent** (where the outcome of one event affects the outcome of the other event) or **independent** (where the outcome of one event does *not* affect the outcome of the other event)? Explain your reasoning.

d. Work with your team to determine all of the possible outcomes of a game of rock-paper-scissors, played by two people (call them Person A and Person B). Be sure to include the word "and." For each outcome, indicate which player wins or if there is a tie. Be prepared to share your strategies for finding the outcomes with the class.

5-45. Is rock-paper-scissors a fair game? How can you tell?

5-46. Imagine that two people, Player A and Player B, were to play rock-paper-scissors 12 times.

a. How many times would you expect Player A to win? Player B to win?

b. Now play rock-paper-scissors 12 times with a partner. Record how many times each player wins and how many times the game results in a tie.

c. How does the experimental probability for the 12 games that you played compare to the theoretical probability that each of you will win? Do you expect them to be the same or different? Why?

5-47. Identify the situations below as either dependent or independent events.

a. Flipping a "heads" on a quarter *and* then flipping another "heads."

b. Choosing a jack from a standard deck of cards, not putting it back in the deck, *and* then choosing a king.

c. Picking a blue marble from a bag of marbles, putting it back, *and* then picking a blue marble again.

d. Rolling a 6 on a number cube three times in a row.

5-48. LEARNING LOG

In your Learning Log, make an entry that summarizes your understanding of independent and dependent events. Explain how to decide if two events are independent or dependent when looking at their likelihood. Give a few examples to support your thinking. Title your notes "Independent and Dependent Events" and include today's date.

METHODS AND MEANINGS

MATH NOTES

Independent and Dependent Events

Two events are **independent** if the outcome of one event does not affect the outcome of the other event. For example, if you draw a card from a standard deck of playing cards but replace it before you draw again, the outcomes of the two draws are independent.

Two events are **dependent** if the outcome of one event affects the outcome of the other event. For example, if you draw a card from a standard deck of playing cards and do not replace it for the next draw, the outcomes of the two draws are dependent.

5-49. For each of the following probabilities, write "dependent" if the outcome of the second event depends on the outcome of the first event and "independent" if it does not.

a. P(spinning a 3 on a spinner after having just spun a 2)

b. P(drawing a red 6 from a deck of cards after the 3 of spades was just drawn and not returned to the deck)

c. P(drawing a face card from a deck of cards after a jack was just drawn and replaced and the deck shuffled again)

d. P(selecting a lemon-lime soda if the person before you reaches into a cooler full of lemon-lime sodas, removes one, and drinks it)

5-50. Skye's Ice Cream Shoppe is Mario's favorite place to get ice cream. Unfortunately, because he was late arriving there, his friends had already ordered. He did not know what they ordered for him. They told him that it was either a waffle cone or a sundae and that the ice cream flavor was apricot, chocolate, or blackberry.

a. Make a list of all of the possible ice cream orders.

b. What is the probability that Mario will get something with apricot ice cream?

c. What is the probability that he will get a sundae?

d. What is the probability that he will get either something with chocolate or a waffle cone with blackberry?

e. What is the probability that he will get orange sherbet?

5-51. On your paper, sketch the algebra tile shape shown at right. Write expressions for the area and perimeter of the shape. Then calculate the area and perimeter of the shape for each x-value.

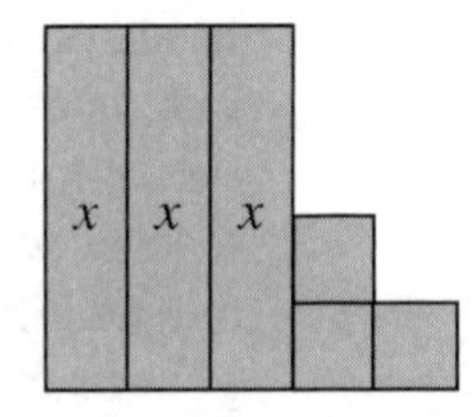

a. $x = 9\text{ cm}$

b. $x = 0.5\text{ cm}$

c. $x = 15\text{ cm}$

5-52. Elin has made twenty-nine note cards for her friends. She plans to send out a total of forty cards. What percentage of the cards has she finished? Represent your work clearly on your paper.

5-53. Copy and simplify the following expressions by combining like terms. Using algebra tiles may be helpful.

a. $3+4x+2+2x+2x$

b. $8x+4-3-x$

c. $7x^2+3x+4+7x^2+3x+4$

d. $5x+4+x+x^2+1$

5.2.4 How can I find all of the outcomes?

Probability Tables

As you may have noticed in Lesson 5.2.3, considering probabilities with more than one event *and* more than two possibilities for each event (such as with the rock-paper-scissors game) can make keeping track of all of outcomes a challenge. In this lesson, you will learn about **probability tables**, a new strategy for organizing all of the possibilities in a complicated game.

5-54. TEN O's

In this game, you will create a strategy to play a board game based on your predictions of likely outcomes. You will place ten O's on a number line. Then your teacher will roll two number cubes and add the resulting numbers. As your teacher rolls the number cubes and calls out each sum, you will cross out an O over the number called. The goal of the game is to be the first person to cross out all ten of your O's.

Talk with your team about the possible outcomes of this game. Then draw a number line like the one below on your own paper. Place a total of ten O's on your number line. Each O should be placed above a number. You should distribute them based on what results you think your teacher will get. More than one O can be placed above a number.

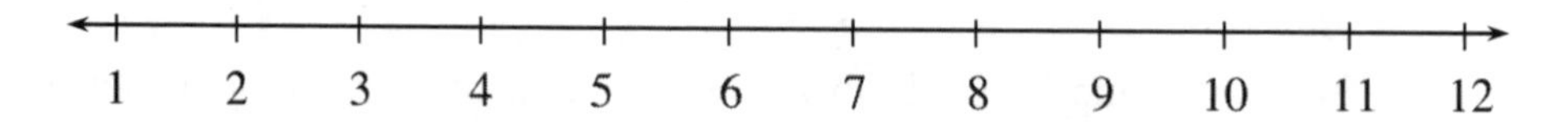

Follow your teacher's instructions to play the game.

5-55. Gerald's strategy for the Ten O's game was to place an O on each number from 1 to 10. He was frustrated that his strategy of placing his ten O's was not working, so he decided to analyze the game.

Gerald began by trying to create a table to list all of the possible combinations of rolls. He made the table at right.

Did he list them all? If so, how can you be sure that they are all there? If not, give examples of a few that he has missed.

Cube 1	Cube 2
1	1
2	2
3	3
4	4
5	5
6	6
1	2
2	3
3	4
4	5
5	6
1	3
2	4
3	5
4	6
1	4
2	5
3	6
1	5
2	6
1	6

5-56. Gerald decided that this method was taking too long, that it was too confusing, and that he made too many mistakes. Even if he listed all of the combinations correctly, he still had to find the sums and then find the theoretical probabilities for each one. Inspired by multiplication tables, he decided to try to make sense of the problem by organizing the possibilities in a **probability table** like the one shown at right.

+	**1**	**2**	**3**	**4**	**5**	**6**
1	2	3				
2	3	4				
3	4					
4						
5						
6						

a. How does Gerald's table represent the two events in this situation? What should go in each of the empty cells? Discuss this with your team and then complete Gerald's table on your own paper.

b. How many total possible number combinations are there for rolling the two cubes? Is each combination listed equally likely? That is, is the probability of getting two 1's the same as that of getting two 2's or a 3 and a 1?

c. How many ways are there to get each sum? Are there any numbers on the game board that are not possible to achieve?

d. What is the theoretical probability for getting each sum listed on the Ten O's game board?

e. Now work with your team to determine a better strategy for Gerald to place his ten O's on the game board that you think will help him to win this game. Explain your strategy and your reasoning.

5-57. Gloria and Jenny each have only one O left on their game board. Gloria's O is at 6, and Jenny's is at 8. Which student is more likely to win on the next roll? Explain.

5-58. Now go back and analyze the game of rock-paper-scissors using a probability table to determine the possible outcomes.

a. Make a probability table and use it to find the probability of Player A's winning and the probability of Player B's winning. Did you get the same answers as before?

b. Do the probabilities for Player A's winning and Player B's winning add up to 1 (or 100%)? If not, why not?

5-59. Imagine that you have a bag with a red block, a blue block, a green block, and a yellow block inside. You plan to make two draws from the bag, replacing the block after each draw.

a. Are these two events (the two draws of a block) independent or dependent? Does it matter if you replace the block each time? Why or why not?

b. Find the probability of getting a red block and a blue block. (Either color can come first.) Be ready to share your method of organizing the possible outcomes.

METHODS AND MEANINGS

MATH NOTES

Probability of Compound Events

Sometimes when you are finding a probability, you are interested in either of two outcomes taking place, but not both. For example, you may be interested in drawing a king or a queen from a deck of cards. At other times, you might be interested in one event followed by another event. For example, you might want to roll a one on a number cube and then roll a six. The probabilities of combinations of simple events are called **compound events**.

To find the probability of *either* one event *or* another event that has nothing in common with the first, you can find the probability of each event separately and then add their probabilities. Using the example above of drawing a king or a queen from a deck of cards:

$\text{P(king)} = \frac{4}{52}$ and $\text{P(queen)} = \frac{4}{52}$ so $\text{P(king or queen)} = \frac{4}{52} + \frac{4}{52} = \frac{8}{52} = \frac{2}{13}$

For two independent events, to find the probability of *both* one *and* the other event occurring, you can find the probability of each event separately and then multiply their probabilities. Using the example of rolling a one followed by a six on a number cube:

$$\text{P}(1) = \frac{1}{6} \text{ and } \text{P}(6) = \frac{1}{6} \text{ so } \text{P(1 then 6)} = \frac{1}{6} \cdot \frac{1}{6} = \frac{1}{36}$$

Note that you would carry out the same computation if you wanted to know the probability of rolling a one on a green cube and a six on a red cube if you rolled both of them at the same time.

5-60. Maggie was at the state fair and decided to buy a sundae from an ice cream stand. The ice cream stand had four flavors of ice cream (chocolate, vanilla, mint chip, and coconut) and two toppings (hot fudge and caramel). How many different sundaes could Maggie create using one scoop of ice cream and one topping? Make a probability table to support your answer.

5-61. The Aloha Stadium in Honolulu, Hawaii, has seats for 50,000 people. At an upcoming football game, a company is planning to give away free hats to people based on where they are sitting.

a. The seats are divided into 40 different sections. If hats are given in only 5 sections, what is the probability of a guest's sitting in a section that gets a hat?

b. The company is going to choose three rows in each section to win the hats. There are 46 rows in a section. If you are sitting in a winning section, what is the probability that you are not sitting in a winning row?

c. The company plans to give away 750 hats. If you buy a ticket to the game, what is the probability that you will receive a hat?

5-62. A lemonade recipe calls for using a ratio of 2 cups of lemon juice for every 4 cups of water.

a. Draw and label a diagram like the one at right to show the percent of lemonade that is water and the percent that is lemon juice.

Old-Fashioned Lemonade

___ cups lemon juice

6 cups lemonade

0%

100%

b. What is the ratio of lemon juice to total liquid?

c. Angel made 10 cups of lemonade. She used 3 cups of lemon juice in her mixture. Did she follow the same recipe? In other words, did she use the same ratio of lemon juice to total liquid?

5-63. Robert found an old game in a closet and wanted to play it. However, a portion of the spinner shown at right could not be read. Find the missing portion of the spinner for Robert.

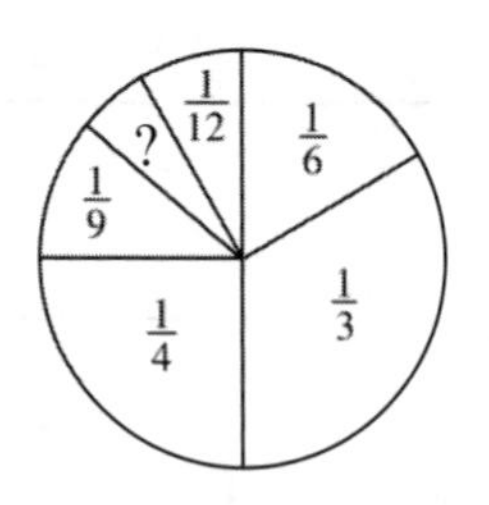

5-64. Copy and complete each of the Diamond Problems below. The pattern used in the Diamond Problems is shown at right.

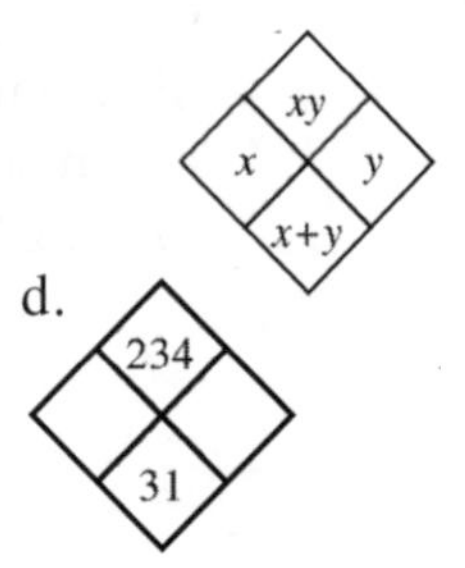

a.
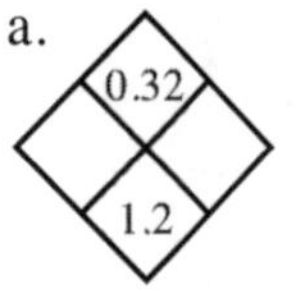

b.
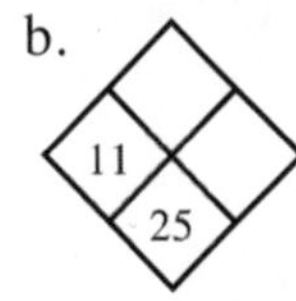

c.
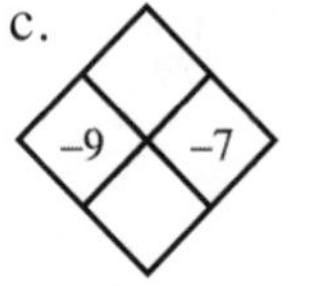

d.

234

31

5.2.5 What if there are more than two events?

Probability Trees

In this lesson you will work with different models for organizing outcomes of multiple events when *both* one event *and* another event occur. Throughout this lesson, use these questions to help focus your team's discussion.

Is there more than one event?

Do *both* one event *and* other events occur?

Are the events independent?

5-65. THE DOUBLE SPIN

A giant wheel is divided into 5 equal sections labeled –2 , –1, 0, 1, and 3. At the Double Spin, players spin the wheel shown at right two times. The sum of their spins determines whether they win.

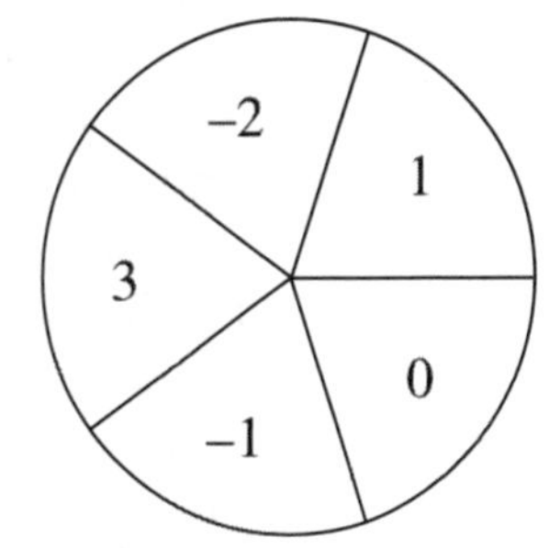

Work with your team to determine probabilities of different outcomes by answering the questions below.

a. Make a list of the possible sums you could get.

b. Which sum do you think will be the most probable?

c. Create a probability table that shows all possible outcomes for the two spins.

d. If Tabitha could choose the winning sum for the Double Spin game, what sum would you advise her to choose? What is the probability of her getting that sum with two spins?

5-66. Scott's job at Crazy Creations Ice Cream Shop is to design new ice cream flavors. The company has just received some new ingredients and Scott wants to be sure to try all of the possible combinations. He needs to choose one item from each category to create the new flavor.

Base Flavor	Chunky Mix-In	Fruit Swirl
Vanilla Chocolate	Hazelnuts Sprinkles Toffee bits	Apricot Plum Berry Grape

a. Without talking with your teammates, list three different combinations Scott could try. Make sure you use the word "and." Then share your combinations with your study team. How many different combinations did you find? Do you think you found all of the possibilities?

b. Creating a list of all of the possibilities would take time and require a lot of writing the same words over and over. Because there are more than two options, a probability table is also challenging. An alternative is creating a **probability tree** to show the different combinations. A probability tree, like the one started at right and on the Lesson 5.2.5 Resource Page, shows the different possibilities branching off each other. In this case, the two segments on the left show the base flavors. Each different mix-in choice branches off of the base flavor, and each fruit swirl branches off each mix-in choice. The first letter of each choice is used to label this diagram.

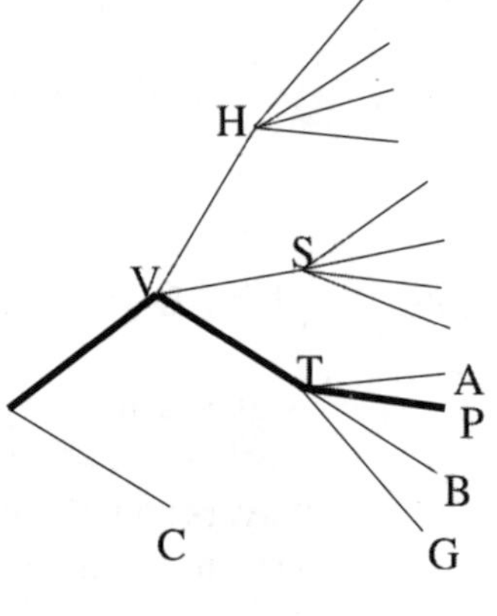

The bold line in the diagram shows the combination vanilla, toffee bits and plum swirl. Complete the probability tree to show all of the possible combinations.

c. How many different flavor combinations are possible? Where do you look on the diagram to count the number of complete combinations?

d. Use your probability tree to help you find the probability that Scott's final combination will include plum swirl.

e. What is the probability that his final combination will include hazelnuts?

5-67. Scott's sister loves hazelnuts and Scott's little brother loves grape.

a. Recall that events are favorable outcomes. List all of the outcomes in Scott's sister's event. List all the outcomes in Scott's little brother's event.

b. Two events are **mutually exclusive** if they have no outcomes in common. Do Scott's sister and little brother have mutually exclusive events?

c. What would two mutually exclusive events in the Crazy Creations Ice-Cream Shop be?

5-68. In a power outage, Rona has to reach into her closet in the dark to get dressed. She is going to find one shirt and one pair of pants. She has three different pairs of pants hanging there: one black, one brown, and one plaid. She also has two different shirts: one white and one polka dot.

a. Draw a probability tree to organize the different outfit combinations Rona might choose.

b. What is the probability that she will wear *both* a polka dot shirt *and* plaid pants?

c. What is the probability that she will not wear the black pants?

d. For what kinds of problems can you also make a probability table? If it is possible, make a probability table for Rona's outfits. Which way of representing the outcomes do you like better?

e. Are the events polka dot and plaid mutually exclusive? Explain.

f. Are the events polka dot and white mutually exclusive? Explain.

5-69. Represent all of the possible outcomes using a list, probability table, or probability tree. Then find the indicated probability in each situation below.

a. You flip a coin three times in a row and get heads exactly twice.

b. You spin the two spinners at right and exactly one spinner lands on 4.

2 3 4

3 4 5 6

c. At the car rental agency, you will be given either a truck or a sedan. Each model comes in four colors: green, black, white, or tan. If there is one vehicle of each color for each model available, what is the probability you will get a green truck?

5-70. LEARNING LOG

In your Learning Log, describe the methods for organizing outcomes in a probability situation that you have learned in the past few lessons, such as systematic lists, probability tables and probability trees. Describe situations for which each tool is appropriate and any advantages and disadvantages with using it. You may want to include an example from your recent work to help you explain. Title this entry "Methods to Organize Probability Outcomes" and label it with today's date.

MATH NOTES

METHODS AND MEANINGS

Probability Models for Multiple Events

To determine all possible outcomes for multiple events when *both* one event *and* the other occur, there are several different models you can use to help organize the information.

Consider spinning each spinner at right once.

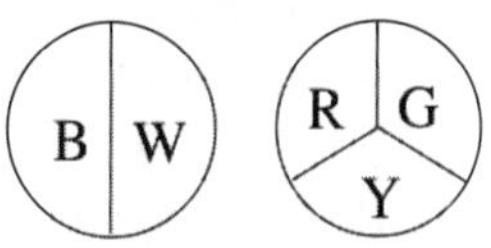

If you use a plan or a pattern to find all of the outcomes in an event, you are making a **systematic list**. For example, assume that you first spin B on spinner 1. Then, list all of the possible outcomes on spinner 2. Next, assume that your first spin is W on spinner 1, and complete the list.

Systematic List

BR WR
BG WG
BY WY

A **probability table** can also organize information if there are exactly two events. The possibilities for each event are listed on the sides of the table as shown, and the combinations of outcomes are listed inside the table. In the example at right, the possible outcomes for spinner 1 are listed on the left side, and the possible outcomes for spinner 2 are listed across the top. The possible outcomes of the two events are shown inside the rectangle. In this table, the top and side are divided evenly because the outcomes are equally likely. Inside the table you can see the possible combinations of outcomes.

Probability Table

	R	G	Y
B	BR	BG	BY
W	WR	WG	WY

A **probability tree** is another method for organizing information. The different outcomes are organized at the end of branches of a tree. The first section has B and W at the ends of two branches because there are two possible outcomes of spinner 1, namely B and W. Then the ends of three more branches represent the possible outcomes of the second spinner, R, G, and Y. These overall possible outcomes of the two events are shown as the six branch ends.

Probability Tree

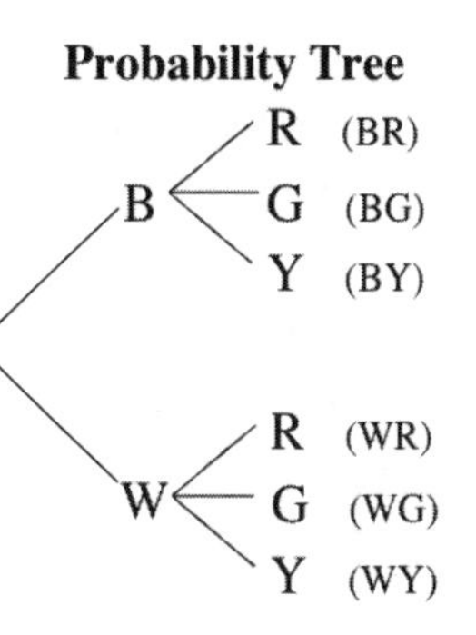

5-71. WALKING THE DOG

Marcus and his brother always argue about who will walk the dog. Their father wants to find a random way of deciding who will do the job. He invented a game to help them decide. Each boy will have a bag with three colored blocks in it: one yellow, one green, and one white. Each night before dinner, each boy draws a block out of his bag. If the colors match, Marcus walks the dog. If the two colors do not match, his brother walks the dog. Marcus's father wants to be sure that the game is fair. Help him decide.

a. Make a probability tree of all of the possible combinations of draws that Marcus and his brother could make. How many possibilities are there?

b. What is the probability that the boys will draw matching blocks? Is the game fair? Justify your answer.

5-72. For Shelley's birthday on Saturday, she received:

- Two new shirts (one plaid and one striped);
- Three pairs of shorts (tan, yellow, and green); and,
- Two pairs of shoes (sandals and tennis shoes).

On Monday she wants to wear a completely new outfit. How many possible outfit choices does she have from these new clothes? Draw a diagram to explain your reasoning.

5-73. In 2009, the federal government budget was \$3.1 trillion (\$3,100,000,000,000). The government was looking to cut costs.

a. If it decided to cut 1%, how much money did it cut?

b. If the government reduced the budget by 7%, how much money did it cut?

c. If the government eliminated \$93 billion (\$93,000,000,000) from the budget, what percentage did it cut?

5-74. Evaluate each expression.

a. $7+(-3)$ b. $(10)(-5)$ c. $-5+6$ d. $(-2)\div(-2)$

5-75. Write expressions for the perimeter and the area of this algebra tile shape. Then simplify each expression by combining like terms.

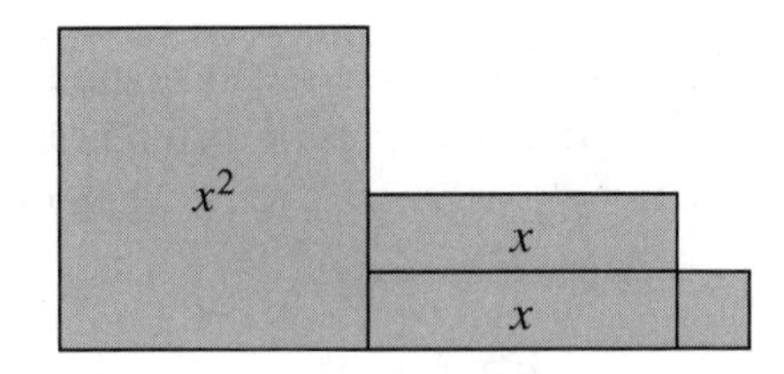

5.2.6 What if the events are not equally likely?

Compound Events

In Lesson 5.2.5, you used systematic lists, probability tables, and probability trees to organize the outcomes of different probability situations. Today you will use a probability table to help organize events when one outcome is more likely than another.

5-76. Nina is buying a new pet fish. At the pet store, the fish tank has an equal number of two kinds of fish: tetras and guppies. Each kind of fish comes in four different colors: yellow, orange, blue, and silver. There are an equal number of each color of fish in the tank.

a. If Nina scoops out a fish at random, what is the probability that she will scoop out a silver tetra? Show how you decided.

b. Nina set up the table below, to organize the different possible outcomes. She represented the kind of fish on one side of her table and the color possibilities on the other. What do the fractions inside her table represent?

	Yellow	Orange	Blue	Silver
Tetra	YT = $\frac{1}{8}$	OT = $\frac{1}{8}$	BT = $\frac{1}{8}$	ST = $\frac{1}{8}$
Guppy	YG = $\frac{1}{8}$	OG = $\frac{1}{8}$	BG = $\frac{1}{8}$	SG = $\frac{1}{8}$

c. As Nina looked at her work, she noticed that her table looked a lot like a rectangle with the area divided into parts. *"Could that help me calculate the probabilities?"* she wondered. She used the length and width of the silver tetra section to set up this equation: $\frac{1}{4} \cdot \frac{1}{2} = \frac{1}{8}$.

How does this equation relate to the length, width, and area of this section of the rectangle? Does this match the probability you found in part (a)?

d. What is the area of the complete large rectangle?

5-77. TESTING THE AREA MODEL

Nina decided to see if thinking about finding area would help find other probabilities. She put three cubes in a bag: two blue cubes and one yellow cube. She pulled one cube out, put it back in the bag, and then drew another.

a. Use a systematic list or a probability tree to organize the possible color combinations she could draw. How many are there? What is P(blue and blue)?

b. This time, Nina made the table at right. Based on the table, what is the probability of drawing two blue blocks? Is this the same probability you found in part (a)?

	B	B	Y
B	BB	BB	BY
B	BB	BB	BY
Y	YB	YB	YY

c. Looking at her work, Edwin said, *"I think I can simplify this diagram."* His rectangle, also known as an area model, is shown at right. What is the area of the section representing blue and blue? Does this match the probability that Nina found?

	B ($\frac{2}{3}$)	Y ($\frac{1}{3}$)
B ($\frac{2}{3}$)	BB	BY
Y ($\frac{1}{3}$)	YB	YY

5-78. The pet store sells a lot of pet food. On a slow day at the pet store, three people buy cat food, two people buy dog food, and one person buys food for a pet snake. If half of the customers pay with cash and half pay with credit card, what is the probability that a customer buying pet food will buy dog food with cash? Set up an area model like Edwin's in part (c) of problem 5-77 to help you find the probability.

5-79. SPINNING ODDS AND EVENS — PART 1

Your team is going to play against your teacher in a game with two hidden spinners. Spinner A has the numbers 2, 3, and 4 on it. Spinner B has the numbers 6, 7, and 8 on it. The rules are:

1. Spin each spinner.
2. Add the results.
3. If the sum is even, one team gets a point. If the sum is odd, the other team gets a point.
4. The first team to earn 10 points wins.

a. Should you choose the odd or even numbers in order to win? Discuss the choices with your team and decide which side to take. Be prepared to justify your choice with mathematics.

b. Play the game at least three times with your teacher. Your teacher will spin the spinners and announce the results. Record the results of each spin and their sum. Is the result odd or even most often? Does this match with your prediction?

c. Make a probability table and determine the theoretical probability for this game.

5-80. SPINNING ODDS AND EVENS — PART 2

Now that you have played the game several times, obtain a Lesson 5.2.6 Resource Page from your teacher and take a close look at the hidden spinners.

a. Are the spinners different from what you expected? How? Be as specific as you can. Do you still think you made the correct choice of odd or even numbers?

b. What assumption about the spinners did you make in part (c) of problem 5-79?

c. What is the probability of spinning each outcome on Spinner A? On Spinner B?

5-81. Raul had imagined that the spinners were divided into equal parts before he saw them. He created the probability table at right to organize the outcomes. *"I thought there would be a $\frac{1}{3}$ chance of spinning a 3 on Spinner A. But now that I see the spinners, I know that is not true. I need to make a new rectangle in order to find the probability."*

	6	7	8
2	8	9	10
3	9	10	11
4	10	11	12

a. Create a new rectangle. Label the top row and left column with the numbers on each spinner and their probabilities.

b. Write a multiplication problem to show the probability of spinning a 3 and a 7. Calculate P(3 and 7).

c. Complete the table to show each possible sum and its probability.

d. What is the probability of spinning an odd sum? What is the probability of spinning an even sum?

e. Did you make the right choice of an odd or even number in problem 5-80? Explain your reasoning.

5-82. **Additional Challenge:** Elliot loves music, especially listening to his music player on shuffle. He has songs stored in four categories: country, blues, rock, and classical. Two fifths of his songs are country songs, one sixth of his songs are classical, one third are blues, and the rest are rock.

a. What is the likelihood that the first two songs will be a country song *and* then a classical?

b. What is the likelihood that *either* a country song *or* a classical song will come up first?

5-83. Darnell designed the spinner at right for a game. It still has one incomplete section.

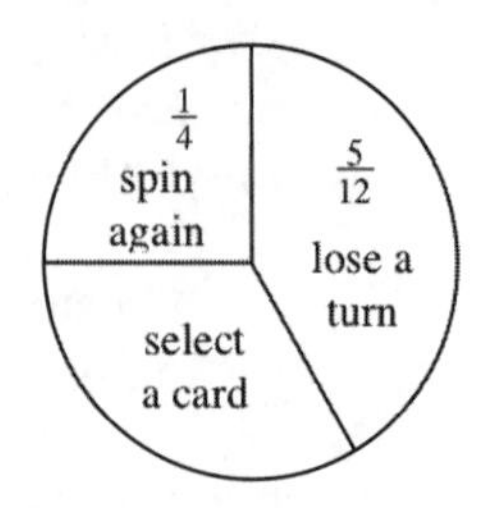

a. Help him figure out the probability of selecting a card on any turn. Show how you got your answer.

b. What is the probability that on any turn you will not get to spin again?

c. Which is more likely: to lose a turn or to select a card? Show how you know.

5-84. Manuel used pattern blocks to build the shapes below. The block marked A is a square, B is a trapezoid, C is a rhombus (a parallelogram with equal sides), and D is a triangle. Find the area of each of Manuel's shapes.

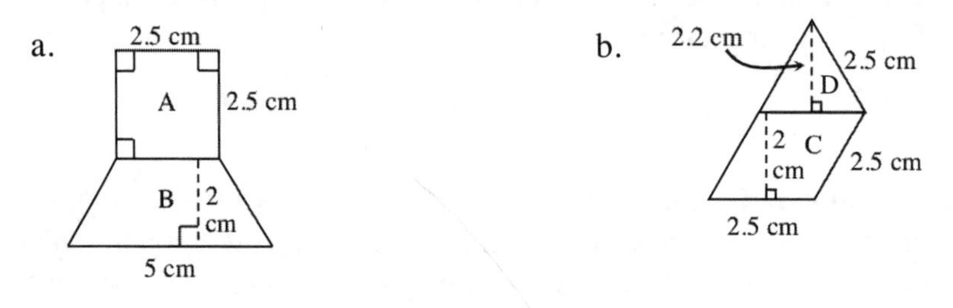

5-85. Rachel is collecting donations for the local animal shelter. So far she has collected \$245, which is 70% of what she hopes to collect. How much money does Rachel plan to collect for the shelter? Show your work.

5-86. Darnell is designing a new game. He will have 110 different-colored blocks in a bag. While a person is blindfolded, he or she will reach in and pull out a block. The color of the block determines the prize according to Darnell's sign at right.

blue → small toy
purple → hat
green → large stuffed animal

a. If he wants players to have a 60% probability of winning a small toy, how many blue blocks should he have?

b. If he wants players to have a 10% probability of winning a large stuffed animal, how many green blocks should he have?

5-87. Simplify each expression below.

a. $1\frac{1}{2}+2\frac{1}{8}$ b. $\frac{4}{5}-\frac{2}{3}+\frac{1}{6}$ c. $5\frac{3}{5}-1\frac{4}{5}$

5-88. Lucas is having yogurt and an apple for a snack. There are five containers of yogurt in the refrigerator: three are raspberry, one is vanilla, and one is peach. There are also two green apples and three red apples.

a. If he reaches into the refrigerator to get a yogurt without looking, what is the probability that Lucas will choose a raspberry yogurt?

b. What is the probability that he will choose a red apple if it is the first item he selects?

c. What is the probability that Lucas will eat a raspberry yogurt and a red apple?

5-89. A bag contains 3 red, 5 yellow, and 7 purple marbles. Find the probability of drawing a purple marble followed by a red marble. The first marble is put back in the bag between draws.

5-90. Use graph paper to complete parts (a) through (c) below.

a. Draw an *xy*-coordinate graph and label each axis. Plot the following ordered pairs: $(2,3),(-2,3),(-2,-3),(2,-3)$. Connect the points in the given order as you plot them. Then connect the fourth point to the first one.

b. Describe the shape on your graph. What is its area? What is its perimeter?

c. Change only two points so that the shape has an area of 32 square units. List your points. Is there more than one answer?

5-91. Jerry bought some pears at the store. He paid $4.59 for 5.4 pounds of pears. What is the unit price of the pears?

5-92. Evaluate the following expressions using the Order of Operations.

a. $7\cdot 8-4(6-2)+18$ b. $6^2-(8\cdot 3)+2^2(7\cdot 3)$

c. $\frac{14}{2}-3(8-6)+7^2$ d. $-9-3(7-2)+\frac{24}{3}$

5.3.1 How can I draw it?

5 - D

Describing Relationships Between Quantities

You may not know it, but you use mathematical thinking every day. You think mathematically when you figure out whether you can afford items you want to buy, or when you read a graph on a website. You also think mathematically when you double a recipe or when you estimate how much longer it will take to get somewhere based on how far you still have to go. Math can describe many of the relationships in the world around you.

Building your interpretation skills and developing ways to represent situations will help you solve problems. In this section, you will learn new ways to show your thinking when using math to solve problems. As you work today, think about the following questions:

How can I represent this with a diagram?

Who has more? Who has less?

5-93. Sometimes using the same words in a slightly different way can change their meaning. Read and compare the two situations below.

Situation 1	Situation 2
Myra has 15 marbles. This is ten less than Dahlia.	Myra has 15 marbles. Dahlia has ten less than Myra.

a. For each situation, draw a picture to represent the marbles each girl has. What is the difference between the problems?

b. In which problem does Myra have more marbles than Dahlia?

c. How many marbles does Dahlia have in Situation 1 above? How many does she have in Situation 2?

5-94. Ellie is building a dollhouse. She has boards that are two different lengths. One long board is 7 inches longer than the total length of three of the short boards.

a. Draw a picture showing how the short and long boards are related.

b. What are some possible lengths of her boards?

c. If one of the long boards is 50 inches long, how long is a short board? Be ready to share your thinking with the class.

5-95. Now read and compare Problems A and B below.

Problem A	Problem B
Dianna has $16. Jairo has twice as much money as Dianna. Who has more money?	Dianna has $16. She has twice as much money as Jairo. Who has more money?

a. Represent each problem with a diagram.

b. Compare the amount of money Jairo has in part (a) to the amount he has in part (b). Explain how you know in which situation he has more money.

5-96. Now you are going to reverse your thinking. Examine the pictures below. Then use words to describe the relationship you see in the pictures. Assume the lengths that appear to be equal are equal.

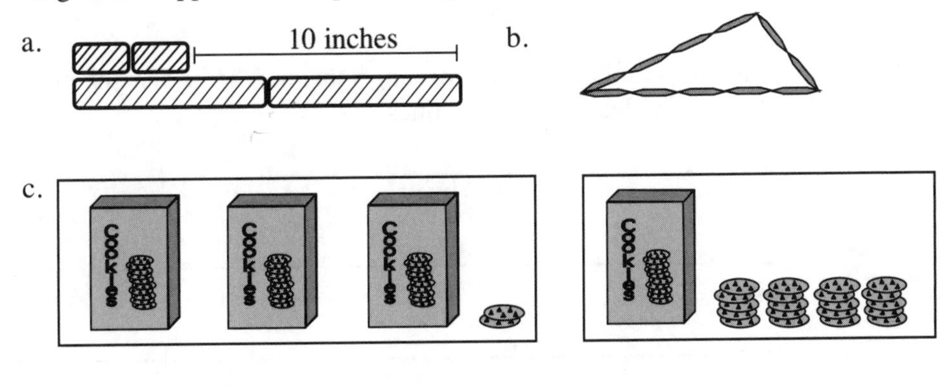

Same number of cookies

5-97. Rich, Arielle, and Kristen just measured how tall they are in feet. Their heights are shown in the bar graph at right.

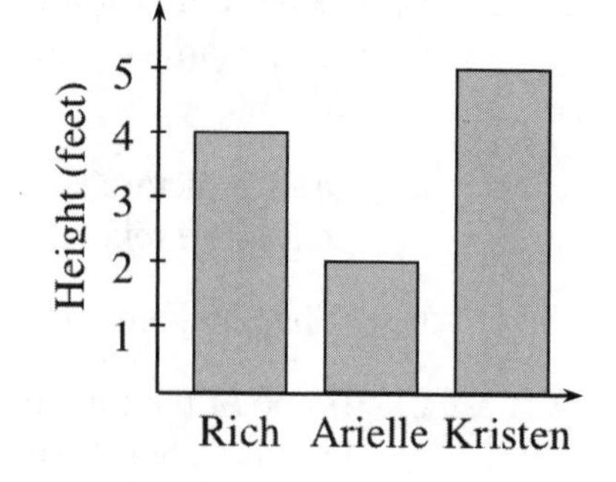

Decide which statements below are true and which statements are false. Rewrite the false statements to make them true.

a. Rich is one foot shorter than Kristen.

b. Arielle is twice as tall as Rich.

c. Kristen is one foot taller than twice Arielle's height.

d. The sum of the three children's height is 10 feet.

5-98. **Additional Challenge:** Represent the description below with a picture.

Ellen is gluing tiles on the four vertical sides of a rectangular planter box. The longer side of the box is covered by six more than two times as many tiles as the shorter side.

5-99. Mr. Nowling's garden has a length that is 7 feet more than twice the width. Draw a diagram to represent this situation. Label each side of the garden, and then write an expression for the perimeter.

5-100. The following number lines are missing some numbers. Use the information provided to complete the number lines.

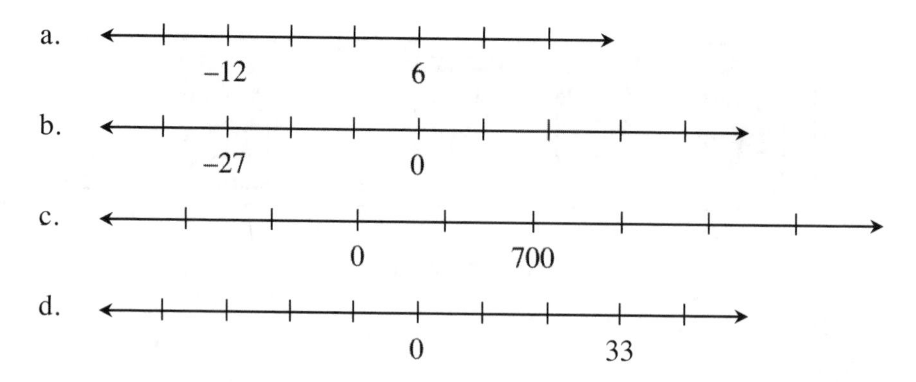

5-101. Lynn was shopping and found a purse that was marked with a discount of "$\frac{1}{3}$ off." If the original cost of the purse was \$80, how much will Lynn pay?

5-102. Evaluate each expression using the Order of Operations.

a. $-4(-4+3)+2^2$

b. $-3-3-3-(-3)$

c. $-17+2(-2)(-2)$

d. $(2+(-3)(5))(3+2(-6))$

5-103. Complete a Proportions Web for the following situation.

A candy-wrapping robot can wrap 434 pieces of candy in 5 minutes. How many pieces of candy can it wrap in any number of minutes?

5.3.2 How can I organize it?

5-D

Solving a Word Problem

You have seen that being able to draw diagrams and describe relationships is helpful for solving problems. In this lesson, you will learn another way to organize your thinking as you solve word problems.

5-104. FENCING THE BASKETBALL COURT

The Parent Club at Post Falls Middle School needs 183 feet of fencing to go around the rectangular outdoor basketball court behind the school gym. The club volunteers will only need to place a fence on three sides of the court, because the wall of the gym will form the fourth side. The length of the court is 32 feet more than the width. One of the shorter sides will be 5 feet shorter than the other one to leave room for a gate.

Your Task: Determine how much fencing will be used on each side of the court. Be prepared to justify your answer and show all of your work. Be sure that someone who is not on your team can read and understand your work.

Discussion Points

What information do you know in the problem?

What do you need to figure out?

What diagram can you draw to represent this situation?

How did you organize your work?

How can a wrong answer help you revise your thinking?

5-105. If another team came to look at your paper for problem 5-104, could that team understand your work? Why or why not? What else could you do to make it so that someone else could make sense of your work just by looking at it?

5-106. Daniel, Ronald, and Zeba decided to organize their thinking in a table using a method they call the 5-D Process. Get a Lesson 5.3.2A Resource Page from your teacher that shows their work. Then answer some of the following questions during the whole-class discussion.

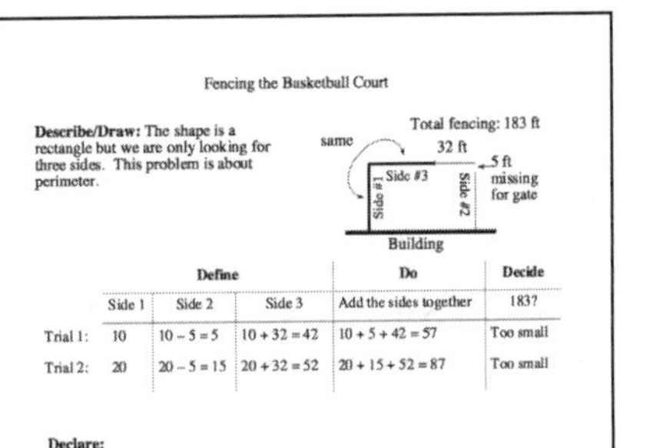

Fencing the Basketball Court

Describe/Draw: The shape is a rectangle but we are only looking for three sides. This problem is about perimeter.

	Define			Do	Decide
	Side 1	Side 2	Side 3	Add the sides together	183?
Trial 1:	10	$10 - 5 = 5$	$10 + 32 = 42$	$10 + 5 + 42 = 57$	Too small
Trial 2:	20	$20 - 5 = 15$	$20 + 32 = 52$	$20 + 15 + 52 = 87$	Too small

Declare:

- *"What are the students <u>Describing and Drawing</u>?"*
- *"What is in the <u>Define</u> columns?"*
- *"What is the <u>Do</u> column used for?"*
- *"What are they trying to <u>Decide</u>?"*
- *"What might the <u>Declare</u> section be for?"*

5-107. While one team was working on problem 5-104, the team members decided to see if a width of 30 feet would use all of the 183 feet of fencing. They figured out that, with a 30-foot width, the length would be 62 feet and the side with the gate would be 25 feet. Only 117 feet of fencing would be used.

What is a logical number that they should try next for the width so that all of the fencing is used? Explain your reasoning.

5-108. Finish problem 5-104 using the 5-D Process. Continue the table you looked at in problem 5-106 to find the answer.

5-109. Use the steps of the 5-D Process to organize and solve each of the questions below. The Lesson 5.3.2C Resource Page may help you set up your table. Be sure to show each of the "D" steps clearly in your solution process.

a. Laura takes very good care of her vehicles. She owns a blue van and a red truck. Although she bought them both new, she has owned the truck for 17 years longer than she has owned the van. If the sum of the ages of the vehicles is 41 years, how old is the van and how old is the truck?

b. Ryan is thinking of a number. When he multiplies this number by 6 and then subtracts 15 from the answer, he ends up with his original number. What number is Ryan thinking of?

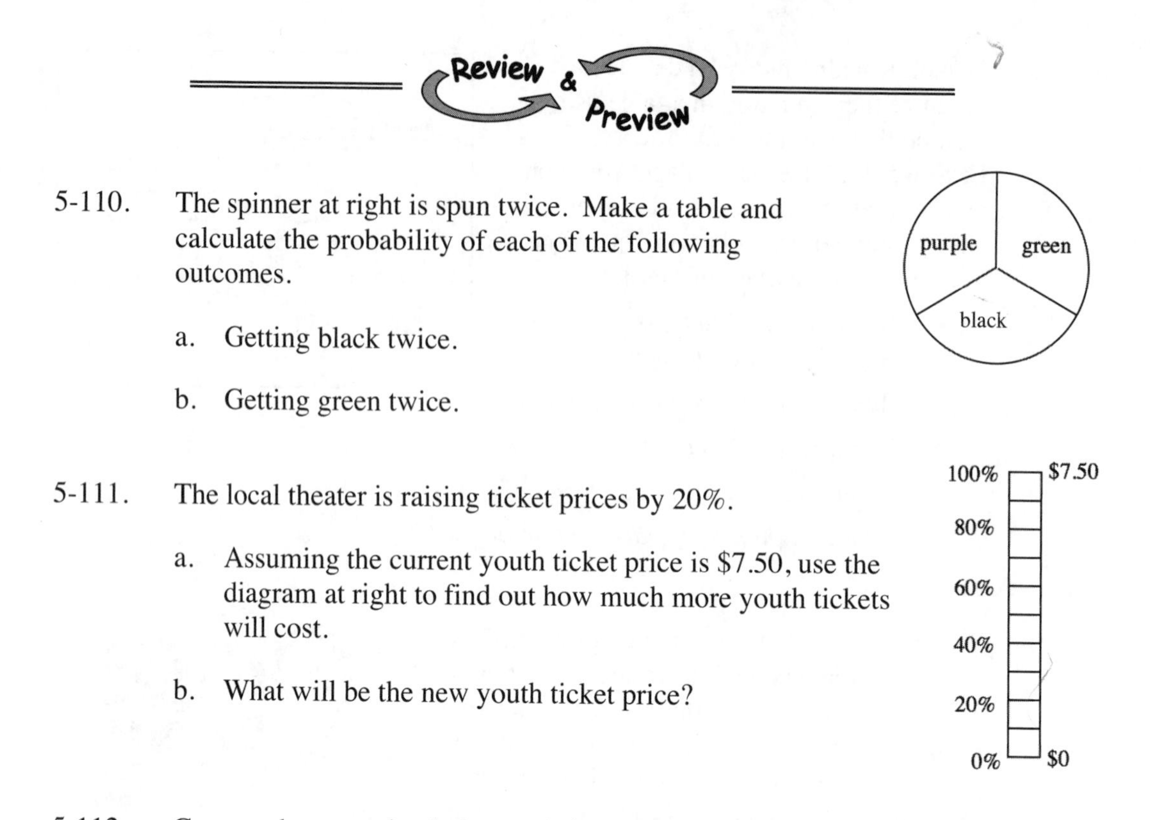

Review & Preview

5-110. The spinner at right is spun twice. Make a table and calculate the probability of each of the following outcomes.

a. Getting black twice.

b. Getting green twice.

5-111. The local theater is raising ticket prices by 20%.

a. Assuming the current youth ticket price is $7.50, use the diagram at right to find out how much more youth tickets will cost.

b. What will be the new youth ticket price?

5-112. Copy each expression below and simplify it using the Order of Operations.

a. $6+4(2+3)^2$ b. $(6+4)(2+3)$ c. $6+4\cdot 2^3+3$

5-113. Write the expression as shown on the Expression Mats. Then simplify by making zeros and combining like terms.

a. x x x

b. x x x x^2

5-114. Look at the algebra tile shape at right.

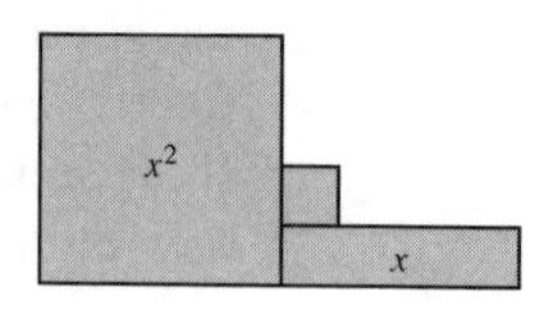

a. Write an algebraic expression for the perimeter of the shape in two ways: first, by finding the length of each of the sides and adding them all together; second, by writing an equivalent, simplified expression.

b. Write an algebraic expression for the area of the shape.

5·3·3 How do I use the 5-D Process?

5 ■ D

Strategies for Using the 5-D Process

Math is used to solve challenging problems that apply to daily life. For example, how much fresh water is on the planet? How many area codes for telephone numbers are needed in a city? Where should a city build transportation lines such as city bus systems and subways to reduce traffic on the freeways? Mathematics can provide helpful insights for the answers to these questions.

When you are trying to solve a new and challenging problem, it is useful to have a strategy. The 5-D Process that you learned about in Lesson 5.3.2 will often work when you are trying to solve a problem you have not seen before.

In this lesson, you will practice using this process to solve more word problems. You will also compare the different ways that your classmates use the 5-D Process to help them. Be sure to write your work neatly and be prepared to justify your reasoning.

As you work using the 5-D Process, consider the questions below.

How can you describe the problem?

How can you decide how to label the columns?

How can you organize the columns?

How can you decide which quantity to start with?
Does it matter which one you choose?

How can you decide which number to try first?

At the end of this lesson, your team may be asked to present your responses to one or more of the target questions above.

5-115. A **scalene triangle** has three unequal side lengths. The medium-length side is 7 cm longer than the shortest side. The longest side is twice as long as the shortest side. The total perimeter is 39 cm. What are the lengths of the sides of the triangle?

5-116. Travis and Angela were playing a "Guess My Numbers" game. Angela told Travis, "I'm thinking of two positive numbers. The difference of my numbers is 4, and the product of my numbers is 96. What are my numbers?" Help Travis find Angela's numbers.

5-117. The Potter Valley basketball team did not record how many baskets each player made during the last game. Jenny remembers that she made three times as many baskets as Grace. Alexis knows that she made six more baskets than Grace. Joan thinks that she made 4 fewer baskets than Grace. Tammy is sure that she made the same number of baskets as Joan. Altogether the five players made 40 baskets. How many baskets did each player make?

5-118. Ms. Pacheco, Mr. Edwards, and Mr. Richards are three math teachers at Turner Middle School. Ms. Pacheco is three years older than Mr. Richards. Mr. Edwards is twice as old as Mr. Richards. The sum of Mr. Richards' age and Mr. Edwards' age is 81. How old is each person?

5-119. Ramon was studying pond life in Doyle Park. In two hours, he counted four more frogs than turtles. The number of crayfish he counted was three more than twice the number of turtles. In total, he counted 54 turtles and crayfish. How many frogs were there?

5-120. Dawn is trying to find the dimensions of a parallelogram. She knows that the base is one unit less than twice the height of the shape. The area is 91 square units. How long are the base and height?

5-121. **Additional Challenge:** If one side of a square is increased by 12 feet and the side connected to it is decreased by three feet, a rectangle is formed. The perimeter of the rectangle is 62 feet. How long was the side of the original square?

5-122. With your team, re-read the focus questions for this lesson, reprinted below:

How can you describe the problem?

How can you decide how to label the columns?

How can you organize the columns?

How can you decide which quantity to start with?
Does it matter which one you choose?

How can you decide which number to test first?

Discuss the strategies you use with the 5-D Process as a team. Be prepared to share your ideas with the class.

MATH NOTES

METHODS AND MEANINGS

Solving Problems with the 5-D Process

The **5-D Process** is an organized method to solve problems. The D's stand for Describe/Draw, Define, Do, Decide, and Declare. An example of this work is shown below.

Problem: The base of a rectangle is 13 centimeters longer than the height. If the perimeter is 58 centimeters, find the base and the height of the rectangle.

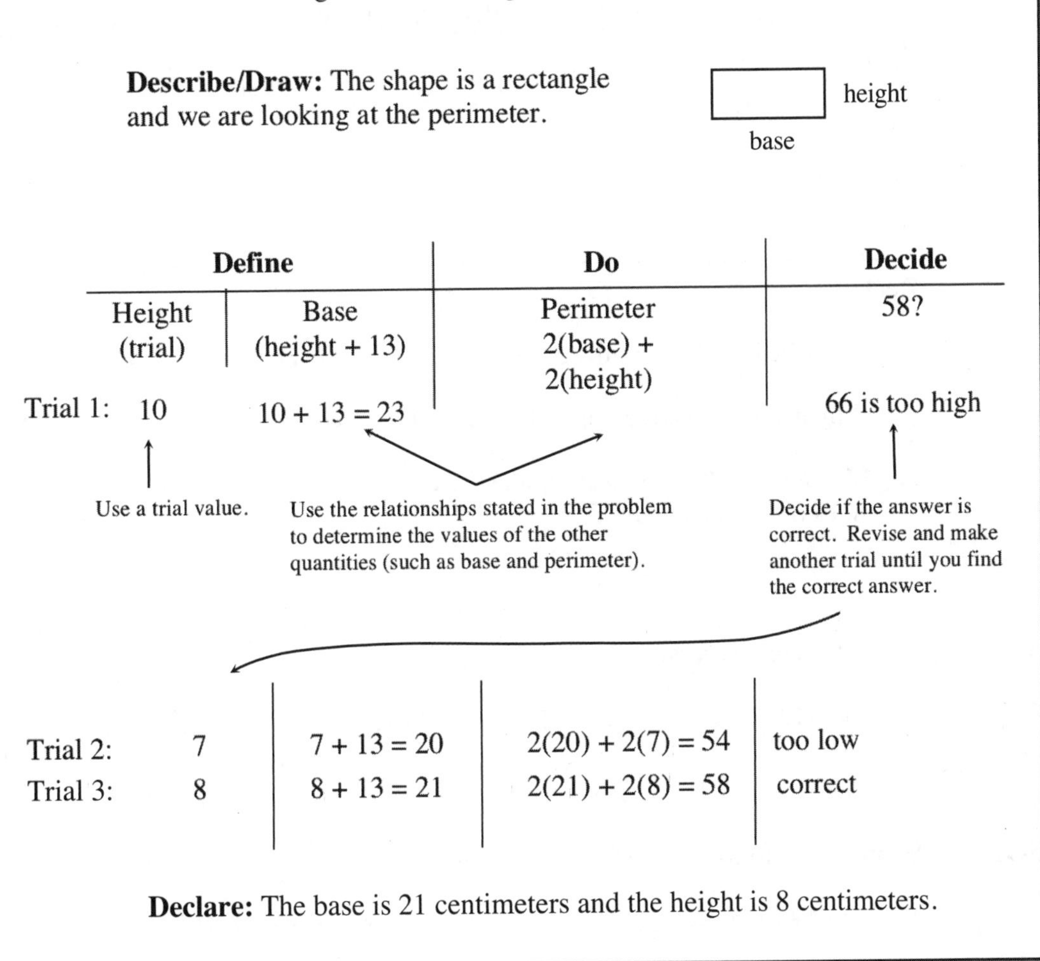

Describe/Draw: The shape is a rectangle and we are looking at the perimeter.

	Define		Do	Decide
	Height (trial)	Base (height + 13)	Perimeter 2(base) + 2(height)	58?
Trial 1:	10	10 + 13 = 23		66 is too high
Trial 2:	7	7 + 13 = 20	2(20) + 2(7) = 54	too low
Trial 3:	8	8 + 13 = 21	2(21) + 2(8) = 58	correct

Declare: The base is 21 centimeters and the height is 8 centimeters.

5-123. If the total area of the rectangle below is 168 square units, how long is each side? To find out how long the x side must be, copy the diagram and table and answer the questions that follow.

Describe/Draw:

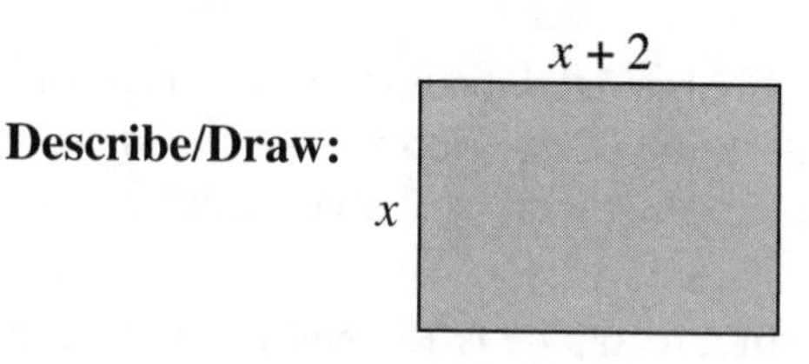

	Define Side #1	Side #2	Do (Side one)·(Side two)	Decide Area = 168?
Trial 1:	10	12		
Trial 2:				

Declare:

a. Describe how the lengths of the two sides are related to each other.

b. Which side of the rectangle does Side #2 represent?

c. Use the 5-D Process to complete the table. Find the lengths of the two sides of the rectangle.

5-124. Evaluate each expression.

a. $\frac{1}{2}(5+13)-4\cdot5$ b. $(5+11)-(24-15)\cdot(3)$ c. $6^2+3\cdot7-9\div3$

5-125. Simplify the following variable expressions.

a. $2x+5+x-6+3x$ b. $x-8+x-5+x+1$

5-126. A radio station is giving away free t-shirts to students in local schools. It plans to give away 40 shirts at Big Sky Middle School and 75 shirts at High Peaks High School. Big Sky Middle School has 350 students, and 800 students attend High Peaks High School.

a. What is the probability of getting a t-shirt if you are a student at the middle school?

b. What is the probability of getting a t-shirt if you are a student at the high school?

c. Are you more likely to get a t-shirt if you are a student at the high school, or at the middle school?

5-127. One student rewrote the expression $17 \cdot 102$ as $17(100+2)$. Then she simplified to get the expression 1700 + 34.

a. Are the three expressions equivalent? Justify your answer.

b. What property of numbers does this demonstrate?

5.3.4 How can I represent it?

Using Variables to Represent Quantities in Word Problems

Today you will continue to use the 5-D Process as you solve word problems. In this lesson, you will use a variable to represent the unknown value in the problem.

Think of these questions as you work on the problems today:

What is the problem asking?

What is the relationship between the quantities involved?

How can I choose which part of the problem to represent with a variable?

5-128. Mai has one mini-box of Choco-Blasters candy, and Warren gave her three more pieces. Samara has two mini-boxes of Choco-Blasters and gave six pieces to Will. Now Mai and Samara have the same number of Choco-Blasters.

How many Choco-Blasters are in a mini-box? Assuming all mini-boxes of Choco-Blasters have the same number of pieces in them, use the 5-D Process to solve this problem.

5-129. Allen's team was working on a problem but did not have time to finish it. They also did not follow the teacher's directions for showing work in the Define section. Discuss with your team what information you can get from Allen's table below.

	DEFINE		**DO**	**DECIDE**
	LENGTH	WIDTH	DOUBLE EACH SIDE AND ADD TOGETHER	TARGET PERIMETER = 36?
TRIAL 1:	3	9	$2(3)+2(9)=24$	TOO SMALL
TRIAL 2:	4	?		

a. Is there enough information in Allen's table to finish the problem? Why or why not?

b. What would you need to know in order to complete Trial 2? Explain your thinking.

5-130. Allen's teammate, Scott, was also working on problem 5-129, but he organized his table differently. As Scott explained his table to Allen, he used the pattern in the first two trials to represent the quantities in the third row with a variable, x.

Look at the table below.

a. How is it different from Allen's table?

b. What does the x in the table represent?

c. In words, describe the relationship between the length and the width.

d. Where did the expression $x+x+(2x+3)+(2x+3)$ come from? Explain your thinking.

	DEFINE		DO	DECIDE
	LENGTH	WIDTH	ADD ALL 4 SIDES TOGETHER	TARGET PERIMETER = 36?
TRIAL 1:	3	$2(3)+3$	$3+3+9+9=24$	TOO SMALL
TRIAL 2:	6	$2(6)+3$	$6+6+15+15=42$	TOO LARGE
	x	$2(x)+3$	$x+x+(2x+3)+(2x+3)$	

5-131. Izzy's team used a 5-D table to solve a problem that involved **consecutive integers**. Consecutive integers are integers that follow each other on a number line. The numbers 1, 2, 3, …, 14, 15, 16, …, or –5, –4, –3, ... are all examples of consecutive integers. The table below shows part of their work on the problem.

Copy the table and finish the problem. After you find a solution, apply Scott's idea from problem 5-130 to add a row that uses a variable to summarize the problem's process.

	DEFINE			DO	DECIDE
	1ST NUMBER	2ND NUMBER	3RD NUMBER	ADD ALL NUMBERS TOGETHER	TARGET SUM = 57
TRIAL 1:	15	$15+1$	$15+2$	$15+16+17=48$	TOO SMALL
TRIAL 2:	20	$20+1$	$20+2$	$20+21+22=63$	TOO LARGE

5-132. Meiko saw someone's expressions in the 5-D Process table below and wanted to reverse the process. The problem involved a bag of green, red, and blue marbles.

	DEFINE			DO	DECIDE
	GREEN	RED	BLUE	TOTAL MARBLES	TOTAL = 71?
TRIAL 1:	15				
	x	$x-2$	$2x+5$	$x+(x-2)+(2x+5)$	

a. One of the variable expressions describes how the number of red marbles compares with the number of green marbles. How can you describe this relationship in words?

b. Based on the variable expressions, use words to describe how the number of blue marbles compares with the number of green marbles.

c. How many total marbles are in the bag?

d. If there are 15 green marbles in the bag, how many red and blue marbles are in the bag? Show your work.

e. Use the information in the table to find the number of green, red, and blue marbles.

5-133. Camille knew that a triangle had one side with a length of 16 inches and another side with a length of 20 inches. She did not know the length of the third side, but she did know that the perimeter was five times the length of the unknown side. How long is the unknown side? Copy the table below and complete the table. You may add as many rows as you need to solve the problem. Remember to summarize the relationships with a row that uses a variable and to complete the Declare sentence.

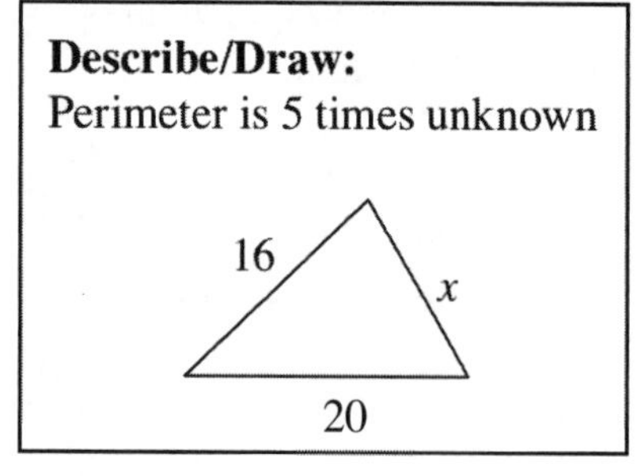

	DEFINE		DO	DECIDE
	UNKNOWN SIDE	PERIMETER	COMPARE SUM TO PERIMETER	SAME?
TRIAL 1:	5	5(5)	$5+16+20\overset{?}{=}25$ $41 \neq 25$	NO

Declare:

5-134. Margaret was working on the problem below.

> Declan earned four times as much money last summer as his sister Gwen. Together they earned \$475. How much did each person earn?

The table below shows the first two trials Margaret made. Based on the results, work with your study team to suggest a number she should try next. (You do not actually need to solve the problem.)

- Is it reasonable for different members of your team to suggest different numbers?
- Are there some numbers that would not be helpful? Explain.

	DEFINE		DO	DECIDE
	GWEN'S EARNINGS	DECLAN'S EARNINGS	ADD BOTH OF THEIR EARNINGS TOGETHER	TARGET SUM = \$475
TRIAL 1:	\$50	4(\$50)	\$50 + \$200 = \$250	TOO SMALL
TRIAL 2:	\$100	4(\$100)	\$100 + \$400 = \$500	TOO LARGE

5-135. Dawn and Myrna's father has asked them to build a rectangular pen for their dog. They have 74 feet of fencing. They want the length to be one more than twice the width. Use the 5-D Process to help Dawn and Myrna find the dimensions (both length and width) of the pen.

5-136. **Additional Challenge:** Use the 5-D Process to find three consecutive integers that have a product of 3360.

5-137. LEARNING LOG

In your Learning Log, describe how you decide which number to use as your first trial in the 5-D Process. Then explain how you use the results of your first trial to choose your next trial number. You may want to include an example from your recent work to help you explain. Title this entry "Defining and Deciding" and label it with today's date.

MATH NOTES

METHODS AND MEANINGS

Consecutive Integers

Consecutive integers are integers that come "one after another" in order (that is, without skipping any of them). For example: 11, 12, and 13 are three consecutive integers. The numbers 10, 12, 14, and 16 are four **consecutive even integers** because in counting up from 10, no even numbers are skipped. Likewise, 15, 17, and 19 are **consecutive odd integers**.

In algebra, it is sometimes necessary to represent a list of consecutive integers. To represent any list in general, you must use variables. It is common to let x represent the first integer. See the examples below of how to write a list of consecutive integers.

Three consecutive integers: $x, x+1, x+2$

Three consecutive odd integers: $x, x+2, x+4$

Three consecutive even integers: $x, x+2, x+4$

Note that consecutive even integers and odd integers look alike because both even integers and odd integers are two apart.

5-138. Think about the mathematical process you use as you solve the following problems. Show your work and your solutions.

a. If there are 100 students in a room and 40 of them are boys, how many are girls?

b. If there are 17 blue and white stripes on a flag and 9 of them are blue, how many are white?

c. If there are 250 pennies and dimes in a box and 130 of them are pennies, how many are dimes?

d. Now it is time to generalize. Imagine you know how many items you have in a collection of two types of things. If you know how many of one of the items you have, how could you find how many of the other item you have?

5-139. If you can travel 156 miles on 4 gallons of gasoline, how far can you travel on 12 gallons? How many miles on 6 gallons? A diagram may help you with your reasoning. Show your work and explain your thinking.

5-140. Use the Distributive Property to simplify the following expressions.

a. $4(x+2)$ b. $-5(9+x)$ c. $7(x-3)$

5-141. Evaluate the following expressions.

a. $-5+2(8-12)$ b. $(-5+2)(8-12)$ c. $-5+2\cdot 8-12$

d. $\frac{1}{2}(-6)(4+10)$ e. $-\frac{2}{3}\cdot 6+15\div(-3)$ f. $(7-2)^2-5\div 5$

5-142. Find the lengths of the missing sides on the similar shapes at right. What is the scale factor?

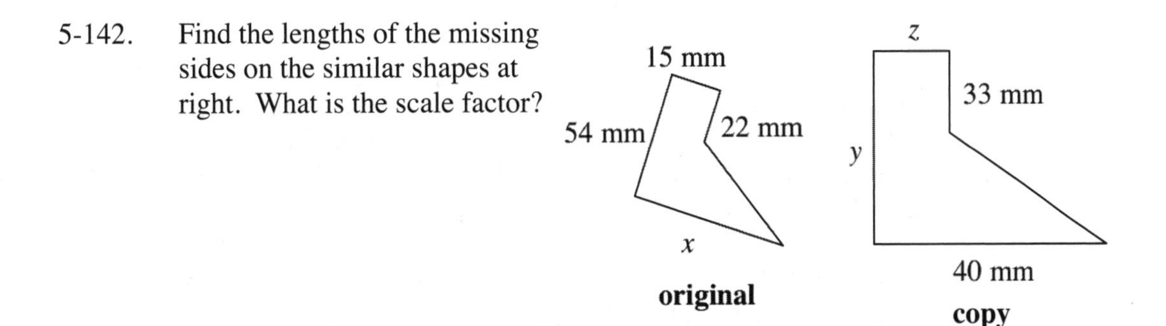

5.3.5 How can I solve it?

5-D

More Word Problem Solving

So far in Section 5.3, you have been using a 5-D Process as a way to organize and solve problems. Today you will continue using this process to solve problems in a variety of situations.

As you work, use the following questions to focus your team's discussion.

What is the problem asking?

What is the relationship between the quantities involved?

How can you decide which part of the problem to represent as x ?

What if a different quantity were represented by x?

5-143. According to many sources, insects are the most diverse group of animals on the planet. The number of species is estimated at between six and ten million. Insects are said to represent more than half of all known living organisms and potentially over 90% of the differing life forms on Earth.

The following problems are about insects and other creepy-crawly creatures. You will use your math skills to find out some fascinating facts about them. Your teacher will assign your team one of the following problems to solve. Be prepared to present your solution, including all steps of your 5-D solving process, to the class.

a. Many insects migrate (travel) between their summer and winter homes. The desert locust migrates about 800 miles farther than the Monarch butterfly every spring, and the pink-spotted hawk moth migrates about 200 miles less than four times the distance of the Monarch butterfly every spring. Laid end to end, the distances traveled by a Monarch butterfly, a desert locust, and a pink-spotted hawk moth is about 12,600 miles every spring. How far does each species travel?

Problem continues on next page. →

5-143. *Problem continued from previous page.*

b. Bees, wasps, and ants all live in colonies that have a queen. The queen of the colony is really the mother of all the insects in the colony. During the spring and summer, many eggs are laid in bee, wasp, and ant colonies all over the world.

Queen bees lay about double the number of eggs in a day that queen ants lay. Queen wasps lay about 600 fewer eggs a day than queen ants do. An average queen bee, ant, and wasp together lay about 2600 eggs a day. How many eggs would each type of queen lay in one day?

c. Flies cannot see much farther than 24 to 36 inches away from their eyes, but that is not due to a lack of lenses – dragonflies have thousands of lenses! In one eye, dragonflies have two thousand more lenses than seven times the number of lenses that houseflies have in one eye. If one housefly eye and one dragonfly eye together have 34,000 lenses, how many lenses do houseflies have in one eye? How many do dragonflies have in one eye?

d. Think you do not have enough room to farm? Think again. You could farm worms under your desk with a commercially available worm farm that measures 16" x 16" x 28". You can buy the worms online. At 1200 worms per pound, you could start your own business just as John did. He's not good at keeping his records, however, and he needs your help.

John buys his worms from two online stores, Worm Heaven and Wiggles R Us. John remembers that he ordered 1200 more than twice as many worms from Worm Heaven as he did from Wiggles R Us. He also knows he has 18,000 worms. How many worms did he order from each store?

Problem continues on next page. →

5-143. *Problem continued from previous page.*

e. There are many kinds of animals that live in and on our bodies, called parasites. Some of the longest parasites live in our intestines. Two of these parasites are roundworms and tapeworms. Their lengths can be quite different, depending on how long they have been living in someone's body.

   One of the longest tapeworms ever measured was three feet less than seven times the length of the longest roundworm ever measured. If you laid these two worms end to end, they would measure an amazing 69 feet! How long was the tapeworm and how long was the roundworm?

f. Did you know that most of the states in this country have official state insects and butterflies? Out of 30 states, the three most common insects are Monarch butterflies, honeybees, and ladybugs. The number of states that have Monarch butterflies as their official insect is one more than the number of states that have ladybugs as their official insect. The number of states that have honeybees as their official insect is three times the number of states with ladybugs as their state insect minus one. How many states have each kind of insect as their state insect?

g. Mosquitoes and other biting insects can cause a great deal of discomfort. They can also spread diseases that threaten public health in many areas of the world. The seed oil of a plant commonly called the physic nut is burned in lamps in India and parts of Africa to repel biting insects, especially mosquitoes. A scientific investigation was done to identify which chemicals in the oil were responsible for deterring mosquitoes. Three chemicals in the oil, specifically palmitic, linoleic, and stearic acids, were tested for find their effectiveness against mosquitoes that spread two deadly diseases in Africa, yellow fever and dengue fever.

   In the study, palmitic acid was determined to be the most effective chemical, providing three times the protection of stearic acid and was ten percentage points higher in protection than linoleic acid. The effectiveness percentages of stearic acid plus linoleic acid together were five percentage points higher than palmitic acid. What is the effectiveness of stearic acid in repelling mosquitoes?

Review & Preview

5-144. The number of girls at Middle School Cyber Summer Camp was six more than twice the number of boys. There were a total of 156 middle school students at the camp. Use the 5-D Process to find the number of boys and the number of girls at camp.

5-145. Copy and complete each of the Diamond Problems below. The pattern used in the Diamond Problems is shown at right.

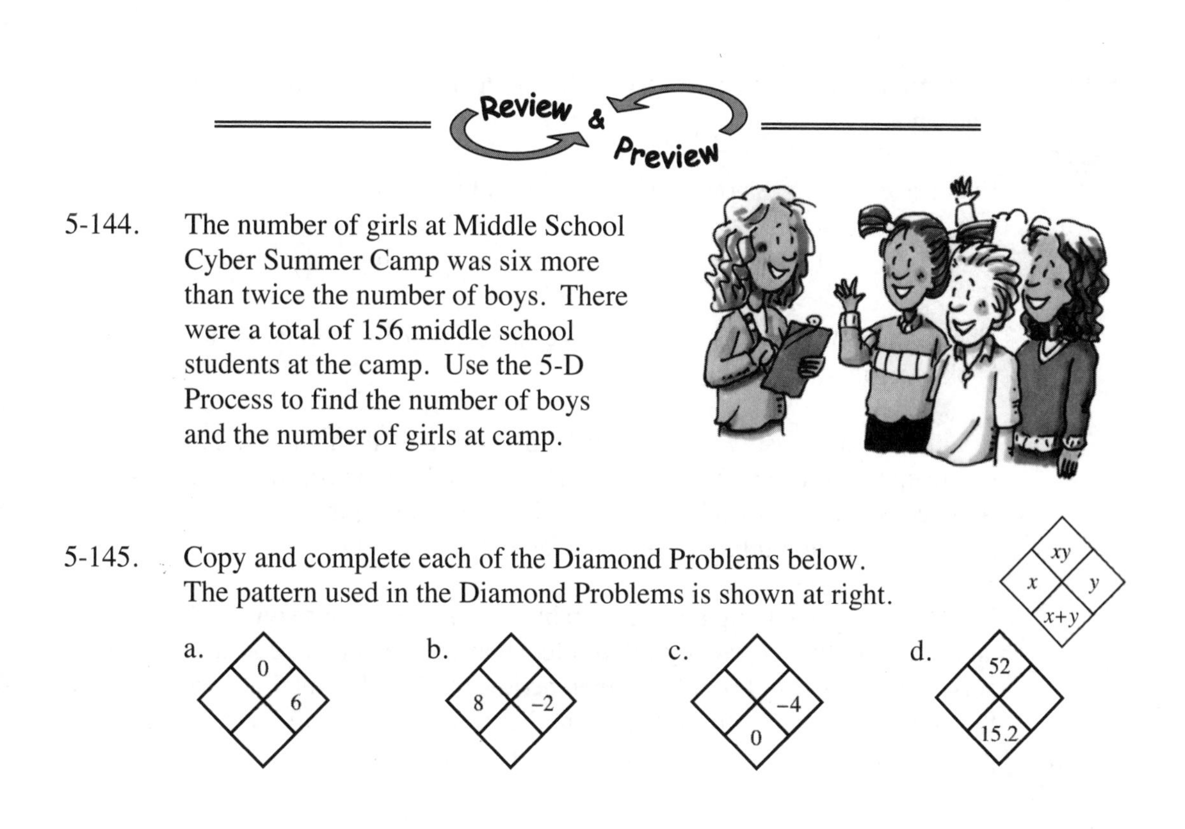

5-146. **Multiple Choice:** Which of the following expressions could be used to find the average (mean) of the numbers k, m, and n?

A. $k+m+n$ B. $3(k+m+n)$ C. $\frac{k+m+n}{3}$ D. $3k+m+n$

5-147. The Giant Prize Wheel at the county fair is evenly divided into 10 sections. One is labeled "Large Prize," three are labeled "Small Prize," and the rest are labeled "No Prize."

a. If you spin once, what is the probability of winning a large prize?

b. If you spin once, what is the probability of winning any prize?

c. If 50 people spin the prize wheel, approximately how many people should expect to win a prize of any kind?

5-148. This problem is a checkpoint for Order of Operations. It will be referred to as Checkpoint 5.

Evaluate each expression using the Order of Operations.

a. $16-2^3 \div 8+5$

b. $(-2+6)^2-\left(\frac{3}{2}\right)\cdot 14+1$

Check your answers by referring to the Checkpoint 5 materials located at the back of your book.

If you needed help solving these problems correctly, then you need more practice. Review the Checkpoint 5 materials and try the practice problems. Also, consider getting help outside of class time. From this point on, you will be expected to do problems like these quickly and easily.

Ideally, at this point you are comfortable working with these types of problems and can solve them correctly. If you feel that you need more confidence when solving these types of problems, then review the Checkpoint 5 materials and try the practice problems provided. From this point on, you will be expected to do problems like these correctly and with confidence.

Chapter 5 Closure What have I learned?

Reflection and Synthesis

The activities below offer you a chance to reflect about what you have learned during this chapter. As you work, look for concepts that you feel very comfortable with, ideas that you would like to learn more about, and topics you need more help with.

① WHAT HAVE I LEARNED?

Doing the problems in this section will help you to evaluate which types of problems you feel comfortable with and which ones you need more help with.

Solve each problem as completely as you can. The table at the end of this closure section provides answers to these problems. It also tells you where you can find additional help and where to find practice problems like them.

CL 5-149. Evan is trying to save $60 to buy new parts for his bike. He has saved 45% of what he needs so far.

a. Draw a diagram to represent this situation.

b. How much has Evan saved so far?

c. How much does Evan still need to save? Write your answer as a dollar amount and as a percent.

CL 5-150. Julia has two children who are four years apart in age. Julia is four times older than her youngest child. The sum of the ages of Julia and her children is 76 years. Use the 5-D Process to find the ages of Julia and each of her children.

CL 5-151. Erika is playing a game where the number of spaces she moves is determined by the spinner at right. Each half of the spinner—left and right—is divided into equal regions as shown.

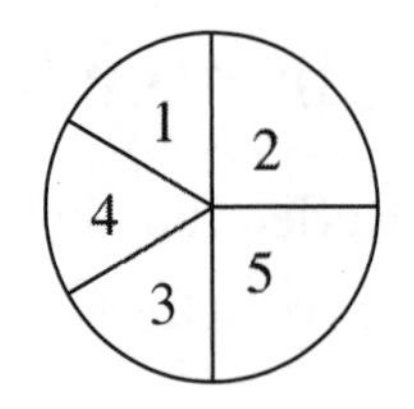

a. What is the probability that Erika will spin an even number on her next spin?

b. If Erika spins a 4, she will land on a space that says, "Get an extra turn." If she then spins a 5, she gets 50 bonus points and will win the game. What is the probability that she can spin a 4 and then a 5?

CL 5-152. Melanie collects stickers. Her favorite stickers have unicorns on them. She has a sheet of stickers that has 2 unicorn stickers on it and 5 dragons. She would like to increase her chances of getting a unicorn sticker when she selects one randomly.

If she takes two sheets of stickers like this and combines them, will she be more likely to select a unicorn sticker? Why or why not?

CL 5-153. Identify the following events as independent or dependent.

a. Reaching into a drawer in the dark, pulling out one sock, and then reaching back in and pulling out another.

b. Selecting a dog biscuit for your dog, feeding it to her, and then getting another one.

c. Rolling a 3 on each of two dice that are tossed at the same time.

d. Spinning a 5 on a spinner and then spinning again and getting a 4.

CL 5-154. Build each collection of tiles represented below on a mat. Name the collection using a simpler algebraic expression, if possible. If it is not possible to simplify the expression, explain why not.

a. $(-x)+5-4x+x-(-3)+(-3x)$

b. Nine plus four times a number, plus three minus seven times the number

c. $3-7x^2+9x$

d. $2x+3x^2-7+(-x^2)$

CL 5-155. Evaluate each expression below.

a. $2\frac{3}{10}-1\frac{2}{5}$

b. $\frac{9}{3}\cdot\frac{4}{5}$

c. $\frac{3}{4}+5\frac{7}{8}$

d. $\frac{2}{9}\cdot(-\frac{3}{7})\cdot(\frac{14}{5})$

e. $-\frac{9}{15}-(-\frac{26}{45})$

f. $5\frac{1}{6}\cdot(-\frac{7}{9})$

CL 5-156. Alaska has a very low population density. It only has 655,000 people in 570,374 square miles. Find the unit rate of density in terms of people per square mile.

CL 5-157. For each of the problems above, do the following:

- Draw a bar or number line that represents 0 to 10.

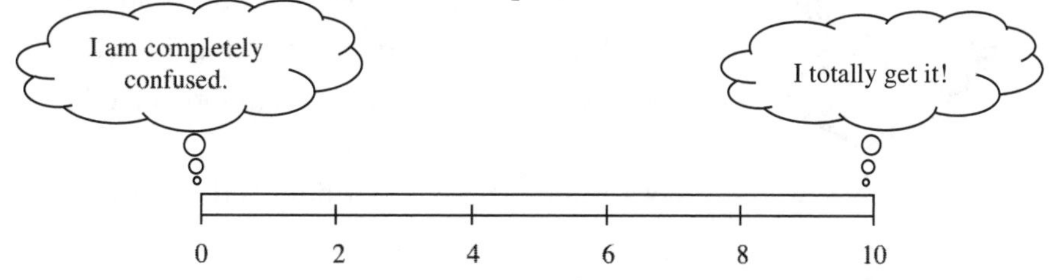

- Color or shade in a portion of the bar that represents your level of understanding and comfort with completing that problem on your own.

If any of your bars are less than a 5, choose *one* of those problems and do one of the following tasks:

- Write two questions that you would like to ask about that problem.
- Brainstorm two things that you DO know about that type of problem.

If all of your bars are a 5 or above, choose one of those problems and do one of these tasks:

- Write two questions you might ask or hints you might give to a student who was stuck on the problem.
- Make a new problem that is similar and more challenging than that problem and solve it.

② WHAT TOOLS CAN I USE?

You have several tools and references available to help support your learning: your teacher, your study team, your math book, and your Toolkit, to name only a few. At the end of each chapter, you will have an opportunity to review your Toolkit for completeness. You will also revise or update it to reflect your current understanding of big ideas.

The main elements of your Toolkit should be your Learning Logs, Math Notes, and the vocabulary used in this chapter. Math words that are new appear in bold in the text. Refer to the lists provided below and follow your teacher's instructions to revise your Toolkit, which will help make it useful for you as you complete this chapter and as you work in future chapters.

Learning Log Entries

- Lesson 5.2.1 – Probability for "Either/Or" Events
- Lesson 5.2.3 – Independent and Dependent Events
- Lesson 5.2.5 – Methods to Organize Probability Outcomes
- Lesson 5.3.4 – Defining and Deciding

Math Notes

- Lesson 5.1.1 – Equivalent Ratios
- Lesson 5.1.2 – Part-to-Whole Relationships
- Lesson 5.2.3 – Independent and Dependent Events
- Lesson 5.2.4 –Probability of Compound Events
- Lesson 5.2.5 – Probability Models for Multiple Events
- Lesson 5.3.3 – Solving Problems with the 5-D Process
- Lesson 5.3.4 – Consecutive Integers

Mathematical Vocabulary

The following is a list of vocabulary found in this chapter. Some of the words have been seen in the previous chapter. The words in bold are words that are new to this chapter. Make sure that you are familiar with the terms below and know what they mean. For the words you do not know, refer to the glossary or index. You might also add these words to your Toolkit so that you can reference them in the future.

5-D Process	**consecutive integers**	**complement**
compound events	desired outcomes	**dependent events**
equivalent ratios	experimental probability	**independent events**
mutually exclusive	outcome	**partition**
percent	possible outcomes	probability
probability table	**probability tree**	proportional relationship
ratio	sample space	**scalene triangle**
simplify	**simulation**	**single event**
systematic list	theoretical probability	variable

Answers and Support for Closure Problems
What Have I Learned?

Note: MN = Math Note, LL = Learning Log

Problem	Solution	Need Help?	More Practice
CL 5-149.	a. \$0, \$60; 0%, 45%, 100% b. \$27 c. \$33 dollars, or 55% of \$60	Lessons 5.1.1 and 5.1.2 MN: 5.1.2	Problems 5-18, 5-19, 5-40, 5-52, 5-85, 5-86, and 5-111
CL 5-150.	Julia is 48. The children are 12 and 16.	Section 5.3 MN: 5.3.3 LL: 5.3.4	Problems 5-38 and 5-144
CL 5-151.	a. $\frac{1}{4}+\frac{1}{6}=\frac{3}{12}+\frac{2}{12}=\frac{5}{12}$ b. $\frac{1}{6}\cdot\frac{1}{4}=\frac{1}{24}$	Lesson 5.2.3 MN: 5.2.5 LL: 5.2.3	Problems 5-49, 5-52, 5-65, 5-81, and 5-83
CL 5-152.	P(unicorn, 1 sheet): $\frac{2}{7}$ P(unicorn, 2 sheets): $\frac{4}{14}=\frac{2}{7}$ They are the same.	Section 5.2 MN: 5.2.4 and 5.2.5 LL: 5.2.5	Problems 5-29, 5-30, 5-39, 5-71, 5-88, and 5-126
CL 5-153.	a. Dependent b. Dependent c. Independent d. Independent	Lesson 5.2.3 MN: 5.2.4 LL: 5.2.3	Problems 5-47 and 5-49
CL 5-154.	a. $-7x+8$ b. $-3x+12$ c. Fully simplified. d. $2x^2+2x-7$	Lessons 4.3.1 and 4.3.3 MN: 4.3.2 LL: 4.3.3	Problems CL 4-124, 5-53, 5-113, and 5-125
CL 5-155.	a. $\frac{9}{10}$ b. $\frac{36}{15}$ or $\frac{12}{5}$ c. $6\frac{5}{8}$ d. $-\frac{84}{315}$ or $-\frac{4}{15}$ e. $-\frac{1}{45}$ f. $-\frac{217}{54}$ or $-4\frac{1}{54}$	Lessons 1.2.6, 2.2.5, and 2.2.6 MN 2.2.5 and 2.3.1 LL: 1.2.8	Problems CL 1-146, CL 2-135, CL 3-136, 5-13, 5-21, and 5-87
CL 5-156.	About 1.15 people per square mile.	Lesson 4.2.3 MN: 4.2.4	Problems CL 4-127, 5-91, and 5-139

5.4 How can I use it? What is the connection?

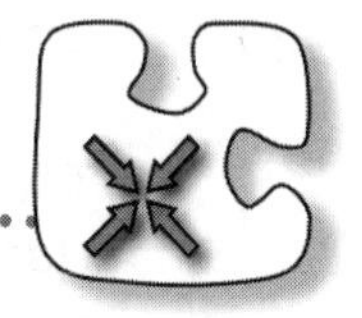

Mid-Course Reflection Activities

The activities in this section review several major topics you have studied so far. As you work, think about the topics and activities that you have done during the first half of this course and how they connect to each other. Also think about which concepts you are comfortable using and those with which you need more practice.

As you work on this activity, keep the questions below in mind.

What mathematical concepts have you studied in this course so far?

What do you still want to know more about?

What connections did you find?

5-ML. MEMORY LANE

Have you ever heard someone talk about "taking a trip down memory lane?" People use this phrase to mean taking time to remember things that have happened in the past, especially events that a group of people shared.

As you follow your teacher's directions to visit your mathematical "memory lane," think about all the activities you have done and what you have learned in your math class so far this year. Your Toolkit should be a useful resource to help you with this activity.

Focus on these four areas as you remember your previous work in this course:

- Working with Signed Numbers
- Probability
- Algebraic Thinking
- Proportional Relationships

5-SH. SCAVENGER HUNT

Today your teacher will give you several clues about mathematical situations. For each clue, work with your team to find all of the situations posted around the classroom or provided on a resource page. Remember that more than one situation – up to three – may match each clue. Once you have decided which situation matches (or which situations match) a clue, justify your decision to your teacher and receive the next clue. Be sure to record your matches on paper.

Your goal is to find the match(es) for each different clue.

Situation #1

Erwin Middle School has 500 boys. $33\frac{1}{3}\%$ of the students are girls. How many students go to this school?

Situation #2

Group: $5 \cdot 3 + (-1) - 2(-6)$

Situation #3

Situation #4

The number of girls in the Middle School Cyber Club was 6 more than double the number of boys, and in total there were 48 middle school students in the Cyber Club. Use the 5-D Process to find the number of boys and girls in the club.

Situation #5

Situation #6

x	7	14	91	9	–12	–36	81
y	$2\frac{1}{3}$	$4\frac{2}{3}$	$30\frac{1}{3}$	3	–4	–12	27

Situation #7

Situation #8

At a school fundraiser, Ryan bought a ticket for $10 to play the "Spin for $" game. In this game, Ryan will spin the spinner shown at right and he will get the given portion of his ticket price back. What is the probability that Ryan will win less than he paid?

Solving
Inequalities and
Equations
6

CHAPTER 6 Solving Inequalities and Equations

In this chapter you will use algebra tiles to compare two expressions on Expression Comparison Mats. In Section 6.1, you will also discover the legal moves that allow you to simplify expressions. Then you will determine which expression is greater or if they are equal. You will also learn how to record solutions to inequalities using number lines with boundary points.

Guiding Questions

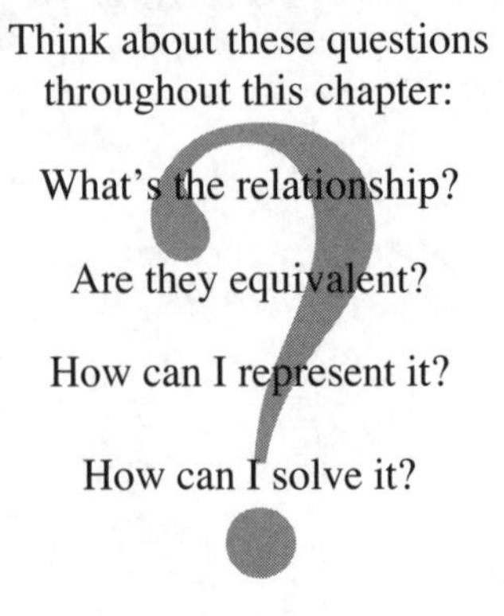

You will extend what you know about comparing expressions to include cases in which expressions are equal. You will build equations on Equation Mats with algebra tiles, write equations with variables, and solve equations without using tiles. Learning how to write and solve equations will provide you a new way to solve word problems without completing a 5-D table. By the end of this chapter, you will learn efficient ways to justify the steps used to solve equations.

In this chapter, you will learn how to:

- Simplify and compare two algebraic expressions.
- Write and solve algebraic inequalities.
- Solve for a variable when two expressions are equal.
- Write and solve an equation to solve a word problem.
- Recognize when an equation has no solution or infinite solutions.

Chapter Outline

Section 6.1 In the first section, you will learn additional strategies for comparing expressions. The strategies will involve maintaining equivalence and determining relationships between expressions. You will also solve inequalities and represent their solutions on a number line.

Section 6.2 Using algebra tiles, here you will explore what you can learn when expressions are equal. Solving equations will also provide you an opportunity to develop efficient simplification strategies and to learn how to know that your solution is correct. You will also consider special cases, such as when an equation has no solution.

6.1.1 How do these compare?

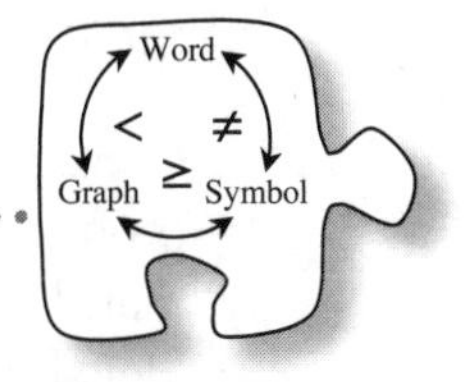

Comparing Expressions

In Chapter 4, you worked with writing and simplifying expressions. As you wrote expressions, you learned that it was helpful to simplify them by combining like terms and removing zeros. In this lesson, you and your teammates will use a tool for comparing expressions. The tool will allow you to determine whether one expression is greater than the other or if they are equivalent ways of writing the same thing (that is, if they are equal).

Remember that to represent expressions with algebra tiles, you will need to be very careful about how positives and negatives are distinguished. To help you understand the diagrams in the text, the legend at right will be placed on every page containing a mat. It shows the shading for +1 and –1. This model also represents a zero pair.

■ = +1
□ = –1

6-1. COMPARING EXPRESSIONS

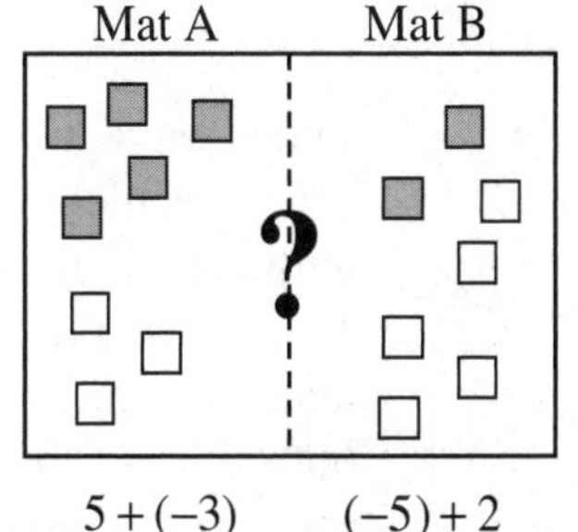

Ignacio and Oliver were playing a game. Each of them grabbed a handful of algebra tiles. They wanted to see whose expression had the greater value.

Two expressions can be compared by dividing the expression mat in half to change it into an **Expression Comparison Mat**. Then the two expressions can be built side by side and compared to see which one is greater.

- Oliver put his tiles on Mat A in the picture above and described it as $5+(-3)$.
- Ignacio put his tiles on Mat B and said it was $(-5)+2$.

With your team, find two different methods to simplify the two expressions so you can compare them. Which side of the mat is larger?

6-2. Using your Expression Comparison Mat, build the two expressions at right. Find a way to determine which side is greater, if possible. Show your work by sketching it on the Lesson 6.1.1B Resource Page. Be ready to share your conclusion and your justification.

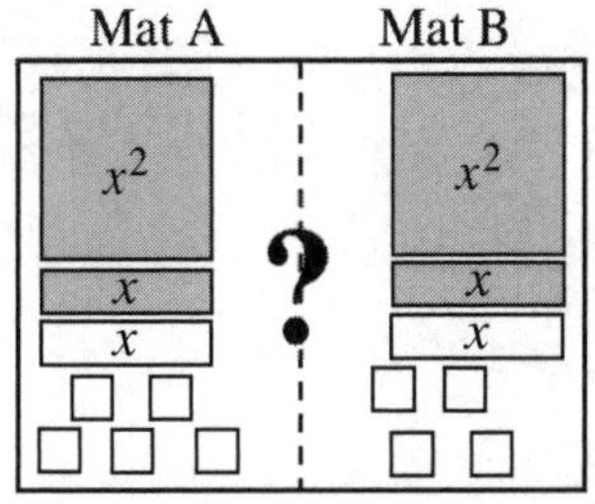

6-3. MORE COMPARING EXPRESSIONS – Is one expression greater?

Consider how you were able to compare the expressions in the previous problems. When is it possible to remove tiles to compare the expressions on the mats? In this problem, you will work with your team to identify two different "legal moves" for simplifying expressions.

Build the mat below using tiles and simplify the expressions. Record your work by drawing circles around the zeros or the balanced sets of tiles that you remove in each step on the Lesson 6.1.1B Resource Page. Which expression is greater?

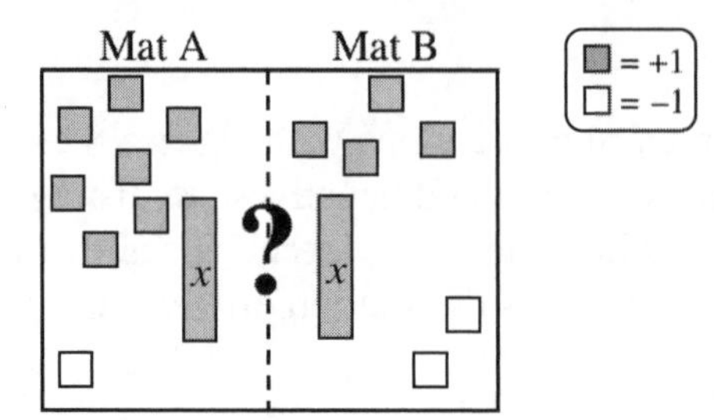

6-4. There are two kinds of moves you could use in problem 6-3 to simplify expressions with algebra tiles. First, you could remove zeros. Second, you could remove matching (or balanced) sets of tiles from both sides of the mat. Both moves are shown in the figures below. Justify why each of these moves can be used to simplify expressions.

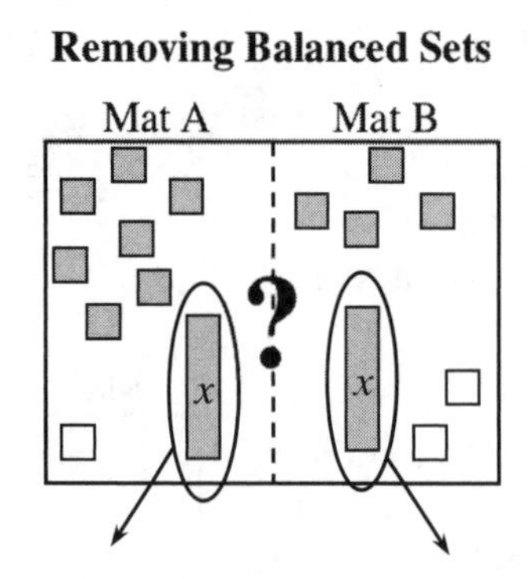

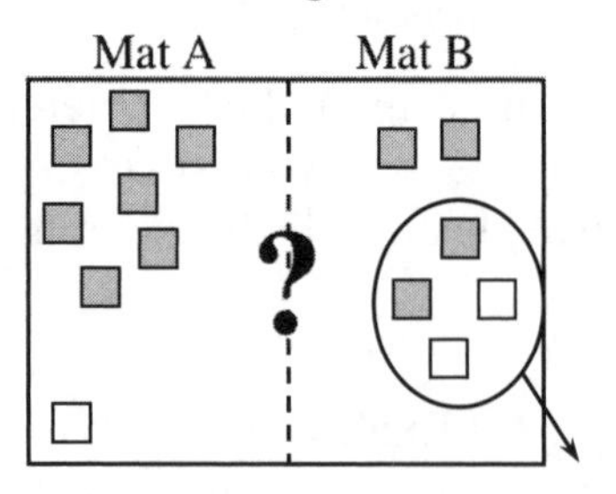

6-5. WHICH SIDE IS GREATER?

For each of the problems below, use the Lesson 6.1.1 Resource Page and:

- Build the two expressions on your mat.
- Write an expression for each side below the mats for parts (a) through (d) OR draw the tiles in the space given on the resource page for parts (e) and (f).
- Use legal moves to determine which mat is greater, if possible. Record your work by drawing circles around the zeros or the balanced (matching) sets of tiles that you remove in each problem.

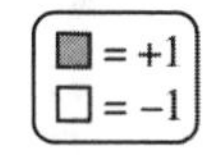

a.

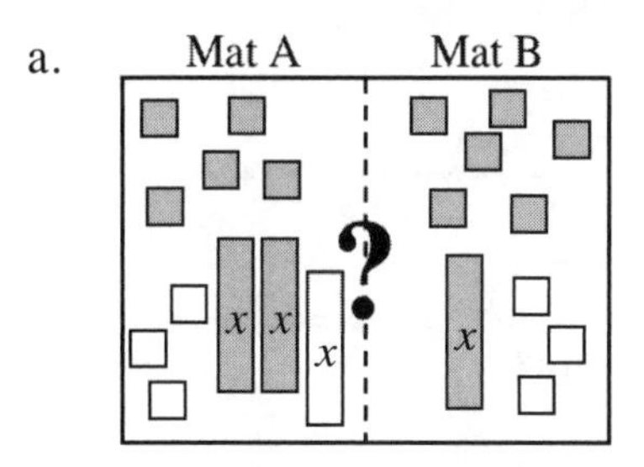

b.

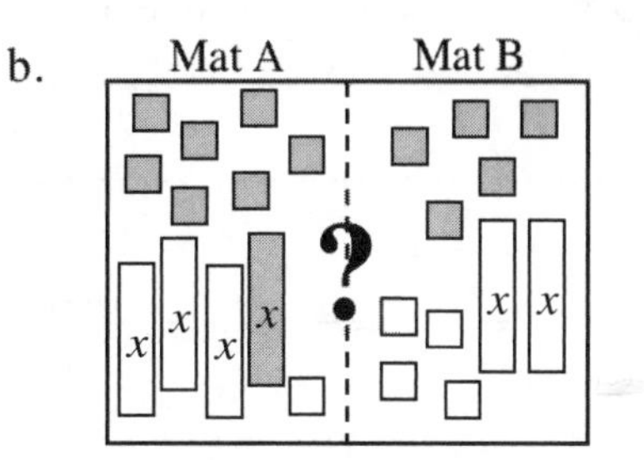

c.

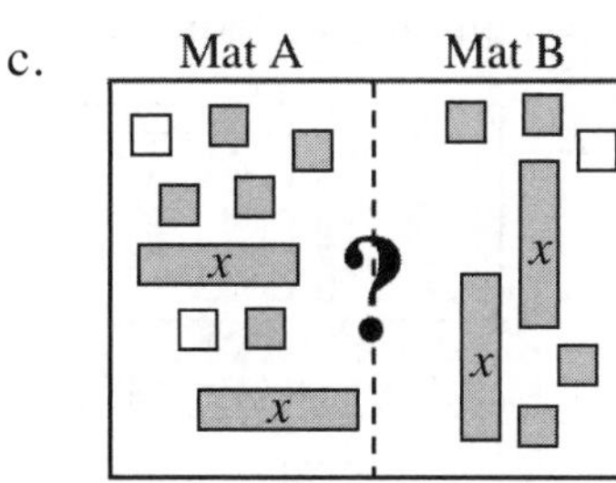

d.

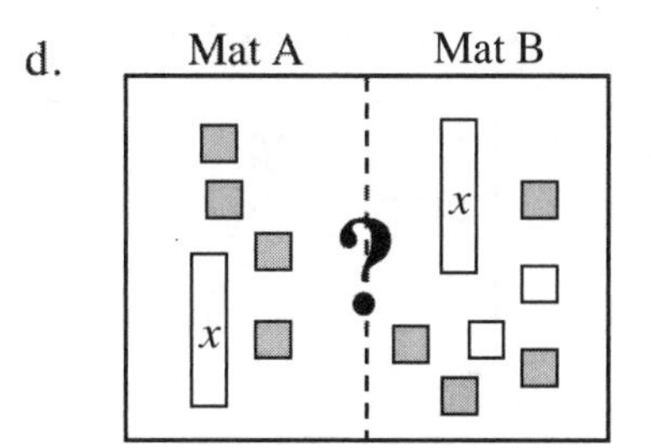

e. Mat A: $3x-4-2$

Mat B: $3(x-1)$

f. Mat A: $5+(-3x)+5x$

Mat B: $x^2+2x+1-x^2$

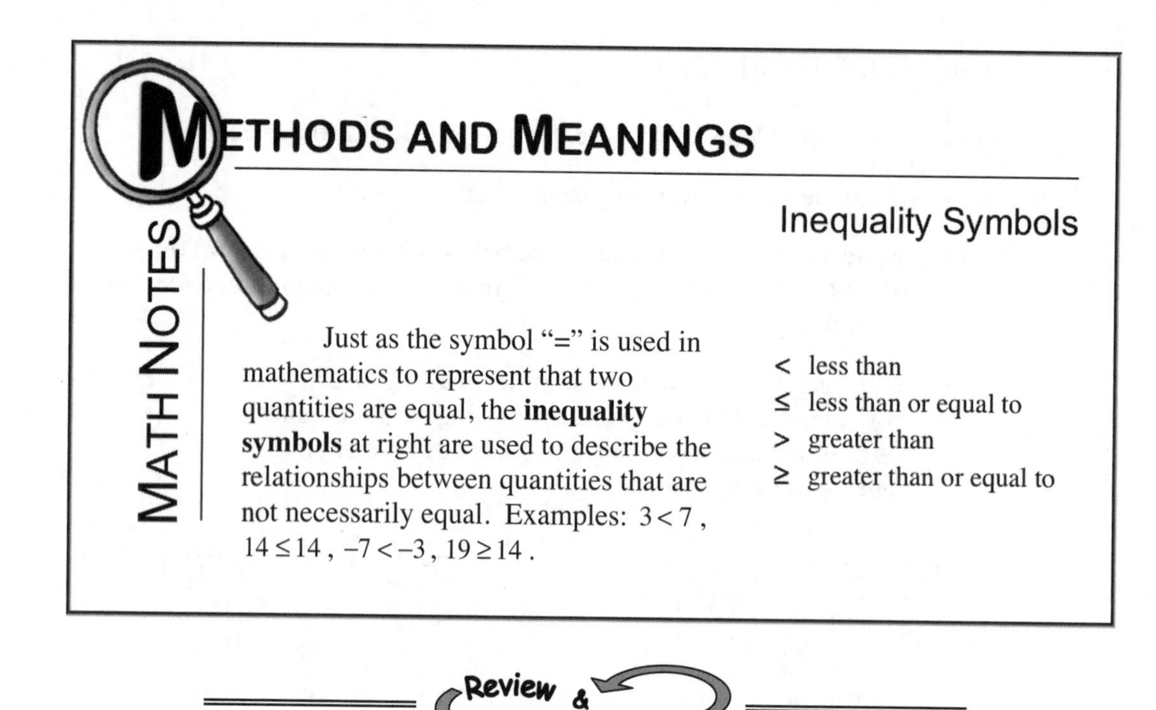

Methods and Meanings

Inequality Symbols

Just as the symbol "=" is used in mathematics to represent that two quantities are equal, the **inequality symbols** at right are used to describe the relationships between quantities that are not necessarily equal. Examples: $3 < 7$, $14 \leq 14$, $-7 < -3$, $19 \geq 14$.

- $<$ less than
- $\leq$ less than or equal to
- $>$ greater than
- $\geq$ greater than or equal to

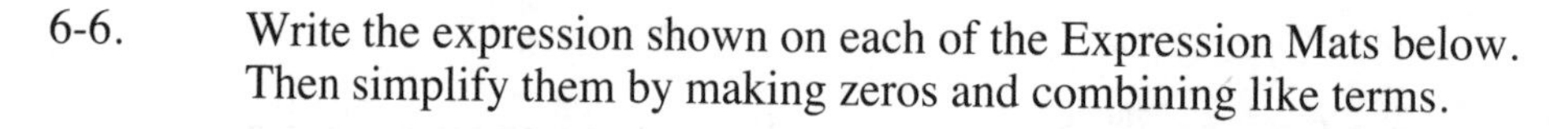

6-6. Write the expression shown on each of the Expression Mats below. Then simplify them by making zeros and combining like terms.

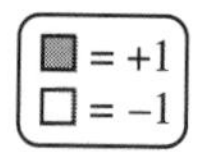

a. 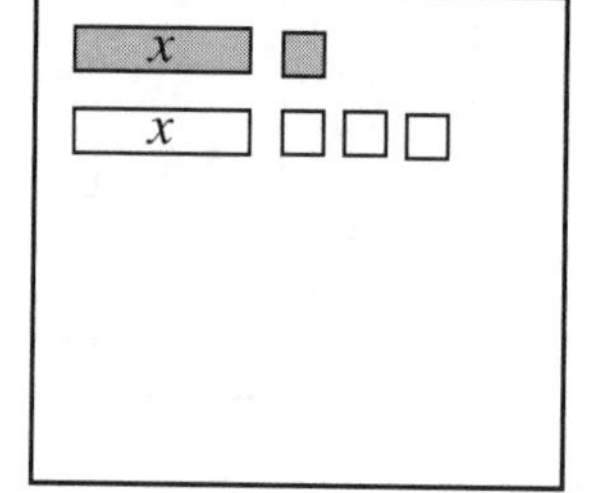

b. 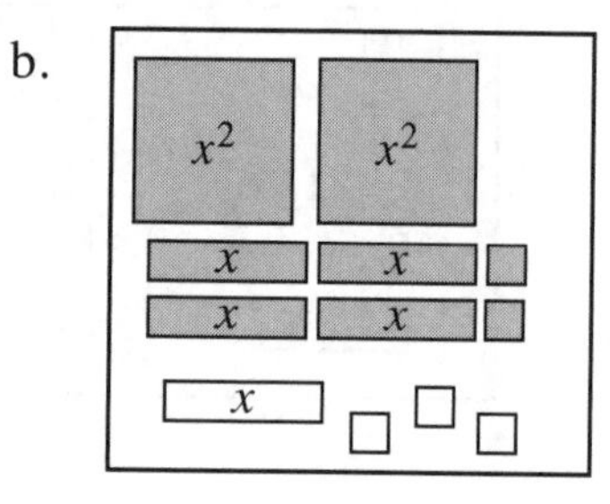

6-7. Which expressions are equivalent to the perimeter of the shape? How do you know?

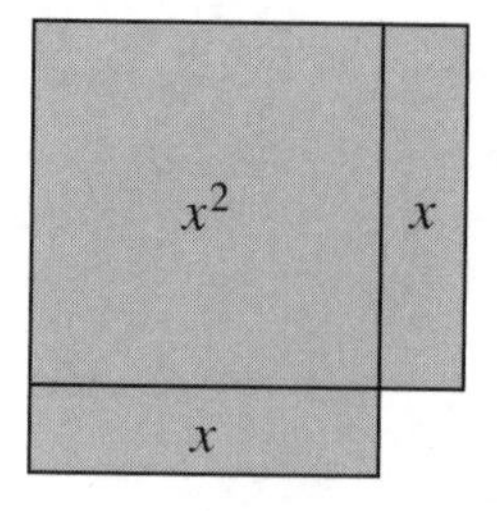

a. $x+3+3x+1$

b. $2x+4+x$

c. $4x+4$

d. $2x+2+2x+2$

6-8. Simplify the following expressions.

a. $-\frac{3}{4}-\frac{2}{5}$
b. $\frac{7}{8}-\frac{2}{3}$
c. $\frac{1}{3}-\frac{5}{6}$
d. $1\frac{2}{3}+(-\frac{2}{5})$
e. $\frac{4}{7}-(-\frac{3}{8})$
f. $-4\frac{1}{2}+3\frac{1}{9}$

6-9. Desmond is rolling a standard six-sided number cube. He plans to roll it 72 times.

a. About how many times would you expect Desmond to roll a 4? Why?

b. About how many times would you expect him to roll an even number? Why?

c. Desmond kept track of his results for all 72 rolls. The table at right shows some of his results.

Based on his partial results, how many times did he roll a 5 or a 6?

Result	Number of Outcomes
1	9
2	14
3	11
4	8

6-10. In parts (a) through (c) below, you will see pairs of quantities. For each pair of quantities, use words to write a sentence that describes the relationship. For example, "$5, $8" could be, "$8 is three more than $5."

a. $13, $39
b. 25 feet, 17 feet
c. 38 lbs., 19 lbs.

6-11. Copy each part below on your paper. Then use the number line to help you fill in < (less than) or > (greater than) on the blank line.

–15 –10 –5 0 5 10 15

a. –5 __ –2
b. 8 __ –1
c. –5 __ 0
d. –15 __ –14

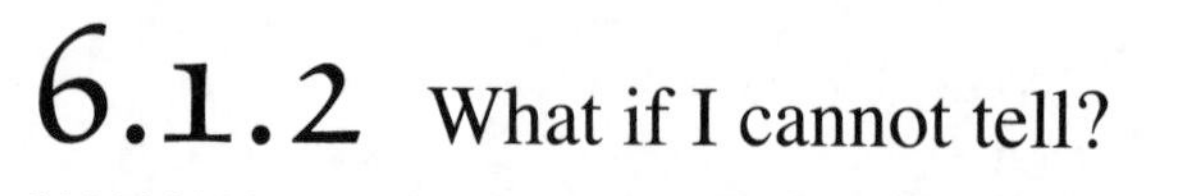

6.1.2 What if I cannot tell?

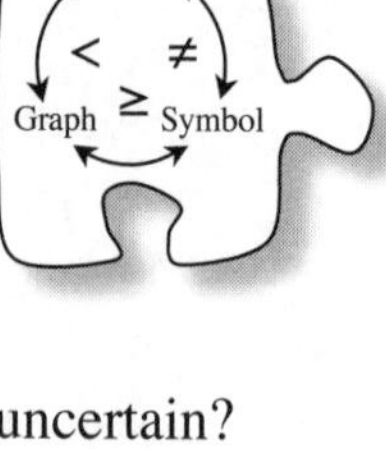

Comparing Quantities with Variables

Have you ever tried to make a decision when the information you have is uncertain? Perhaps you have tried to make plans on a summer day only to learn that it *might* rain. In that case, your decision might have been based on the weather, such as, "I will go swimming if it does not rain, or stay home and play video games if it does rain." Sometimes in mathematics, solutions might depend on something you do not know, like the value of the variable. Today you will study this kind of situation.

6-12. For each of the problems below, build the given expressions on your Expression Comparison Mat. Then use the simplification strategies of removing zeros and simplifying by removing matching pairs of tiles to determine which side is greater, if possible. Record your steps on the Lesson 6.1.2 Resource Page.

■ = +1
□ = −1

a.

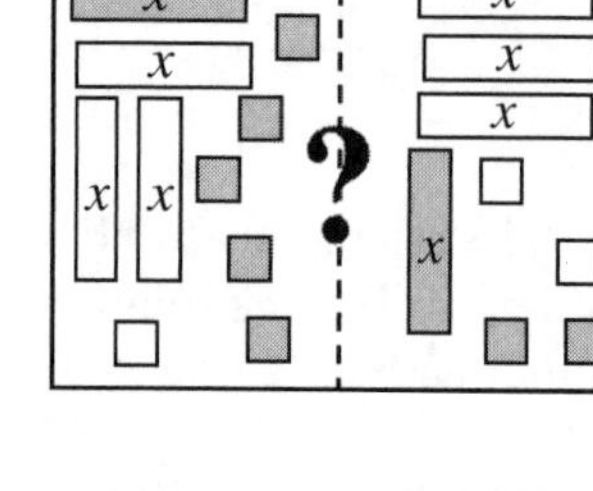

b. Mat A: $2(x+3)-4$

Mat B: $3x+(-1)-x+4$

c.

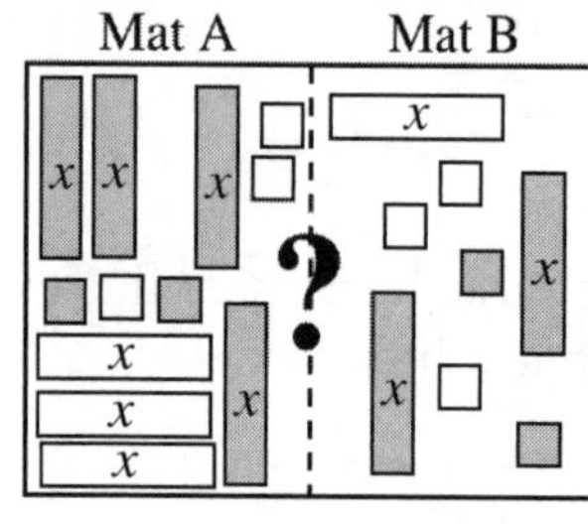

d.

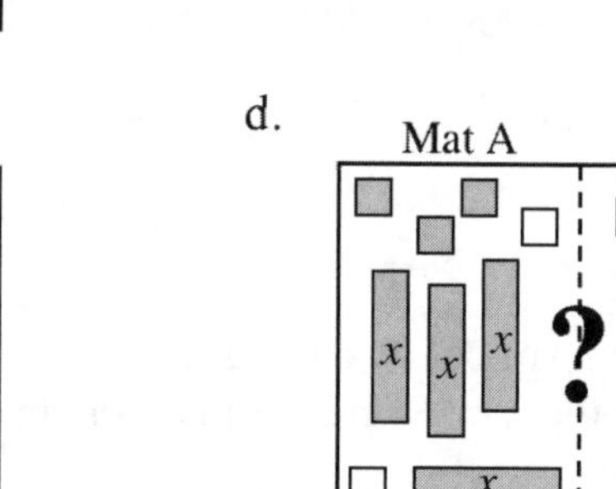

6-13. WHAT HAPPENED?

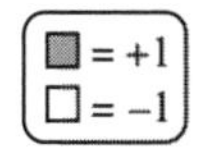

When Ignacio and Oliver compared the expressions in part (d) of problem 6-12, they could not figure out which side was greater.

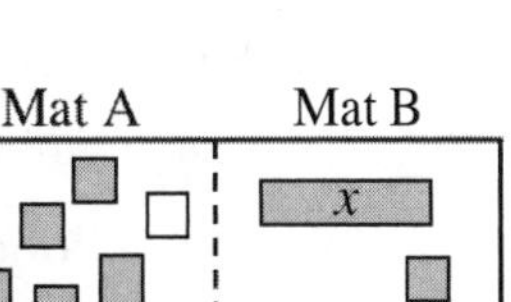

a. Is it always possible to determine which side of the Expression Comparison Mat is greater (has the greater value)? Why or why not? Be prepared to share your reasoning.

b. How is it possible for Mat A to have the greater value?

c. How is it possible for Mat B to have the greater value?

d. In what other way can Mat A and B be related? Explain.

6-14. Ignacio and Oliver are playing another game with the algebra tiles. After they simplify two new expressions, they are left with the expressions on their mats shown at right. They could not tell which part of the mat is greater just by looking.

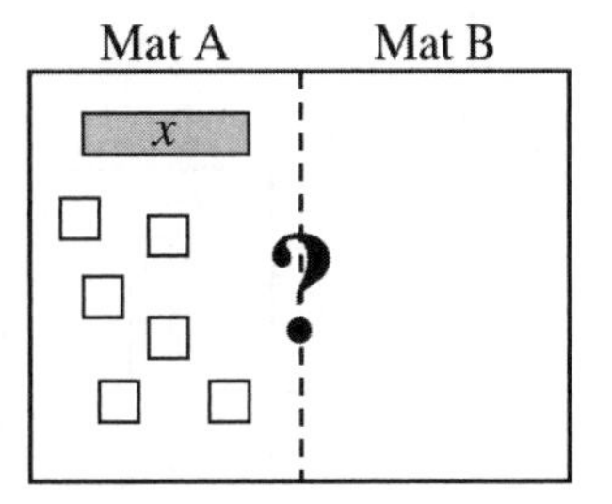

a. One way to compare the mats is to separate the x-tiles and the unit tiles on different sides of the mat. Work with your team to find a way to have only x-tiles on Mat A. Make sure that you are able to justify that your moves are legal.

b. Using the same reasoning from part (a), what would you do to have only the variable on Mat B in the Expression Comparison Mat at right?

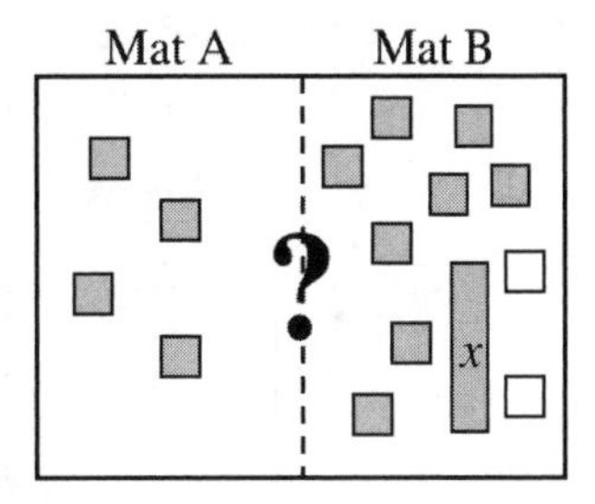

c. Write a short note to Ignacio and Oliver explaining this new strategy. Feel free to give it a name so it is easier for them to remember.

6-15. Ignacio and Oliver are trying to decide if there are other ways to change expressions on the Expression Comparison Mat without affecting which side is greater. They have invented some new strategies and described them below.

Your Task: For each of the moves below:

- Build the Expression Comparison Mats on your paper.
- Follow each set of directions for the mat shown in each strategy below.
- Determine if the move in the strategy is valid for maintaining the relationship between the two expressions. Be prepared to justify your response.

Strategy #1

"If you have a mat like the one drawn below, you can add the same number of tiles to both sides. In this case, I added 3 negative tiles to both sides."

Strategy #2

"On a mat like the one below, I added +3 to Mat A and added –3 to Mat B."

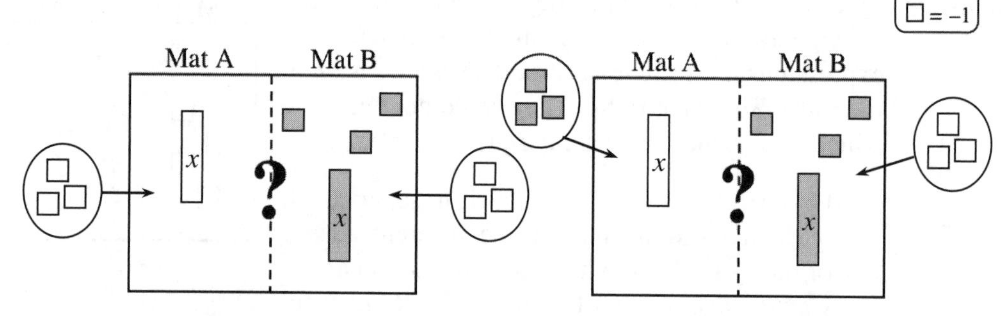

Strategy #3

"To simplify, I removed a positive x-tile from one side and a negative x-tile from the other side."

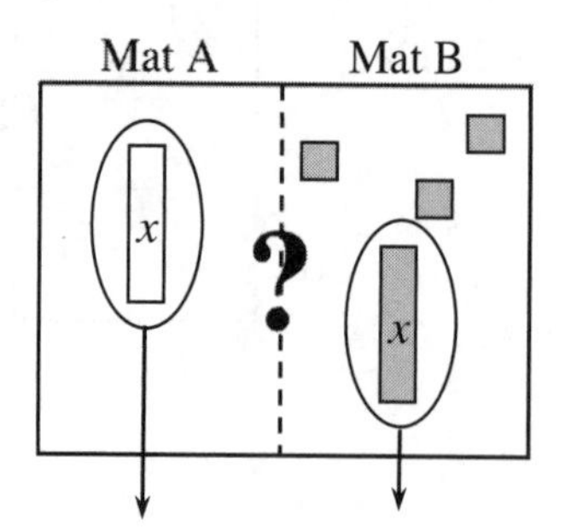

Strategy #4

"On a mat like the one below, I would add three zero pairs to Mat B."

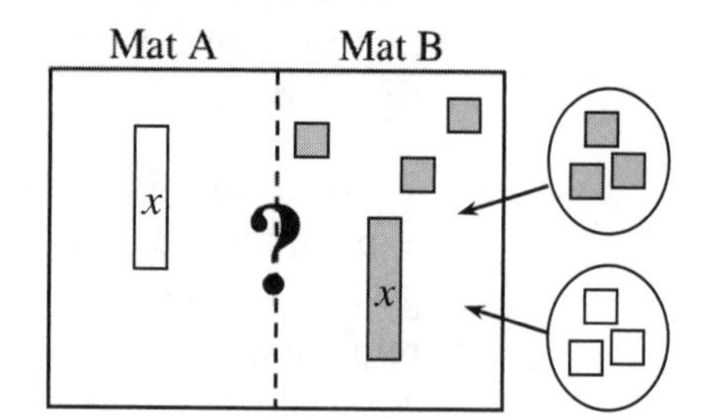

6-16. LEARNING LOG

In your Learning Log, summarize the methods that your team and class developed in the last two lessons to simplify expressions on the Expression Comparison Mat. Label your Learning Log entry "Simplifying Expressions (Legal Moves)" and include today's date.

6-17. Write an algebraic expression for each mat below. Then use the legal moves that you have developed to simplify each mat. If possible, decide which expression is greater.

■ = +1
□ = −1

a. Mat A | Mat B

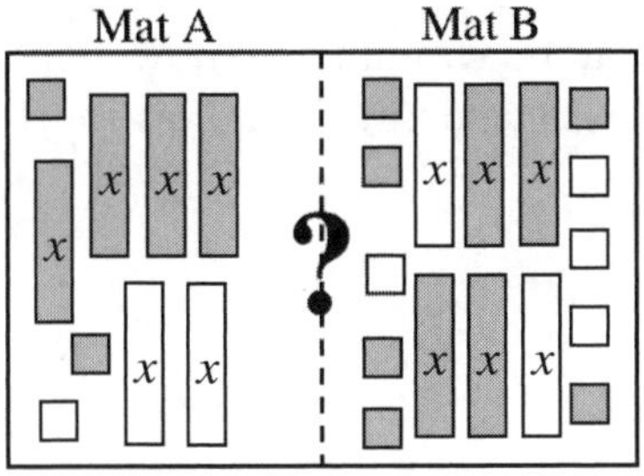

b. Mat A | Mat B

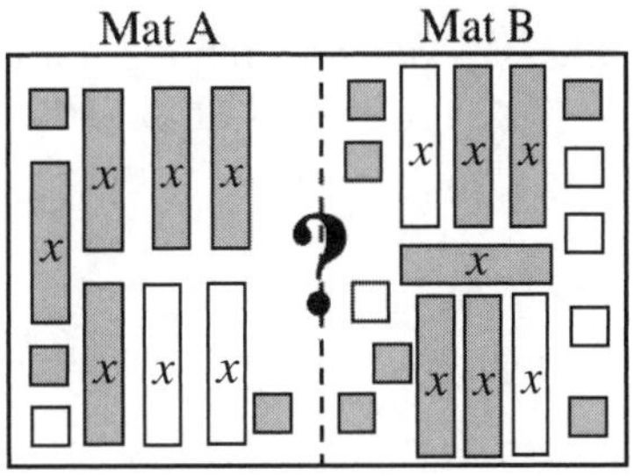

6-18. When solving a problem about the perimeter of a rectangle using the 5-D Process, Herman built the expression below.

$$\text{Perimeter} = x + x + 4x + 4x \text{ feet}$$

a. Draw a rectangle and label its sides based on Herman's expression.

b. What is the relationship between the base and height of Herman's rectangle? How can you tell?

c. If the perimeter of the rectangle is 60 feet, how long are the base and height of Herman's rectangle? Show how you know.

6-19. Evaluate the expressions below.

a. $5^2 \cdot (-3) - 4 \cdot 6 + 7$

b. $-3 \cdot (6 + 4 \cdot 2)$

c. $9 + 8 \div (-4) - 12$

d. $2^3 - 3 \cdot 4 + 6(-1 + 2)$

e. $4 + (3 + 4)^2$

f. $\frac{8-13}{10}$

6-20. Write each of the following expressions in two ways, one with parentheses and one without. For example, $4(x-3)$ can be written $4x-12$.

a. A number reduced by 3 and then multiplied by 2.

b. A number increased by 7 and then multiplied by 5.

c. Ten times a number, and then add twenty.

6-21. Graph these points on a coordinate grid: $A(-2,0)$, $B(0,4)$, $C(4,1)$, $D(2,-3)$. Connect the points in order, with point D connected to point A. What shape have you created?

6-22. Alan was paying a dinner check, but he was not sure how much he should tip for his bill of \$27.38. If a 15% tip is standard, about how much should Alan leave for the server?

6.1.3 Where do the solutions begin and end?

One Variable Inequalities

■ = +1
□ = −1

You have used Expression Comparison Mats to compare two expressions and have found that sometimes it is possible to determine which expression is greater. In this lesson, you will again compare expressions. This time, you will find the values for the variable that make one expression greater than the other.

6-23. Maria has been recording her work to see which side of an Expression Comparison Mat is greater, but she has been called away. Garth looked at her work, but he cannot figure out what Maria did to get from one step to another.

Mat A	**Mat B**
$5x+2+(-6)$	$2x+2+(-8)$
$5x+(-4)$	$2x+(-6)$
$3x+(-4)$	-6
$3x$	-2

Look at Maria's work above and help Garth by building the expressions on your mat and simplifying them. Write him a note explaining what Maria did to get from one step to another.

6-24. Compare the expressions $2 + 2x + (-3)$ on Mat A and $2x + (-4) + 1$ on Mat B using algebra tiles. Use Maria's method of recording to show your steps. Make sure you record each step so that your teacher or others could see what you did on your Expression Comparison Mat.

a. Which mat is greater?

b. Use symbols such as $<$, $=$, or $>$ to show the relationship between the final expressions on Mat A and Mat B.

6-25. Maria and Garth were playing a game with the algebra tiles. They each grabbed a handful of tiles and put them on the Expression Comparison Mat at right to see whose side had greater value.

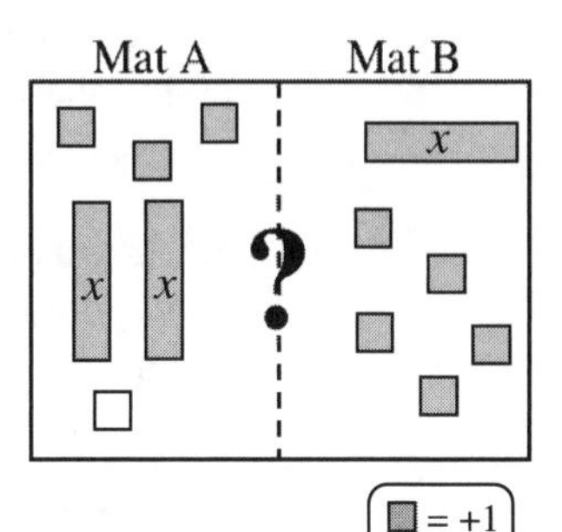

Maria said, *"I have Mat A and my side has more value."* Garth, who had Mat B, disagreed with her.

a. Write expressions for Mat A and Mat B.

b. Work with your team to simplify the expressions on the Expression Comparison Mat while carefully recording your work for each step on your paper with symbols. Can you tell whose side is greater? Why or why not?

c. With your team, find at least four values for x that would make the expression on Maria's side (Mat A) greater than the expression on Garth's side (Mat B). Be prepared to share your values with the class.

d. Any value for x that makes Mat A greater than Mat B is a solution to the inequality $2x+3+(-1)>x+5$. This is read, *"Two x plus three plus negative one is greater than x plus five."*

Share your solutions with another team and see if you have the same solutions as the other team does.

6-26. Karla had a hard time keeping track of all of the solutions to the inequality in problem 6-25 in her head. She decided to try to organize her answers. First she needed to know more about the problem.

a. Is there a greatest number that is a solution? Discuss this question with your team and be prepared to share your ideas with the class.

b. Is there a smallest number that is a solution? Again, be prepared to share your team's thinking with the class.

c. What is special about the point where the solutions end? (This number is called the **boundary point**.) In other words, what relationship does this number have to the two expressions being compared?

d. Karla was tired of listing so many solutions and wanted a quick way to show all of the solutions to this inequality. She decided to draw a number line like the one below.

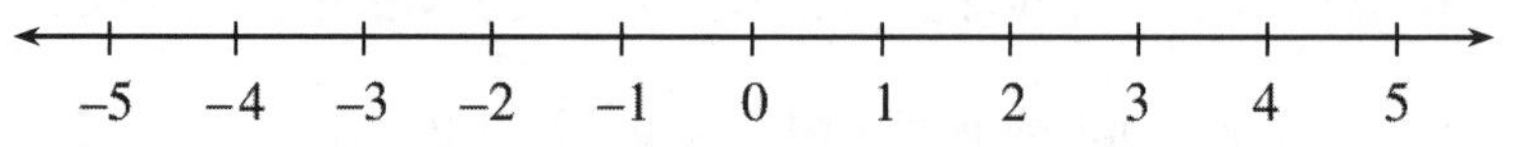

On your own paper, draw a number line such as the one above then follow your teacher's directions to represent the answer to this question on your number line.

6-27. Now consider the inequality $2x+5<3$, which can be read *"Two x plus five is less than 3."*

■ = +1
□ = –1

Build the inequality on your Expression Comparison Mat and record each step on your paper using symbols. Work with your team to describe the least and greatest solutions to the inequality and draw your solution on a number line. Be prepared to justify your ideas.

6-28. Jerry and Ken were solving the inequality $6>2x+2$. They set up the inequality on their Expression Comparison Mat and simplified it.

a. Write a sentence in words to represent the original inequality.

b. What did they get on each side of the mat when they simplified? Record your work on your paper.

c. Graph all the solutions to this inequality on a number line.

MATH NOTES

METHODS AND MEANINGS

Algebra Vocabulary

Variable: A letter or symbol that represents one or more numbers.

Expression: A combination of numbers, variables, and operation symbols. An expression does not contain an equal sign. For example, $2x + 3(5 - 2x) + 8$. Also, $5 - 2x$ is a smaller expression within the larger expression.

Term: Parts of the expression separated by addition and subtraction. For example, in the expression $2x + 3(5 - 2x) + 8$, the three terms are $2x$, $3(5 - 2x)$, and 8. The expression $5 - 2x$ has two terms, 5 and $2x$.

Coefficient: The numerical part of a term. In the expression $2x + 3(5 - 2x) + 8$, 2 is the coefficient of $2x$. In the expression $7x - 15x^2$, both 7 and 15 are coefficients.

Constant term: A number that is not multiplied by a variable. In the example above, 8 is a constant term. The number 3 is not a constant term because it is multiplied by a variable inside the parentheses.

Factor: Part of a multiplication expression. In the expression $3(5 - 2x)$, 3 and $5 - 2x$ are factors.

6-29. Graph each of the following inequalities on a number line.

a. $x > 3$ b. $x \le 5$ c. $x \ge -4$

6-30. Write an algebraic expression for each situation. For example, 5 less than a number can be expressed as $n - 5$.

a. 7 more than a number b. Twice a number

6-31. MATH TALK

Read the Math Notes box in this lesson to review commonly used algebra vocabulary. Then consider the expression below as you answer the following questions.

$$3x^2+7-2(4x+1)$$

a. Name the constant term.

b. What are the two factors in $2(4x+1)$? What are the two factors in $4x$?

c. Write an expression with a variable m, a coefficient –3, and a constant of 17.

d. Use the words coefficient, constant term, term, expression, and variable, to discuss $4x^2+11y-37$.

e. Use the words factor, product, quotient, and sum to describe the parts of $\frac{5-m}{n}-2-8(m+n)$.

6-32. Hector has a part-time job at a garage. He gets a paycheck of \$820 every four weeks.

a. Hector has to pay 15% of his income in taxes. How much money does he pay in taxes each paycheck? Show your thinking with a diagram and calculations.

b. Hector took a 1-week vacation, so his next paycheck will only be for 3 weeks of work. What percentage of his regular pay should he expect to receive? How much is that?

c. The garage owner is impressed with Hector's work and is giving him a 10% raise. How much will Hector be paid when he receives his next 4-week paycheck?

6-33. A fair number cube labeled 1, 2, 3, 4, 5, and 6 is rolled 100 times. About how many times would you expect the number 3 to appear?

6-34. Find the perimeter and area of each algebra tile shape below. Be sure to combine like terms.

a.

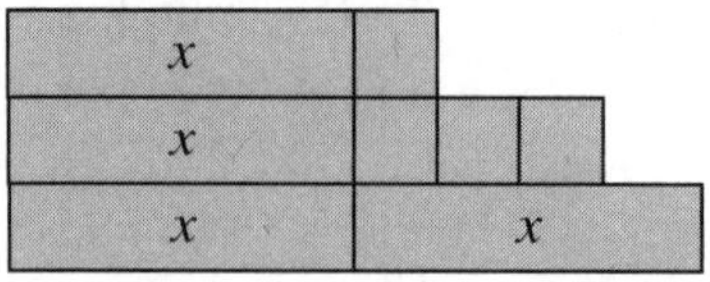

b.

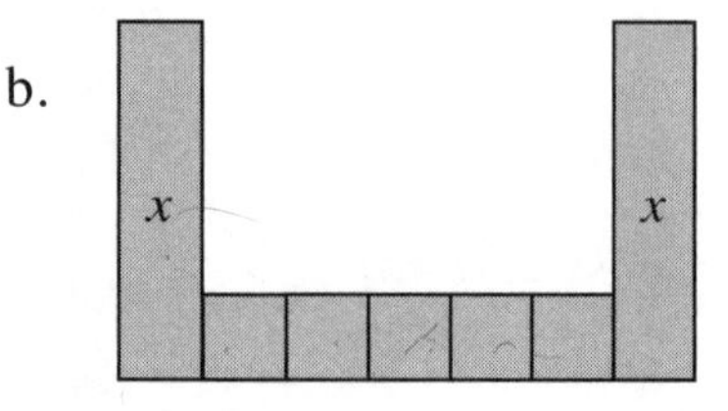

6.1.4 How can I find all solutions?

Solving One Variable Inequalities

In this lesson, you will work with your team to develop and describe a process for solving linear inequalities. As you work, use the following questions to focus your discussion.

What is a solution?

What do all of the solutions have in common?

What is the greatest solution? What is the smallest solution?

6-35. Jerry and Ken were working on solving the inequality $3x-1 \le 2x$. They found the boundary point and Ken made the number line graph shown at right.

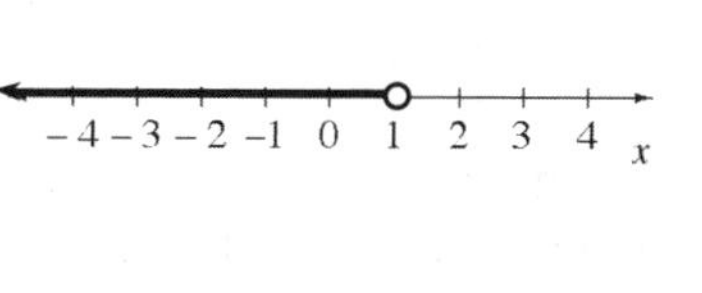

Jerry noticed a problem. *"Doesn't the line at the bottom of the ≤ symbol mean that it includes the equal part? That means that $x=1$ is also a solution. How could we show that?"*

"Hmmm," Jerry said. *"Well, the solution $x=1$ would look like this on a number line. Is there a way that we can combine the two number lines?"*

Discuss this idea with your team and be prepared to share your ideas with the class.

6-36. The diagram at right shows three possible ways to represent inequality statements. Review the meanings of the inequality symbols >, <, ≥, and ≤ with your team. Then, generate the two missing representations from each inequality described in parts (a) through (c) below.

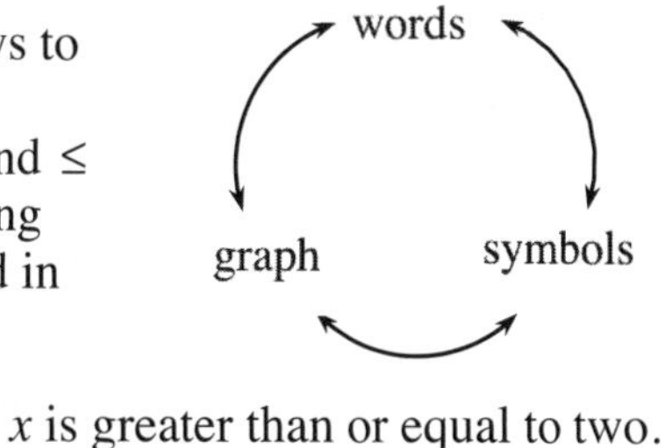

a. $x < -1\frac{1}{2}$

b. x is greater than or equal to two.

c. –4 –3 –2 –1 0 1 2 3 4 x

6-37. WHEN IS THE BOUNDARY POINT INCLUDED?

Represent the solution for each of the variables described below as an inequality on a number line and with symbols.

a. The speed limit on certain freeways is 65 miles per hour. Let x represent any speed that could get a speeding ticket.

b. You brought \$10 to the mall. Let y represent any amount of money you can spend.

c. To ride your favorite roller coaster, you must be at least five feet tall but less than seven feet tall. Let h represent any height that can ride the roller coaster.

6-38. Ellie was still working on her dollhouse. She has boards that are two different lengths. One long board is 54 inches.

a. The length of the short board is unknown. Ellie put three short boards end-to-end and then added her 12-inch ruler end-to-end. The total length was still less than the 54-inch board. Draw a picture showing how the short and long boards are related.

b. Write an inequality that represents the relationship between the short boards and 54 inches shown in your diagram in part (a). Be sure to state what your variable represents.

c. What are possible lengths of the short board? Show your answer as an inequality and on a number line.

6-39. Jordyn, Teri, and Morgan are going to have a kite-flying contest. Jordyn and Teri each have one roll of kite string. They also each have 45 yards of extra string. Morgan has three rolls of kite string plus 10 yards of extra string. All of the rolls of string are the same length. The girls want to see who can fly their kite the highest.

a. Since Jordyn and Teri have fewer rolls of kite string, they decide to tie their string together so their kite can fly higher. Write at least two expressions to show how much kite string Jordyn and Teri have. Let x represent the number of yards of string on one roll.

b. Write an expression to show how much kite string Morgan has. Again, let x be the number of yards of string on one roll.

c. How long does a roll of string have to be for Jordyn and Teri to be able to fly their kite higher than Morgan's kite? Show your answer as an inequality and on a number line.

d. How long does a roll of string have to be for Morgan to be able to fly her kite higher than Jordyn and Teri's kite? Show your answer as an inequality and on a number line.

e. What length would the roll of string have to be for the girls' kites to fly at the same height?

6-40. **Additional Challenge:** Travis loves trains! Today he is beginning a train ride from Madison, Wisconsin all the way to Seattle, Washington.

Shortly after the train left the station in Madison, Travis fell asleep. When he woke up, it was dark outside and he had no idea how long he had been asleep. A fellow passenger told him they had already passed La Crosse, which is 135 miles from Madison. If the train travels at an average speed of 50 miles per hour, at least how long has Travis been asleep? Represent this problem with an inequality and then solve it.

6-41. LEARNING LOG

Work with your team to describe each step of your process for finding boundary points and deciding what part of the number line to shade. Then write down each step in your Learning Log. Be sure to illustrate your ideas with examples. Title this entry "Finding Boundary Points" and label it with today's date.

METHODS AND MEANINGS

MATH NOTES

Graphing Inequalities

To solve and graph an inequality with one variable, first treat the problem as if it were an equality and solve the problem. The solution to the equality is called the **boundary point**. For example, to solve $x-4 \geq 8$, first solve $x-4=8$. The solution $x=12$ is the boundary point for the inequality $x-4 \geq 8$.

Since the original inequality is true when $x=12$, place your boundary point on the number line as a solid point. Then test one value on either side in the *original* inequality by substituting it into the original inequality. This will determine which set of numbers makes the inequality true. Write the inequality solution and extend an arrow onto the number line in the direction of the side that makes the inequality true. This is shown with the examples of $x=8$ and $x=15$ above. Therefore, the solution is $x \geq 12$ (also shown on the number line).

Test: $x=8$	**Test:** $x=15$
$(8)-4 \geq 8$	$(15)-4 \geq 8$
$4 \geq 8$	$11 \geq 8$
FALSE!	TRUE!

When the inequality is < or >, the boundary point is *not* included in the answer. On a number line, this would be indicated with an open circle at the boundary point. For example, the graph of $x<7$ is shown below.

6-42. Solve each of the following inequalities. Represent the solutions algebraically (with symbols) and graphically (on a number line).

a. $3x-3<2-2x$

b. $\frac{4}{5}x \geq 8$

6-43. Determine whether each of the numbers below is a solution to the inequality $3x-2<2-2x$. Show all of your work.

a. 2

b. $\frac{1}{2}$

c. -3

d. $\frac{2}{3}$

6-44. Evaluate the expressions below using $x=-2$, $y=-5$, and $z=3$.

a. xyz

b. $3(x+y)$

c. $\frac{z+2}{y}+1$

6-45. On your paper, sketch the algebra tile shape at right. Write an expression for the perimeter, and then find the perimeter for each of the given values of x.

a. $x=7$ cm

b. $x=5.5$ cm

6-46. Alden found a partially completed 5-D table:

	Define			Do	Decide Target 74
Trial 1:	15	$2(15)=30$	$15+2=17$	$15+30+17=$	62 too small
Trial 2:	18	$2(18)=36$	$18+2=20$	$18+36+20=$	74 just right

a. Create a word problem that could have been solved using this table.

b. What words would you put above the numbers in the three empty sections in the "Trial" and "Define" parts of the table?

c. What word(s) would you put above the "Do" column?

6-47. Beth is filling a small backyard pool with a garden hose. The pool holds 30 gallons of water. After 5 minutes, the pool is about one fourth full.

a. Assuming that the water is flowing at a constant rate, about how much water is going into the pool each minute?

b. About how long will it take to fill the pool?

6.2.1 What values make expressions equal?

Solving Equations

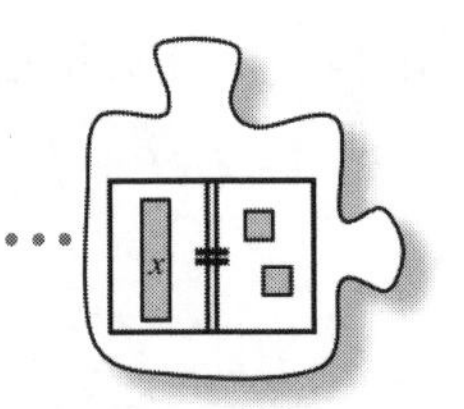

In the last section, you figured out how to determine what values of x make one expression greater than another. In this lesson, you will study what can be learned about x when two expressions are equal. As you work today, focus on these questions:

What if both sides are equal?

Is there more than one way to simplify?

What value(s) of x will make the expressions equal?

6-48. CHOOSING A PRICE PLAN

Sandeep works at a bowling alley that currently charges players $3 to rent shoes and $4 per game. However, his boss is thinking about charging $11 to rent shoes and $2 per game.

a. If a customer rents shoes and plays two games, will he or she pay more with the current price plan or the new price plan? Show how you know.

b. If the customer bowls 7 games, which price plan is cheaper?

6-49. WILL THEY EVER BE EQUAL?

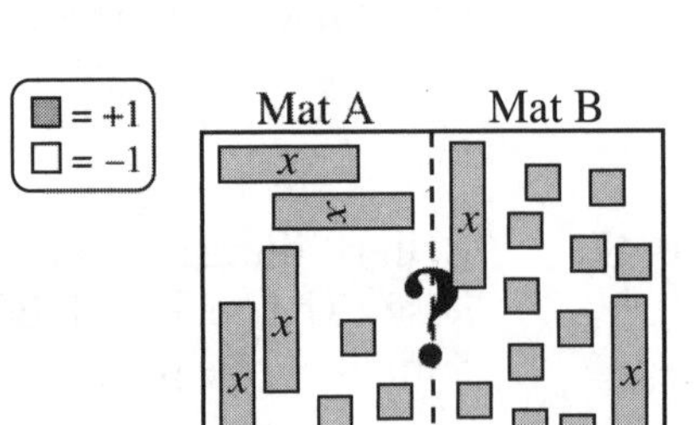

Sandeep decided to represent the two price plans from problem 6-48 with the expressions below, where x represents the number of games bowled. Then he placed them on the Expression Comparison Mat shown at right.

Original price: $4x+3$ New price: $2x+11$

a. Are his expressions correct? Find both the original and new prices when $x=2$ and then again when $x=7$ games. Did you get the same prices as you found in problem 6-46?

Problem continues on next page. →

6-49. *Problem continued from previous page.*

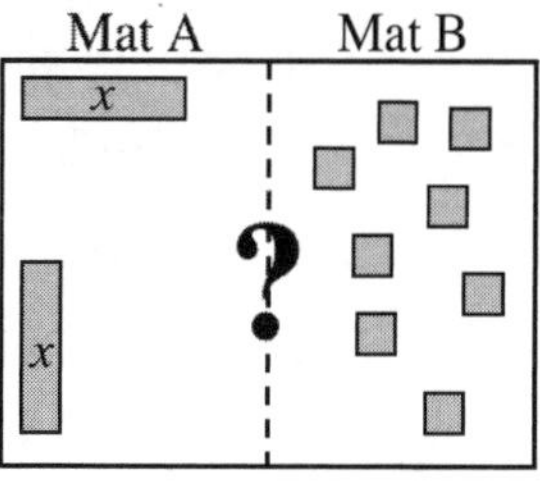

b. Sandeep then simplified the expressions on the mat. What steps did Sandeep take to simplify the mat to this point?

c. Sandeep noticed that for a certain number of games, customers would pay the same amount no matter which price plan his boss used. That is, he found a value of x that will make $4x+3=2x+11$. How many games would that customer bowl? What was the price he paid? Explain.

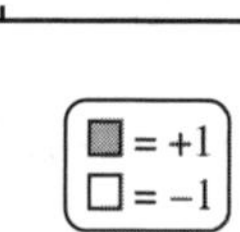

d. The value of x you found in part (c) is called a **solution** to the equation $4x+3=2x+11$ because it makes the equation true. That is, it makes both expressions have the same value.

   Is $x=6$ also a solution? How can you tell?

6-50. SOLVING FOR *X*

When the expressions on each side of the comparison mat are equal, they can be represented on a mat called an **Equation Mat**. Obtain a Lesson 6.2.1 Resource Page and algebra tiles from your teacher. Now the "=" symbol on the central line indicates that the expressions on each side of the mat are equal.

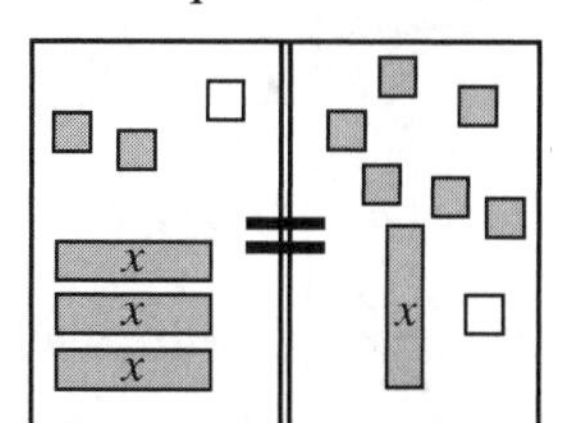

a. Build the equation represented by the Equation Mat at right on your own mat using algebra tiles.

b. On your paper, record the original equation represented on your Equation Mat.

c. Simplify the tiles on the mat as much as possible. Record what is on the mat after each legal move as you simplify each expression. What value of x will make the expressions equal?

6-51. Amelia wants to solve the equation shown on the Equation Mat at right. After she simplified each expression as much as possible, she was confused by the tiles that were left on the mat.

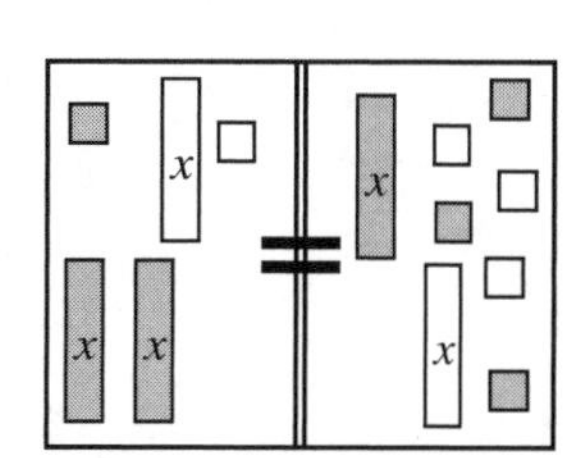

a. What was Amelia's original equation?

b. Remove any zero pairs that you find on each side of the Equation Mat. What happens?

c. What is the solution to this equation? That is, what value of x makes this equation true? Explain your reasoning.

6-52. Amelia now wants to solve the equation $2x+2+(-3)=5x+8$. Help her find the value of x that makes these expressions equal. Be sure to:

- Build the expressions using algebra tiles on your Equation Mat.
- Draw the mat on your paper.
- Simplify the mat to help you figure out what value of x makes this equation true. Be sure to record your work in symbols on your paper.

6-53. **Additional Challenge:** Try the number puzzle below.

Pick any number, add 20, multiply your answer by 2, and subtract 30 from the result. Then, divide your answer by 2 and subtract your original number.

a. What is the result?

b. Try it with several different numbers. Is the result the same every time?

c. Using a variable (such as n) to represent the starting number, show why the final result is always the number 5.

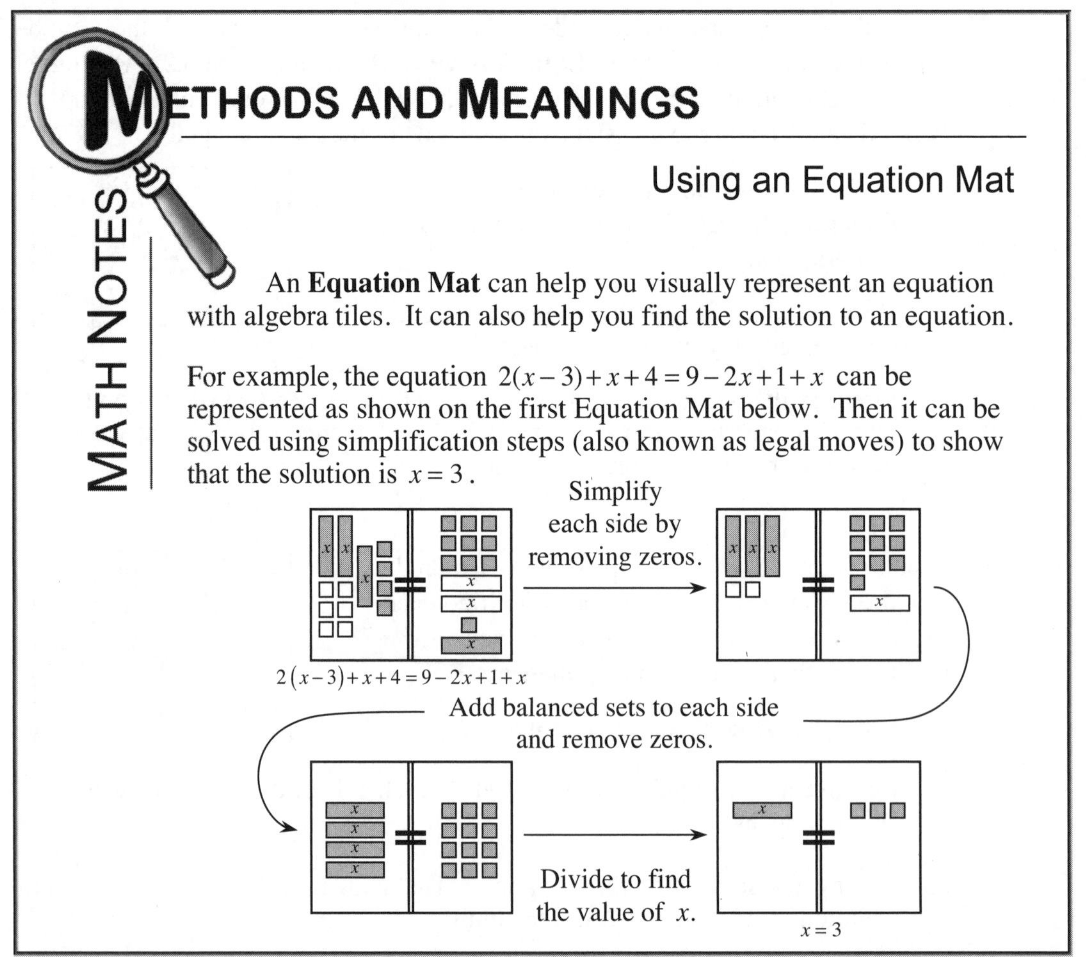

Using an Equation Mat

An **Equation Mat** can help you visually represent an equation with algebra tiles. It can also help you find the solution to an equation.

For example, the equation $2(x-3)+x+4=9-2x+1+x$ can be represented as shown on the first Equation Mat below. Then it can be solved using simplification steps (also known as legal moves) to show that the solution is $x=3$.

6-54. Consider the Equation Mat at right.

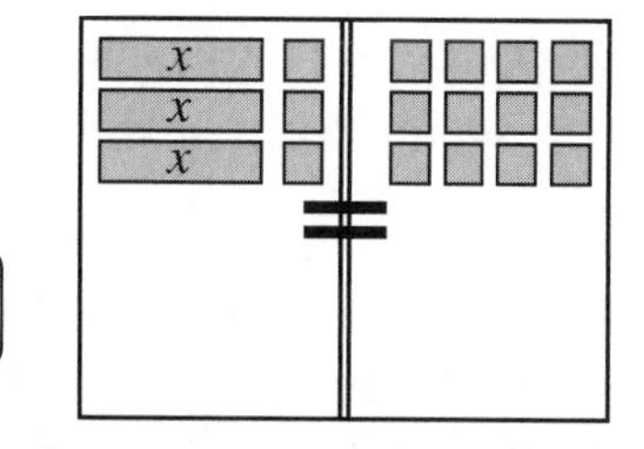

a. Write the original equation represented.

b. Simplify the tiles on the mat as much as possible. What value of x will make the two expressions equal?

6-55. When Lakeesha solved the equation $3(x + 1) = 12$ from problem 6-54, she reasoned this way:

"Since 3 groups of (x + 1) equals 3 groups of 4, then I know that each group of (x + 1) must equal 4."

a. Do you agree with her reasoning? Explain.

b. How can the result of Lakeesha's reasoning be written?

c. Verify that your answer from problem 6-54 will make the equation you wrote in part (b) true.

6-56. In problems 6-54 and 6-55, $3(x + 1)$ could also be written as $3x + 3$ by using the Distributive Property. The expression $3(x + 1)$ is a product, while $3x + 3$ is a sum. For each expression below, write an equivalent expression that is a product instead of a sum. This process of writing an expression in the form of factors (multiplication) is called **factoring**.

a. $75x - 50$ b. $32x^2 + 48x$ c. $-40m - 30$ d. $63m^2 - 54m$

6-57. Evaluate the expression $5 + (-3x)$ for the given x-values.

a. $x = 3$ b. $x = \frac{1}{3}$ c. $x = -3$

6-58. Which fractions below are equivalent? Explain how you know.

A. $\frac{20}{5}$ B. $\frac{-20}{5}$ C. $\frac{20}{-5}$ D. $\frac{-20}{-5}$ E. $-\frac{20}{5}$

6-59. Simplify each expression.

a. $8.4(7x - 4) + 3.9$ b. $\frac{1}{4} + \frac{4}{5}\left(\frac{3}{4}x - 1\frac{1}{9}\right)$

6.2.2 How do I know that it is correct?

Checking Solutions and the Distributive Property

Sometimes a lot can depend on the solution of a problem. For example, when businesses calculate the cost of packaging and shipping a product, they need to come up with an accurate value. If they miscalculate by only $0.01 per package but ship one million packages per year, this small miscalculation could be costly.

Solving a problem is one challenge. However, once it is solved, it is important to have ways to know whether the solution you found is correct. In this lesson, you will be solving equations and finding ways to determine whether your solution makes the equation true.

6-60. Chen's sister made this riddle for him to solve: *"I am thinking of a number. If you add two to the number then triple it, you get nine."*

a. Build the equation on an Equation Mat. What are *two* ways that Chen could write this equation?

b. Solve the equation and show your work by writing the equation on your paper after each legal move.

c. When Chen told his sister the mystery number in the riddle, she said he was wrong. Chen was sure that he had figured out the correct number. Find a way to justify that you have the correct solution in part (b).

6-61. Now solve the equation $4(x+3)=8$. Remember to:

- Build the equation on your Equation Mat with algebra tiles.
- Simplify the equation using your legal moves.
- Record your work on your paper.
- Solve for x. That is, find the value of x that makes the equation true.

6-62. CHECKING YOUR SOLUTION

When you solve an equation that has one solution, you get a value for the variable. But how do you know that you have done the steps correctly and that your answer "works"?

a. Look at your answer for problem 6-61. How could you verify that your solution is correct and convince someone else? Discuss your ideas with your team.

b. When Kelly and Madison compared their solutions for the equation $2x-7=-2x+1$, Kelly got a solution of $x=2$ and Madison got a solution of $x=-1$. To decide whether the solutions were correct, the girls decided to check their answers to see if they made the expressions equal.

Finish their work below to determine whether either girl has the correct solution.

Kelly's Work	Madison's Work
$2x-7 \stackrel{?}{=} -2x+1$ $2(2)-7 \stackrel{?}{=} -2(2)+1$	$2x-7 \stackrel{?}{=} -2x+1$ $2(-1)-7 \stackrel{?}{=} -2(-1)+1$

c. When checking, Kelly ended up with $-3=-3$. Does this mean that her answer is correct or incorrect? If it is correct, does this mean the solution is $x=-3$ or $x=2$? Explain.

d. Go back to problem 6-61 and show how to check your solution for that problem.

6-63. Kelly solved the equation $4(x+3)=8$ from problem 6-61. Her work is shown at right.

$$4(x+3)=8$$
$$x+3=2$$
$$x+3+(-3)=2+(-3)$$
$$x=-1$$

a. If $4(x+3)=8$, does $x+3$ have to equal 2? Why?

b. What did Kelly do to remove the 3 unit tiles from the left side of the equation? Does this move affect the equality?

c. If Kelly were solving the equation $3(x-5)=9$, what might her first step be? What would she have after that step? You may want to build this equation on an Equation Mat to help make sense of her strategy.

6-64. Now practice this new solving skill by building each of the equations below with tiles, solving for x, and checking your solution for each equation. Record your work.

a. $4(x+1)+1+(-x)=10+x$

b. $-1+2x-x=x-8+(-x)$

c. $5+2(x-4)=4x+7$

d. $9-3x=1+x$

e. $3x+3-x+2=x+5$

f. $4=3(2x+1)-11$

METHODS AND MEANINGS

MATH NOTES

Equations and Inequalities

Equations always have an equal sign. **Inequalities** have one of inequality symbols defined in the Lesson 6.1.1 Math Note. To **solve** an equation or inequality means to find all values of the variable that make the relationship true. The solution can be shown on a number line. See the examples below.

Solve this equation:

$x+3=7$

The solution is:

$x=4$

Solve this inequality:

$x-2<5$

The solution is:

$x<7$

Review & Preview

6-65. Substitute the given solution into the corresponding equation to check it. Then decide if the solution is correct or incorrect.

a. $5x+8=3x-2$ Solution: $x=-5$

b. $2(x+1)+6=20-3x$ Solution: $x=4$

6-66. During this chapter, you will use your new solving skills to solve word problems. Think about and use the strategies you already have to answer the questions below.

a. Andy is 4 years older than Eduardo. If Andy is x years old, write an expression to represent Eduardo's age.

b. In Eduardo's collection, the number of butterflies is 12 more than twice the number of moths. If there are x moths, write an expression to represent the number of butterflies he has.

6-67. Evaluate the expressions $3x - 2$ and $4x + 4$ for the following values of x. When you have found the value for each expression, write a statement using $<$, $>$, or $=$ that shows how the two values are related.

a. $x = 0$ b. $x = -6$ c. $x = 5$ d. $x = -2$

6-68. Victor wants to play "Guess My Number." Use the clues below to figure out his number. Each part is a new game.

a. "*When you double my number and subtract 9, you get my original number. What is my number?*"

b. "*When you double my number and add 5, you get 17. What is my number?*"

6-69. Find the perimeter and area of each triangle below.

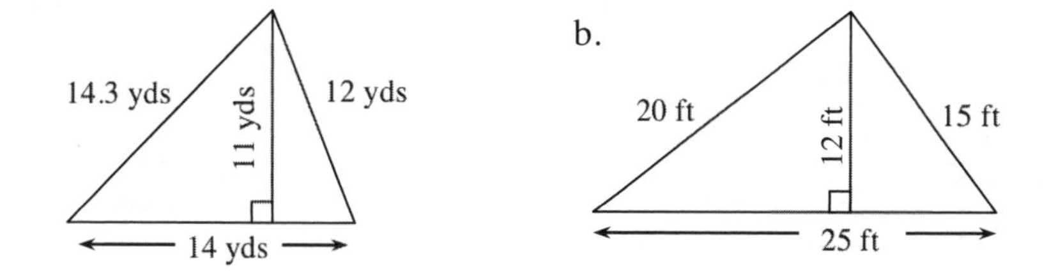

6-70. To solve the following problem, use the 5-D Process. Define a variable and write an expression for each column of your table.

In the first three football games of the season, Carlos gained three times as many yards as Alston. Travis gained ten yards more than Carlos. Altogether, the three players gained a total of 430 yards. How many yards did Carlos gain?

6.2.3 How can I record it?

Solving Equations and Recording Work

In this lesson, you will continue to improve your skills of simplifying and solving more complex equations. You will develop ways to record your solving strategies so that another student can understand your steps without seeing your Equation Mat. Consider these questions as you work today:

How can I record the steps I use to solve?

How can I record what is on the Equation Mat after each step?

6-71. Gene and Aidan were using algebra tiles to solve equations. Aidan was called away.

Help Gene finish by completing the table shown below and on the Lesson 6.2.3 Resource Page.

Mat A	Mat B	Steps taken
$2x+2(2x+1)+(-3x)+(-6)$	$4x+3+(-3)+x+8$	Original Equation
		1. Use the Distributive Property.
$3x+(-4)$	$5x+8$	2.
		3. Subtract $3x$ from both sides.
-12	$2x$	4.
		5. Divide both sides by 2.

6-72. Aidan was frustrated that he needed to write so much when solving an equation. He decided to come up with a shortcut for recording his work to solve a new equation.

As you look at Aidan's recording below of how he solved $2x+4=-12$, visualize an Equation Mat with algebra tiles. Then answer the questions for each step below.

$$2x + 4 = -12$$
$$\quad -4 \quad -4$$
$$\frac{2x}{2} = \frac{-16}{2}$$
$$x = -8$$

a. What legal move does writing -4 twice represent?

b. What legal move does circling the $+4$ and the -4 represent?

c. What does the box around the $\frac{2}{2}$ represent?

d. Why did Aidan divide both sides by 2?

e. Check Aidan's solution in the original equation. Is his solution correct?

6-73. The method of recording the steps in the solution of an equation is useful only if you understand what operations are being used and how they relate to the legal moves on your Equation Mat.

Find the work shown at right on your resource page for this lesson.

$$x + (-4) + 6x = 3x - 1 + 5$$
$$-4 + 7x = 3x + 4$$
$$7x = 3x + 8$$
$$4x = 8$$
$$x = 2$$

a. For each step in the solution, add the missing work below each line that shows what legal moves were used. You may want to build the equation on an Equation Mat.

b. Check that the solution is correct.

6-74. For each equation below, solve for x. You may want to build the equation on your Equation Mat. Record your work in symbols using Aidan's method from problem 6-72. Remember to check your solution.

a. $-2x+5+2x-5=-1+(-1)+6x+2$

b. $3(4+x)=x+6$

6-75. Oliver is building a train depot for his model railroad. As his final step, he needs to apply rain gutters around the roof of the rectangular building. He has 52 cm of rain gutters. The length of the depot is 19 cm. Explore how Oliver can find the width of the depot by answering the questions below.

a. Find the width of the depot using arithmetic (that is, solve the problem without using any variables). Record your steps.

b. Use w to represent the width of the depot. Write an algebraic equation that shows the perimeter is 52 cm, and solve your equation. Record your steps.

c. Which method, the arithmetic or algebraic, did you prefer? Why?

6-76. For each equation below, solve for x. You may want to build the equation on your Equation Mat. Record your work and check your solution.

a. $5x+(-x)-1=11-2x$

b. $3(-x+2)+x-1=-x-3$

6-77. Genny is confused. She simplified an equation and ended up with the mat shown at right. What is the value of x?

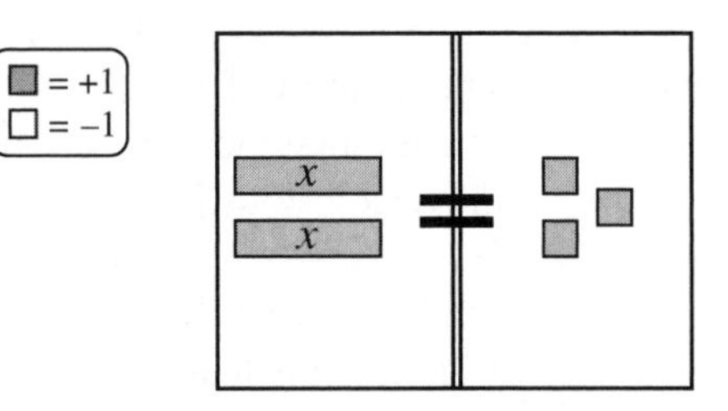

6-78. Maggie's mom agrees to let Maggie buy small gifts for some of her friends. Each gift costs \$4. Maggie's mom gave her a budget of \$19. When Maggie went online to order the gifts, she discovered there was a \$7 shipping fee no matter how many gifts she bought.

a. Use arithmetic (without variables) to determine how many gifts Maggie can buy. Record your steps.

b. Write an algebraic equation to determine how many gifts Maggie can buy with \$19, and solve your equation. Record your steps.

c. Compare and contrast the two methods of solving the problem.

6-79. Your teacher will explain the way you will be working on solving the equations below for x. You may want to build the equations on your Equation Mat. Record your work and check your solution.

a. $2(x+1)+3=3(x-1)$

b. $-2x-2=3(-x+2)$

c. $3+4(2-x)=3x+(-x)-7$

d. $6(3-x)+(-20)=10+3(4x+2)$

6-80. LEARNING LOG

In your Learning Log, explain what it means to solve an equation. What is a solution? Be sure to give an example. Title this entry "Solving Equations and Checking Solutions" and include today's date.

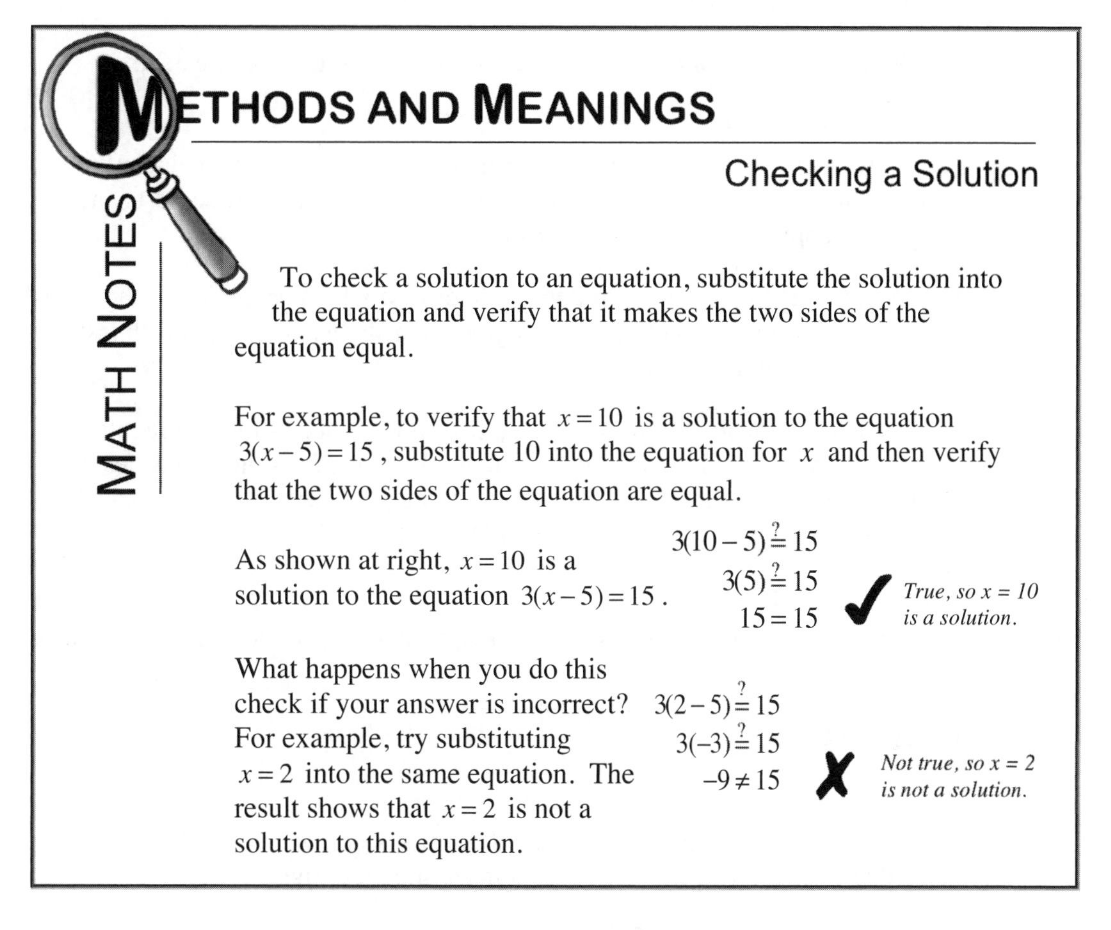

METHODS AND MEANINGS

MATH NOTES

Checking a Solution

To check a solution to an equation, substitute the solution into the equation and verify that it makes the two sides of the equation equal.

For example, to verify that $x = 10$ is a solution to the equation $3(x-5) = 15$, substitute 10 into the equation for x and then verify that the two sides of the equation are equal.

As shown at right, $x = 10$ is a solution to the equation $3(x-5) = 15$.

$$3(10-5) \stackrel{?}{=} 15$$
$$3(5) \stackrel{?}{=} 15$$
$$15 = 15$$

✓ *True, so x = 10 is a solution.*

What happens when you do this check if your answer is incorrect? For example, try substituting $x = 2$ into the same equation. The result shows that $x = 2$ is not a solution to this equation.

$$3(2-5) \stackrel{?}{=} 15$$
$$3(-3) \stackrel{?}{=} 15$$
$$-9 \neq 15$$

✗ *Not true, so x = 2 is not a solution.*

6-81. Solve each equation below for x. Check your final answer.

a. $4x = 6x - 14$

b. $3x + 5 = 50$

6-82. Forty percent of the students at Pinecrest Middle School have a school sweatshirt. There are 560 students at the school. Draw a diagram to help you solve each problem below.

a. How many students have a school sweatshirt?

b. If 280 students have school t-shirts instead of sweatshirts, what percentage of the school has a t-shirt?

c. What percentage of the school does not have a t-shirt or a sweatshirt?

6-83. Latisha wants to get at least a B+ in her history class. To do so, she needs to have an overall average of at least 86%. So far, she has taken three tests and has gotten scores of 90%, 82%, and 81%.

a. Use the 5-D Process to help Latisha determine what percent score she needs on the fourth test to get the overall grade that she wants. The fourth test is the last test of the grading period.

b. The teacher decided to make the last test worth twice as much a regular test. How does this change the score that Latisha needs on the last test to get an overall average of 86%? Support your answer with mathematical work. You may choose to use the 5-D Process again.

6-84. Factor each expression. That is, write an equivalent expression that is a product instead of a sum.

a. $20y-84$

b. $24b^2+96b$

6-85. Copy and complete each of the Diamond Problems below. The pattern used in the Diamond Problems is shown at right.

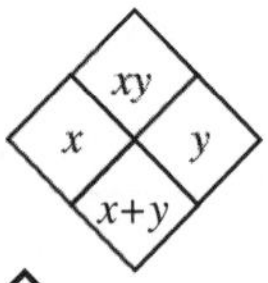

xy
x
y
$x+y$

a.
13
14

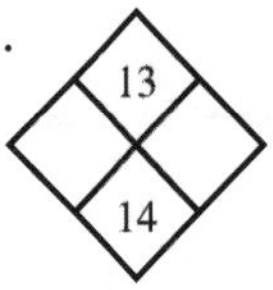

b.
16
−2

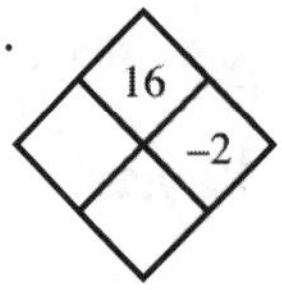

c.
−4.2
−3

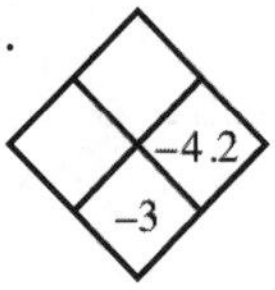

d.
0
15

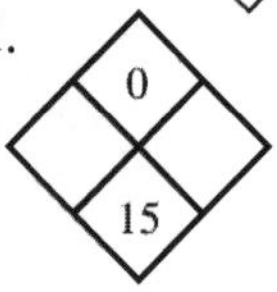

6-86. A cattle rancher gave $\frac{1}{3}$ of his land to his son and kept the remaining $\frac{2}{3}$ for himself. He kept 34 acres of land. How much land did he have to begin with?

6-87. Solve each equation. Record your work and check your solution.

a. $5(x-2)+(-9)=-7(1-x)$

b. $-6x-7=-1(-9+2x)$

6-88. Simplify each expression.

a. $\frac{73}{100}\cdot(-\frac{2}{7})$

b. $0.4\cdot 0.3$

c. $-\frac{63}{80}+\frac{7}{10}$

d. $5\frac{1}{9}+8\frac{2}{5}$

e. $-\frac{9}{17}-\frac{1}{2}$

f. $-1.2+(-\frac{3}{5})$

6-89. Sketch the parallelogram shown at right, and then redraw it with sides that are half as long.

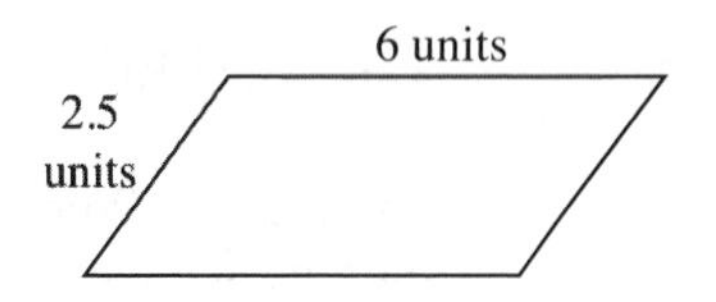

a. Find the perimeters of both the original and smaller parallelograms.

b. If the height of the original parallelogram (drawn to the side that is 6 units) is 2 units, find the areas of both parallelograms.

6-90. Evaluate the expression $10-2x$ for the x-values given below.

a. $x=2$

b. $x=\frac{1}{2}$

c. $x=-2$

6-91. Set up a four quadrant graph and graph the points below to make the four-sided shape $PQRS$.

$P(-2,4)\quad Q(-2,-3)\quad R(2,-2)\quad S(2,3)$

a. What shape is $PQRS$?

b. Find the area of the shape.

6-92. Write and solve an inequality for the following situation.

Robert is painting a house. He has 35 cans of paint. He has used 30 cans of paint on the walls. Now he needs to paint the trim. If each section of trim takes $\frac{1}{2}$ can of paint, how many sections of trim can he paint? Show your answer as an inequality with symbols, in words, and with a number line. Make sure that your solution makes sense for this situation.

6.2.4 How can I represent it?

Using a Table to Write Equations from Word Problems

In the last few lessons, you used algebra tiles and Equation Mats to solve problems in which variables represented specific numbers. The tile and Equation Mat tools are related to the processes you have used to solve word problems in which a specific value is unknown. Today you will connect these two tools and the expressions you wrote using a part of the 5-D Process to extend your repertoire for solving problems.

6-93. THE 5-D PROCESS REVISITED

Use the 5-D Process to set up the following problem. Complete only *three* trials. Even if you do not yet know the solution, wait for your teacher's instructions.

The Great Lakes contain the largest amount of fresh water on the surface of the planet. Combined, the five lakes (Superior, Michigan, Huron, Erie, and Ontario) contain 84% of North America's and 21% of the world's surface fresh water.

The amount of water in Lake Superior is 1720 cubic miles more than the amount of water in Lake Michigan. Lake Huron has 330 cubic miles of water less than Lake Michigan. If the total amount of water in the three lakes is 4930 cubic miles, how much water is in each lake?

Check the reasonableness of the amounts of water you found for each lake by using estimation strategies: Does the total volume of the three lakes seem reasonable?

6-94. GO FOR THE GOLD

As you saw in problem 6-93, sometimes organizing your thinking using the 5-D Process to solve a word problem involves a lot of work. Sometimes the tables are very complicated or the numbers require many trials to find the answer. How can your new equation-solving skills help you solve word problems? Read the following word problem and then answer the questions below.

While looking at the country of Jamaica's results from the 2008 Beijing Olympics, Gemma noticed that the number of gold medals Jamaica received was twice the number of silver medals. She also realized that Jamaica received 1 fewer bronze medal than silver medals. Altogether, Jamaica received 11 medals.

a. Gemma started by setting up the 5-D Process table below. What did she define x to represent?

Define			**Do**	**Decide**
# Gold	# Silver	# Bronze	Total Number of Medals	11?
$2x$	x	$x-1$		

b. How did she represent the number of gold and bronze medals?

c. Write an equation for the total number of medals.

d. Solve your equation in part (c). What is the value of x? What does this represent?

e. How many gold medals did Jamaica earn? Explain how you know.

6-95. Solve the following word problems by writing and solving an equation. You may choose to use the 5-D Process and create a table to help you build your equation. It may be helpful first to do one or two trials with numbers to help establish a pattern. Whatever strategy you use, do not forget to define the variable by stating what x represents. Finally, check your answer.

a. A person's height is positively associated with his or her arm span (the distance between the ends of the fingertips as arms are held out on each side of the body). One of the tallest men in history had an arm span measuring 7 inches more than his height. The combined total of his arm span and height was 221 inches. How tall was this man?

b. Have you ever tried to hold your breath? Humans can only hold their breath an average of one minute. However, other animals can hold their breath for much longer.

A Greenland whale can hold its breath three times as long as a beaver, and a hippopotamus can hold its breath five minutes less than a beaver. If you added the time a Greenland whale, beaver, and hippopotamus can hold their breath, you would get 95 minutes! How long can a beaver hold its breath?

6-96. LEARNING LOG

In Chapter 5, you learned about variables and using the 5-D Process to solve problems. In this chapter, you simplified expressions using algebra tiles and focused on solving equations.

In your Learning Log, describe how variables and equations can be used to solve word problems. Use an example problem to help make your explanation clear. Title this entry "Using the 5-D Process to Write and Solve Equations" and label it with today's date.

METHODS AND MEANINGS

MATH NOTES

Defining a Variable

When you write an equation, it is important to **define the variable** carefully. You need to be clear about what you are talking about so that someone else looking at your work understands what the variable represents. This step is an important habit to develop because it is an important step in solving many different math problems.

For example, suppose you have this problem:

> At the neighborhood grocery store, grapes cost \$3 a pound. If Belinda spent \$5.40 on grapes, how many pounds of grapes did she buy?

One equation you could write is $3x = 5.4$, if you know what x stands for. The variable x should be clearly defined, such as $x = \text{pounds of grapes}$, rather than just $x = \text{grapes}$. You could also write $g = \text{pounds of grapes}$, since any letter may be used as a variable.

6-97. For the end-of-year party, Mt. Rose Middle School ordered 112 pizzas. There were eight fewer veggie pizzas than there were pepperoni pizzas. There were three times as many combo pizzas as pepperoni pizzas. Use the 5-D Process to define a variable and write an equation for this situation. Then determine how many of each kind of pizza were ordered.

6-98. Consider the equation $7 = 3x - 5$.

a. Stanley wants to start solving the equation by adding 5 to both sides, while Terrence first wants to subtract 7 from both sides. Will both strategies work? Is one strategy more efficient than the other?

b. Solve $7 = 3x - 5$. Show your steps.

6-99. The two triangles at right are similar shapes.

a. What is the scale factor from shape A to shape B?

b. Find the missing side lengths.

c. If you wanted to make shape A smaller instead of bigger, what is a scale factor you could use?

6-100. Find the area and perimeter of each of the following figures.

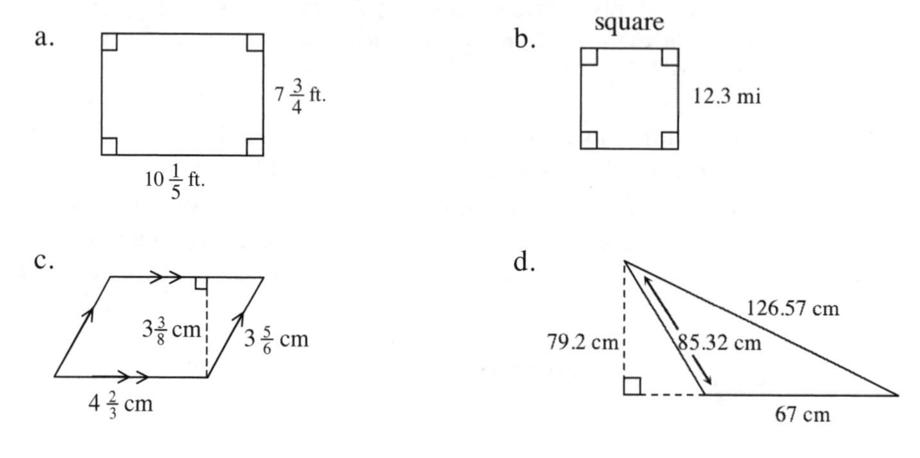

6-101. Factor each expression by writing it as a product instead of a sum.

a. $90k-60$

b. $30d^2-18d$

6-102. Write an expression for each mat at right.

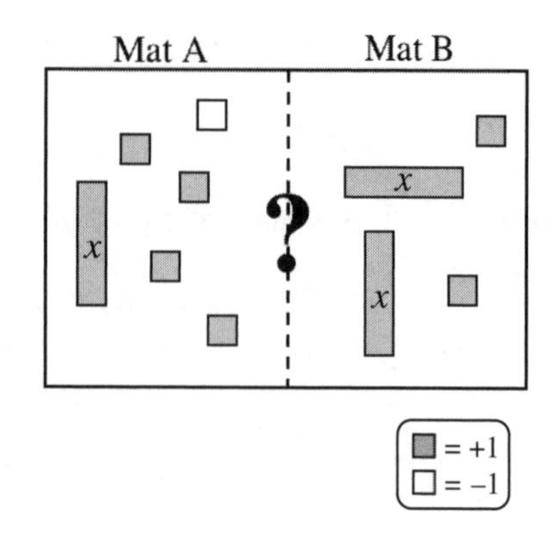

a. Simplify each mat to determine which expression is greater, if possible.

b. If $x=3$, would your answer to part (a) change? Explain.

c. If $x=-2$, would your answer change? Explain.

6.2.5 How can I model it?

Writing and Solving Equations

Engineers investigate practical problems to improve people's quality of life. To investigate solutions to problems, they often build models. These models can take various forms. For example, a structural engineer designing a bridge might build a small replica of the bridge. Civil engineers studying the traffic patterns in a city might create equations that model traffic flows into and out of a city at different times.

In this lesson, you will be building equations to model and solve problems based on known information. As you work today, keep the following questions in mind.

What does x represent in the equation?

How does the equation show the same information as the problem?

Have I answered the question?

6-103. Today your team will be responsible for solving a problem and sharing your solution with the class on a poster. It is important that your poster communicates your thinking and reasoning so that people who look at your poster understand how you solved the problem. Your poster should include:

- Connections between the words in the problem and the relationships in your table and/or equation. Connections can be made with arrows, colors, symbols, and/or labels.
- Variables that are defined completely.
- An equation to represent the problem.
- Your solution to the problem.
- The answer declared in a sentence.
- An estimation verifying that the total of your solutions is reasonable.

Begin by solving one of the problems below and writing an equation. Make sure to define the variable you use and answer the question(s) being asked. Using the 5-D Process, including numerical trials, may be helpful.

a. Hong Kong's tallest building, Two International Finance Center, is 88 stories tall. The former Sears Tower in Chicago is eight stories taller than the Empire State Building in New York City. If all of the buildings were stacked on top of each other, the combined heights would have 300 stories. How many stories does the Sears Tower have?

Problem continues on next page. →

6-103. *Problem continued from previous page.*

b. Have you ever driven or walked across a suspension bridge? There are many suspension bridges in the world of different lengths that allow people to travel across rivers, bays, and lakes.

The Mackinac Bridge in Michigan is 1158 meters long. The Tsing Ma Bridge in Hong Kong is 97 meters longer than the Golden Gate Bridge in California. Together, all three bridges have a length of 3815 meters. How long is the Tsing Ma Bridge?

c. Elevations found in the United States range from California's Death Valley at 282 feet below sea level to Alaska's Mount McKinley, also known as Denali, at 20,320 feet above sea level.

The highest elevation in Delaware is 106 feet higher than the highest elevation in Florida. Louisiana's highest elevation is 190 feet higher than Florida's highest elevation. If you climbed from sea level to the highest points in Delaware, Florida, and Louisiana, you would only climb 1331 feet. How high is the highest elevation in each of the three states?

d. Most states in the United States are divided into counties. Some counties are very large, while some are very small. Different states have different numbers of counties. Pennsylvania has five less than twice as many counties as Oregon. Florida has one less county than Pennsylvania. Together, the three states have 169 counties. How many counties does each of these three states have?

e. A train from Washington, D.C. to Chicago stops first in Pittsburgh and then in Cleveland. The distance from Washington, D.C. to Pittsburgh is 30 miles less than twice the distance from Pittsburgh to Cleveland. The distance from Cleveland to Chicago is 220 miles more than the distance between Pittsburgh and Cleveland. If the entire train ride is 710 miles, how far is the train ride from Cleveland to Chicago?

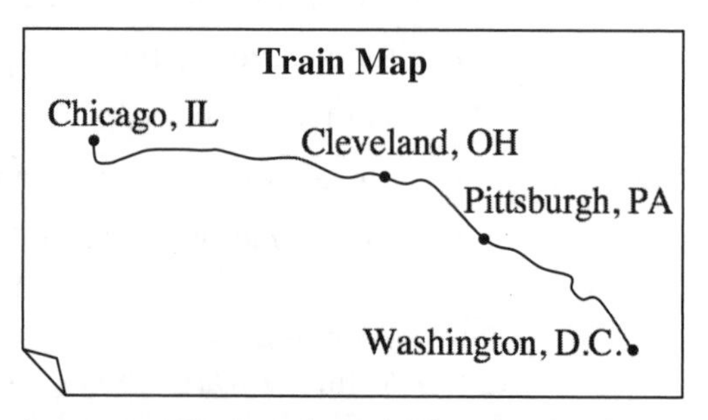

Review & Preview

6-104. Solve the following equations using any method. Show your work and check your solution.

a. $2x+16=5x+4$ b. $3x-5=2x+14$ c. $5x-5=x+15$

6-105. Write an algebraic expression for each situation.

a. Three less than a number.

b. Nine more than three times a number.

c. Two less than five times a number.

6-106. A triangle has a base that is three times longer than its height. It has an area of 486 sq cm.

Use the 5-D Process to find the base and height of the triangle. Write a variable expression for each column of your table.

6-107. Kandi has a bag of marbles. She has 5 black, 3 white, 2 green, and 4 orange marbles. Kandi reaches into the bag without looking and pulls out a marble.

a. What is the probability that she will pull out a green marble?

b. If she does get a green marble and does not put it back in the bag, what is the probability that she will now pull the other green marble from the bag?

c. Assume that Kandi does get the second green marble and does not return it to the bag. What is the probability that she will now pull another green marble from the bag?

6-108. Which of the equations below represent proportional relationships? If the relationship is proportional, identify the constant of proportionality. If the relationship is not proportional, explain why.

a. $y=\frac{3}{4}x+2$ b. $y=\left(4\frac{2}{3}\right)x$ c. $y=3(x-1)$

6-109. The diagram at right represents an acrobat's sequence of moves on a tightrope, where m represents the distance in feet that she covers each time she does a leap.

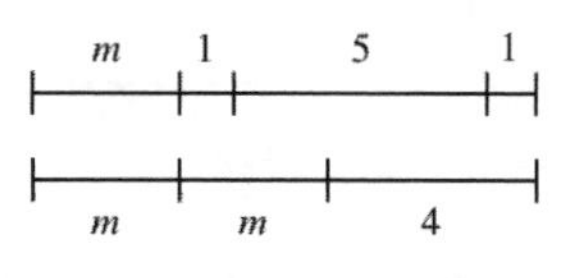

a. How long is each of her leaps? How can you tell?

b. Write and solve an equation to find the length of each leap.

c. How long is the tightrope?

6-110. Solve the following equations using any method. Show your work and check your solution.

a. $3x+10=25$ b. $5(x-2)=30$ c. $2x-9=x+7$

6-111. Use the 5-D Process to solve the following problem. Write an expression to represent each column of your table.

Yosemite Falls, the highest waterfall in the United States, is actually made up of three smaller falls. The Lower Yosemite Falls is 355 feet shorter than the Middle Cascades Falls. The Upper Yosemite Falls is 80 feet more than twice the Middle Cascades Falls. If the entire set of waterfalls is 2425 feet long, how tall is each of the smaller waterfalls?

6-112. Evaluate the following expressions.

a. $7x+8$ when $x=9$ b. $6(y-11)$ when $y=-6$

c. $45-5m+7$ when $m=-4$ d. $-2t+9$ when $t=-20$

6-113. Here are some new distances with given lengths to help Cecil cross the tightrope. Find at least two ways to get Cecil across for each situation. Write your solutions in symbolic form.

a. Span of tightrope: 19 feet Given lengths: 4, 5, 7 feet

b. Span of tightrope: 25 feet Given lengths: 3, 6, 7 feet

c. Span of tightrope: 23 feet Given lengths: 5, 2, 9 feet

6-114. Walter walked 15.5 blocks from his house to work. It took him 35 minutes. What is his rate in blocks per hour?

6-115. Jana's mom gave her $100 to shop for some new school clothes. She is at the store and has picked out a pair of pants that cost $49.50. She wants to spend the rest of her money buying various colors of a shirt that is on sale for $12.99. Write an inequality that can be used to calculate the number of shirts she can buy. Solve your inequality. How many shirts can Jana buy?

6.2.6 Is there always a solution?

Cases With Infinite or No Solutions

Are all equations solvable? Are all solutions a single number? Think about this: Annika was born first, and her brother William was born 4 years later. How old will William be when Annika is twice his age? How old will William be when Annika is exactly the same as his age?

In this lesson, you will continue to practice your strategies of combining like terms, removing zeros, and balancing to simplify and compare two expressions. You will also encounter unusual situations where the solution may be unexpected. As you work today, focus with your team on these questions:

What if both sides are not equal?

Are there many values of x that will make the expressions equal?

Is there always a solution?

6-116. Many students believe that every equation has only one solution. However, in the introduction to this lesson you might have noticed that if Annika was four years older than her brother, William, they could never be the same age. Some situations have one solution, others have no solution, and still others have all numbers as solutions.

For each of the following equations, reason with your team to decide if the answer would be "One solution," "No solution," or "All numbers are solutions." If there is a single number solution, write it down. If you are not sure how many solutions there are, have each member of your team try a number to see if you can find a value that makes the equation work.

a. $x = x$

b. $x + 1 = x$

c. $x = 2x$

d. $x + x = 2 + x$

e. $x + x = x - x$

f. $x + x = 2x$

g. $x \cdot x = x^2$

h. $x - 1 = x$

6-117. Use the 5-D Process to write an equation for the problem below. Then answer the question.

Kelly is 6 years younger than her twin brothers Bailey and Larry. How old will Kelly be when the sum of her brothers ages is 12 more than twice Kelly's?

6-118. SPECIAL CASES, Part One

Use the equation $8+x+(-5)=(-4)+x+7$ to complete parts (a) through (c).

a. Build the equation on your Equation Mat and simplify it as much as possible. Record your steps and what you see when you have simplified the equation fully. Draw a picture of your final mat.

b. Have each member of your team test a different value for x in the original equation, such as $x=0$, $x=1$, $x=-5$, $x=10$, etc. What happens in each case?

c. Are there any solutions to this equation? If so, how many?

6-119. SPECIAL CASES, Part Two

Use the equation $x+x+2=2x$ to complete parts (a) through (c).

a. Build the equation on your Equation Mat and simplify it as much as possible. Record your steps and what you see when you have simplified the equation fully. Draw a picture of your final mat.

b. Have each member of your team test a different value for x in the equation, such as $x=0$, $x=1$, $x=-5$, $x=10$, etc. What happens? Is there a pattern to the results you get from the equation?

c. Did you find any values for x that satisfied the equation in part (a)? When there is an imbalance of units left on the mat (such as $2 = 0$), what does this mean? Is $x = 0$ a solution to the equation?

6-120. Keeping these special cases in mind, continue to develop your equation-solving strategies by visualizing and solving each equation below. Remember to build each equation on your mat, if needed, to simplify as much as possible, and to solve for x. Identify if one number is the solution, if any number is the solution, or if there is no solution. Record your steps.

a. $-x+2=4$

b. $-3+x=2(x+3)$

c. $5x+3+(-x)=2x+1+2x+3$

d. $3x+7+(-x)+-2=2x+5$

e. $4+-3x=2$

f. $3x+3=4+x+(-1)$

6-121. **Additional Challenge:** For each of the parts below, create your own equation (involving at least three steps) that has the given solution.

a. $x=-2$

b. $x=\frac{1}{2}$

c. no solution

d. all numbers

METHODS AND MEANINGS

MATH NOTES

Solutions to an Equation With One Variable

A **solution** to an equation gives the value(s) of the variable that makes the equation true.
For example, when 5 is substituted for x in the equation at right, both sides of the equation are equal. Therefore, $x=5$ is a solution to this equation. Some equations have several solutions, such as $x^2=25$, where $x=5$ or -5.

$$4x-1=2x+9$$
$$4(5)-1=2(5)+9$$
$$19=19$$

Equations may also have no solution or an infinite (unlimited) number of solutions.

Notice that no matter what the value of x is, the left side of the first equation will never equal the right side. Therefore, it could be said that $x+2=x+3$ has **no solution**.

Equation with no solution:

$$x+2=x+3$$
$$2\neq 3$$

However, in the equation $x-2=x-2$, no matter what value x has, the equation will always be true. All numbers can make $x-2=x-2$ true. Therefore, it could be said that the solution for the equation $x-2=x-2$ is **all numbers**.

Equation with infinitely many solutions:

$$x-2=x-2$$
$$-2=-2$$

6-122. Simplify and solve each equation below for x. Show your work and record your final answer.

a. $24+2x=3x+2(3\cdot 4)$

b. $24+3x=3x+3(7-1)$

c. $2(12+x)=2x+24$

6-123. Show the "check" for each of these problems and write whether the solution is correct or incorrect.

a. For $3x+2=x-2$, does $x=0$?

b. For $3(x-2)=30+x-2-x+2$, does $x=12$?

6-124. Some steps in solving an equation are more efficient than others. Complete parts (a) through (d) to determine the most efficient first step to solve the equation $34=5x-21$.

a. If both sides of the equation were divided by 5, then the equation would be $\frac{34}{5}=x-\frac{21}{5}$. Does this make the problem simpler? Why or why not?

b. If you subtract 34 from both sides, the equation becomes $0=5x-55$. Does this make the equation simpler to solve? Why or why not?

c. If you add 21 to both sides, the equation becomes $55=5x$. Does this suggestion make this a problem you can solve more easily? Why or why not?

d. All three suggestions are legal moves, but which method will lead to the most efficient solution? Why?

6-125. Alex has a job delivering newspapers. He puts 20% of his earnings each week into his college savings account. Each week he puts \$16 into the account.

a. Draw a diagram to represent this situation. How much money does Alex earn each week?

b. Alex spends 10% of his earnings on snacks each week. How much does he spend?

c. When Alex has worked for one year, he will get a raise that is equal to 15% of his current earnings. How much more money will he earn each week?

6-126. Factor each expression below.

a. $16x-4$

b. $-10x+5x^2$

c. $30y-24x$

6-127. Each of the diagrams below represents a sequence for an acrobat on a tightrope. Each letter represents the unknown length of a trick. For each part below, write and solve an equation to figure out how far the acrobat travels during each trick (that is, the length represented by each letter). Show how you know your answer is correct.

a. Find x.

x | 7 | x

13

b. Find j.

j | j | 15 | j

27

c. Find n.

n | n | 6 | 6 | 6 | 6

44

6.2.7 Which method should I use?

Choosing a Solving Strategy

Today you will practice writing equations from word problems and solving them using any of the tools you know. You are developing an efficient set of tools to solve any word problem, such as the 5-D Process and algebra tiles. Having a variety of methods will allow you to choose the one that makes sense to you and ultimately makes you a stronger mathematician.

6-128. Nick tried to use a symbolic method to solve $3x-6=27$, but he may have made a mistake. His work is shown at right. If he did make a mistake, on which step did he first make a mistake, and what was his mistake? If he did not make a mistake, check his solution and write "all correct."

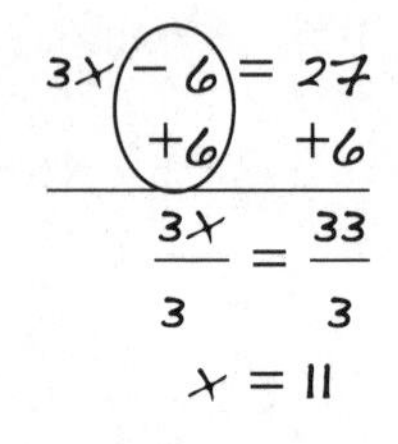

6-129. Nick represented the equation $3(2x+4)=-6$ on the Equation Mat at right.

a. Choose a strategy to solve for x. You may continue to use algebra tiles, or you may use symbols on paper.

b. Check your answer. If your answer does not make the equation true, try solving the equation using a different strategy.

= +1
= −1

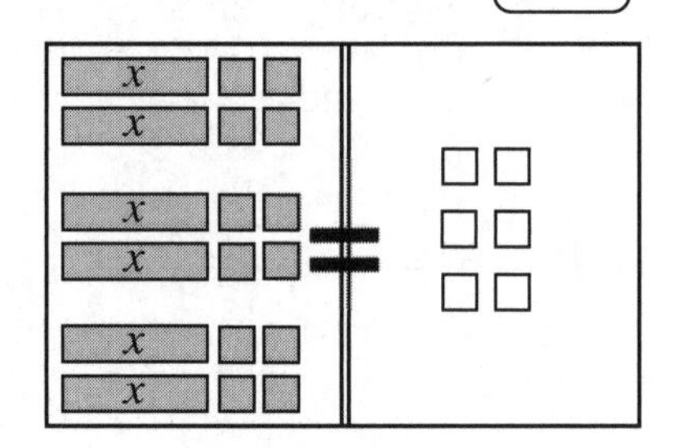

6-130. Read the problem below, and then answer the questions in parts (a) and (b).

Cisco and Misty need to construct a chicken coop for their famous egg-laying hens. The hens need at least 108 square feet of living space. The space available allows Cisco and Misty to make the length of the coop 3 feet longer than the width and to create exactly 108 square feet of area. What are the dimensions of the coop?

a. Laura tried to use an Equation Mat for this problem but got stuck and decided to use a different strategy. Why do you think she decided not to use the Equation Mat?

b. Now choose a different method to solve this problem, such as the 5-D Process or writing and solving an equation. Even if you solve an equation and do not use the table from the 5-D Process, you still need to define how you are using variables and remember to write your answer in a sentence. Check your answer.

6-131. Below is a problem started with a 5-D table.

Describe/Draw: 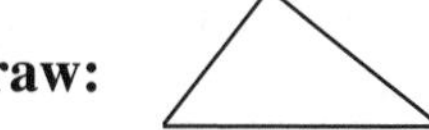

We want to find the side lengths so the perimeter is 35 m.

	Define			**Do**	**Decide**
	Side 1	Side 2	Side 3	Perimeter	Target: 35 m
Trial 1	5	$5+2=7$	$7+4=11$	$5+7+11=23$	23 *Too small*
	x	$x+2$	$(x+2)+4$	$x+(x+2)+(x+2+4)=35$	

a. Write the word problem that could have accompanied this 5-D table.

b. What is your preferred method to solve this problem: algebra tiles, an equation, or the 5-D Process?

c. Decide on a method to solve this problem, use your method to find your answer, and write a Declare statement for your answer.

6-132. Apiologists (scientists who study bees) have found that the number and types of bees in a hive is based on the amount of nectar and pollen available. Within a hive are three types of bees that help the queen: workers, drones, and nurses.

In a recent study of a hive, it was found that there was a total of 4109 bees, not including the queen. There were thirty-three more nurses than drones. The number of workers was twelve more than six times the number of drones. How many of each type of bee was in the hive?

Choose a method to solve this problem, such as the 5-D Process or writing and solving an equation. Even if you solve an equation and do not use the table from the 5-D Process, you still need to define how you are using variables and remember to write your answer in a sentence. Check your answer with estimation to make sure that it is reasonable.

6-133. Use any method to solve the following equations. Show your work and check your solutions.

a. $3x+4=-5$

b. $3(x+4)=-3$

c. $3(x+4)=x+2(x+6)$

d. $3x+4=3x-4$

Review & Preview

6-134. One way of thinking about solving equations is to work to get the variable terms on one side of the equation and the constants on the other side. Consider the equation $71=9x-37$.

a. As a first step, you could subtract 71 from both sides, or divide both sides by 9, or add 37 to both sides of the equation. Does one of these steps get all of the variable terms on one side of the equation and the constants on the other?

b. Solve $71=9x-37$ for x. Show your steps.

6-135. For each equation below, solve for x. Sometimes the easiest strategy is to use mental math.

a. $x-\frac{2}{3}=\frac{1}{3}$

b. $4x=6$

c. $x+4.6=12.96$

d. $\frac{x}{7}=\frac{3}{7}$

6-136. Due to differences in gravity, a 100-pound person on Earth would weigh about 38 pounds on Mars and 17 pounds on the moon.

a. What would a 150-pound person on Earth weigh on Mars? Explain your reasoning with words or a diagram.

b. What would a 50-pound person on Earth weigh on the moon? Explain your reasoning with words or a diagram.

c. **Additional Challenge:** If an astronaut on the moon weighed about 34 pounds, what would that astronaut weigh on Mars? Show how you know.

6-137. Evaluate each expression.

a. $1.2 - 0.8$

b. $-4 - (-2)$

c. $-\frac{6}{11} - (-\frac{1}{4})$

d. $\frac{2}{3} \cdot \frac{2}{5}$

e. $0.6 \cdot 8$

f. $-\frac{5}{4} \cdot \frac{8}{13}$

6-138. Rewrite each fraction below as an equivalent fraction, as a decimal, and as a percent.

a. $\frac{6}{18}$

b. $\frac{7}{20}$

c. $\frac{9}{10}$

d. $\frac{4}{25}$

6-139. This problem is a checkpoint for writing and evaluating algebraic expressions. It will be referred to as Checkpoint 6.

Change each phrase into an algebraic expression.

a. Six more than x.

b. Five less than y.

c. Twice a number x, increased by 3.

d. The product of 5 and y.

e. Evaluate each expression in parts (a) through (d) using $x = 5$ or $y = 8$.

Check your answers by referring to the Checkpoint 6 materials located at the back of your book.

Ideally, at this point you are comfortable working with these types of problems and can solve them correctly. If you feel that you need more confidence when solving these types of problems, then review the Checkpoint 6 materials and try the practice problems provided. From this point on, you will be expected to do problems like these correctly and with confidence.

Chapter 6 Closure What have I learned?

Reflection and Synthesis

The activities below offer you a chance to reflect about what you have learned during this chapter. As you work, look for concepts that you feel very comfortable with, ideas that you would like to learn more about, and topics with which you need more help.

① SUMMARIZING MY UNDERSTANDING

In this chapter, you have used algebra tiles and an Equation Mat as tools for solving equations. You have also represented your solution steps on an Equation Mat and with algebraic symbols. Today you will use what you have learned about equations in this chapter to show connections between all of these methods. To start, consider the following problem.

Jamee is working to solve an equation. She did the work shown below. With your team, answer the questions that follow:

Jamee's work: Original problem: $3(2x-4)=2(2x+5)$

Step 1: $6x-12=4x+10$

Step 2: $2x=-2$

- Explain what Jamee did at each step.
- What is her solution?
- Is her solution correct? Justify your answer. If it is not, find her error and the correct answer.

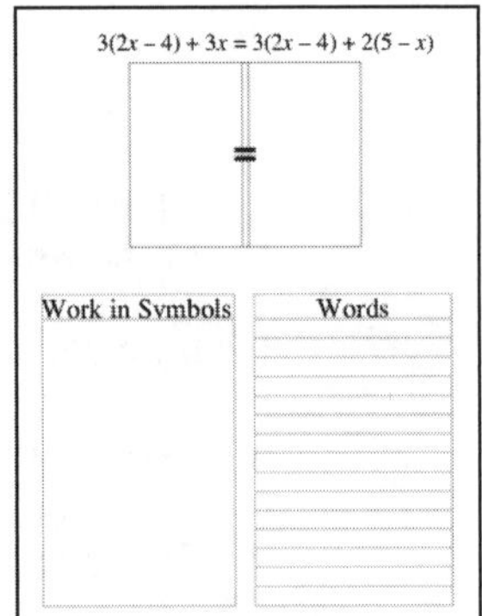

Obtain a Chapter 6 Closure Resource Page (shown at right) from your teacher. Follow the directions below to demonstrate your understanding of solving equations with an Equation Mat, algebraically (with numbers and symbols), and in words.

Part 1: Sketch the equation on the mat on the resource page. You may also want to build it with algebra tiles.

Part 2: Complete each step to solve the equation. Represent each step on the mat, with symbols, and in words. As you work, ask questions to clarify your thinking and understanding. Make sure you can give reasons for each step.

Part 3: Color-code the matching steps in each representation. For example, if your second step is to combine like terms, label this step with green in the symbols, on the mat, and in words. Use a new color to code each step.

② WHAT HAVE I LEARNED?

Doing the problems in this section will help you to evaluate which types of problems you feel comfortable with and which ones you need more help with.

Solve each problem as completely as you can. The table at the end of this closure section provides answers to these problems. It also tells you where you can find additional help and where to find practice problems like them.

CL 6-140. Consider the Equation Mat at right.

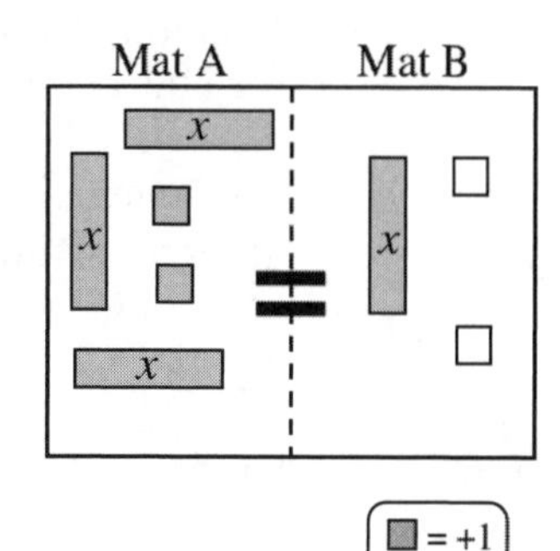

a. Write the original equation represented.

b. Simplify as needed. Record all steps of your work. What value of x will make the two sides equal?

c. Check your solution.

CL 6-141. Write the expressions for the Expression Mats at right.

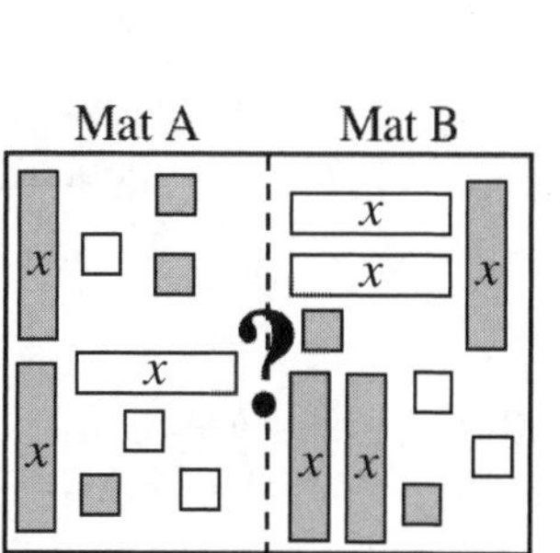

a. Simplify each mat to determine which side is greater.

b. If $x = 4$, would your answer to part (a) change? Explain.

CL 6-142. Serena found the spinner at right. Help her find the probability of spinning each of the following colors on the spinner.

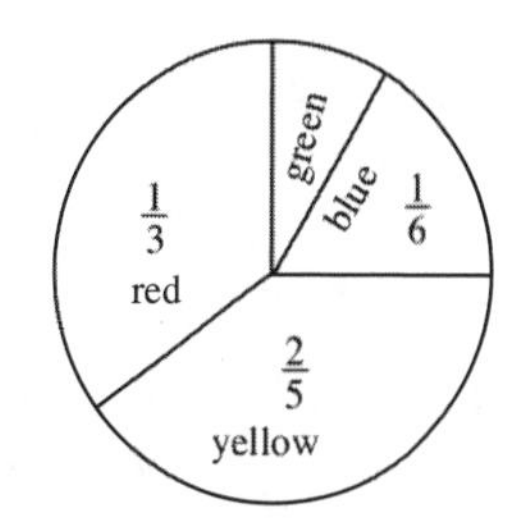

a. What is the P(yellow or blue)?

b. What is the P(not red)?

c. What is the P(green)?

CL 6-143. The shapes at right are similar.

a. What is the scale factor from shape A to shape B?

b. What are the lengths of the missing sides?

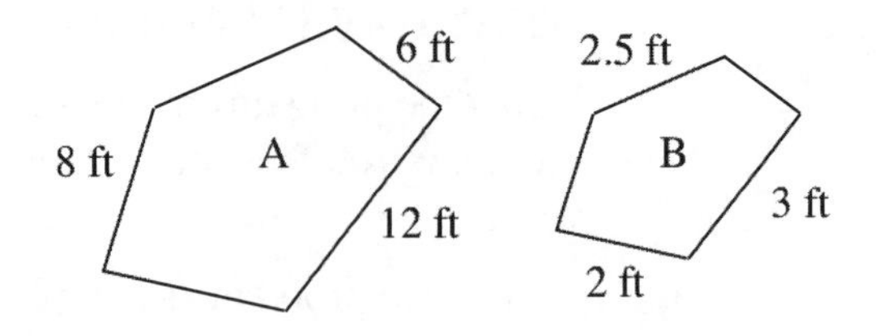

CL 6-144. Solve this problem by using the 5-D Process or writing and solving an equation. No matter which you method you use, be sure to define your variable and write an equation to represent the relationship.

A rectangle has a perimeter of 30 inches. Its length is one less than three times its width. What are the length and width of the rectangle?

CL 6-145. Kindra would like to have at least \$1500 in her savings account.

a. If she starts with \$61 in her savings account, write an inequality to show how much she wants to have.

b. How much does Kindra need to save? Show your solution as an inequality with symbols, in words, and on a number line.

CL 6-146. Alejandra has been practicing her free-throw shots as she gets ready for basketball season. At her last practice, she made 70% of her shots from the free-throw line. If she shot the ball 130 times:

a. How many times did she make a free-throw?

b. How many times did she miss? What percentage of her shots did she miss?

CL 6-147. Copy and complete each of the Diamond Problems below. The pattern used in the Diamond Problems is shown at right.

xy, x, y, $x+y$

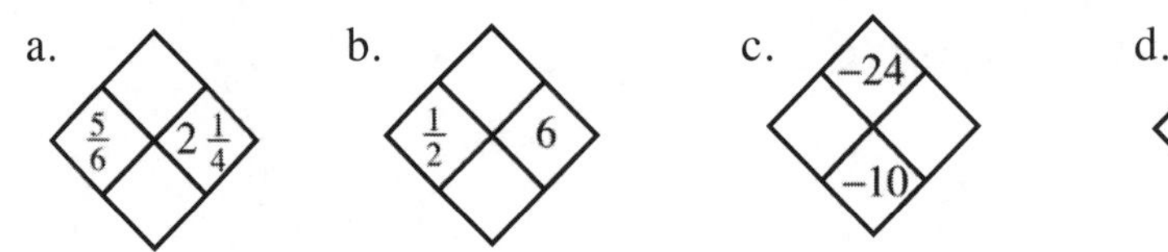

CL 6-148. Simplify each expression.

a. $\frac{3}{8}+(-\frac{4}{6})-\frac{1}{3}$

b. $-\frac{5}{7}+\frac{4}{9}-(-\frac{2}{3})$

c. $\frac{2}{5}\cdot\frac{3}{8}-\frac{3}{4}$

d. $-\frac{6}{11}+(-\frac{2}{3})-\frac{5}{6}$

e. $-\frac{2}{3}\cdot\left(2\frac{1}{4}\right)\cdot\frac{3}{4}$

f. $\frac{5}{7}+(-\frac{1}{3})-(-\frac{1}{2})$

CL 6-149. For each of the problems above, do the following:

- Draw a bar or number line that represents 0 to 10.

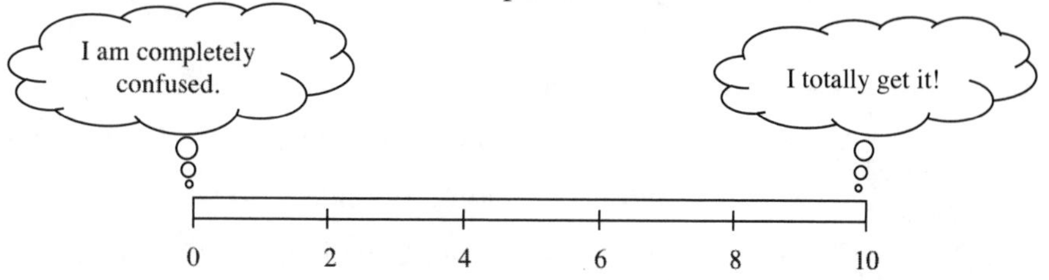

- Color or shade in a portion of the bar that represents your level of understanding and comfort with completing that problem on your own.

If any of your bars are less than a 5, choose *one* of those problems and do one of the following tasks:

- Write two questions that you would like to ask about that problem.
- Brainstorm two things that you DO know about that type of problem.

If all of your bars are a 5 or above, choose one of those problems and do one of these tasks:

- Write two questions you might ask or hints you might give to a student who was stuck on the problem.
- Make a new problem that is similar and more challenging than that problem and solve it.

③ WHAT TOOLS CAN I USE?

You have several tools and references available to help support your learning: your teacher, your study team, your math book, and your Toolkit, to name only a few. At the end of each chapter, you will have an opportunity to review your Toolkit for completeness. You will also revise or update it to reflect your current understanding of big ideas.

The main elements of your Toolkit should be your Learning Logs, Math Notes, and the vocabulary used in this chapter. Math words that are new appear in bold in the text. Refer to the lists provided below and follow your teacher's instructions to revise your Toolkit, which will help make it useful for you as you complete this chapter and as you work in future chapters.

Learning Log Entries

- Lesson 6.1.2 – Simplifying Expressions (Legal Moves)
- Lesson 6.1.4 – Finding Boundary Points
- Lesson 6.2.3 – Solving Equations and Checking Solutions
- Lesson 6.2.4 – Using the 5-D Process to Write and Solve Equations

Math Notes

- Lesson 6.1.1 – Inequality Symbols
- Lesson 6.1.3 – Algebra Vocabulary
- Lesson 6.1.4 – Graphing Inequalities
- Lesson 6.2.1 – Using an Equation Mat
- Lesson 6.2.2 – Equations and Inequalities
- Lesson 6.2.3 – Checking a Solution
- Lesson 6.2.4 – Defining a Variable
- Lesson 6.2.6 – Solutions to an Equation With One Variable

Mathematical Vocabulary

The following is a list of vocabulary found in this chapter. Some of the words have been seen in the previous chapter. The words in bold are words that are new to this chapter. Make sure that you are familiar with the terms below and know what they mean. For the words you do not know, refer to the glossary or index. You might also add these words to your Toolkit so that you can reference them in the future.

5-D Process	**boundary point**	**coefficient**
constant term	Distributive Property	equation
Equation Mat	evaluate	expression
Expression Comparison Mat	**factor**	**factoring**
inequality	**inequality symbols**	proportional relationship
ratio	**solution**	simplify
term	variable	

Answers and Support for Closure Problems
What Have I Learned?

Note: MN = Math Note, LL = Learning Log

Problem	Solution	Need Help?	More Practice
CL 6-140.	a. $3x+2=x-2$ b. $x=-2$ c. $3(-2)+2=-2-2$ $-6+2=-4$ $-4=-4$	Lessons 6.2.1, 6.2.2, and 6.2.3 MN: 6.2.1, 6.2.2, 6.2.3, and 6.2.6 LL: 6.1.2 and 6.2.3	Problems 6-54, 6-81, 6-98, 6-104, 6-110, 6-122, and 6-129
CL 6-141.	a. $x=x$, The mats are equal in value. b. No, the mats will be equal for any value of x.	Lessons 6.1.1 and 6.1.2 MN: 6.1.1 LL: 6.1.2	Problems 6-17 and 6-102

Problem	Solution	Need Help?	More Practice
CL 6-142.	a. P(yellow or blue) = $\frac{2}{5}+\frac{1}{6}=\frac{17}{30}$ b. P(not red) = $1-\frac{1}{3}=\frac{2}{3}$ c. P(green) = $1-\frac{1}{3}-\frac{2}{5}-\frac{1}{6}=\frac{1}{10}$	Lessons 1.2.2 and 5.2.3 MN: 1.2.3 and 5.2.5 LL: 5.2.3	Problems CL 5-151 and 6-107
CL 6-143.	a. $\frac{1}{4}$ b. On shape A, the missing sides are 10 and 8 feet; on shape B, the missing sides are 2 and 1.5 feet.	Lesson 4.1.1 MN: 4.1.2	Problems CL 4-125, 5-22, 5-142, and 6-99
CL 6-144.	The length is 11 in. and the width is 4 in. If x = width, one possible equation would be $x+(3x-1)+x+(3x-1)=30$.	Lessons 5.3.2, 5.3.3, and 6.2.4 MN: 5.3.3 and 6.2.4 LL: 5.3.4 and 6.2.4	Problems CL 5-150, 6-70, 6-83, 6-97, 6-106, and 6-111
CL 6-145.	a. $\$61+x\geq\$1500$ b. $x\geq\$1439$; She needs to save more than or equal to $1439. 0 500 1000 1500 2000	Lessons 6.1.3 and 6.1.4 MN: 6.1.1, 6.1.4, and 6.2.2 LL: 6.1.4	Problems 6-29, 6-42, 6-92, and 6-115
CL 6-146.	a. 91 b. 39 shots, 30%	Lessons 5.1.1 and 5.1.2 MN: 5.1.2	Problems CL 5-149, 6-22, 6-32, 6-82, and 6-125
CL 6-147.	a. $\frac{15}{8}$ and $3\frac{1}{12}$ b. 3 and $6\frac{1}{2}$ c. –12 and 2 d. 16 and –3	Problem 2-16	Problems CL 4-123 and 6-85
CL 6-148.	a. $-\frac{15}{24}=-\frac{5}{8}$ b. $\frac{25}{63}$ c. $-\frac{24}{40}=-\frac{3}{5}$ d. $-\frac{135}{66}=-2\frac{1}{22}$ e. $-\frac{9}{8}=-1\frac{1}{8}$ f. $\frac{37}{42}$	Lessons 1.2.6, 2.2.5, and 2.2.6 MN: 2.2.5 and 2.3.1 LL: 1.2.8	Problems CL 5-155, 6-8, and 6-88

Proportions and Percents
7

CHAPTER 7 Proportions and Percents

When traveling in a car, have you ever asked, "*When are we going to get there?*" Did you know that you could use mathematics to answer that question? In Section 7.1, you will use diagrams, like the ones you used for percents, to find the relationship between rate, time, and distance.

Then you will revisit scale factors and connect them to percents. You will learn how to simplify difficult problems by rewriting equations to remove fractional and decimal coefficients. Finally, you will investigate how to find the percent increase, percent decrease, and simple interest.

Guiding Questions

Think about these questions throughout this chapter:

How is it changing?

What is the relationship?

What is the connection?

How can I represent it?

What strategy should I use?

You have studied many different proportional relationships, including scale drawings, unit pricing, penny towers, and gas mileage. You will explore more about proportional relationships in Section 7.2 as you learn additional strategies for solving them.

In this chapter, you will learn how to:

- Solve problems involving distance, rate, and time.
- Solve equations that have fractional or decimal coefficients.
- Find the whole amount if you only know a percentage of it, and vice versa.
- Calculate simple interest.
- Set up and solve proportional equations.

Chapter Outline

Section 7.1 You will identify the relationship between distance, rate, and time and will use it to solve word problems. You will connect your work with percents and scale factors to solve new problems involving part-whole relationships. You will also develop strategies to solve equations with fractional and decimal coefficients. Finally, you will explore percent change and simple interest.

Section 7.2 This section reviews and extends the idea of proportional relationships that you studied in Chapter 4. You will learn new strategies for solving proportional situations.

7.1.1 What is the relationship?

Distance, Rate, and Time

In this course, you have looked at several relationships between two sets of information and investigated how one piece of information can or cannot be found from the other. To continue your investigation of proportional relationships from Chapter 4, you will look at the mathematical relationship between distance, rate, and time. Later, in the final section of this chapter, you will identify proportional relationships and use your understanding of proportionality to solve problems.

7-1. George stood on the train platform and waved goodbye to his sister as she left for summer camp. Later, as he was getting in his car to drive home, he saw a light flashing inside the train station and heard an announcement that his sister's train had malfunctioned and was stuck on the tracks. George had a map of the train's route and decided to drive to where the train was stuck and pick up his sister.

How can he figure out where the train is? What information would help him to figure it out? Be prepared to share your ideas with the class.

7-2. TOYS

If you needed to predict how far a car, train, or plane had gone, it would be helpful to know something about how fast it was going and how long it had been moving. You will work with your team to investigate the relationship between distance, speed (or rate), and time in the following experiment.

Problem continues on next page. →

7-2. *Problem continued from previous page.*

Obtain a meter stick, a toy (such as a wind-up car), a long piece of paper, and a stopwatch from your teacher. Put the paper on the floor, draw a starting line near one end of it, and place the toy on the edge of the paper facing the starting line as shown at right. Place the toy a short distance behind the starting line so that it can reach a constant speed by the time it gets to the starting line.

Read the directions below for taking data *before* starting your toy.

Directions for Taking Data

1. Appoint a Timer, a Toy-starter, a Marker, and a Measurer.
2. The Toy-starter should start the toy.
3. As the front end of the toy reaches the starting line, the Timer should start the stopwatch.
4. When five seconds have passed, the Timer calls out "Now." At this moment, the Marker makes a mark (without touching the toy) at the place on the paper where the front end of the toy is. This process repeats at ten seconds, fifteen seconds, etc. for at least twenty seconds or until the toy has reached the end of the paper.
5. The Measurer measures each distance in centimeters *from the starting line*.

a. Do a "dry run" of the experiment one time *without collecting data*, and talk with your team about how, exactly, you will collect the data.

b. Work with your team to take data comparing the time that has passed (in seconds) to the distance (in cm) that the toy is from the starting line, following the directions above.

c. Obtain a Lesson 7.1.1 Resource Page from your teacher. Work with your team to organize your data into a table and graph it. Be prepared to share your table and graph with the class. Then think about the following questions.

   i. Where does your graph begin? Should your graph "stop"? Would it make sense to continue your graph to show how your toy would travel if you were to continue measuring for more time?

   ii. How far would you expect your toy to have traveled after 7 seconds have passed? What about after 2.3 seconds? Does it make sense to connect the points on the graph? Why or why not?

7-3. What is the unit rate of your toy? That is, approximately how far does your toy travel each second? How can you see this in your table? How can you see it on your graph? Be prepared to explain your ideas to the class.

7-4. How can you use your answer to problem 7-3 to write an equation relating the time the car has been moving to the distance it has traveled? Work with your team to write an equation relating distance and time.

7-5. If your toy were twice as fast, how far would it travel each second? How would you see this in the table? How would you see it on the graph? Again, be prepared to explain your ideas to the class.

7-6. If your toy travels at a constant speed, then the distance your toy has traveled and the time it has taken are related to each other proportionally. In a **proportional relationship**, two quantities are related by a **constant of proportionality** (or a **constant multiplier**). For your toy, the constant of proportion is called the **rate**. In this case, it is also the speed.

Where else in this course have you seen two quantities related by a constant multiplier? Work with your team to come up with examples of proportional relationships and be ready to contribute your ideas to the class discussion.

7-7. Answer each of the following questions and be ready to explain how you could use your table or graph to get each answer.

a. What distance would your toy travel in 9 seconds?

b. How far would your toy travel in 25 seconds?

c. How many seconds would it take your toy to travel 300 cm?

7-8. Bella wants to use her toy car to deliver a secret note to Edward, who is sitting all the way across the cafeteria, approximately 20 meters from her. She plans to get the car started and then leave the cafeteria so Edward will not see her. If her car travels at 1.1 meters per second, about how much time will she have to get out of the cafeteria before Edward gets the note?

7-9. **Additional Challenge:** Gloria and David's toys crossed the starting line at exactly the same time and are traveling in the same direction. Gloria's toy travels at 40 centimeters per second, and David's toy travels 35 centimeters per second. After 20 seconds, how far apart will their toys be? Be prepared to explain your thinking to the class.

MATH NOTES

METHODS AND MEANINGS

Histograms and Stem-and-Leaf Plots

A **histogram** is similar to a bar graph in that each bar represents data in an interval of numbers. The intervals for the data are shown on the horizontal axis, and the frequency (number of pieces of data in each interval) is represented by the height of a bar above the interval.

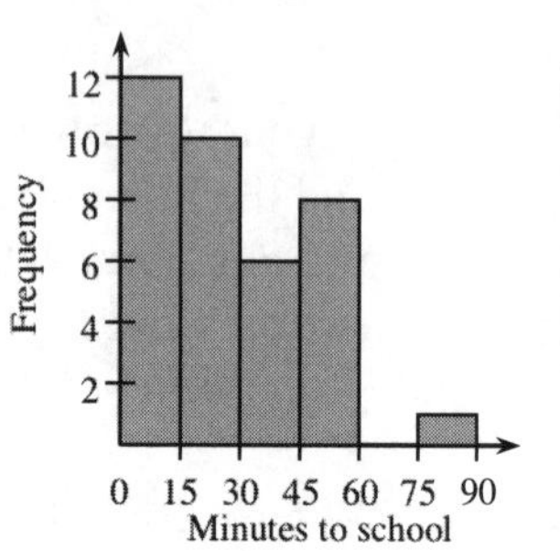

The labels on the horizontal axis represent the lower end of each interval. For example, the histogram at right shows that 10 students take at least 15 minutes but less than 30 minutes to get to school.

Histograms are used to display numeric data with an order, while bar graphs display data in categories where order generally does not matter.

A **stem-and-leaf plot** shows the same data as a histogram, but it shows the individual values from a set of data and how the values are distributed. The "stem" part of the graph represents all of the digits in a number except the last one. The "leaf" part of the graph represents the last digit of each of the numbers.

Example: Students in a math class received the following scores on their tests: 49, 52, 54, 58, 61, 61, 67, 68, 72, 73, 73, 73, 78, 82, and 83. Display the test score data on a stem-and-leaf plot.

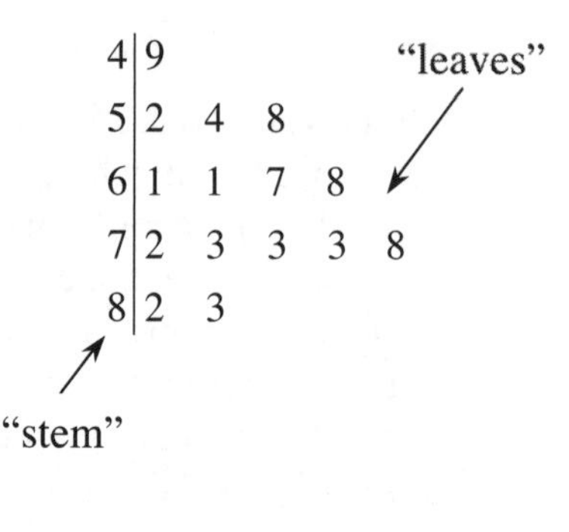

7-10. It took Ivan $7\frac{1}{2}$ hours to drive 412.5 miles at a constant speed. How fast was he driving? Show how you know.

7-11. Make a graph to show the relationship between distance and time for a bicycle that travels 10 miles every hour.

7-12. Twenty-five percent of the students at Marcus Garvey Middle School bring their lunches from home. 225 students do not bring their lunch. How many students attend the school? Draw and label a diagram to show the number and percent of each group of students.

7-13. Copy and rewrite the following expressions by combining like terms, making zeros, and using the Distributive Property. Visualizing the expressions by using algebra tiles may be helpful.

a. $(-3)+4x+2+2x+2x$

b. $-8x+4+(-3)$

c. $7x^2+3x+4+7x^2+3x+4$

d. $5(x-4)$

7-14. Sao can text 1500 words per hour. He needs to text a message with 85 words. He only has 5 minutes between classes to complete the text. Can he do it in 5 minutes?

7-15. Find the new dimensions of the figure given at right when it is enlarged by a scale factor of 2.5. Then find the perimeter and area of the original and enlarged figures.

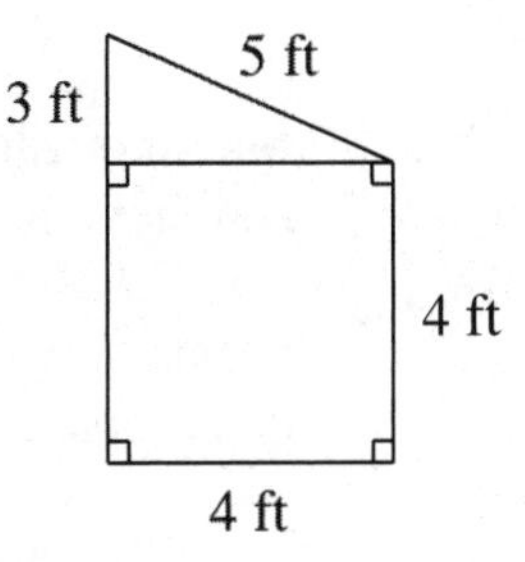

7.1.2 How can I make it smaller or bigger?

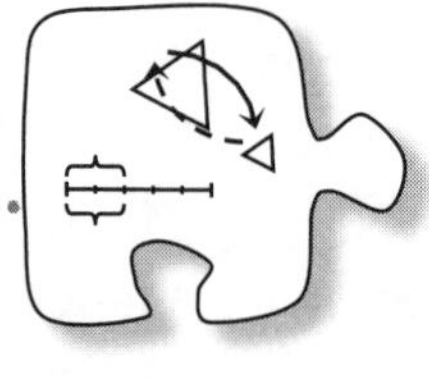

Scaling Quantities

In Chapter 5, you learned how to find the percent of a number by making a diagram to relate the part to the whole and find the desired portion. This calculation is fairly straightforward if the percent is a multiple of 10, like 40%, or can be thought of as a fraction, like $\frac{1}{4} = 25\%$. However, it can be more challenging if the percent is something like 6.3% or 84.5%.

Today you will connect what you have learned previously about the relationship between distance, rate, and time to the idea of scale factors. You will learn how to use a scale factor to find the corresponding lengths of similar figures. This idea will add a powerful new tool to your collection of problem-solving strategies that will help you to calculate percents.

7-16. Dana is training for a bicycle race. He can ride his bike 25 miles per hour.

One day, when he had been riding for $\frac{3}{5}$ of an hour, he had to stop and fix a flat tire. How many miles had he ridden when he stopped? The diagram below may be useful.

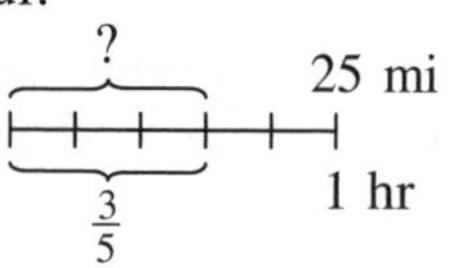

7-17. Matt thought about problem 7-16 and drew the diagram at right. Look at Matt's drawing and decide how he is thinking about this problem.

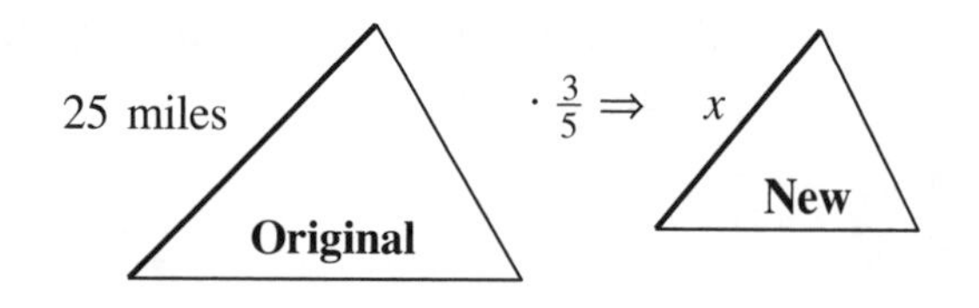

a. Write an equation that uses the scale factor to find x.

b. What connection is Matt making between finding a distance using the rate and time (as you did in problem 7-16) and using a scale factor with similar figures? How are the situations alike and how are they different?

7-18. In the two previous problems, $\frac{3}{5}$ is used in two ways: first, as *time* in the rate problem $\frac{25 \text{ miles}}{1 \text{ hr}} \cdot \frac{3}{5} \text{ hrs}$, and second, as the *scale factor* in the similar triangle problem used to find three fifths of 25 miles. Both of these situations resulted in an equivalent calculation: $25 \cdot \frac{3}{5} = 15$. How else could this be written?

a. Using the portions web shown at right, work with your team to find two other ways to write the equation $25 \cdot \frac{3}{5} = 15$. For example, one way might be $25 \cdot \frac{6}{10} = 15$.

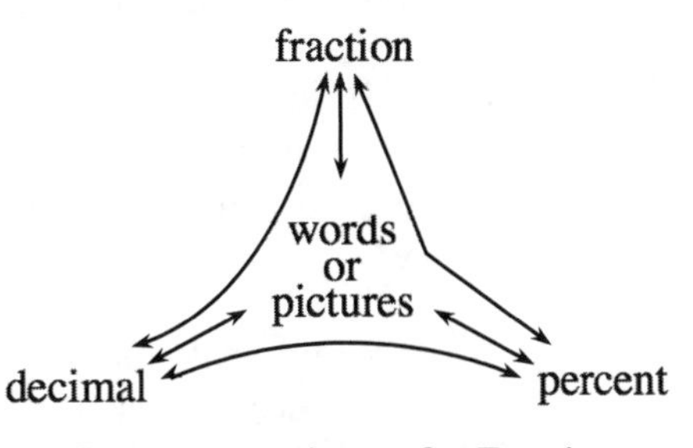

Representations of a Portion

b. If you did not already find it, what percent would be equivalent to $\frac{3}{5}$? Use this percent to write a statement in words and symbols that is equivalent to $25 \cdot \frac{3}{5} = 15$.

c. Use the idea of scaling to find the following values. Write an expression using either a fraction or a percent, and then find the result.

i. 90% of 25 miles *ii.* 8% of $75 *iii.* 25% of 144

7-19. Josea went out to dinner at an Indian restaurant. The total bill was $38. She wanted to leave a 15% tip.

a. If you use the idea of scaling to find the tip amount, what would she need to multiply by? As you talk about this with your team, consider:

- How could you represent this multiplier as a fraction?
- How could you represent it as a decimal?
- Does it make a difference which representation, fraction or decimal, you use to solve this problem?
- Which do you think will be easier?

b. How much should Josea leave for the tip? Show your calculations.

c. If Josea changes her mind and wants to leave a 20% tip instead, how much will this be?

7-20. While shopping for a computer game, Isaiah found one that was on sale for 35% off. He was wondering if he could use $\frac{35}{100}$ as a multiplier to scale down the price to find out how much he would have to pay for the game.

a. If Isaiah uses $\frac{35}{100}$ as a scale factor (multiplier), will he find the price that he will pay for the game? Why or why not?

b. There is scale factor (multiplier) other than 35% that can be used to find the sale price. What is it? Draw a diagram to show how this scale factor is related to 35%. Label the parts of your diagram "discount" and "sale price" along with the relevant percents.

c. How much will Isaiah have to pay for the game if the original price is $40? Show your strategy.

MATH NOTES

METHODS AND MEANINGS

Quartiles and Interquartile Range (IQR)

Quartiles are points that divide a data set into four equal parts (and thus, the use of the prefix "quar" as in "quarter"). One of these points is the median, which you learned about in Chapter 1, since it marks the middle of the data set. In addition, there are two other quartiles in the middle of the lower and upper halves: the **first quartile** and the **third quartile**.

Suppose you have this data set: 22, 43, 14, 7, 2, 32, 9, 36, and 12.

To find **quartiles**, the data set must be placed in order from smallest to largest. Then divide the data set into two halves by finding the median of the entire data set. Next find the median of the lower and upper halves of the data set. (Note that if there are an odd number of data values, the median is not included in either half of the data set.) See the example below.

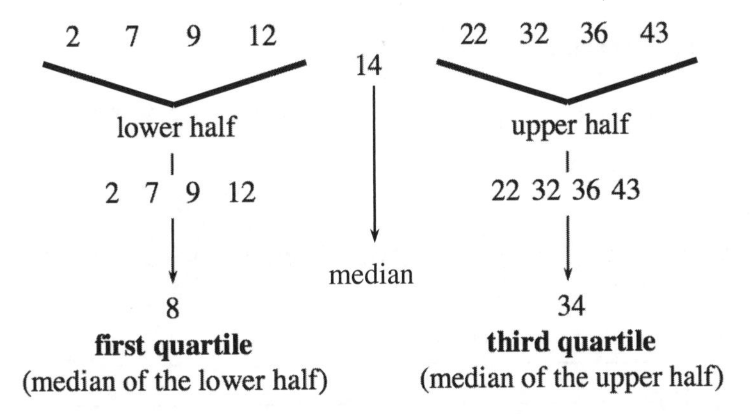

The **interquartile range** (**IQR**) is one way (along with range) to measure the spread of the data. Statisticians often prefer using the IQR to measure spread, because it is not affected much by outliers or non-symmetrical distributions. The IQR is the range of the middle 50% of the data. It is calculated by subtracting the first quartile from the third quartile. In the above example, the IQR is 26 (34 – 8 = 26).

7-21. Ameena's boat travels 35 miles per hour. The best fishing spot in the lake is 27 miles away from her starting point.

a. If she drives her boat for $\frac{2}{3}$ of an hour, will she make it to the best fishing spot on the lake?

b. How long will Ameena need to drive to get to the best fishing spot on the lake? Express your answer in both a portion of an hour and in minutes.

7-22. Use the triangles below right to answer the questions that follow.

a. What is the scale factor from A to B?

b. What is the scale factor from B to A?

c. What is the relationship of the scale factors?

7-23. Simplify each expression.

a. $\frac{1}{2}x+\frac{7}{12}+\frac{3}{5}x-\frac{2}{3}$

b. $5.3-2.8x-7.1+3.9x$

7-24. Copy the diagram below on your paper. Use the given information to fill in all of the missing labels.

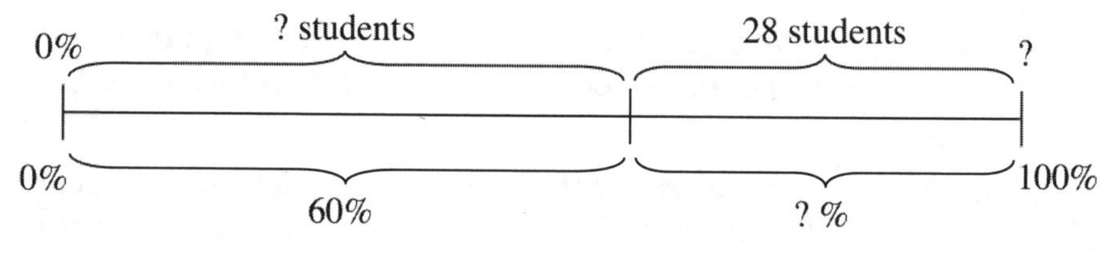

7-25. Alan is making a bouquet to take home to his grandmother. He needs to choose one kind of greenery and one kind of flower for his bouquet. He has a choice of ferns or leaves for his greenery. His flower choices are daisies, carnations, and sunflowers.

a. Draw a tree diagram to show the different bouquets he could make. How many are there?

b. What is the probability that he will use ferns?

c. What is the probability that he will not use sunflowers?

d. What is the probability that he will use leaves and carnations?

7-26. Read the Math Notes box in this lesson and use the information to complete the following problems.

The daily high temperatures in degrees Fahrenheit for the last two weeks in Grand Forks, North Dakota were 7, 1, –3, 0, 4, –1, 2, 5, 7, 7, 3, –2, –4, and –5.

a. Calculate the median temperature.

b. Find the first and third quartiles (Q1 and Q3).

c. What is the interquartile range (IQR)?

7.1.3 Which multiplier should I use?

Solving Problems Involving Percents

As you have seen many times in this course, there is usually more than one way to solve a problem. When a problem uses portions (fractions, decimals, or percents), there are different ways to write the numbers and different solving strategies to choose from. Today you will look at the different multipliers that can scale a quantity and see what each of them will help you find. As you work with your team today, consider the questions below.

What multiplier (scale factor) should I use?

How can I write an equation?

7-27. Hugo and his family were shopping and purchased a new bed. The bed was a great deal at 60% off of the original cost. The bed originally cost $245.

a. Draw a diagram for this situation.

b. If Hugo scales (multiplies) the original price of the bed by 60%, what will his result represent?

c. What should Hugo scale (multiply) the original price by to find the new price of the bed?

d. Work with your team to find the sale price of the bed in two different ways, that is, using two different multipliers (scale factors). How do your answers from your two methods compare?

7-28. Hugo's older sister, Sandra, had the same summer job for the past two years. Last year, she worked the entire summer and was paid a salary of $3,000. This summer, she is going to get a 6% raise in pay. To figure out how much she will make, Sandra drew the following diagram.

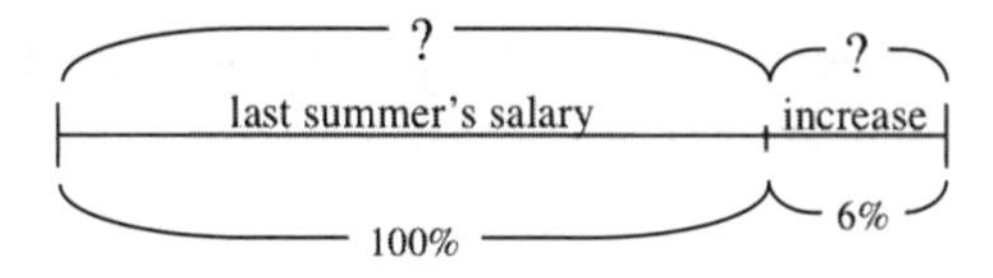

a. Copy the diagram on your paper and fill in the missing information.

b. Since Sandra's salary is increasing, does it make sense that her scale factor (multiplier) should be less than 1, equal to 1, or more than 1? Why?

c. The diagram shows Sandra's original salary and the amount of the increase. What is the scale factor (multiplier) between her original salary and her new salary? That is, what number could Sandra multiply the original salary by to get the new salary?

d. Show two ways that use different scale factors (multipliers) that Sandra can use to compute her new salary.

7-29. Miranna teaches gymnastics lessons at summer camp. She is paid $12.50 per hour.

a. If Miranna were offered a raise of 100% per hour, what would her new hourly rate be? What percent of her original pay would she be paid?

b. Miranna is offered a raise of 75% of her hourly rate to teach a private lesson. How much per hour would she be paid for the private lesson? What percent of her original pay would she get?

c. What is the relationship between the percent raise that Miranna gets and her new pay as a percent of her original pay? How is this related to the scale factor (multiplier) between her original pay and her new pay?

7-30. Liam was working on a problem and drew a diagram like the one below. He then wrote the equation $(\$72)(0.14) = x$. Does his equation agree with his diagram?

- If you agree, then solve his equation for x.
- If you disagree, write and solve a new equation that will find x in his diagram.

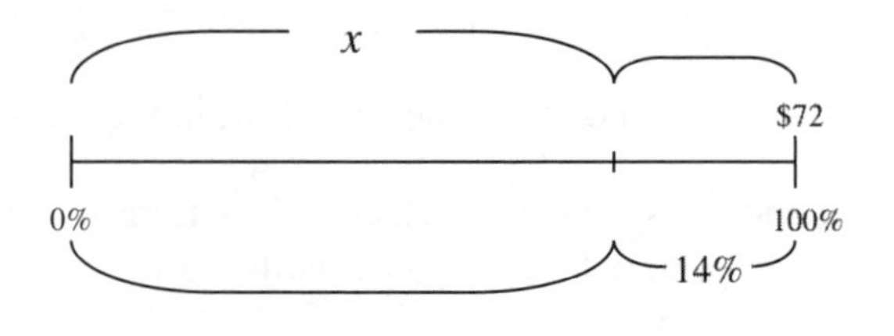

7-31. **Additional Challenge:** Ramon went to the corner store and bought more notebook paper to do his homework. The cost for the paper was $7.50, but he also had to pay the 8.1% sales tax. How much will the notebook paper cost Ramon? If Ramon gives the clerk $10, how much change should he receive?

7-32. LEARNING LOG

In your Learning Log, describe how you scale a quantity. For example, how do you know what multiplier (scale factor) to use? How can you tell if your multiplier should be more than one? Title your entry "Scaling Quantities" and include today's date.

MATH NOTES

METHODS AND MEANINGS

Describing Data Distributions

Distributions of data are typically described by considering the **center**, **shape**, **spread**, and **outliers**.

Center: The median best represents the center (or a "typical" data value) if the distribution is not symmetrical or if there are outliers. Either the mean or the median is appropriate for describing the center of symmetrical distributions with no outliers.

Shape: The shape is the overall appearance of the data when it is displayed in a histogram or stem-and-leaf plot. Is the distribution fairly symmetrical? Uniform? Single peaked? Skewed? Does it have large gaps or clusters?

Spread: Spread is a measure of the variability of the data, that is, how much scatter there is in the data. For non-symmetrical data or data with outliers, use the interquartile range (IQR) to describe the spread, since it is based on median. For symmetrical data with no outliers, either the mean absolute deviation, which is based on the mean, or the IQR are appropriate measures of spread. The range is not usually the best measure of the scatter in data, because it considers only the maximum and the minimum values and not what is occurring in between.

Outliers: An outlier is any data point that is far removed from the bulk of the rest of the data.

7-33. A homeowner must reduce the use of his home's electricity. The home currently consumes 25.7 kwh (kilowatt hours) of electricity per day, and the homeowner must reduce the use by 20%. Find the amount of electricity that will be used after the reduction in two different ways, using two different scale factors.

7-34. Copy and simplify the following expressions by combining like terms, making zeros, and using the Distributive Property. Using algebra tiles may be helpful.

a. $(-1)+4x+2+2x+x$

b. $-8x+4+(-3)+10x$

c. $(-4)+1x^2+3x+4$

d. $2(3x-2)$

7-35. Study the following division problems and the diagrams that represent them. Answer the question below each diagram.

a. $8 \div \frac{1}{3}$

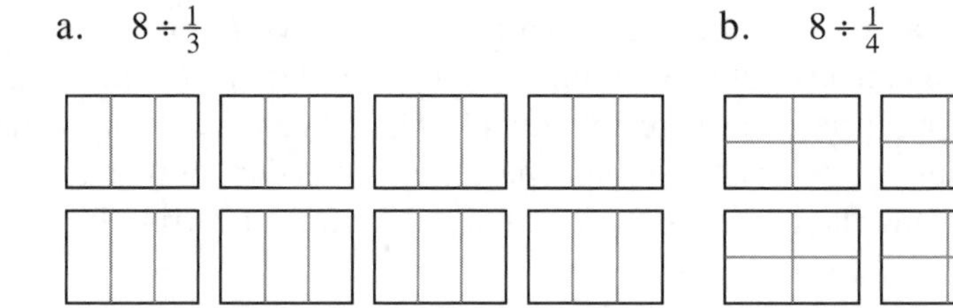

How many thirds?

b. $8 \div \frac{1}{4}$

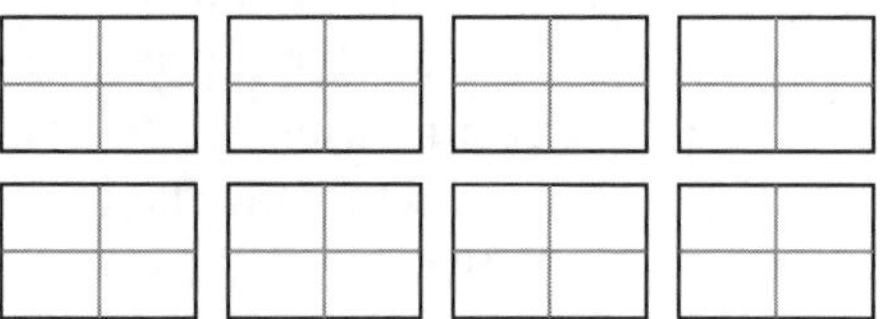

How many fourths?

7-36. The table at right shows speed limits in some foreign countries in kilometers per hour. One kilometer is equal to 0.6 miles. What are these speed limits in miles per hour?

Speed Limits in km per hour		
Country	Country Roads	Motorways
Australia	100	110
South Africa	100	120
Great Britain	96	112
Turkey	90	90

7-37. Simplify each expression.

a. $18 \div \frac{3}{4}$

b. $\frac{2}{3}(9-6)+40$

c. $15 \div 5+\frac{1}{2} \cdot\left(-\frac{4}{7}\right)$

d. $-\frac{7}{10}+(-\frac{5}{12})-(\frac{1}{4})$

e. $4.25-7.06$

f. $\frac{7}{8}-(-\frac{1}{10})+(-\frac{3}{5})$

7-38. Read the Math Notes boxes in this lesson and in the previous lesson. Use the information to complete the following problems.

The coach of the girls' basketball team weighed each player. Their weights in pounds were 120, 122, 126, 130, 133, 147, 115, 106, 120, 112, and 142.

a. Make a stem-and-leaf plot of the team players' weights.

b. Make a histogram of the teams' weights.

c. Describe the shape and spread of the data. That is, is it symmetric or non-symmetric? Does it have more than one peak or only one? Is it tightly packed together or widely spread out?

d. Does this data have any outliers? Which measure of center, mean or median, would be appropriate to use to describe the typical weight?

e. What is the typical weight of a player on the team?

f. What is the range of the data?

7.1.4 How can I solve it?

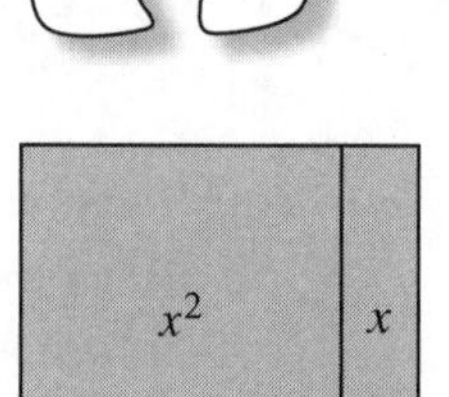

Equations with Fraction and Decimal Coefficients

Throughout this course, you have worked with quantities represented in multiple ways. You have seen that $\frac{12}{16}$, 0.75, 75%, and $\frac{3}{4}$ each represent the same portion even though they *look* different. In your work with algebra tiles, you visualized and described perimeters in different ways. For example, the perimeter of the algebra tiles at right can be described by the expressions $3x+2+x$, $x+1+x+1+x+x$, or $4x+2x+2-2x$ units.

In this lesson, you will develop strategies to solve a new type of equation: equations with coefficients that are fractions. Recall that coefficients are the numerical part of a term, such as the 5 in $5x$ and the $\frac{2}{3}$ in $\frac{2}{3}x^2$. You will choose between different strategies based on how the problem is represented, what diagram you draw, or whether you represent the situation with an equation. As you explore solving strategies today, keep these questions in mind:

How can I represent it?

How are the representations related?

What is the best approach for this equation?

7-39. ARE WE THERE YET?

The Sutton family took a trip to see the mountains in Rocky Mountain National Park. Linda and her brother, Lee, kept asking, *"Are we there yet?"* At one point, their mother answered, *"No, but what I can tell you is that we have driven 100 miles and we are about $\frac{2}{5}$ of the way there."*

Linda turned to Lee and asked, *"How long is this trip, anyway?"* They each started thinking about whether they could determine the length of the trip from the information they were given.

Linda's Method

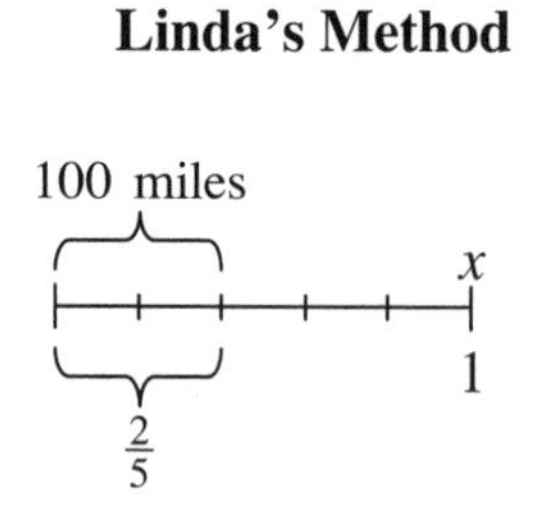

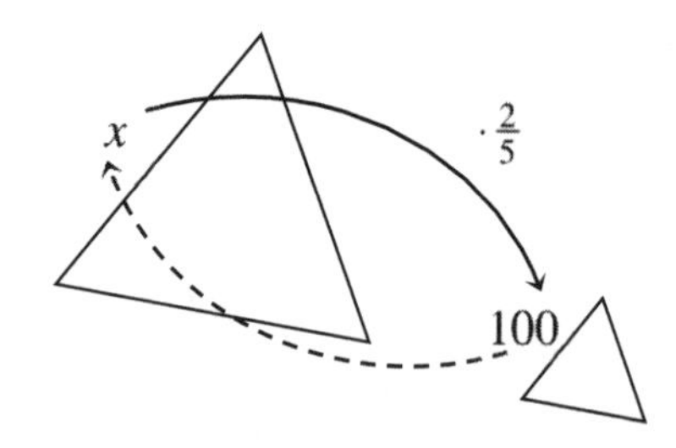

Lee's Method

Problem continues on next page. →

7-39. *Problem continued from previous page.*

a. Explain how both Linda's work and Lee's work illustrate the situation described by their mother. What does x represent in each diagram?

b. What equation could represent this situation? Use the scale factor (multiplier) to represent this situation in an equation. Let x represent the total distance in miles.

c. Is the answer going to be more or less than 100 miles? Explain your thinking.

7-40. Linda remarked to Lee, "*When I look at my diagram, I see that the total distance is two-and-a-half times the distance we've driven.*"

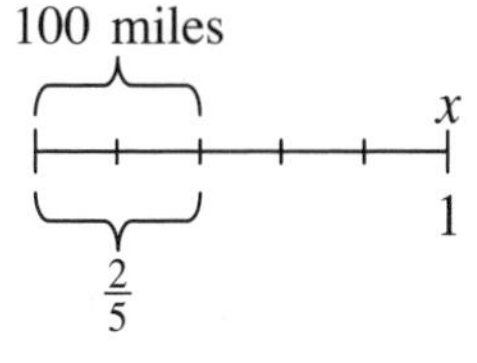

a. Do you agree? How can you add labels to Linda's diagram to show $2\frac{1}{2}$ times the distance?

b. How long is the trip? Show how you know.

7-41. Lee thinks what he knows about similar triangles can help.

a. Review problem 7-22, which involved similar triangles. How are the scale factors related?

b. How can the relationship of the scale factors between similar shapes help Lee? Find the missing scale factor in his diagram at right. That is, what could he multiply 100 by to solve for x?

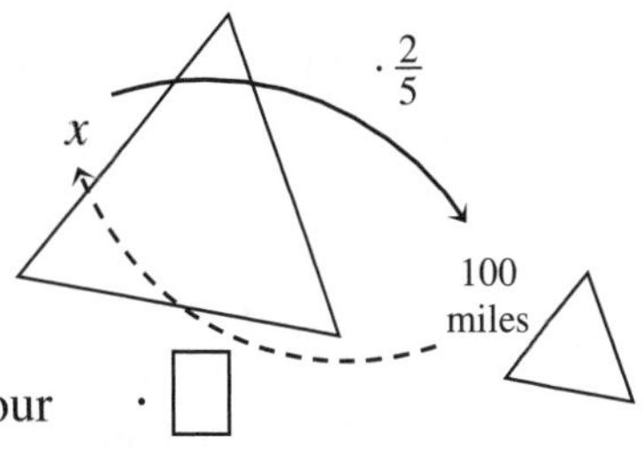

c. Use the new scale factor to find x. Does your answer agree with the one you found in part (b) of problem 7-40?

7-42. As Linda and Lee were talking about the problem (from problem 7-39), their mother overheard and offered them another strategy: *"Here is how I would start solving the problem."* She showed them the work at right.

$$\frac{2}{5}x = 100$$

$$\frac{\frac{2}{5}x}{\frac{2}{5}} = \frac{100}{\frac{2}{5}}$$

a. *"I see a Giant One!"* exclaimed Lee. Where is the Giant One? Help rewrite the left side of the equation.

b. One way of making sense of $\frac{100}{\frac{2}{5}}$ is as $100 \div \frac{2}{5} = ?$.

This could be read, *"How many two fifths are in one hundred wholes?"* With your team, find one way to explain how you could figure out how many two fifths are in 100.

7-43. Lee began to wonder how his diagram could help him solve his mother's equation (from problem 7-42). He showed his work below.

$$\frac{2}{5}x = 100$$

$$\frac{5}{2}\left(\frac{2}{5}x\right) = (100)\frac{5}{2}$$

a. How does Lee's work relate to the similar-triangles diagram? What is $\frac{5}{2}\left(\frac{2}{5}x\right)$ equal to?

b. Finish Lee's work to solve for x. Then check your solution.

7-44. Linda and Lee wondered how these new equation-solving strategies would work with different equations. They made up more equations to try to solve. Copy the equations below on your paper and solve each equation using one of the strategies from this lesson. How did you decide which strategy to use?

a. $\frac{9}{2}x = 27$

b. $12 = \frac{2}{7}x$

c. $-\frac{3}{4}x = 21$

METHODS AND MEANINGS

MATH NOTES

Scaling

When a quantity is increased or decreased by a specific proportion of the original amount, it is changed by a specific scale factor (also called a multiplier). Quantities are **scaled up** when they are increased by multiplying by a number greater than one or **scaled down** when they are decreased by multiplying by a number between (but not including) zero and one.

For example, if a music system is on sale for 25% off its original price of $500, the discount can be found by multiplying by 25%:

$$\text{discount} = 0.25(\text{original price}) = 0.25(\$500) = \$125$$

The full price (100%) minus the discount (25%) would result in the sale price, which in this case is 75% of the original. The sale price can also be found by scaling:

$$\text{sale price} = 0.75(\text{original price}) = 0.75(\$500) = \$375$$

Scaling can be used to enlarge and reduce side lengths of similar shapes, or to increase or decrease times, distances, and other related quantities.

7-45. Mr. Anderson's doctor has advised him to go on a diet. He must reduce his caloric intake by 15%. He currently eats 2800 calories per day. Calculate his new daily caloric intake rate in two different ways, using two different multipliers.

7-46. Last month, a dwarf lemon tree grew half as much as a semi-dwarf lemon tree. A full-size lemon tree grew three times as much as the semi-dwarf lemon. Together, the three trees grew 27 inches. Write and solve an equation to determine how much each tree grew. Make sure you define your variable.

7-47. Enrique is saving money to buy a graphing calculator. So far he has saved \$30. His math teacher told him he has saved 40% of what he will need. How much does the calculator cost?

7-48. A principal made the histogram at right to analyze how many years teachers had been teaching at her school.

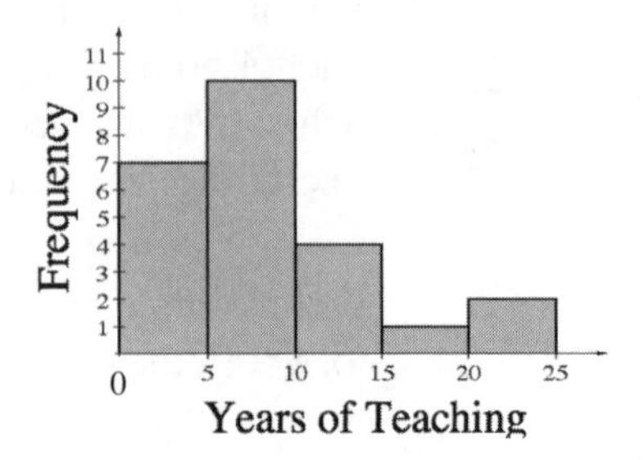

a. How many teachers work at her school?

b. If the principal randomly chose one teacher to represent the school at a conference, what is the probability that the teacher would have been teaching at the school for more than 10 years? Write the probability in two different ways.

c. What is the probability that a teacher on the staff has been there for fewer than 5 years?

7-49. Lue is rolling a random number cube. The cube has six sides, and each one is labeled with a different number 1 through 6.

a. What is the probability that he will roll a 5 or a 3 on one roll?

b. What is the probability that he will roll a 5 and then a 3 in two rolls?

c. What is the probability that he will roll a sum of 12 in two rolls?

7-50. This problem is a checkpoint for simplifying expressions. It will be referred to as Checkpoint 7A.

a. $4x^2+3x-7+(-2x^2)-2x+(-3)$ b. $-3x^2-2x+5+4x^2-7x+6$

Check your answers by referring to the Checkpoint 7A materials located at the back of your book.

Ideally, at this point you are comfortable working with these types of problems and can solve them correctly. If you feel that you need more confidence when solving these types of problems, then review the Checkpoint 7A materials and try the practice problems provided. From this point on, you will be expected to do problems like these correctly and with confidence.

7.1.5 How can I eliminate the fractions?

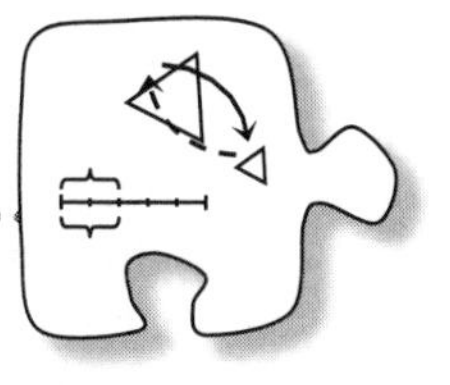

Creating Integer Coefficients

Often, one of the best ways to deal with a challenging task is to find a way to make the task easier. For example, lifting a heavy weight can be made easier with a lever or pulley. Mathematical problems are very similar; often, a challenging problem can be changed to create a new problem that is much easier to solve. In this lesson, you will develop strategies for rewriting a complicated equation into an equivalent equation that is more familiar and easier to solve.

7-51. COMMUNITY SERVICE

The community service club at North Middle School is planning to paint apartments at the local senior citizen center next week. The club needs your help to determine how many apartments they should be able to paint in a day. Earlier in the year, when only $\frac{4}{7}$ of the students worked, they painted 9 apartments in one day. Next week, all of the students are available.

a. Assume that all of the student workers contribute equally to the work. If x represents the number of apartments that can be painted by all of the students in the club, use a multiplier and your understanding of scaling to represent this situation as an equation.

b. Choose a strategy to solve your equation in part (a). What does your answer represent? Be ready to share your strategy.

7-52. HOW CAN I MAKE WHOLES?

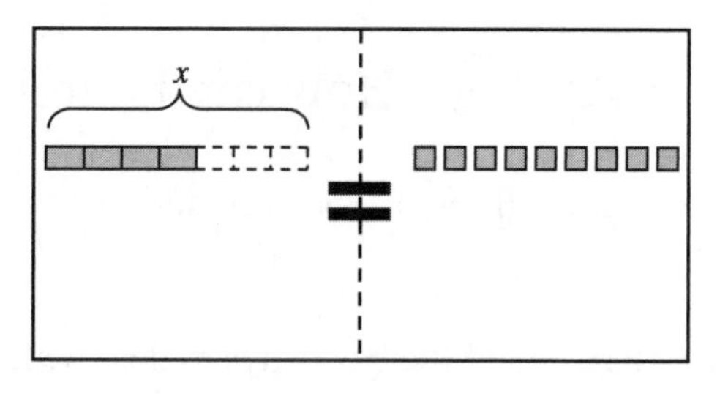

Janice, the club's president, began to think about how she could visualize $\frac{4}{7}x$ to help her solve her equation (from problem 7-51). She recalled using algebra tiles to represent x. In her mind, she visualized the diagram at right.

a. Does this Equation Mat represent your equation from problem 7-51? Why or why not?

b. Janice recognized that these numbers were not easy to work with, since she did not have whole tiles. After working on her paper for a while, she said, *"Maybe I can make whole tiles using more than one set of partial tiles."* She drew the diagram shown at right.

What is her new equation as represented in this picture?

c. With your team or class, discuss Janice's strategy for solving this equation. During your discussion, answer the following questions (in any order):

- What made Janice's strategy different than what you did in Lesson 7.1.4?
- How many sets of $\frac{4}{7}x$ did Janice use to get a whole number of algebra tiles?
- Why did the right-hand side of the equation change?
- How does the number of sets Janice used relate to the equation you wrote in part (a)?

7-53. Will the strategy of turning fractions into integers from problem 7-52 work with other equations, such as $\frac{2}{3}x = 8$? Consider this question as you answer the questions below.

a. How many sets of $\frac{2}{3}x$ would make a whole number of x-tiles?

b. Solve for x using Janice's method from problem 7-52. How could you record your work on your paper?

c. Show how your solution is also the number of two thirds in 8 wholes (written $8 \div \frac{2}{3}$).

7-54. Janice wondered if the method of creating whole-number x-terms would work with decimals. Suppose an item was marked 15% off and the sale cost was \$36.21. She wrote the equation below:

$$0.85x = 36.21$$

a. Why did she write 0.85 in her equation?

b. Is there a number she can multiply both sides of the equation by to get an integer coefficient (so there is no decimal)? If so, list at least one. If not, explain why not.

c. Use Janice's strategy to solve the equation. What was the original price of the item?

d. Does this method work for all equations with decimal coefficients? What if you wanted to solve the equation $1.2x = 14$? What about $0.999x = 71.2$? Discuss these equations with your team and write down your conclusion.

7-55. Solve each equation below by changing the number that x is being multiplied by (the coefficient of x) to an integer. Check your answer.

a. $\frac{5}{6}x = 4$

b. $0.8x = 19$

c. $\frac{5}{3}x = 12$

d. $0.12x = 1$

7-56. LEARNING LOG

In your Learning Log, summarize at least two strategies to solve an equation with fractional (or decimal) coefficients. Provide an example for each strategy and include a diagram. Title this entry "Solving Equations with Fractional Coefficients" and include today's date.

MATH NOTES

METHODS AND MEANINGS

Box Plots

A **box plot** (sometimes called a "box-and-whisker plot") displays a summary of data using the median, quartiles, and extremes of the data. The box contains "the middle half" of the data. The right segment represents the top 25% of the data, and the left segment represents the bottom 25% of the data. A box plot makes it easy to see where the data are spread out and where they are concentrated. The larger the box, the more the data are spread out.

To construct a box plot using a number line that shows the range of the data, draw vertical line segments above the median, first quartile, and third quartile. Then connect the lines from the first and third quartiles to form a rectangle. Place a vertical line segment above the number line at the highest and lowest data values. Connect the minimum value to the first quartile and the maximum value to the third quartile using horizontal segments. The box plot is shown below for the data set 2, 7, 9, 12, 14, 22, 32, 36, and 43.

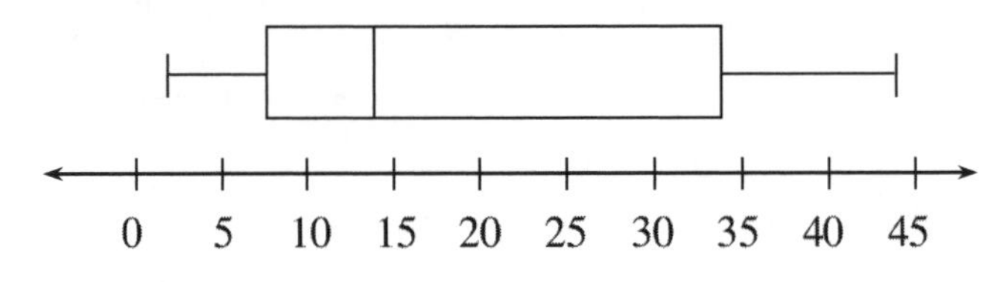

7-57. Erika is tracking the depth of the water in her local creek. Her first twelve measurements are below, in inches:

16 15 13 12 17 14 11 9 11 9 10 9

a. Find the median, first quartile (Q1), and third quartile (Q3).

b. Create a box plot for the data. Read the Math Notes box in this lesson to review how to make a box plot.

c. What is the interquartile range (IQR) for Erika's data?

7-58. If $\frac{1}{4}$ of x is 16, what is $\frac{3}{4}$ of x? Justify your answer in more than one way.

7-59. LuAnn talked on her cell phone for 180 minutes, using $\frac{3}{7}$ of her total monthly minutes. Find out how many total minutes LuAnn gets to talk in one month using at least two different methods.

7-60. Write the inequality represented by each graph.

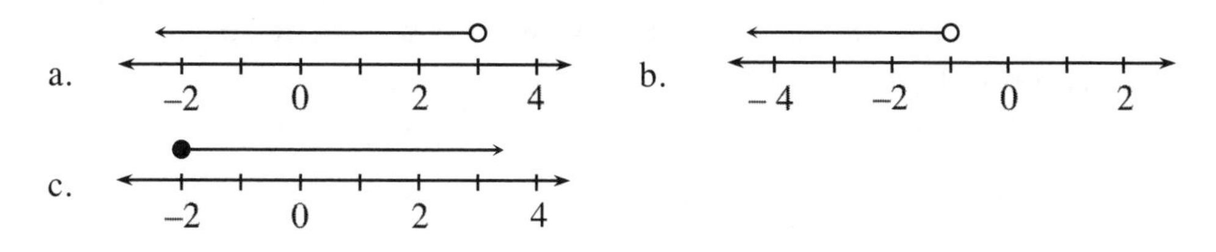

7-61. *Tires R Us* is having a 30%-off sale. Find the savings on a tire that regularly costs \$45.

7-62. Simplify each expression.

a. $3.3(x+4)$

b. $9-5\frac{1}{2}x-3(-2x+1)$

c. $2.2(3.1+x)+3x$

7.1.6 How can I solve complicated equations?

Creating Integer Coefficients Efficiently

In this lesson, you will continue to develop strategies to rewrite a complicated equation into an equivalent equation that is more familiar and easier to solve.

7-63. Chari volunteers over the summer in a veterinarian's clinic. The doctor has told Chari to determine the correct dose of medicine to give to the cat, Sweetie, who weighs 9.5 pounds. The dosage (in ml) for a 9.5-pound cat is given by x in the formula below.

$$\frac{2x}{3}+\frac{4}{3}=\frac{10}{3}$$

Chari had never solved such a complicated equation before. She thought about how Janice visualized algebra tiles in problem 7-52 and wondered if that could help. Chari visualized the following diagram.

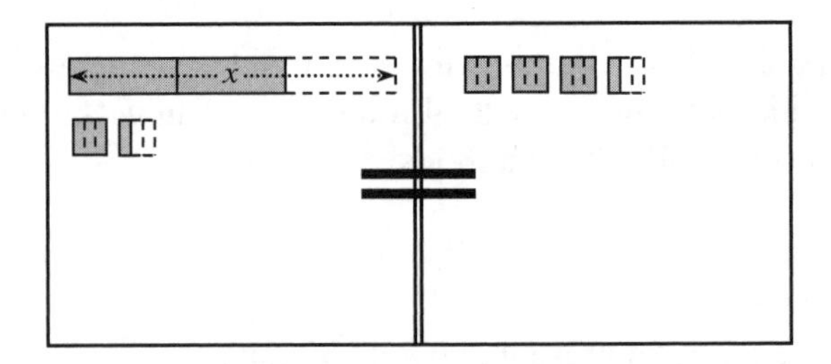

Help Chari rewrite the equation with integers. Determine the correct dose of medicine to give to Sweetie.

7-64. Examine the equation below.

$$\frac{x}{4}-\frac{5}{6}=7$$

a. Multiply each term by 4. What happened? Do any fractions remain?

b. If you have not already done so, decide how you can change your result from part (a) so that no fractions remain. Then solve the resulting equation.

c. Multiplying $\frac{x}{4}-\frac{5}{6}=7$ by 4 did not eliminate all the fractions. What could you have multiplied by to get rid of all the fractions? Explain how you got your answer and write the equivalent equation that has no fractions.

d. Solve the resulting equation from part (c) and check your solution in the original equation.

7-65. The method you used in problem 7-64 to eliminate fractions from an equation can be called **Fraction Busters**, because the multiplication of the equation by a common denominator or several of the denominators eliminates, or "busts," the fractions. The result is an equation with no fractions.

Chari is attempting to solve the equation below.

$$\frac{2b}{3}-\frac{1}{6}=\frac{b}{2}$$

a. What is a common denominator for these fractions? Discuss with your team how you could use the common denominator to eliminate the fractions in Chari's equation.

b. If you have not already done so, find an equivalent equation without fractions.

c. Solve for b and check your answer.

7-66. Chari is worried that Sweetie is too thin. The doctor tells Chari that the weight of a typical cat like Sweetie is given by w in the formula below. A healthy cat is within 2 pounds of the typical weight. Is Sweetie too thin?

$$\frac{3w}{10}+\frac{w}{5}=5.5$$

7-67. Work with your team to solve the following equations. Can you find a number to multiply by that will eliminate all of the fractions in one step?

a. $\frac{5x}{6}+\frac{11}{4}=\frac{17}{3}$ b. $\frac{x}{6}=\frac{1}{12}+\frac{x}{8}$ c. $\frac{x}{3}-\frac{2}{5}=\frac{4}{15}+\frac{2x}{9}$

7-68. Use Fraction Busters in reverse to rewrite the equations below with smaller integer coefficients to make them easier to solve. Solve each equation and check your solution.

a. $300x-1500=2400$ b. $36-3r=18-6r$

7-69. Rewrite the equations below to make them easier to solve. Solve each equation and check your solution.

a. $0.04x+0.16=0.06+0.08x$ b. $4r^2+48=4r+24+4r^2-8r$

c. $\frac{33}{2}+\frac{3y}{5}=\frac{7y}{10}+15$ d. $\frac{4}{x}+11=\frac{35}{3}$

MATH NOTES

METHODS AND MEANINGS

Solving Equations with Algebraic Fractions (also known as Fraction Busters)

Example: Solve $\frac{x}{3}+\frac{x}{5}=2$ for x.

$$\frac{x}{3}+\frac{x}{5}=2$$

This equation would be much easier to solve if it had no fractions. Therefore, the first goal is to find an equivalent equation that has no fractions.

The lowest common denominator of $\frac{x}{3}$ *and* $\frac{x}{5}$ *is* 15.

$$15\cdot\left(\frac{x}{3}+\frac{x}{5}\right)=15\cdot 2$$

To eliminate the denominators, multiply all of the terms on both sides of the equation by the common denominator. In this example, the lowest common denominator is 15, so multiplying all of the terms (both sides) in the equation by 15 eliminates the fractions. Another approach is to multiply all of the terms in the equation by one denominator and then by the other. Either way, the result is an equivalent equation without fractions.

$$15\cdot\frac{x}{3}+15\cdot\frac{x}{5}=15\cdot 2$$

$$5x+3x=30$$

$$8x=30$$

$$x=\frac{30}{8}=\frac{15}{4}=3.75$$

Check: $\frac{3.75}{3}+\frac{3.75}{5}=2$

$1.25+0.75=2$ ✓

In this course, the number used to eliminate the denominators is called a **Fraction Buster**. Now the equation looks like many you have seen before, and it can be solved in the usual way.

Once you have found the solution, remember to check your answer.

7-70. Use the Fraction Busters to solve the following problems.

a. $\frac{3}{2}+\frac{2x}{5}=\frac{7}{10}$

b. $\frac{-8x}{5}+\frac{1}{6}=\frac{-5x}{3}$

7-71. Find the value of x that makes each equation true.

a. $-4.9x=9.8$

b. $\frac{8}{21}=-\frac{2}{7}x$

c. $\frac{3}{5}+x=\frac{2}{3}$

7-72. Trina planted 43 plants in her garden last week. She planted twice as many cucumbers as zucchini and eight more tomatoes than cucumbers. Write and solve an equation to find the number of each kind of plant in her garden. If you need to, use the 5-D Process to help you organize your thinking. Be sure to define your variable.

7-73. Complete the scaling for each number line below.

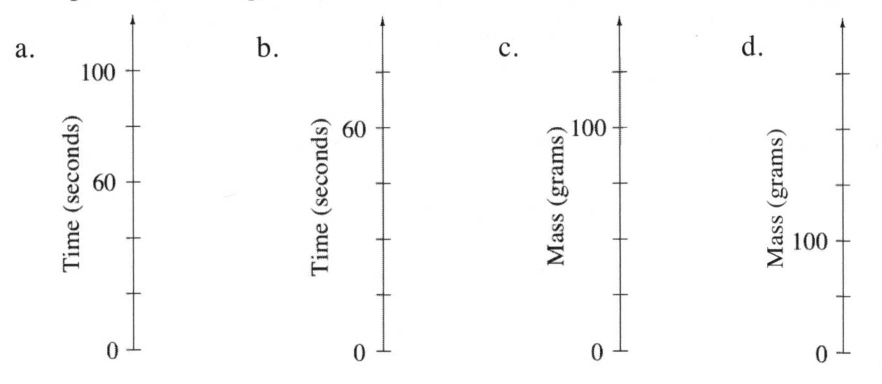

7-74. Mt. Rose Middle School collected canned food to donate to a local charity. Each classroom kept track of how many cans it collected. The number of cans in each room were 107, 55, 39, 79, 86, 62, 65, 70, 80, and 77. The principal displayed the data in the box plot below.

a. What is the interquartile range of the data?

39 62 73.5 80 107
30 40 50 60 70 80 90 100 110

b. The main office staff collected 55 cans, the counseling staff collected 89 cans, and the custodial staff collected 67 cans.

On grid paper, make a new box plot that includes this data. Clearly label the median and the first and third quartiles.

7-75. Ages of golfers participating in a golf tournament were 44, 48, 40, 25, 28, 37, 29, 34, 45, 51, 43, 35, 38, 57, 50, 35, 47, 30, 61, 43, 44, 60, 46, 43, 33, 45, 42, 34, 32, and 74.

a. Create a stem-and-leaf plot for this data.

b. Use the stem-and-leaf plot to create a histogram.

c. Describe the shape and spread of the data. Are there any apparent outliers?

d. Use the appropriate measure of center to describe the "typical" age of golfers at the tournament.

7.1.7 Percent of what?

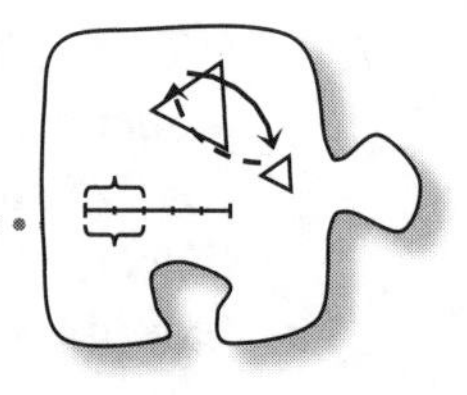

Percent Increase and Decrease

Perhaps you have heard an adult say something like, *"When I was growing up, it only cost a dime to go to the movies!"* The rate at which prices increase over a period of time, called **inflation**, is one of the many things that mathematics can help you understand. In this lesson, you will be using diagrams and computations to calculate the way quantities (like cost or height) change.

As you work today, keep the following questions in mind.

Is it increasing or decreasing?

What is it changing from?

By how much did it change?

7-76. WHAT IS THE PERCENT INCREASE?

Several years ago, Joe started a lawn-care business. Due to rising costs, he needs to increase his prices. He is concerned, however, because he has heard that if he raises his rates more than 33%, he might lose business. At right is a letter he sent to his clients.

> *Dear Valued Customer,*
>
> *After several years of business, Mowcare is increasing its price for lawn service. Since the cost of gas and other supplies has increased, we need to raise our prices. Our prices will increase from $12.50 per hour to $15 per hour. We hope you continue to be happy with the quality of our work.*
>
> *Sincerely,*
> *Joe*

Joe began to wonder about how the increase in his fees could be expressed in terms of a percent.

a. Joe wants to determine the scale factor (multiplier) for the price increase and wrote the following equation:

$$12.50x = 15$$

Explain how this expression represents this situation. What does x represent?

b. Solve the equation above to determine the scale factor for his change in fees. Represent this multiplier (scale factor) as a fraction, as a decimal, and as a percent.

Problem continues on next page. →

7-76. *Problem continued from previous page.*

c. How could this situation be represented with a line diagram? With your team, copy and complete the diagram below. Then answer and do the following:

- Which portion of the diagram corresponds to the original price? Circle and label this part "original."
- Which portion of the diagram corresponds to the change in price? Circle and label this part "change."

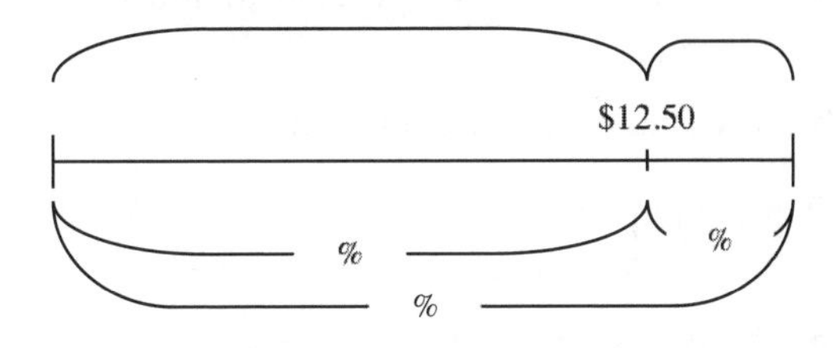

d. When Joe raised his rates, what was the **percent increase**? That is another way of asking: What percent of the original price did the price change? Should Joe expect to lose business?

7-77. Paige needs your help! She wants to convince her grandmother to let her sign up for a rock-climbing class. The class normally costs $50, but the school is offering a special price of $34. Paige's grandmother wants to know what percent of the cost of the class she would save.

a. Without calculating, estimate the percent of the discount.

b. With your team, determine the percent change in the price of the class. Use the prompts below to help guide your team's discussion.

- Draw a diagram or write an equation that represents the situation.
- What is the original (whole) value? Indicate this on your diagram or in your equation.
- What percent is the change? Find and indicate this on your diagram or in your equation.
- Does this situation represent an increase or decrease?

7-78. The **percent change** is a comparison of the amount of change to the original amount. If a number increases from the original amount, it is called **percent increase**. If the number decreases from the original, it is called a **percent decrease**.

a. What is the percent change from $30 to $33? Is this a percent increase or decrease? To answer this question:

- Draw a diagram to represent the problem.
- Determine if it is a percent increase or decrease.
- Calculate the percent change.

b. What is the percent change from $33 to $30? Is this a percent increase or decrease? To answer this question:

- Draw a diagram to represent the problem.
- Determine if it is a percent increase or decrease.
- Calculate the percent change.

c. If both parts (a) and (b) above have a change of $3, why are the percent changes different? Explain.

7-79. To attract new customers, a shoe company called Shoe Fits will raise its prices 10% and then offer a 10%-off coupon.

a. Without doing any calculations, consider the following question: If a coupon is used, do you think the final price will be more than, less than, or the same as the original price? Discuss this with your team and be ready to share your thinking with the class.

b. Akari wants to use a coupon to buy a pair of shoes that originally cost $46. What will the increased price be? What will be the price after the 10%-off coupon is used? Show all calculations. Does this result confirm your answer to part (a)?

c. Akari had assumed that if the price increased 10% and then he received a 10% discount, it would return to the original price. Explain why this did not happen.

MATH NOTES

METHODS AND MEANINGS

Percent Increase or Decrease

A **percent increase** is the amount that a quantity has increased, represented as a percent of the original amount. A **percent decrease** is the amount that a quantity has decreased, written as a percent of the original amount. You can write an equation to represent a percent change that is an increase or decrease using a scale factor or multiplier:

amount of increase or decrease = (% change)(original amount)

Example 1: A loaf of bread increased in price from \$0.29 to \$2.89 in the past 50 years. What was the percent increase?

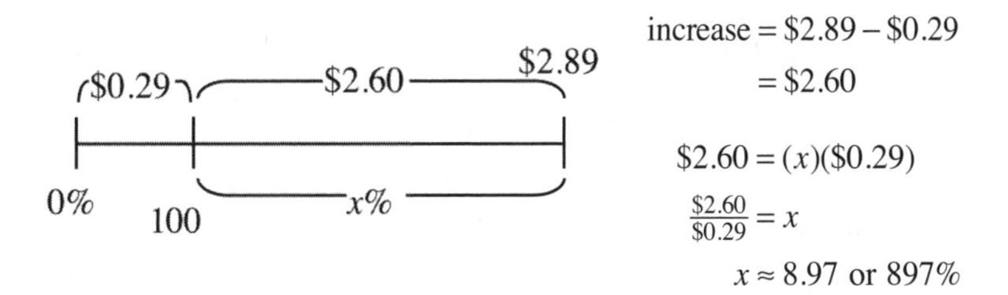

$$\text{increase} = \$2.89 - \$0.29 = \$2.60$$

$$\$2.60 = (x)(\$0.29)$$

$$\frac{\$2.60}{\$0.29} = x$$

$$x \approx 8.97 \text{ or } 897\%$$

Example 2: Calculator prices decreased from \$59 to \$9.95. What was the percent decrease?

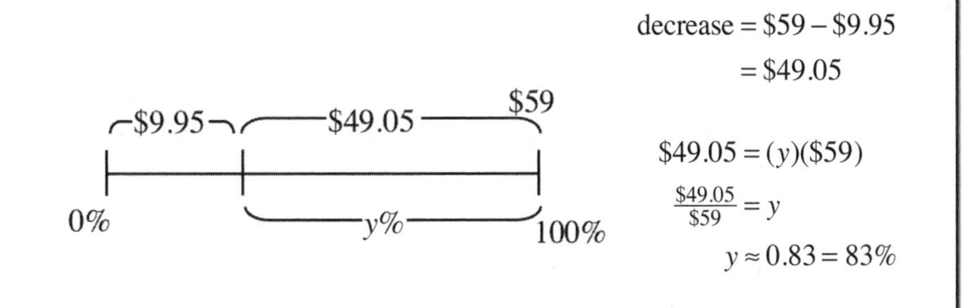

$$\text{decrease} = \$59 - \$9.95 = \$49.05$$

$$\$49.05 = (y)(\$59)$$

$$\frac{\$49.05}{\$59} = y$$

$$y \approx 0.83 = 83\%$$

7-80. Joe wanted to know more about how the cost of fertilizer for his lawn-care business was changing. The cost of a bag of fertilizer just increased from \$8 to \$15. What is the percent increase of the price? Represent the change as a fraction, as a percent, and as a decimal.

7-81. Solve each equation. Show all work.

a. $0.85x = 200$

b. $\frac{7}{6}x = 140$

7-82. Ms. Poppy has finished grading her students' tests. The scores were 62, 65, 93, 51, 55, 76, 79, 85, 55, 72, 78, 83, 91, and 82.

a. Find the median.

b. Find the quartiles.

c. Find the IQR.

d. Find the mean.

7-83. Mr. Crow, the head groundskeeper at High Tech Middle School, mows the lawn along the side of the gym. The lawn is rectangular, and the length is 5 feet more than twice the width. The perimeter of the lawn is 250 feet.

a. Use the 5-D Process to find the dimensions of the lawn.

b. Use the dimensions you calculated in part (a) to find the area of the lawn.

7-84. Evaluate the inequality below for the following listed values of x. Decide if the value makes the statement true or false. Show your work.

$$3x - 3 \geq 2x + 3$$

a. $x = -3$

b. $x = 9.5$

c. $x = 6$

d. $x = 10\frac{1}{2}$

7-85. Mr. Takaya can eat three slices of pizza in five minutes. If he continues to eat at the same rate, how long will it take him to eat the whole pizza, which has twelve slices? How many slices could he eat in half of an hour?

7.1.8 How does it change over time?

Simple Interest

When banks lend money, they charge **interest**, which is a fee for letting the borrower use the money. Interest is usually expressed as a percent of the amount borrowed and is added to the amount that the borrower owes. For example, a bank might charge someone an 8% annual (yearly) interest rate for borrowing $500. In addition, if you have money in a savings account, banks generally pay interest to you on the money in the account. So by leaving your money in a bank, you can earn more money.

There are different ways of calculating interest, and each one creates different patterns of growth. As you work with your team to investigate one kind of interest called **simple interest**, ask these questions to focus your discussion:

What patterns do you see?

How can you show the connection?

7-86. RENTING THE HALL

The student council is planning a spring celebration. Unfortunately, to rent a hall for the event, they will need to pay a deposit in advance of the event. Since they have not started selling tickets yet, they asked the Parent-Teacher Association for a loan of $825 for the hall rental. The PTA agreed, but said it would charge 2% simple interest each week until the loan is paid back.

Ms. Becker, the student-council advisor, explained to the students that the amount of the loan ($825) is called the **principal** amount. Until the loan is paid back, 2% (called the weekly **interest rate**) of the principal amount will be added each week to the amount owed.

a. How much money in interest will the PTA charge each week?

b. If the student council borrows $825, how much will it owe after 1 week? After 3 weeks? Show your calculations.

c. How much would the student council owe two months (8 weeks) from now? Be prepared to justify your strategy.

7-87. The student-council members realized that they would also need funds before the event to pay the DJ and photographer a deposit. They will need a second loan of $1000 to pay for these two expenses.

a. If the PTA also charges them 2% weekly simple interest for this loan, how much will be added to this loan each week?

b. The PTA has decided that to cover its costs, it only needs to earn $18 interest each week. What percent weekly interest should the PTA charge the student council for this loan? Be prepared to share your strategy.

7-88. A loan agreement between the student council and the PTA has finally been reached, but the PTA will not loan the full $1825 requested. To make sure everyone understands the agreement, the PTA created the table below.

Number of Weeks	Calculations	Total Loan Amount
0	$1250	$1250
1	$1250 + $18.75	$1268.75
2	$1250 + $18.75 + $18.75	$1287.50
3		
4		

a. Based on this table, how much will the student council borrow? What is the percent interest?

b. How much will the student council owe after 3 weeks? After 4 weeks? Show your calculations.

c. How is the amount of money that the student council owes changing each week? Show how this change can be found in your table.

d. The student-council president wants to be able to check quickly how much the student council owes at any point. Use your table to write a variable expression that shows the amount of money the club owes the PTA after any number of weeks. Make sure to define your variable.

e. The president figured out that if the student council does not pay off the loan by the end of the school year, it would owe $1500. How many weeks of school are left? Use your expression from part (d) to write and solve an equation to answer this question.

7-89. SHOPPING AROUND

The treasurer of the student council decided to look into other funding options for the DJ and the photographer. With your team, examine how each loan would grow and find a way to compare the loans. Assume that a month is 4 weeks. Then find answers to the questions below.

The local bank offered to loan the student council \$955 for 1% weekly simple interest.	The Math Club offered to loan the student council \$940 for 4.5% monthly simple interest.	The Booster Club offered to loan the student council \$960 and would add \$36 interest each month.

a. Which loan would grow most quickly? That is, which has the most interest added each month?

b. What is the monthly interest rate the Booster Club is offering? Show how you got your answer.

c. For which loan would the student council owe the most money overall after 3 months? Justify your answer.

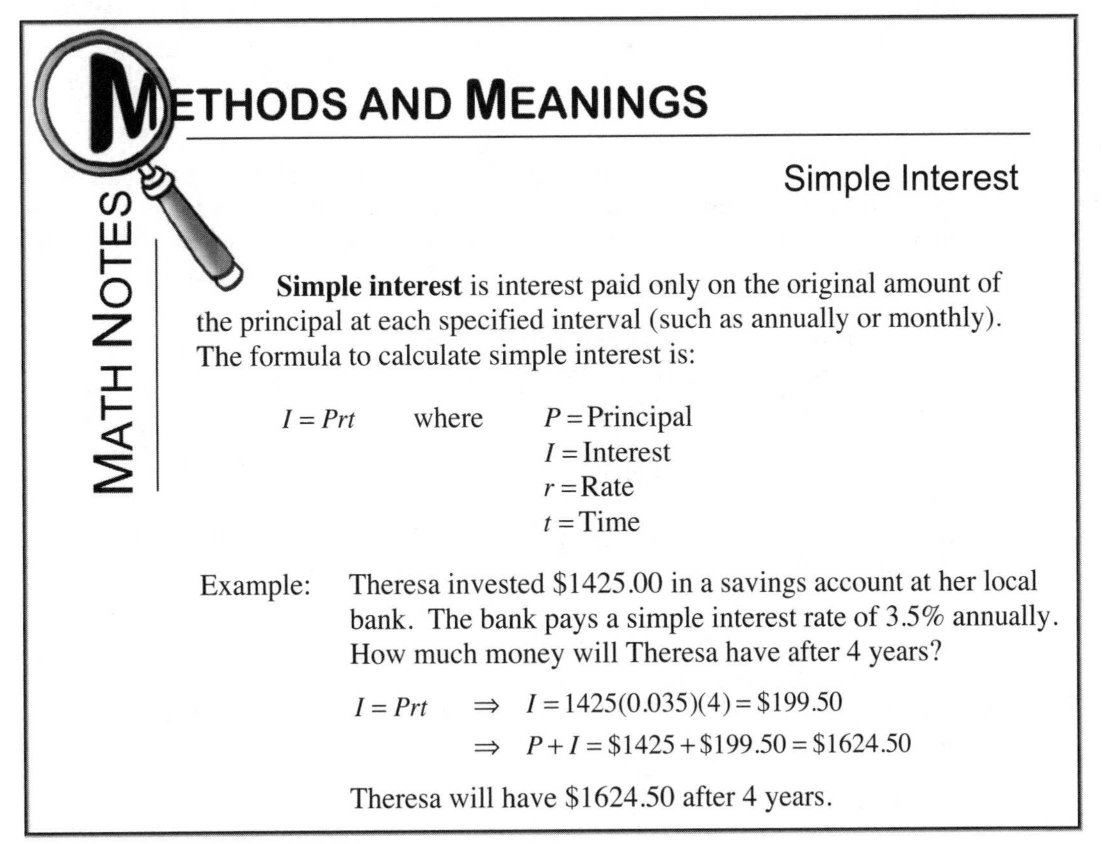

METHODS AND MEANINGS

MATH NOTES

Simple Interest

Simple interest is interest paid only on the original amount of the principal at each specified interval (such as annually or monthly). The formula to calculate simple interest is:

$I = Prt$ where $P =$ Principal
$I =$ Interest
$r =$ Rate
$t =$ Time

Example: Theresa invested \$1425.00 in a savings account at her local bank. The bank pays a simple interest rate of 3.5% annually. How much money will Theresa have after 4 years?

$$I = Prt \quad \Rightarrow \quad I = 1425(0.035)(4) = \$199.50$$

$$\Rightarrow \quad P + I = \$1425 + \$199.50 = \$1624.50$$

Theresa will have \$1624.50 after 4 years.

7-90. Ida wants to buy a car, but she currently does not have any money. The car she wants costs \$2500. Consider her two options and decide which loan she should take.

a. She could borrow \$2500 at a monthly interest rate of 4% simple interest and pay the total after 12 months. Write a simple-interest expression and calculate what she would owe at the end of 12 months.

b. She could borrow \$2500 at a weekly interest rate of 1% simple interest and pay the total after 12 months. Show calculations and a written explanation to justify your answer.

7-91. The Jones family wants to remodel their kitchen. They have saved \$23,000 in the last two years. Their contractor says the remodel will cost \$40,000. They can borrow the difference at a monthly interest rate of 2% simple interest. If they pay the loan off in six months, how much will they have paid?

7-92. The electronics department is having a No Sales Tax Sale! In addition, all of the items in the department are on sale for 25% off. Wyatt is looking at a music player that normally costs \$120. He has \$95 to spend, and he is wondering if he has enough money to buy it.

a. Wyatt sketched the diagram at right. Use the work he started to find 25% of \$120. Is this the price he will pay?

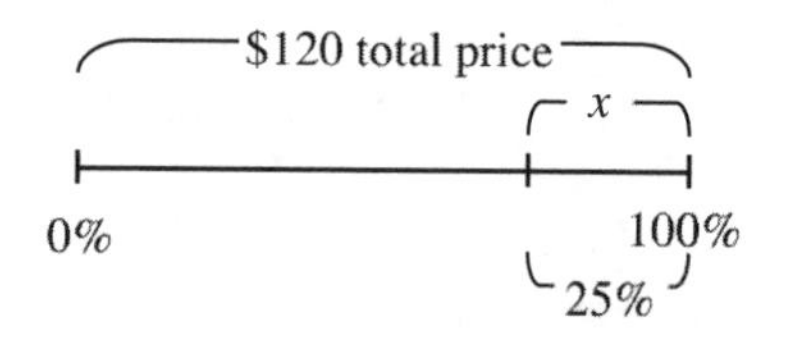

b. Does Wyatt have enough money?

c. Would he have enough money if he had to pay the 5.5% sales tax on the sale price?

7-93. For each equation below, solve for x. Show the process you use to check your answer.

a. $x-\frac{2}{5}=1\frac{3}{5}$

b. $5x=0$

c. $x-14.6=2.96$

7-94. Marty is saving money to buy a new computer. He received $200 for his birthday and saves $150 of each week's paycheck.

Does this situation represent a proportional relationship? If it does, identify the constant of proportionality. If it does not, explain why not.

7-95. Elvin found the box plot below in the school newspaper.

Number of hours spent watching TV each week

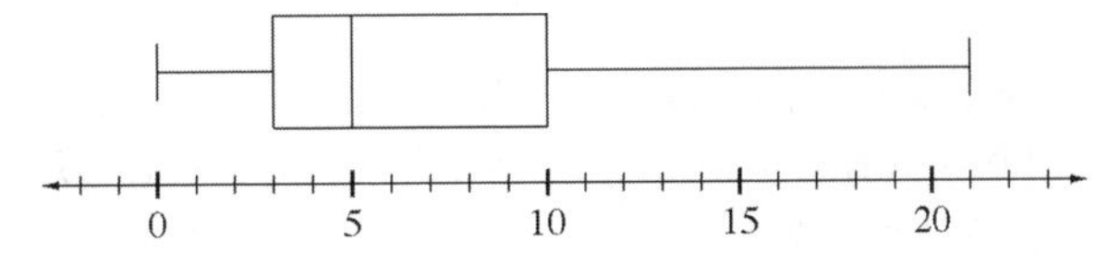

a. Based on the plot, what percent of students watch more than 10 hours of television each week?

b. Based on the plot, what percent of students watch less than 5 hours of television each week?

c. Can Elvin use the plot to find the mean (average) number of hours of television students watch each week? If so, what is it? Explain your reasoning.

d. Can he use the plot to find the median? If so, what is it? Explain your reasoning.

7.2.1 What is the missing number?

Finding Missing Information in Proportional Relationships

Throughout this course, you have made connections between different representations of proportional relationships. In this lesson, all of these ideas will come together to uncover a new strategy for finding missing quantities in proportional relationships.

7-96. In Chapter 4, Kaci was trying to figure out how many pounds of Havarti cheese she could buy for \$10, knowing that 3 pounds costs \$7.50. She wrote the equivalent ratios below.

$$\frac{3 \text{ pounds}}{\$7.50} = \frac{x}{\$10}$$

Work with your team to brainstorm a list of all of the methods that you can think of that Kaci could use to find the information she is missing. Be prepared to share your ideas with the rest of the class.

7-97. Graeme knows that he earns \$4.23 every half hour. He wanted to know how much money he would earn after one full week of work (40 hours). He wrote the equivalent ratios below and quickly sees a way to find his answer.

$$\frac{\$4.23}{\frac{1}{2} \text{ hour}} = \frac{x}{40 \text{ hours}}$$

a. What do you think Graeme is thinking of doing?

b. Solve Graeme's equation.

c. Graeme wants to know how long it will take him to earn \$1000. Write and solve an equation to help him figure it out.

7-98. Shiloh knows that it takes 5 cups of flour to make 2 recipes of cookies. He has 13 cups of flour left in his cupboard. He wants to know how many recipes he can make. He wrote the equivalent ratios below.

$$\frac{5 \text{ cups}}{2 \text{ recipes}} = \frac{13 \text{ cups}}{x \text{ recipes}}$$

This equation looked difficult to solve, so he decided to ask his friend Carolyn for help. Carolyn said,

"If it takes 5 cups of flour to make 2 recipes, then it takes $2\frac{1}{2}$ cups of flour for each recipe. This is the multiplier. Can't you just use the multiplier to write an equation?"

Carolyn then wrote the equation $F = 2\frac{1}{2}R$ where F stands for cups of flour and R stands for the number of recipes. As Carolyn wrote the equation below, she said, *"Then I would solve this equation to find out the number of recipes."*

$$13 = 2\tfrac{1}{2}R$$

a. Compare Shiloh and Carolyn's equations. Are they correct? Why or why not?

b. Which equation is easiest to solve? Solve it.

c. Does your solution work in both Shiloh and Carolyn's equations?

7-99. Find the missing information in each set of equivalent ratios below, using any method. Be sure that you record your process so that others can see what you did.

a. $\frac{2}{15} = \frac{x}{5}$

b. $\frac{x}{100} = \frac{7}{8}$

c. $\frac{0.2}{2} = \frac{1}{x}$

d. $\frac{y}{11.2} = \frac{4}{7}$

Review & Preview

7-100. Find the missing value in each of the pairs of equivalent ratios below.

a. $\frac{x}{10}=\frac{6}{15}$ b. $\frac{12}{9}=\frac{8}{x}$ c. $\frac{16}{38}=\frac{200}{m}$

7-101. Samantha's parents are going to paint her room. Her color choices for the walls include three different shades of white, four shades of tan, two shades of blue, three shades of green, and four shades of pink. What is the probability that she will randomly select any shade of blue or pink?

7-102. The local sports shop has backpacks on sale for \$28. The original price was \$40. What is the percent decrease for the backpack price?

7-103. Simplify the expressions below.

a. $\frac{3}{4}-\frac{1}{3}+(-\frac{5}{24})$ b. $\frac{10}{12}\div\frac{1}{4}$ c. $3\frac{1}{2}\cdot1\frac{3}{8}$

d. $-\frac{20}{7}\div\frac{1}{3}$ e. $-\frac{8}{25}\cdot(-\frac{15}{32})$ f. $\frac{9}{4}\div(-\frac{2}{3})$

g. $\frac{8}{21}+(-\frac{3}{7})$ h. $\frac{7}{4}\cdot(-\frac{2}{5})\cdot\frac{3}{5}$

7-104. Stephanie is earning simple interest of 3.5% on her money each month. She currently has \$1325 in her account. What will her balance be in 5 months?

7-105. Eduardo's friends guessed how many jelly beans were in a jar at his birthday party. Here are their guesses: 75, 80, 95, 92, 100, 72, 71, 60, 65, 88, 60, 152.

a. Make a histogram to display the data.

b. Make a box plot to display the data.

c. Which measure of center is most appropriate for this data? Why?

d. Which data display most clearly shows the median of the data?

7.2.2 How can I find the missing value?

Solving Proportions

You have examined several proportional situations (such as the price of yogurt versus the number of pounds of yogurt) and non-proportional situations (such as the value of a college fund over time). Today you will continue to develop strategies for solving proportional equations.

7-106. J.R. reduced figure A at right to create similar figure B.

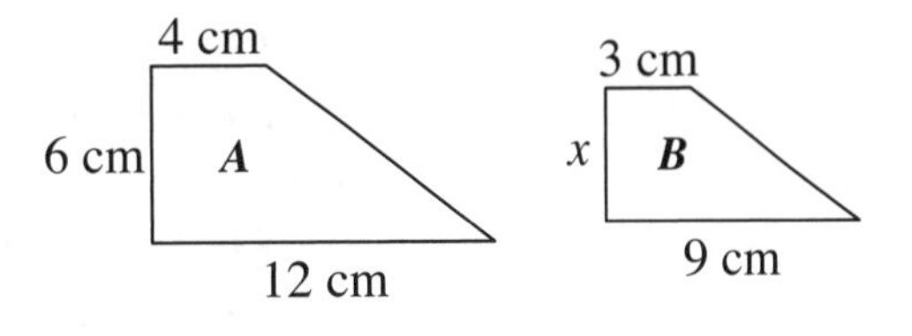

a. Write all of the ratios that compare the corresponding sides of figure B to figure A. What is the relationship between these ratios? How do you know?

b. One of the relationships between the sides can be written as $\frac{3}{4}=\frac{x}{6}$. Find two different ways to find the value of x in this equation. Is your answer reasonable? Be ready to share your strategies with the class.

7-107. MULTIPLE STRATEGIES

J.R.'s team is trying to find multiple ways to solve $\frac{3}{4}=\frac{x}{6}$ from problem 7-106. With your team, analyze each of the strategies below. Some of these strategies might be the same as what you came up with in problem 7-106. However, others may be new. Work to understand each strategy so that you can use it to solve a new problem.

a. J.R. wants to use a **Giant One** to help find the value of x. Explain how he can find a value to use as a numerator and denominator in a Giant One, then find the value of x.

$$\frac{3}{4}\cdot\left[\frac{\ }{\ }\right]=\frac{x}{6}$$

Problem continues on next page. →

7-107. *Problem continued from previous page.*

b. Looking at J.R.'s work, Leticia said, *"I see it differently. We just need to find some number that when divided by 6 you get $\frac{3}{4}$. We can undo the division by multiplying each side of the proportion by 6 like this."* Then Leticia showed J.R. the work below.

$$\left(\frac{6}{1}\right)\frac{3}{4}=\frac{x}{6}\left(\frac{6}{1}\right)$$

With your team, explain how Leticia's idea works. Are the two ratios still equal? Why did she choose to multiply by 6? Simplify each side of the equation.

c. Avner asked, "*But if multiplying both sides by 6 gets rid of the denominator of the x, then can we use the same strategy to get rid of the 4 in the other denominator? Like when we do Fraction Busters, right?*" Discuss Avner's question and decide if undoing both denominators using a Fraction Buster is a reasonable strategy. Does this help solve the equation?

$$\frac{3}{4}=\frac{x}{6}$$

$$\frac{4\cdot 6}{1}\left(\frac{3}{4}\right)=\left(\frac{x}{6}\right)\frac{4\cdot 6}{1}$$

$$(6)(3)=(x)(4)$$

Avner's work

7-108. Use the strategies from problem 7-107 to solve the problems below.

a. Use Leticia's method of undoing division to solve this proportion: $\frac{p}{22.5}=\frac{7}{5}$. When you find p, replace the value in the original proportion to confirm that the two ratios are equal.

b. Write and solve a proportional equation for x for the similar triangles at right. Then use Avner's method of undoing both denominators (Fraction Busters) to solve for x.

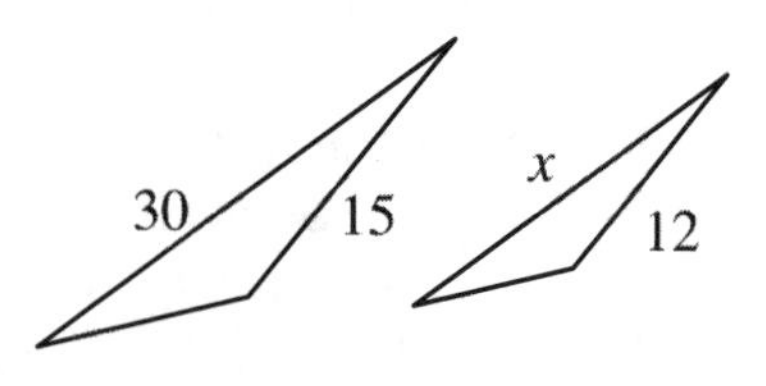

c. An apple-juice container has a tiny hole in it, so it is slowly leaking. If the container leaks three ounces every 19 minutes, how long will it take for the 16 ounces of juice in the container to leak out? Write a proportional equation and solve with J.R.'s strategy of using a Giant One.

7-109. For each problem below, decide if the situation is proportional. If the problem is proportional, say so, and then solve the problem using any strategy you choose. If the problem is not proportional, explain why not, and then solve the problem.

a. Steve drove 130 miles from Portland to Tacoma in 2 hours. If he continues to drive at the same speed, how long will it take him to drive 390 miles?

b. At an amusement park, you pay a $15 entrance fee and then $4 for each ride you go on. How much will it cost you to go on seven rides?

c. Armando has collected 39 bottle caps in the past three months. At this rate, how many bottle caps will he have in five months?

d. The grocery store sells 3 limes for 99 cents. At this rate, how much will a dozen limes cost?

e. Margarit drove her friends to a movie. She drove for 30 minutes at 10 miles per hour in heavy traffic, and then she drove for 15 minutes at 40 miles per hour. How far did she travel in those 45 minutes?

7-110. After Ramona had solved several proportional equations, she noticed a pattern. *"When we eliminated both of the fractions by multiplying by both denominators, we ended up with something that looks like we just multiplied diagonally."*

$$\frac{10}{4} = \frac{x}{7}$$
$$(7)(10) = (x)(4)$$

a. What does she mean? For each of the proportions below, apply Ramona's diagonal multiplying pattern and determine whether the result is a true mathematical equation. Will her pattern always work?

i. $\frac{8}{10} = \frac{12}{15}$ *ii.* $\frac{6}{4} = \frac{9}{6}$ *iii.* $\frac{15}{3} = \frac{20}{4}$

b. Use Ramona's pattern to solve the equation $\frac{2}{5} = \frac{11}{x}$ for x.

7-111. LEARNING LOG

In this section, you have used a number of different strategies for finding missing information in proportional relationships.

In your Learning Log, show each of these methods. Include examples to show your thinking. Title this entry "Methods for Finding Missing Information in Proportional Relationships" and label it with today's date.

MATH NOTES

METHODS AND MEANINGS

Solving Proportions

An equation stating that two ratios are equal is called a **proportion**. Some examples of proportions are shown at right.

$$\frac{6\text{ mi}}{2\text{ hr}}=\frac{9\text{ mi}}{3\text{ hr}}$$

$$\frac{5}{7}=\frac{50}{70}$$

When two ratios are known to be equal, setting up a proportion is one strategy for solving for an unknown part of one ratio. For example, if the ratios $\frac{9}{2}$ and $\frac{x}{16}$ are equal, setting up the proportion $\frac{x}{16}=\frac{9}{2}$ allows you to solve for x.

Strategy 1: One way to solve this proportion is by using a **Giant One** to find the equivalent ratio. In this case, since 2 times 8 is 16, so use $\frac{8}{8}$ for the Giant One.

$\frac{x}{16}=\frac{9}{2}\cdot\frac{8}{8}$ and $\frac{9\cdot 8}{2\cdot 8}=\frac{72}{16}$, which shows that $\frac{x}{16}=\frac{72}{16}$, so $x=72$.

Strategy 2: Undoing division. Another way to solve the proportion is to think of the ratio $\frac{x}{16}$ as, "x divided by 16." To solve for x, use the inverse operation of division, which is multiplication. Multiplying both sides of the proportional equation by 16 "undoes" the division.

$$\frac{x}{16}=\frac{9}{2}$$
$$\left(\frac{16}{1}\right)\frac{x}{16}=\frac{9}{2}\left(\frac{16}{1}\right)$$
$$x=\frac{144}{2}=72$$

Strategy 3: Use cross multiplication. This is a solving strategy for proportions that is based on the process of multiplying each side of the equation by the denominators of each ratio and setting the two sides equal. It is a shortcut for using a **Fraction Buster** (multiplying each side of the equation by the denominators).

Complete Algebraic Solution (Fraction Busters)

$$\frac{x}{16}=\frac{9}{2}$$
$$2\cdot 16\cdot\frac{x}{16}=\frac{9}{2}\cdot 2\cdot 16$$
$$2\cdot x=9\cdot 16$$
$$2x=144$$
$$x=72$$

Cross Multiplication

$$\frac{x}{16}=\frac{9}{2}$$
$$\frac{x}{16}\times\frac{9}{2}$$
$$2\cdot x=9\cdot 16$$
$$2x=144$$
$$x=72$$

Review & Preview

7-112. Solve the proportions using any strategy you choose. Show all of your steps.

a. $\frac{35}{70}=\frac{x}{100}$

b. $\frac{12}{33}=\frac{m}{11}$

c. $\frac{x}{15}=\frac{12}{75}$

d. $\frac{4}{32}=\frac{10.5}{x}$

7-113. Triangle ABC is similar to triangle DEF.

a. Find the scale factor from triangle ABC to triangle DEF.

b. Find x.

c. Find y.

7-114. Write an equation to represent the situation below and answer the question. You may use the 5-D Process to help you.

Andrew just opened a new office-supply store. He has been keeping track of how many customers visit his store. During his second week, he had 18 more customers than he did the first week. The third week, he had four less than twice as many customers as he had during the second week. In his fourth week of business, he had 92 customers. If he had 382 customers in total during his first four weeks of business, how many customers did he have during the second week?

7-115. For each equation below, solve for x. Sometimes the easiest strategy is to use mental math.

a. $x-\frac{3}{5}=1\frac{2}{5}$

b. $5.2+x=10.95$

c. $2x-3.25=7.15$

d. $\frac{x}{16}=\frac{3}{8}$

7-116. Jessica wants to make a spinner that has all of the following characteristics. Sketch a possible spinner for Jessica. Be sure to label each section of the spinner with a name and with its theoretical probability.

- Blue, red, purple, and green are the only colors on the spinner.
- It is half as likely to land on blue as to land on red.
- It is three times as likely to land on purple as green.
- There is a 50% probability of landing on either blue or red and a 50% probability of landing on either purple or green.

7-117. This problem is a checkpoint for displays of data. It will be referred to as Checkpoint 7B.

For the information in parts (a) and (b), create a histogram. For the information in parts (c) and (d), create a box plot and then identify the quartiles and interquartile range.

a. Hours spent doing after school sports each weekday by students:
$0, 4, 0, 1, 1, 1, \frac{1}{2}, 1\frac{1}{2}, 2, 2, \frac{1}{2}, 2, 2, 2, 1\frac{1}{2}, 1\frac{1}{2}, 1, 1, 2, 4, \frac{1}{2}, \frac{1}{2}, 2$

b. Amount of time spent solving a math puzzle (minutes) by study teams:
3, 15, 18, 14, 10, 14, 19, 8, 14, 14, 15, 19, 9

c. Average number of text messages sent per day by a group of friends:
47, 52, 50, 47, 51, 46, 49, 46, 48

d. Number of points scored by the basketball team during a season:
76, 90, 75, 72, 93, 82, 70, 85, 80

Check your answers by referring to the Checkpoint 7B materials located at the back of your book.

Ideally, at this point you are comfortable working with these types of problems and can solve them correctly. If you feel that you need more confidence when solving these types of problems, then review the Checkpoint 7B materials and try the practice problems provided. From this point on, you will be expected to do problems like these correctly and with confidence.

Chapter 7 Closure What have I learned?

Reflection and Synthesis

The activities below offer you a chance to reflect about what you have learned during this chapter. As you work, look for concepts that you feel very comfortable with, ideas that you would like to learn more about, and topics you need more help with.

① SUMMARIZING MY UNDERSTANDING

This section gives you an opportunity to show what you know the main math ideas in this chapter.

With a partner, obtain an envelope from your teacher. Follow the directions below to demonstrate your understanding of solving equations with rate, including those with fractional coefficients.

Part 1: Decide which one of you is going to work a problem and which one of you is going to listen. (You will do both jobs before you finish this lesson, so you are just choosing the job you will do first.) The partner working the problem should draw a problem out of the envelope.

Part 2: **If you are working the problem**, clearly show all of your work on your paper, draw diagrams, and label them completely. Explain what you are thinking to your partner as you work.

If you are the listener, pay attention to what your partner is saying as he or she solves the problem. When your partner is finished, you must tell him or her whether or not you agree with the solution and why or why not.

Part 3: Trade jobs with your partner. The partner now working the problem should draw a new problem out of the envelope and explain the solution to the listener.

Two example problems are shown below.

Problem A	Problem F
Omar has been riding his bicycle at a speed of 15 mph for 48 miles. How long has he been riding?	At Maple Middle School, 34% of the students are in seventh grade. If there are 1300 students at the school, how many students are NOT in seventh grade?

② WHAT HAVE I LEARNED?

Doing the problems in this section will help you to evaluate which types of problems you feel comfortable with and which ones you need more help with.

Solve each problem as completely as you can. The table at the end of this closure section provides answers to these problems. It also tells you where you can find additional help and where to find practice problems like them.

CL 7-118. Aja and Emilie were riding their skateboards. They knew that they could ride 3 miles in 20 minutes. Use your problem-solving strategies to find out how far the girls can ride in 45 minutes.

CL 7-119. Harley was eating pizza and had already eaten six pieces before his sister, Samantha, got home. Samantha was worried that she was not going to get a fair share of the pizza and wanted to know how many pieces were in the pizza originally. Harley told her, "*I have only eaten* $\frac{3}{8}$ *of the pizza.*" Help Samantha figure out how many pieces of pizza there were to start with.

CL 7-120. Marcus has a summer job where he makes $45 a day. Yesterday, his boss told him that he was getting a raise to $63 a day because he was such a hard worker. What is the percent increase in Marcus' salary?

CL 7-121. Simplify and solve the following equations.

a. $5x+2=-3x-14$

b. $\frac{2}{3}x+1=x-4$

c. $0.5x-0.5=0.75x+1-x$

d. $5x+6-2x=3x-7$

CL 7-122. Joe is using his allowance money to download songs from the Internet. He can download them at a rate of eight songs every 10 minutes. Jasmine, who is downloading songs with the money she made from her part-time job, can download at a rate of 12 songs every 15 minutes. Who is downloading songs faster?

CL 7-123. Solve the inequality $8+x\leq 3$ and graph the solutions on a number line.

CL 7-124. A biologist was sitting near a pond and noticed a large number of dragonflies. He also saw both frogs and fish trying to eat the dragonflies. He counted a total of 89 fish, frogs, and dragonflies. He noticed that there were four times as many dragonflies as fish and that the frogs were five more than twice the number of fish.

Use the 5-D Process to determine how many fish, frogs, and dragonflies the biologist counted.

CL 7-125. Find the probability of each of the following events. Show all of your work.

a. Flipping a penny and getting a "heads" and then flipping a nickel and getting a "tails."

b. Rolling a 5 on a standard number cube and picking a 10 or a jack from a standard deck of playing cards.

CL 7-126. For each of the problems above, do the following:

- Draw a bar or number line that represents 0 to 10.

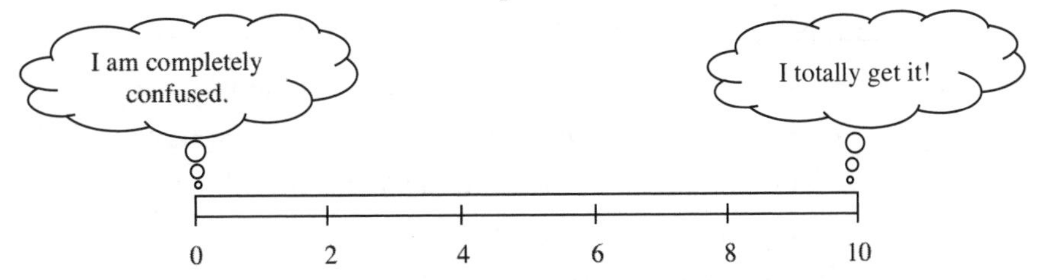

- Color or shade in a portion of the bar that represents your level of understanding and comfort with completing that problem on your own.

If any of your bars are less than a 5, choose *one* of those problems and do one of the following tasks:

- Write two questions that you would like to ask about that problem.
- Brainstorm two things that you DO know about that type of problem.

If all of your bars are a 5 or above, choose one of those problems and do one of these tasks:

- Write two questions you might ask or hints you might give to a student who was stuck on the problem.
- Make a new problem that is similar and more challenging than that problem and solve it.

③ WHAT TOOLS CAN I USE?

You have several tools and references available to help support your learning: your teacher, your study team, your math book, and your Toolkit, to name only a few. At the end of each chapter, you will have an opportunity to review your Toolkit for completeness. You will also revise or update it to reflect your current understanding of big ideas.

The main elements of your Toolkit should be your Learning Logs, Math Notes, and the vocabulary used in this chapter. Math words that are new appear in bold in the text. Refer to the lists provided below and follow your teacher's instructions to revise your Toolkit, which will help make it useful for you as you complete this chapter and as you work in future chapters.

Learning Log Entries

- Lesson 7.1.3 – Scaling Quantities
- Lesson 7.1.5 – Solving Equations with Fractional Coefficients
- Lesson 7.2.2 – Methods for Finding Missing Information in Proportional Relationships

Math Notes

- Lesson 7.1.1 – Histograms and Stem-and-Leaf Plots
- Lesson 7.1.2 – Quantities and Interquartile Range (IQR)
- Lesson 7.1.3 – Describing Data Distributions
- Lesson 7.1.4 – Scaling
- Lesson 7.1.5 – Box Plots
- Lesson 7.1.6 – Solving Equations with Algebraic Fractions (also known as Fraction Busters)
- Lesson 7.1.7 – Percent Increase or Decrease
- Lesson 7.1.8 – Simple Interest
- Lesson 7.2.2 – Solving Proportions

Mathematical Vocabulary

The following is a list of vocabulary found in this chapter. Some of the words have been seen in the previous chapter. The words in bold are words that are new to this chapter. Make sure that you are familiar with the terms below and know what they mean. For the words you do not know, refer to the glossary or index. You might also add these words to your Toolkit so that you can reference them in the future.

box plot	coefficient	constant of proportionality
Fraction Busters	**first quartile**	**Giant One**
histogram	**interest**	**interquartile range (IQR)**
mean	median	measure of central tendency
outlier	**principal**	**percent change**
proportional	rate	scale
similar	**stem-and-leaf plot**	**third quartile**

Answers and Support for Closure Problems
What Have I Learned?

Note: MN = Math Note, LL = Learning Log

Problem	Solution	Need Help?	More Practice
CL 7-118.	The girls can ride $6\frac{3}{4}$ miles in 45 minutes.	Lessons 7.1.1, 7.1.2, 7.2.1, and 7.2.2 MN: 7.1.4, 7.2.2 LL: 7.1.3, 7.2.2	Problems 7-14, 7-21, 7-59, and 7-85
CL 7-119.	There were 16 pieces in the pizza.	Lessons 7.1.4 and 7.1.5 LL: 7.1.5	Problems 7-47, 7-58, and 7-92
CL 7-120.	Marcus' salary increased by 40%.	Lesson 7.1.7 MN: 7.1.7	Problems 7-76, 7-78, 7-80, and 7-102
CL 7-121.	a. $x=-2$ b. $x=15$ c. $x=2$ d. no solution	Lessons 7.1.4, 7.1.5, and 7.1.6 MN: 7.1.6 LL: 7.1.5	Problems 7-44, 7-81, 7-93, and 7-115
CL 7-122.	They are downloading at the same rate.	Lessons 4.2.3 MN: 4.2.4	Problem CL 4-147, CL 5-156, and 7-10
CL 7-123.	$x \le -5$ 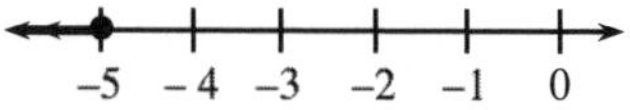	Section 6.1 MN: 6.1.1, 6.1.4 LL: 6.1.4	Problems CL 6-145, 7-60, and 7-84
CL 7-124.	12 fish, 29 frogs, 48 dragonflies	Section 5.3 MN: 5.3.3 LL: 5.3.4	Problems CL 5-150, 7-83, and 7-114
CL 7-125.	a. $\frac{1}{2}\cdot\frac{1}{2}=\frac{1}{4}$ b. $\frac{1}{6}\cdot\frac{2}{13}=\frac{2}{78}=\frac{1}{39}$	Section 5.2 MN: 5.2.4 and 5.2.5 LL: 5.2.1 and 5.2.5	Problems CL 5-151, CL 6-142, 7-25 7-49, and 7-101

8
Statistics and Angle Relationships
wedge
2 7 12 11 15 8 4 10
8 iron
5 9 11 12 13

CHAPTER 8 Statistics and Angle Relationships

You may not have noticed, but many homework problems in Chapter 7 helped prepare you for this chapter's work with data. The homework problems equipped you with tools for comparing two sets of data and making inferences about the data based on evidence.

After revisiting data display and analysis in Section 8.1, in Section 8.2 you will look at how to design a good survey. You will learn more about the kinds of questions to ask and the group that you would select to answer them.

In Section 8.3, your focus will shift from statistics toward geometry. You will begin by learning about angles. Specifically, you will learn how to classify them by their sizes and by their relationships to other angles. Then you will build triangles and quadrilaterals with specific characteristics and compare them to each other.

Guiding Questions

Think about these questions throughout this chapter:

How can I describe the data?

How do the data sets compare?

How can I select a good sample?

What can I conclude?

How can I measure it?

In this chapter, you will learn how to:

- Describe, analyze and compare sets of data using measures of central tendency, such as mean and median, and using the variation, including range and inter quartile range (IQR).
- Attempt to find random and representative samples to complete a survey.
- Identify angles by their characteristics and use correct vocabulary to describe and name them.
- Construct triangles and quadrilaterals with given side lengths and/or angles and predict if they will be unique shapes.

Chapter Outline

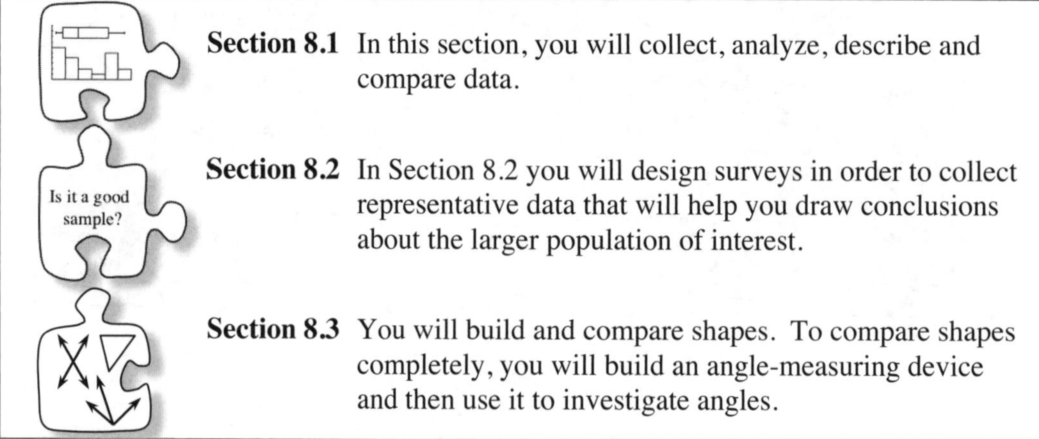

Section 8.1 In this section, you will collect, analyze, describe and compare data.

Section 8.2 In Section 8.2 you will design surveys in order to collect representative data that will help you draw conclusions about the larger population of interest.

Section 8.3 You will build and compare shapes. To compare shapes completely, you will build an angle-measuring device and then use it to investigate angles.

8.1.1 Which tool is more precise?

Measurement Precision

Do the lengths of the object you are measuring or the tool you choose to measure with affect how precise your measurement is likely to be? In this section, your class will explore this question by analyzing the results of an experiment. As you work with your team, think about the questions that follow.

What am I measuring?

What unit is being repeated?

What can I do to make my measurement more precise?

8-1. WHICH TOOL GIVES A MORE PRECISE MEASUREMENT?

Have you heard the expression, "Measure twice, cut once"? This advice refers to the care that professionals such as carpenters and fashion designers need to take to measure precisely so that all of the parts of their creations fit together correctly. Careful, correct measurements also ensure that they do not waste materials. Does it matter what tool they use to make their measurements?

Imagine using two different tools, such as a 12-inch ruler and a continuous measuring tape, to measure a length of your classroom or the width of a basketball court (in inches). How might the measurements that you get compare?

Discuss the following questions with your team. Be prepared to share your ideas with the rest of the class.

- Would you get the same measurement with each tool?
- Why might the measures be different? Should they be the same?
- Which tool do you think would give you a more precise measurement, that is, one that is closer to the *true* length of the classroom?

8-2. Now you and your class will gather data to test your ideas about the precision of measuring the same length with two different tools.

Your Task: As directed by your teacher, measure the specified length in the classroom to the nearest inch twice, each time using a different tool (a 12-inch ruler and a single measuring tape, for example). Although you will share tools with your team and work together to make sure the measures are recorded properly, *each person* in the team should measure the length twice, once with each tool.

8-3. Once your team members have each made their measurements, compare the results within your team by answering the following questions:

- Which tool seems to measure more precisely?
- What do you think is the actual length of the classroom? How did you decide?
- Which tool do you think gave you a better answer?

8-4. Add your data to the class data table.

a. Examine the sets of data. Record any initial observations you can make.

b. Are there any measures that look very different from the others? These extreme values are called **outliers**, because they are far away from most of the data. What could you do to help you see any outliers better?

c. Sometimes an outlier can reveal that an error or misunderstanding has occurred. Decide as a class if any data needs to be deleted or corrected due to an error or misunderstanding.

d. What is the range for each set of data? How do the ranges compare? For each set of data, what is the median? What is the first quartile? The third quartile?

8-5. Creating visual representations of data makes data sets easier to compare.

a. Make a histogram for each set of data. Make sure to use the same scale for both histograms.

b. Create box plots for the two sets of data. Put both box plots on the same number line and use the same scale as you did for your histogram.

c. Compare the center, shape, spread, and outliers for the two sets of data using the histograms and the box plots. Do the data sets seem to show the same value for the length of the classroom?

8-6. WHICH MEASUREMENT IS BEST?

So what is the actual measure? Clearly you have multiple measurements from which to choose. How can you decide what is the best estimate of the length of the classroom?

Look at the data set for each tool, along with their histograms and box plots, and consider the center, shape, spread, and outliers. With your team, discuss what you can learn from each of these pieces of information about the precision (consistency) of each measuring tool, as well as about the length of the classroom. Which of the many numbers that you could choose is the best estimate for the *actual* length of the classroom? Why? What do you think accounts for the greater consistency of one tool?

8-7. IS MEASUREMENT ALWAYS APPROXIMATE?

As you have seen, the measurements that you made are approximate. Is this always true? Can you imagine a way to measure something that would be exact without any variability? Discuss this with your team and be prepared to share your ideas with the class.

8-8. Ms. Whitney has thirteen students who did extra credit assignments to raise their grades. The scores on the assignments were 96, 45, 89, 100, 100, 77, 67, 84, 98, 33, 60, 97, and 100.

a. Make a stem-and-leaf plot of this data.

b. Find the median, and the first and third quartiles.

8-9. Simplify each expression.

a. $-\frac{4}{5}+\frac{7}{12}$ b. $\frac{5}{9}+(-\frac{1}{4})$ c. $-\frac{3}{7}\cdot\frac{11}{12}$ d. $-1\frac{2}{3}\cdot\frac{4}{5}$

8-10. Solve the equations below for the variable. Be sure to check your answer.

a. $3(2x-1)+2=5x$ b. $600x+200=500x$

8-11. Write an equation to represent this problem and find the unknown side lengths. Use the 5-D Process to help you organize your thinking and to define your variables, if you need to do so. Remember to define your variable.

A trapezoid has a perimeter of 117 cm. The two shortest sides have the same length. The third side is 12 cm longer than one short side. The final side is 9 cm less than three times one short side. How long is each side of the trapezoid?

8-12. Four pieces of taffy cost 25 cents. Complete the table below.

Taffy (# of pieces)	4	16	8	80	24	32	40
Cost (in dollars)							

8-13. Mrs. Ferguson, your school librarian, asks you to conduct a survey of how many books students read during the year. You get the following results: 12, 24, 10, 32, 12, 4, 35, 10, 8, 12, 15, 20, 18, 25, 21, and 9.

a. Use the data to create a histogram. Use a bin width of 10 books. (Remember, if a value falls on the line, place it in the upper bin.)

b. Is the mean or median a better measure of the center? Find the value of whichever is more appropriate.

c. Make a box plot of the data.

d. Describe the center, shape, spread, and outliers of the distribution.

8-14. Copy and complete each of the Diamond Problems below. The pattern used in the Diamond Problems is shown at right.

xy
x y
$x+y$

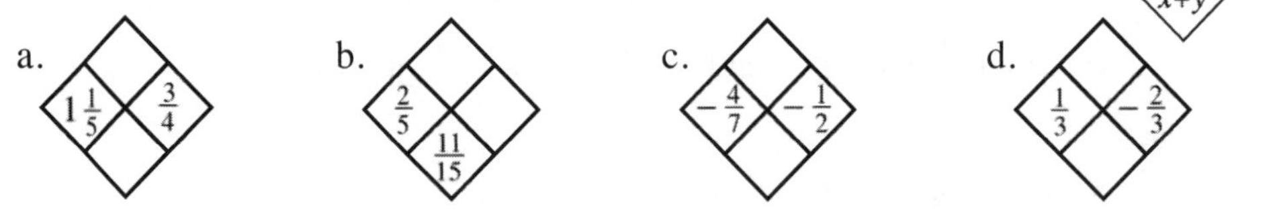

8-15. Solve the following equations using any method. Show your work and check your solution.

a. $5x + 20 = 3x + 4$ b. $7x - 4 = 3x + 8$ c. $2x + 6 = x - 9$

8-16. Mariana and Felix were in science class and were using a test kit to measure the amount of calcium in milk. They measured the amount of calcium in 1 cup of milk 10 times and got a mean of 294.6 mg. They looked up the amount of calcium that is typically in milk and found out it was 290 mg per 1 cup. Percent error finds the difference between the actual value and measured value and the compares that difference to the actual value as a percentage. Find the percent error of Mariana and Felix's measurement.

8-17. If five songs can be downloaded for $6, what is the cost of seven songs?

8-18. Roger has a bag of marbles. There are 6 red, 4 blue, 3 white, and 7 green marbles in the bag. If he draws one marble, replaces it, and then draws another, find the following probabilities. Write your answer as a fraction and a percent.

a. P(red, red)

b. P(not white, green)

c. P(blue or white, red)

d. Find the answer for part (a) above if Roger does not replace the marble before selecting the second one.

8.1.2 How can I compare the results?

Comparing Distributions

In Lesson 8.1.1, you compared the results of two different methods of measuring to answer the question, "Which measuring tool is more precise?" Today you will continue to develop your methods for comparing two distributions of data.

8-19. Josh is just starting a round of golf. This first hole is 130 yards long. He needs to decide which club to use for his first shot. He has kept careful records about how close his first shots came to the hole, all from this same distance. His records include data from his use of two different golf clubs, a wedge and an 8-iron, over the past year.

Wedge, distance to hole (yards): 0 3 1 2 7 2 15 25 5 22
8-iron, distance to hole (yards): 19 12 12 8 3 11 5 7 10 13 8 10 11 20

a. Create a histogram and box plot for each of the clubs. Place the box plot above the histogram on the same number line for each club to make a combination plot. Use a bin width of 5 yards.

b. To find the "typical" distance that Josh hits the ball from the hole with a wedge, is the mean or the median a better choice? Find the typical distance Josh hits the ball from the hole with a wedge and compare it to the typical distance he hits the ball with an 8-iron.

c. Advise Josh which club to use. Explain your thinking.

8-20. It is just as important to consider the spread of the data as it is to consider the center when comparing data sets.

a. Calculate the Interquartile Range (IQR) for each golf club in the previous problem. With which club is Josh more consistent?

b. If Josh decided to use the 8-iron, he could "typically" expect to hit the ball so that it lands between 8 and 12 yards from the hole. This is indicated by the box on the box plot display and corresponds with the IQR. If Josh decided to use the wedge, what is a "typical" interval of distances from the hole he could expect the ball to land?

c. Compare the typical interval of distances for the 8-iron with the interval you found for the wedge. Do you wish to modify your advice to Josh? Explain.

8-21. Mr. Webb has only one more starting position available on his basketball team, but two students have tried out for it. He wants to choose the student who is likely to score the most points.
The two students from whom he can choose are described below.

a. In her most recent games, Jana scored: 7 46 9 6 11 7 9 11 19 7 9 11 9 55 11 7 points, while Alejandra scored 13 15 9 18 13 17 17 15 points. Which girl has the higher average (mean) number of points?

b. Which student do you think Mr. Webb should select and why? Use parallel box plots (two box plots on the same number line) to support your explanation.

c. Why was the mean not a good measure of the girl's typical performance?

d. Calculate the IQR to measure the variability of each girl's performance.

e. Who had the higher median and by how many points? How large is the difference between the medians measured by how many IQRs would fit into it?

8-22. Gregory and his sister shared a computer at home. In order to be fair, they kept track of how much time they spent socializing with friends each day for the last two weeks. Their usage in minutes follows:

Gregory: 49 48 51 52 68 40 73 68 61 60 69 55 51 59

His sister: 49 45 37 63 56 57 62 50 42 48 55 64 40 42

Make a parallel box plot to compare their usage. Is their median usage notably different from each other? If the usage is notably different, how much more did one of them use the computer than the other, measured in number of IQRs?

MATH NOTES

METHODS AND MEANINGS

Comparing Box Plots

One way to visually represent a distribution of collected data is with a **combination histogram and box plot**. The box plot is graphed on the same x-axis as the histogram. See Alejandro's scores at right.

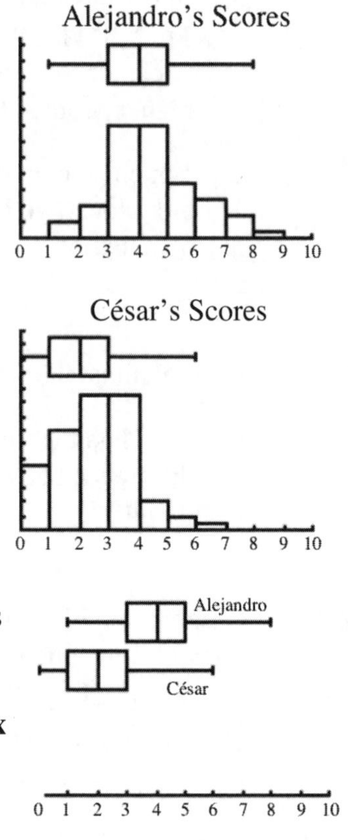

To compare two distributions, a second combination histogram and box plot is drawn *with the same scale* as the first histogram. The two combination plots can then be lined up exactly on top of each other so that differences are readily observable. Compare Alejandro's scores from above to César's scores at right.

Sometimes comparing only the two box plots is enough to be able to compare the distributions. When two box plots are drawn on the same axis, they are called **parallel box plots**. An example is shown at right.

8-23. The two histograms below show how precisely Lue threw 50 darts with his right hand and then 50 with his left hand. Study the two histograms.

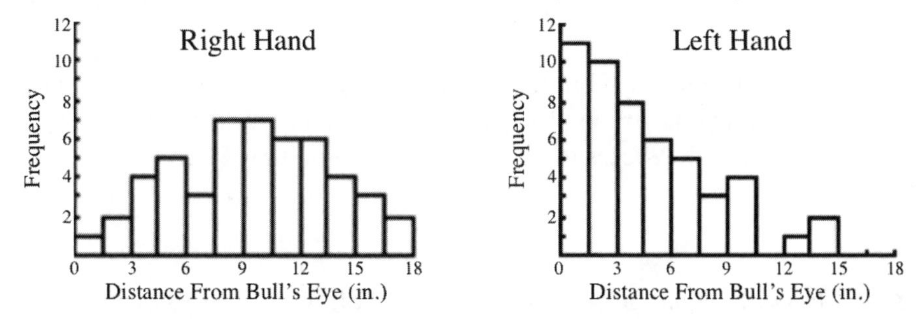

a. Estimate what the box plots would look like and make a parallel box plot.

b. Compare the center, shape, spread, and outliers between Lue's left hand and right hand.

c. Is Lue more precise throwing with his right hand or with his left hand?

d. Use the box plot to estimate how many IQRs above the median Lue's better hand is. Explain your thinking.

8-24. Find the missing lengths or values on the diagram below. Assume that the line is evenly divided.

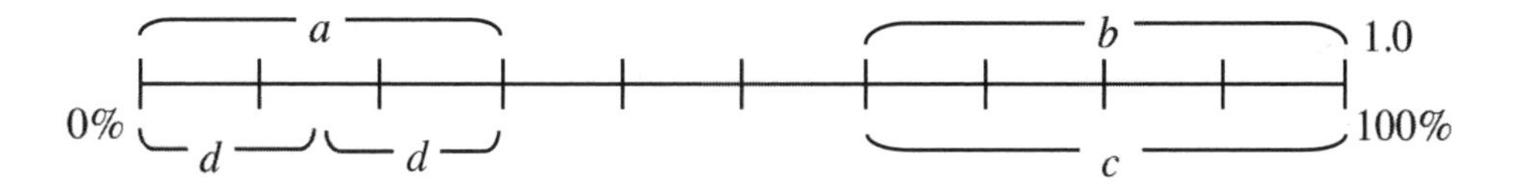

8-25. Joaquin has agreed to lend his younger brother \$45 so that he can buy a new tank for his pet lizard. Joaquin is charging his brother 2% simple interest per month. If his brother pays him back in 6 months, how much will Joaquin get back?

8-26. Michaela holds her state high school record for the 500-meter freestyle swimming event. She can swim the event in 4 minutes and 50 seconds. At this same rate, how far will she swim in 10 minutes?

8-27. Mrs. Chen has two brothers. Mark is 7 years older than Mrs. Chen and Eric is 11 years younger than Mrs. Chen. The sum of all three of their ages is 149. Use the 5-D Process to determine the age of Mrs. Chen.

8-28. For each equation below, solve for x. Show the process you use to check your answer.

a. $2\frac{1}{2}=x-1\frac{1}{4}$

b. $5x=2x+12$

c. $x-14.6=8.02$

8.2.1 Is the survey fair?

Representative Samples

If you want to know what a bowl of soup tastes like, do you need to eat all of the soup in the bowl? Or can you get a good idea of the taste by trying a small sample?

When you conduct a survey, it is not usually possible for you to survey every person in the **population** you are interested in, such as *all* female teenage shoppers or *all* of the students at your school. Instead, statisticians collect information about a **sample** (a portion) of the population. However, finding a **representative sample** (a sample that represents the whole population well) is not easy.

8-29. As the social director of the Class Council, Ramin would like to survey a few students about their interests.

When Ramin analyzes the results from the survey, he wants to make claims about the interests of *all* of the students in his school. If he were to survey only students on the Class Council, for example, it might be hard to make claims about what all students think. Students who are on the Class Council may not have the same social interests as other students. Consider this idea as you think about the samples described below.

a. If Ramin wanted to generalize the opinions of all students at his school, would it make sense to go to the grocery store and survey the people there? Why or why not?

b. If he wanted to generalize the opinions of all students at his school, would it make sense to ask all of his friends at school? Why or why not?

c. If he wanted to generalize the opinions of all students at his school, would it make sense to ask every third person who entered the cafeteria at lunch? Why or why not?

8-30. There are a variety of ways to choose samples of the population you are studying. Every sample has features that make it more or less representative of the larger population. For example, if you want to represent all of the students at your school, but you survey all of the students at school 30 minutes after the last class has ended, you are likely to get a disproportionate number of students who play school sports, attend after-school activities, or go to after-school tutoring.

a. If you ask the opinion of the people around you, then you have used a **convenience sample**. If you took a convenience sample right now, what would be some features of the sample? Would you expect a convenience sample to represent the entire student population at your school? Why or why not?

b. If you email or create an online questionnaire then you have used a **voluntary response sample**. What are some features of the people in a volunteer response sample? Could it represent the sample of all of the students at school accurately?

c. You use a **cluster sample** if you first divide the students into smaller groups so that each smaller group represents all of the students at your school. Then you randomly select one or more of these groups to sample. How might you divide the students at your school into groups that each represent the whole school? Explain. Are there any reasons that these clusters might not be fully representative of all the students at your school?

8-31. From what population is each of these samples taken? Write down the actual population for each of these sampling techniques.

Method of Sampling	Description of Actual Population
Call every hundredth name in the phone book.	People with phones who also have their numbers listed
Survey people who come to the "Vote Now" booth at the high school football game.	
Ask every tenth student entering a high school football game.	
Haphazardly survey students during the morning break.	
Text response to an online "instant" poll.	
Hand out surveys in the library before school.	
Survey all students in Period 1 English classes.	

8-32. A study at the University of Iowa in 2008 concluded that children that play violent video games are more aggressive in real life. Children ages 9 to 12 were studied to determine how much they played violent video games; peers and teachers were asked how much these students hit, kicked, and got into fights with other students.

a. Can you legitimately conclude from this study that teenagers who play violent video games tend to be more aggressive? Why or why not?

b. Can you legitimately conclude from this study that children ages 9 to 12 who play violent video games are more likely to commit violent crimes? Why or why not?

c. Can you legitimately conclude from this study that children ages 9 to 12 who play violent video games tend to hit and kick more in school?

d. Can you legitimately conclude from this study that playing a lot of violent video games will cause 9 to 12-year-old students to become more violent at school?

8-33. Addie was helping children in a kindergarten class learn to read. She was curious how old the typical child was when they entered kindergarten. It was not practical to look up the school records of all 100 kindergarteners. So on the first day of school, Addie took a sample: she asked the parent of the first fifteen students to be dropped off at the school how old (in months) their child was. Her data is listed below.

67 61 69 72 71 65 67 67 57 68 71 72 61 59 62

Make an **inference** (a statistical prediction) of the mean age of Kindergarten children at the school.

8-34. **Additional Challenge:** Create a survey question that will help you to better know the students in your school. Tell when and where you would ask the question so that you asked a representative sample of the students in the school.

MATH NOTES

METHODS AND MEANINGS

Types of Samples from a Population

When taking a survey, the **population** is the group of people about whom the information is to be gathered. For example, if you wanted to conduct a survey about what foods to serve in the cafeteria, the population would be the entire student body. Since it is not usually convenient to survey the total population, different kinds of **samples** may be used.

A **representative sample** is a subgroup of the population that matches the general characteristics of the entire population. If you choose to sample 10% of the students, you would need to include an equivalent fraction of students from each grade and an equivalent ratio of male to female students as the larger population.

A **convenience sample** is a subgroup of the population where it is easy to collect data. Only sampling the students in your homeroom, for example, would be convenient, but would not necessarily accurately represent the entire school.

A **cluster sample** is a subgroup of the population that contains a common characteristic. Sampling only the eighth graders, in the above example, would be a cluster sample. Again, this sample would not necessarily represent the entire school.

A **voluntary response sample** contains only the sample of the population that chose to respond. This also would not necessarily represent the entire population.

8-35. Suppose you were conducting a survey to try to determine what portion of voters in your small town support a particular candidate for mayor. Consider each of the following methods for sampling the voting population of your town. State whether each is likely to produce a representative sample and explain your reasoning.

a. Ask every voter on your block.

b. Randomly pick one house from each block in the neighborhood and survey the homeowner.

c. Survey each person at the I-Jump Pancake Restaurant after church on Sunday morning.

d. Ask people who are leaving the twice-yearly town hall meeting.

e. Visit every tenth person on the county's voter registration list.

8-36. Calculate the percent change in each problem below.

a. Robert wanted to buy a computer game that cost \$25 last week. This week when he went back to buy the game, the price was \$35. What was the percent of increase in the price?

b. Susan bought a jacket on sale. The original price of \$35 was marked down to \$25. What was the percent discount because of the sale?

c. Why were your answers to parts (a) and (b) different?

8-37. Simplify each expression.

a. $\frac{12}{5} \div \frac{7}{10}$ b. $\frac{9}{4} \div (-\frac{1}{3})$ c. $-\frac{3}{5} \div (-\frac{1}{6})$

8-38. Find the area and perimeter of each shape below. Show your steps and work. Note: Diagrams are not drawn to scale.

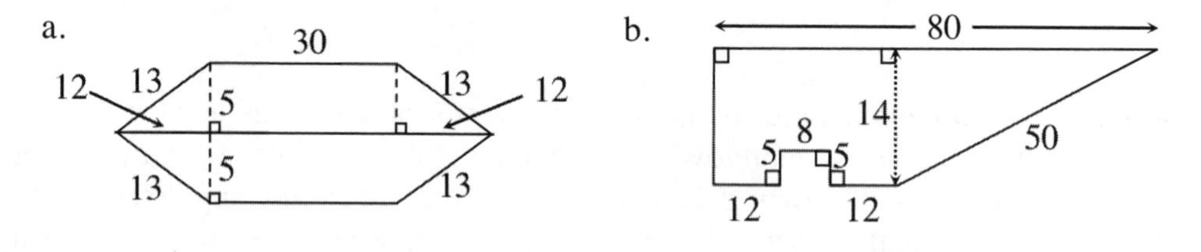

8-39. The recommended speed on a scenic road is 35 mph. Driving too fast is a hazard, but so is driving too slowly. Safe speeds s may be described by the inequality $|35 - s| \le 10$.

a. Find a list of at least 5 safe speeds.

b. Determine how to show the entire set of possible values (solutions) for s by graphing them on a number line.

8-40. Simplify and solve each equation below for x. Show your work and check your answer.

a. $24 = 3x + 3$

b. $2(x - 6) = x - 14$

c. $3(2x - 3) = 4x - 5$

d. $\frac{3}{4}x = 2x - 5$

8.2.2 How close is my sample?

Is it a good sample?

Inference from Random Samples

In the previous lesson, you studied the randomness of various sampling populations. If you wanted to know the average height of the trees in a forest, you would not want to measure every tree in the forest. You would take a sample of the trees and measure them to give you a good prediction of the average height of all the trees.

If you measured 10 trees and found the mean, you would get a number that describes those 10 trees, but how well does that number describe all of the trees in the entire forest? Let's investigate similar situations.

8-41. The sighting of American robins in yards is considered a sign that spring has arrived. You would like to know the average weight of an American robin in your town.

a. Of course you cannot weigh every robin in town, even if you could figure out how to catch them all. A sample seems like a good idea. Read the Math Notes box, "Random Samples," that follows this lesson.

Think about how you can take a random sample from the population of robins in the envelope provided by your teacher. What things would be important to do? Discuss this with your team.

b. Now take a random sample of ten robins from your envelope and record their weights. Each member of your team should do the same thing with their own random sample.

c. Calculate the mean of your sample. Do you think that your mean is representative of the population? What inferences can you make about the population from your sample?

d. Compare your estimate of the population mean to the means of the other students in your team. Is your mean the true average weight for all American robins in town? Are any of your teammates' numbers the true average? How can you explain any differences between the means?

8-42. Your estimate of the mean will probably be a little larger or smaller than the true average weight of robins. Let's explore how much larger or smaller your estimate might be than the true average.

a. Follow your teacher's directions to add your estimate of the population mean to the list with the rest of the class' estimates. Then, make a combination histogram and box plot of the data. Use a bin width of 5g on your histogram.

b. What causes variation in the sample means? That is, why are some of the sample means on your class graph so much larger or smaller than others? Why are so many of the sample means bunched up in the middle?

c. Within what interval do you suppose is the true mean weight of American robins?

8-43. Cyrus plays volleyball in county-wide tournaments. He wondered what portion of volleyball players prefer plain water over sports drinks during intense games.

a. At his next tournament, Cyrus selected 50 random players from all the teams to ask about their preference. 78% preferred plain water. What inference can Cyrus make about *all* the volleyball players in the county?

b. What additional information would Cyrus gain if it was practical to take many samples at many tournaments in the county?

c. If many samples could be taken, the distribution of percentages in each of the samples might look like this:

% preferring water: 84% 71% 73% 83% 80% 80%
79% 77% 81% 72% 81% 78%

Make a box plot of the sample means. With this additional information, make a new statement about volleyball players and water.

8-44. LEARNING LOG

Make an entry in your Learning Log titled "Inferences From Random Samples" and add today's date. Then discuss with your team and answer the following questions for your Learning Log entry. Why would you want to take a sample instead of just testing the entire population? What is the best way to take a sample from a population? Why are random samples more representative of the population than other kinds of samples? What additional information would you have if you could take many samples from the same population? What information can you get from a random sample?

METHODS AND MEANINGS

MATH NOTES

Random Samples

There are many techniques for taking samples from populations. You are familiar with convenience samples, voluntary response samples, and cluster samples. However, a **random sample** is the best way to get a sample that is most representative of the population.

If you were conducting a survey, you might think it would be a good idea to pick some athletes, some band members, and some honor students to represent the school. The problem with intentionally sampling students is that it is too easy to miss an important group of students. By *randomly* picking students you would get some athletes, some band members, and some honor students. But most importantly, you would also get some students that you forgot about or did not know about, such as, the drama club students.

A random sample is representative of the whole population. Therefore, you can use random samples to make **inferences** (predictions) about characteristics of the whole population, without having to measure every single item in the population.

8-45. Athena was working on her Girl Scout silver award and was wondering what percentage of people support the Girl Scouts financially through cookie sales outside the grocery store.

At the next cookie sale, Athena kept track of how many customers at the grocery store walked by the cookie table and how many stopped to purchase cookies. 32% of families stopped and purchased cookies at the table.

Athena continued collecting data at several different grocery stores around town. Here are the percent of those who bought cookies at each store:

32% 29% 19% 31% 30% 24% 38% 33% 42% 25% 22% 27%

Make a box plot of the samples, then make a new statement about what proportion of people (in what interval) you can expect to buy Girl Scout cookies at the grocery store.

8-46. Bee is tiling her kitchen floor using square tiles that are 1 foot long on each side. The rectangular floor is 13 feet by 7 feet.

a. If she has 86 tiles, does she have enough to cover the floor? If not, how many more does she need?

b. Does she have enough to tile just around the edges of the kitchen? If so, how many leftover tiles will she have? If not, how many more will she need? Draw a picture and show your work.

8-47. Draw an isosceles trapezoid (a trapezoid with two equal, non-parallel sides). Label the top base 6 cm and the height 4 cm. If the area of this trapezoid is 36 square cm, what is the length of the other base? You may find it helpful to use the 5-D Process to write an equation to solve.

8-48. Simplify each expression.

a. $\frac{5}{12}+(-\frac{7}{8})-(-\frac{1}{6})$

b. $-\frac{11}{15}-\frac{4}{5}-(-\frac{57}{60})$

c. $4\frac{1}{12}+(-1\frac{5}{6})$

d. $-\frac{7}{11}\cdot\frac{8}{9}$

e. $\frac{1}{3}\cdot\frac{1}{2}+\frac{5}{6}$

f. $-\frac{4}{6}\cdot(-\frac{9}{2})$

8-49. Solve these equations for x. Check your answers.

a. $2(x+4.5)=32$

b. $6+2.5x=21$

c. $\frac{x}{9}=\frac{5}{16}$

8-50. Autumn and her friends had dinner at their favorite restaurant, and the bill came to $60. They decided to leave 18% of the bill for a tip. Without using a calculator, help them compute how much money is 18% of the bill.

8.3.1 What is an angle?

Introduction to Angles

Have you ever watched a dance team performing a routine in which each person moves and spins in perfect unison? Each dancer always knows exactly how many times to turn and the direction in which he or she should end up facing. In this lesson, you will develop ways to describe turns by investigating angles and look at angles inside shapes.

8-51. MY HEAD IS SPINNING!

What does it mean to "do a three-sixty (360)"? What about "a one-eighty (180)"?

a. Your teacher will instruct you to stand up and "do a 360," that is, to turn 360°. Then your teacher will instruct you to "do a 180," that is, to turn 180°.

b. Work with your team to design a clear and consistent way to draw diagrams to represent these movements. Be sure your diagrams include something that shows the direction a person would face at the beginning and the end of the turn as well as the size of the turn in between.

c. What would it mean to "do a 90," or to turn 90°? What about "a 45"? Add diagrams for these movements. Be prepared to explain your diagrams to the class.

8-52. When your teacher asked you to "do a 360," how did you know what to do? "360" refers to turning in a full circle, that is, turning completely around right back to where you started. The most common unit used to measure rotation is a **degree** and there are 360 degrees in one full rotation.

Get a copy of the Lesson 8.3.1A Resource Page, which has a diagram of the angle shown at right. Work with your team to *estimate* the measure of this angle in degrees. Be prepared to explain how you determined your estimate.

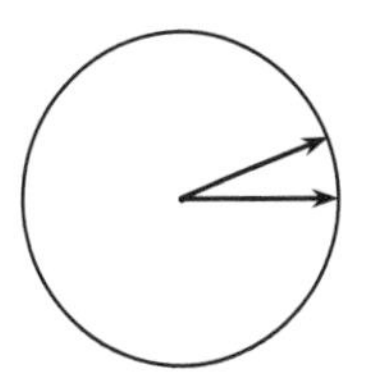

8-53. ANGLE RULERS

How can you measure angles accurately using degrees? In this activity, you will build a device (you can call it an "angle ruler") to help you measure angles in degrees.

Your Task: Get a copy of the Lesson 8.3.1B Resource Page, which contains a diagram like the one at right. Work with your team to find a way to fold and label the resource page multiple times to make it into an "angle ruler." The ruler is started with 0° and includes a mark for 180°. Be sure to design your angle ruler so that you can measure common angles such as 30°, 45°, 60°, 90° and 135°. Be prepared to explain your strategy.

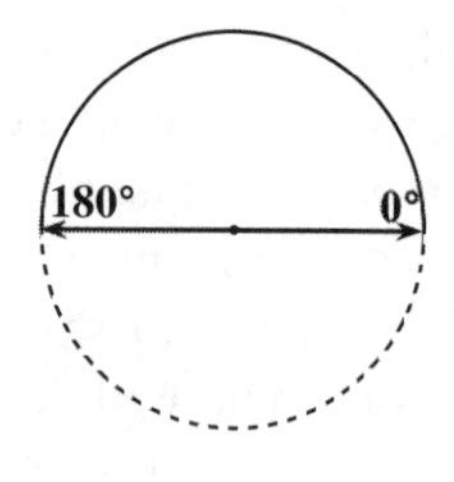

Discussion Points

How can we partition it into pieces of equal angle?

How big is this angle in degrees?

Can we subdivide it any further?

8-54. Use your new "angle ruler" to measure the angle you estimated in problem 8-52. Check with your teacher to see if your measurement is reasonable. How accurate is your new measurement tool?

8-55. Actually, "angle rulers" exist. They are called **protractors**.

a. Get a protractor from your teacher. Compare it with the one that you made. In what ways are they similar and in what ways are they different?

b. Hunter used a protractor to measure the angle at right. He got 60°. Is his answer reasonable? Explain why or why not.

c. When measuring an angle with a protractor, is it necessary to line up one side of the angle with the 0° or 180° mark? If you did not, how would you figure out what the measure of the angle was? Explain.

8-56. Estimate the angles formed in the diagrams below *without measuring*. Be ready to explain your estimates.

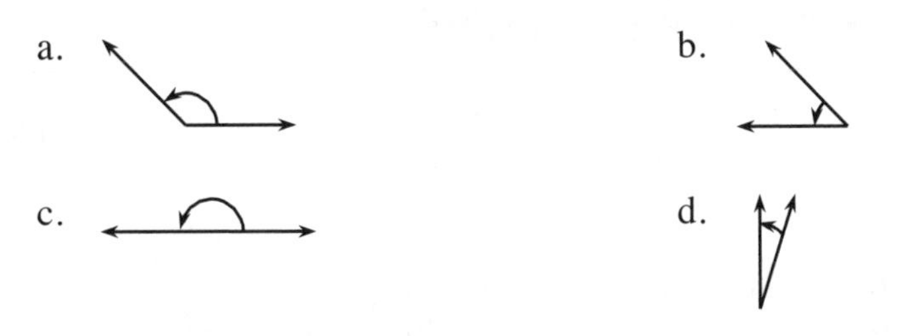

8-57. Angles can be thought of as the result of a rotation or turn. They can also help you to describe shapes.

Get a Lesson 8.3.1C Resource Page, which has larger diagrams of each of the figures below. First *estimate*, then *measure* the indicated angles in degrees.

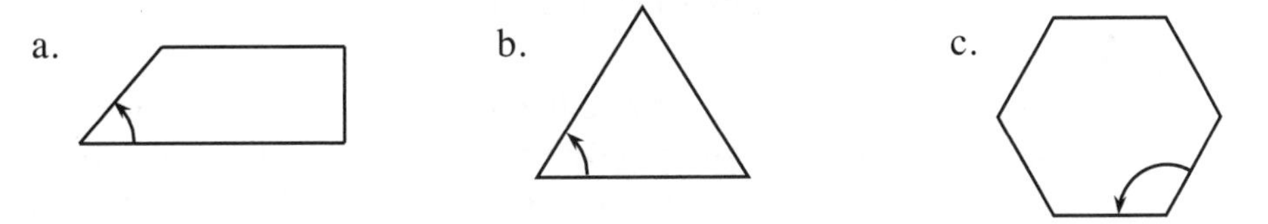

8-58. UNIQUE UNITS

Additional Challenge: Does a complete rotation *have to be* broken into exactly 360 small parts? What if you used a different unit?

a. Work with your team to invent a *new* unit to measure angles. Give it a name and decide how many of your units fit into a full circle.

b. Draw diagrams to represent angles resulting from a full turn, a half-turn, a quarter-turn, and $\frac{1}{8}$ of a turn and then label the measurement of each angle with your new unit. Be prepared to share your diagrams with the rest of the class and to explain how to measure with your unit.

c. Examine the diagram at right. Estimate the measure of this angle in your new unit. Be prepared to explain how you got your estimate.

8-59. LEARNING LOG

In your Learning Log, explain what an angle is and how you can estimate the measure of an angle in degrees. Include diagrams to explain your thinking. Title this entry "Angles" and label it with today's date.

MATH NOTES

Angles

To understand the meaning of an angle, picture two rays starting at a single point called the **vertex** of the angle, as shown in the diagram at right. (A **ray** is a part of a line that starts at a point and goes on without end in one direction.) An **angle** is formed by two rays (or line segments) that have the same starting point (or **endpoint**). The **measure** of an angle is how many degrees you rotate your starting ray to get to the ray on the opposite side of an angle. One way to visualize an angle is as a measure of how "open" the gap is between the two rays.

angle

Angles are named by their size in comparison to a right angle. That is, they are named according to whether they are less than, greater than, or equal to a right angle. An **acute angle** measures less than 90°. An **obtuse angle** measures more than 90° and less than 180°. The little box in an angle indicates that it is a **right angle**, which measures 90°). A **straight angle** measures 180° and forms a straight line.

acute angle | right angle | obtuse angle | straight angle

Review & Preview

8-60. Estimate the measure of each angle below.

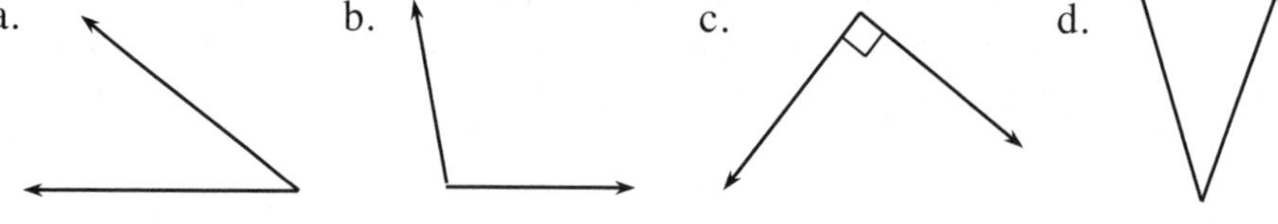

8-61. Write an equation that represents each diagram below and find the value of the variable.

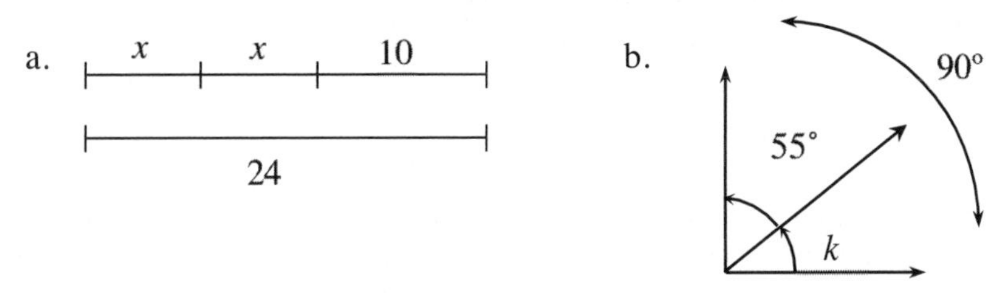

8-62. Simplify each expression.

a. $\frac{9}{15} \div \frac{4}{3}$ b. $-\frac{19}{20} + \frac{4}{5}$ c. $-\frac{8}{9} \div (-\frac{2}{5})$ d. $3\frac{1}{2} \div 1\frac{1}{7}$

e. $-\frac{3}{4} - (-\frac{11}{16})$ f. $\frac{2}{9} \cdot \frac{14}{15} \cdot (-\frac{9}{10})$ g. $-10\frac{4}{5} + (-\frac{3}{8})$ h. $\frac{12}{5} \div (-\frac{1}{10})$

8-63. Ms. Carpenter asked each of her students to record how much time it takes them to get from school to home this afternoon. The next day, students came back with this data, in minutes: 15, 12, 5, 55, 6, 9, 47, 8, 35, 3, 22, 26, 46, 54, 17, 42, 43, 42, 15, 5.

a. Create a combination histogram and box plot to display this information. Use a bin width of 10 minutes.

b. Find the mean and the median. Why does neither plot seem very adequate in describing the center of this distribution? How could you better describe a "typical" trip home?

c. Considering the situation, make a conjecture as to why this data has a shape with two peaks.

8-64. Kirk's grandparents are really enjoying their portable music players and have downloaded many more albums. Maude now has 225 albums, 135 of which are heavy metal. Claude now has 450 albums, 270 of which are heavy metal. Which of Kirk's grandparents has a higher probability of listening to heavy metal?

8-65. Josue called his father to say that he was almost home. He had traveled 61.5 miles, which was $\frac{3}{4}$ of the way home. Write and solve an equation to calculate the total distance he will travel to get home.

8.3.2 What kind of angle is it?

Classifying Angles

If you look around you, you will see angles everywhere. Angles are important in construction, sports, and art. In the previous lesson, you learned how to measure angles using a protractor. Today you will classify angles and use your protractor to identify special angles.

8-66. In geometry, an **angle** is formed by two rays with a common endpoint. A **ray** is a line that has an endpoint and extends infinitely in a particular direction. The point where the two rays intersect is called the **vertex** of the angle.

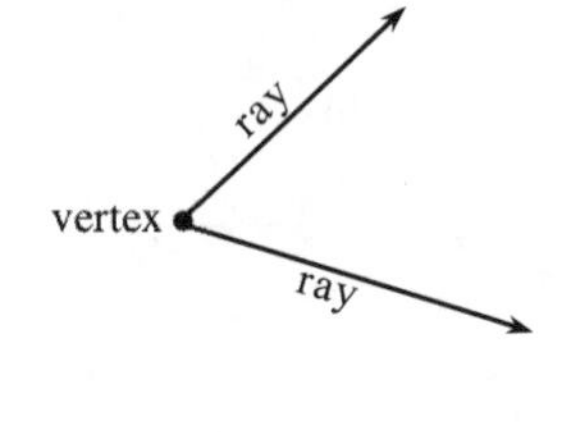

One of the most common angles is a right angle. A **right angle** measures 90°. If an angle measures less than 90°, it is called an **acute angle**. If an angle measures more than 90° but less than 180°, it is called an **obtuse angle**.

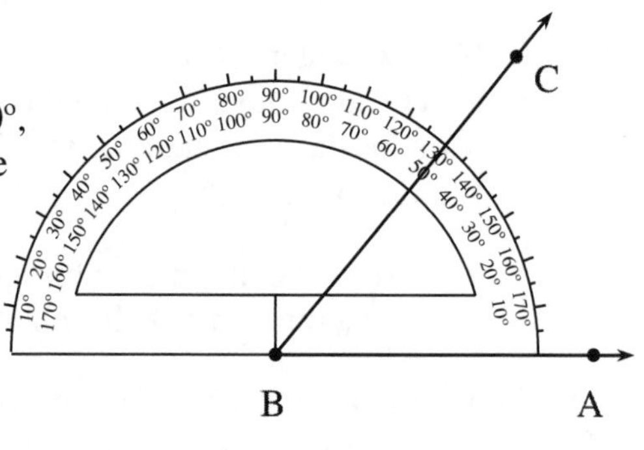

Use a protractor to find the measure of each angle, and then classify it according to its measure.

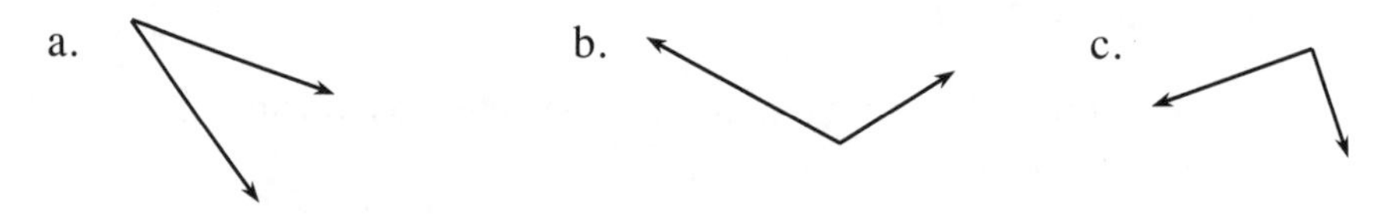

d. A straight line is also called a **straight angle**. Draw a straight angle on your paper. What is the measure of a straight angle?

8-67. The diagrams below show some students' use of protractors. Explain what each student needs to do to find the correct angle measure.

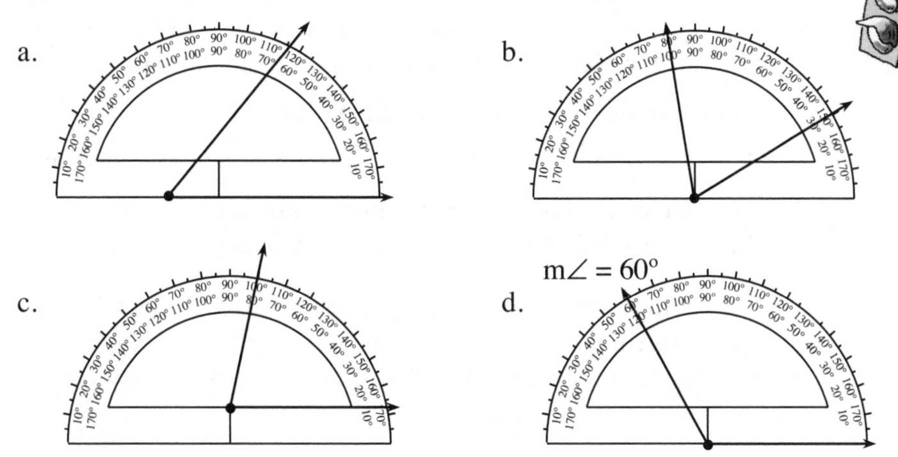

8-68. **Complementary angles** are two angles with a sum of 90°.

Supplementary angles are two angles with a sum of 180°.

a. Use your protractor to measure each of the angles below and determine which angles are complementary and which angles are supplementary.

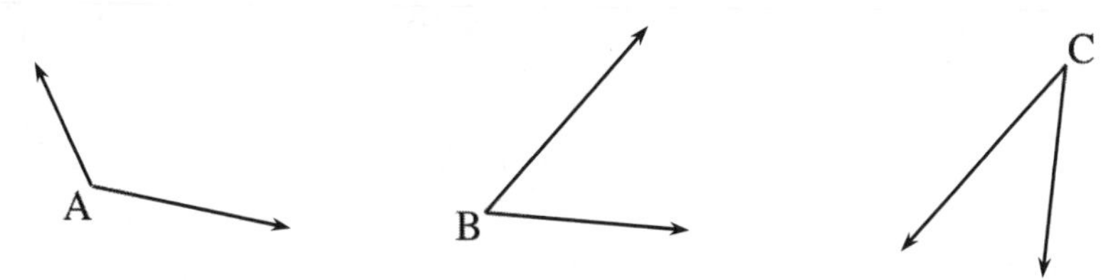

b. With your team, come up with a strategy for remembering the definitions of complementary and supplementary.

8-69. ADJACENT ANGLES

Angles that share that same vertex and one side are referred to as **adjacent angles**. "Adjacent" in the English language means "next to." For two angles to be adjacent, they must satisfy the following three conditions:

1. The two angles must have a common (shared or same) side.
2. They must have a common vertex (a common starting point for all sides).
3. They can have no interior points in common (no overlap is permitted). The common side must be between the two angles.

Copy each of the figures below onto your paper. Determine which pairs of angles are adjacent and which are not by checking to see if each angle pair satisfies all three conditions. Write "yes" or "no" next to each figure. If you write "no," give a short explanation.

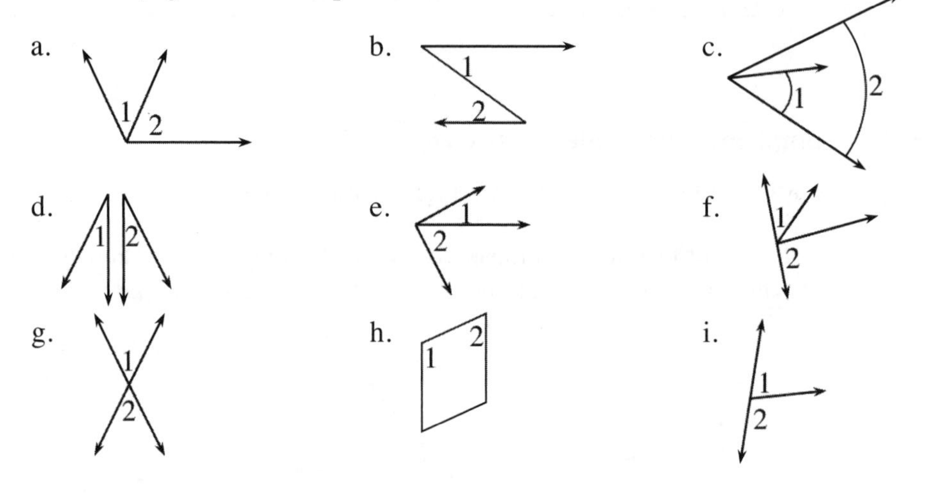

8-70. VERTICAL ANGLES

Angles formed by two intersecting lines that are not adjacent are called **vertical angles**. In the diagram at right, angles 1 and 2 are vertical angles.

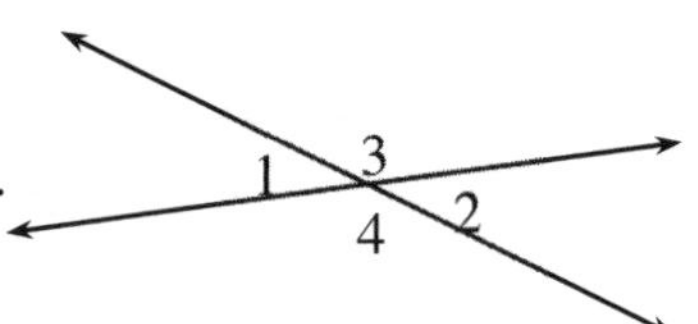

a. What can you say about angles 3 and 4?

b. Use your protractor to measure each of the four angles. What do you notice?

c. Draw a pair of vertical angles on your paper. Each team member should draw angles with different measures. Measure your vertical angles. What do you think is true about the measures of vertical angles?

8-71. Find the measure of the missing angles.

a. $\angle 1 = 75°$

$\angle 2 = ?$

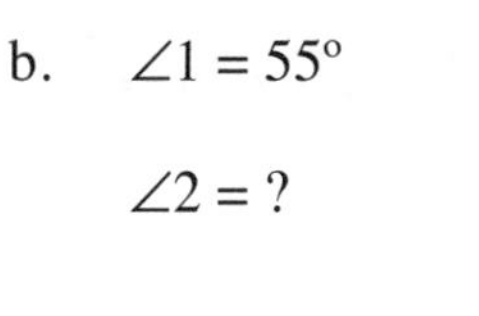

b. $\angle 1 = 55°$

$\angle 2 = ?$

c. $\angle 1$ and $\angle 2$ are complementary

$\angle 1 = 27°$

$\angle 2 = ?$

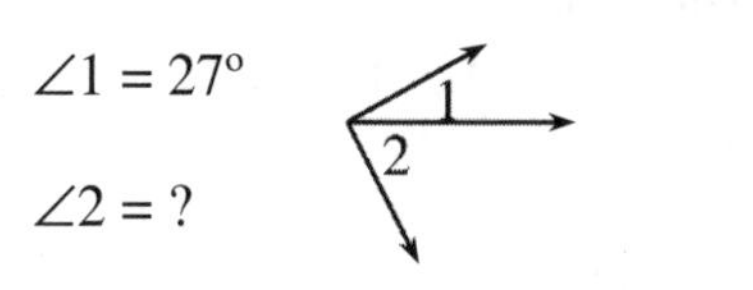

d. $\angle 1$ and $\angle 2$ are supplementary

$\angle 1 = 30°$

$\angle 2 = ?$

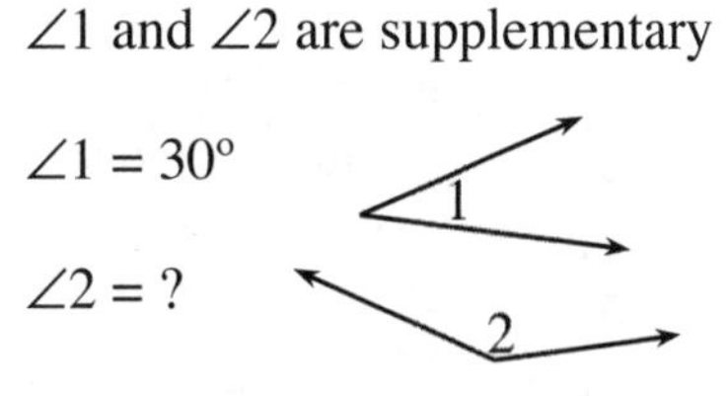

8-72. The problems below describe other situations where some angles have been put together to create larger angles. For each problem below, write an equation to represent the situation and then answer the question.

a. Three angles that all have the same measure and one 36° angle combine to make a 90° angle, as shown in the diagram at right. What is the measure of each of the three unmarked angles?

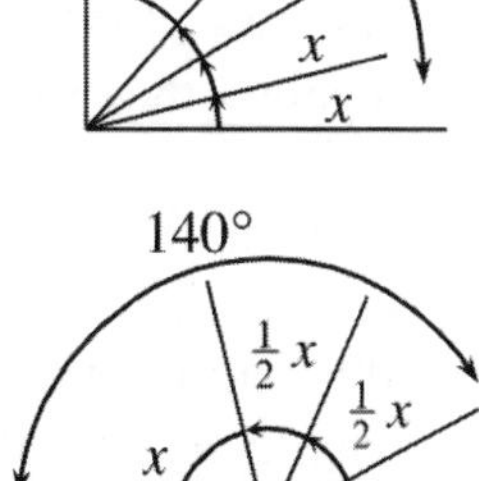

b. **Additional Challenge:** One angle and two other angles that are each half as large as the first combine to create an angle that measures 140°, as shown in the diagram at right. What are the measures of each of the angles?

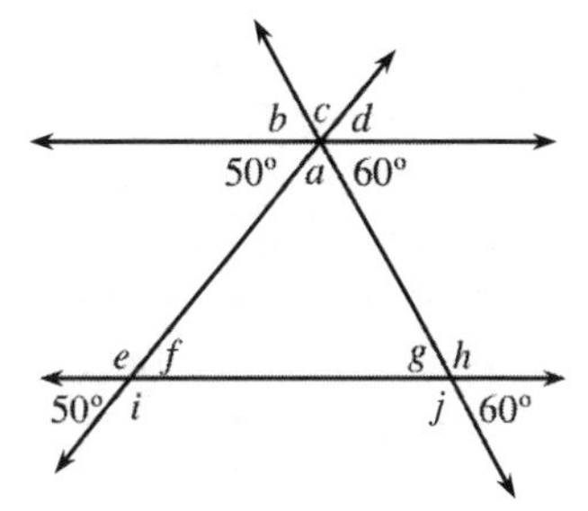

8-73. **Additional Challenge:** Determine the size of all of the angles labeled with variables.

METHODS AND MEANINGS

MATH NOTES

Angle Relationships

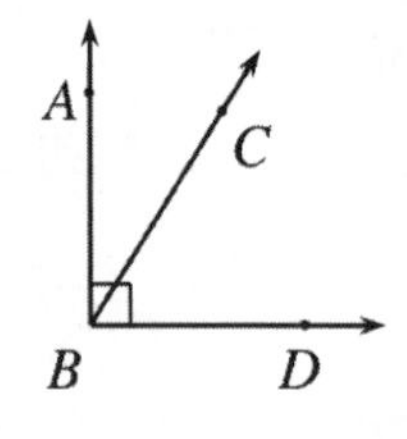

It is common to identify angles using three letters. For example, $\angle ABC$ means the angle you would find by going from point A, to point B, to point C in the diagram at right. Point B is the **vertex** of the angle (where the endpoints of the two sides meet) and $\overrightarrow{BA}$ and $\overrightarrow{BC}$ are the rays that define it. A **ray** is a part of a line that has an endpoint (starting point) and extends infinitely in one direction.

If two angles have measures that add up to 90°, they are called **complementary angles**. For example, in the diagram above right, $\angle ABC$ and $\angle CBD$ are complementary because together they form a right angle.

E F H G

If two angles have measures that add up to 180°, they are called **supplementary angles**. For example, in the diagram at right, $\angle EFG$ and $\angle GFH$ are supplementary because together they form a straight angle.

Two angles do not have to share a vertex to be complementary or supplementary. The first pair of angles at right are supplementary; the second pair of angles are complementary.

120° 60°

Supplementary

40° 50°

Complementary

Adjacent angles are angles that have a common vertex, share a common side, and have no interior points in common. So $\angle c$ and $\angle d$ in the diagram at right are adjacent angles, as are $\angle c$ and $\angle f$, $\angle f$ and $\angle g$, and $\angle g$ and $\angle d$.

c d f g

Vertical angles are the two opposite (that is, non-adjacent) angles formed by two intersecting lines, such as angles $\angle c$ and $\angle g$ in the diagram above right. $\angle c$ by itself is not a vertical angle, nor is $\angle g$, although $\angle c$ and $\angle g$ together are a pair of vertical angles. Vertical angles always have equal measure.

8-74. Alexander and Santiago put five pattern blocks together with one vertex of each block touching, as shown in the diagram at right. Work with your team to find the measure of the smaller angle of a beige rhombus.

8-75. Use the vocabulary terms you learned today to classify the following angle pairs. Use the terms complementary, supplementary, adjacent, and vertical.

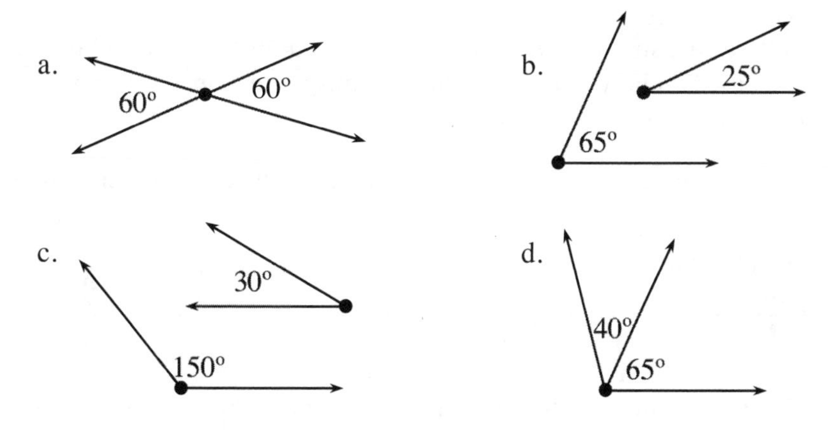

8-76. Graph the following points on a coordinate graph: $A(-3,-3)$, $B(3,0)$, $C(3,6)$, $D(-3,6)$. Connect the points as you plot them. Then connect point A to point D.

a. Describe the shape you have created.

b. Identify the types of angles at points A, B, C, and D.

8-77. Scientists studying prehistoric birds have estimated the weights (in grams) of two different sub-species of birds. The data they collected is shown below.

Pre-emergent thrushes:

$$49, 54, 52, 58, 61, 72, 73, 78, 73, 82, 83, 73, 61, 67, 68$$

Post-emergent thrushes:

$$65, 35, 48, 29, 57, 87, 94, 68, 86, 73, 58, 74, 85, 91, 88, 97$$

a. Create a parallel box plot to compare the weights of these two sub-species of birds.

b. Would the mean accurately represent the middle of the data? Why or why not?

c. A fossil of a bird is found. Scientists estimated that its weight must have been around 75 grams. Which sub-species was the bird most likely a member of? Explain.

8-78. A candy store's specialty is taffy. Customers can fill a bag with taffy and the price is based on how much the candy weighs. The store charges $2 for 10 ounces of taffy.

a. Copy the table below and fill in the missing values. Add three more entries.

Amount of taffy (ounces)	2	5	10	12	15	20
Price ($)			$2			$4

b. Graph the values in the table. Let x represent the number of ounces and y represent the price in dollars.

c. Is this situation proportional? Explain your reasoning.

8-79. Write an equation to represent this situation and answer the question. Use the 5-D Process to help you define a variable and write an equation if necessary.

Ella is trying to determine the side lengths of a triangle. She knows that the longest side is three times longer than the shortest side. The medium side is ten more than twice the shortest side. If the perimeter is 142 cm, how long is each side?

8.3.3 How can I build it?

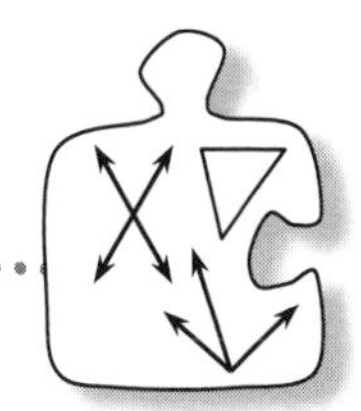

Constructing Shapes

Architects and drafters make careful drawings of the buildings that they design. The drawings represent how the building should be constructed. They show the thickness of the walls and where doors, windows, and pipes will be. To make these precise diagrams, professionals often use special computer software. However, some architects still prefer to draw diagrams by hand at least some of the time. They use special drawing tools that look something like those in the drawing at right, including a right triangle tool and a protractor.

Building plans are just one example of a precise geometric drawing. Mathematicians have used these basic tools to draw accurate diagrams for other reasons. In mathematics, making a **construction** is the process of using a straightedge and compass to solve a problem or create a geometric diagram. Constructing shapes that meet different guidelines can help you understand many of the specific characteristics of those shapes. In this lesson, you will use given conditions to construct your own shapes.

8-80. Without looking at anyone else's work, each member of your team should draw a triangle with one angle that measures 60° and one side that is 1.5 cm long.

a. When each member of your team has finished, check the drawings of your teammates by trading papers and measuring the sides and angles. Does everyone have a triangle that matches the given description? If not, come up with a strategy for drawing accurately sized angles and line segments. Are all of the triangles the same as one another?

b. Measure each of the three angles in your triangle. What is the sum of the three angles? Share your answer with your team. Make a conjecture about the sum of the angles in a triangle.

8-81. Again, without looking at each others papers, have each member of your team draw a quadrilateral with one angle that measures 30°, one angle that measures 60°, and one side that is 5 cm long.

a. Again, when each member of your team is finished, check the drawings of your teammates by trading papers and measuring the sides and angles. Does everyone have a quadrilateral that matches the given description? Are all of the quadrilaterals the same as one another?

b. Measure each of the four angles in your quadrilateral. What is the sum of the four angles? Share your answer with your team. Make a conjecture about the sum of the angles in a quadrilateral.

8-82. All measurements have a small degree of error and measurements made by people can vary quite a bit as you discovered in Lesson 8.1.1 and 8.1.2. Using technology to construct shapes can give you more accurate information and allow you to test more situations more quickly.

a. First, check your conclusions from problem 8-80 using technology. Work with a partner to make a triangle with the same conditions as those given in problem 8-80 using the technology tool (or the Lesson 8.3.3 Resource Page). Verify your results from problem 8-80. That is, does each of your triangles look the same as the one that you made in problem 8-80? Is the sum of the angles for each triangle still the same?

b. Now use the same technology tool or resource page materials to create the quadrilaterals that you and your partner made in problem 8-81. Again, verify your results that the quadrilaterals look the same as those that you made by hand and that the sum of angles for each is the same.

8-83. On your own, write down two specific conditions for a triangle. Then trade papers with someone in your team and draw the triangle specified. Check to see if your partner drew the triangle correctly. If they did not, verbally help them to draw it correctly. Do not draw the triangle for them.

8-84. On your own, write down three specific conditions for a drawing a quadrilateral. Then trade paper with a different person in your team and have them draw your quadrilateral. Check to see if they drew the quadrilateral correctly. If they did not, verbally help them to draw it correctly. Do not draw the quadrilateral for them.

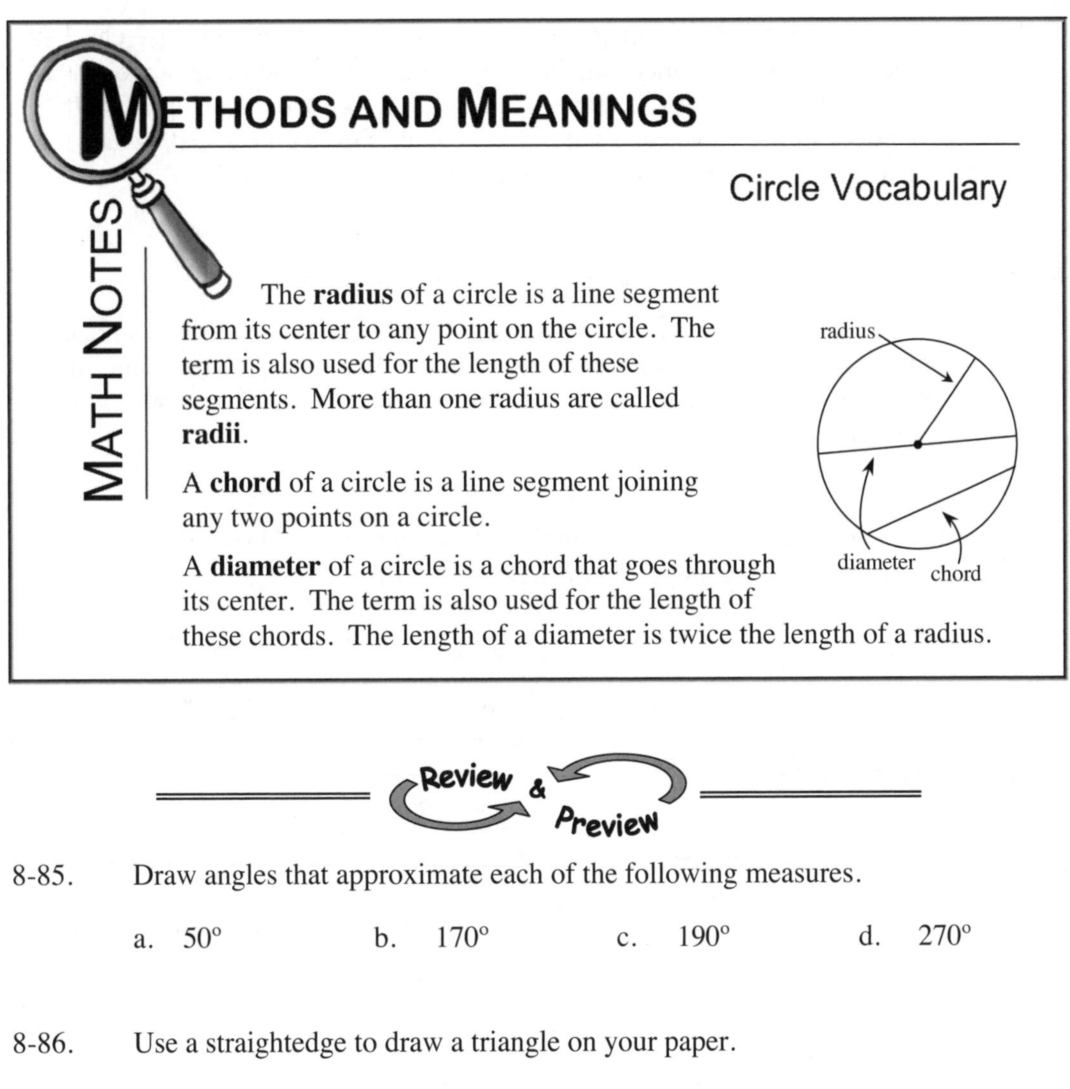

Methods and Meanings

Math Notes

Circle Vocabulary

The **radius** of a circle is a line segment from its center to any point on the circle. The term is also used for the length of these segments. More than one radius are called **radii**.

A **chord** of a circle is a line segment joining any two points on a circle.

A **diameter** of a circle is a chord that goes through its center. The term is also used for the length of these chords. The length of a diameter is twice the length of a radius.

Review & Preview

8-85. Draw angles that approximate each of the following measures.

a. 50° b. 170° c. 190° d. 270°

8-86. Use a straightedge to draw a triangle on your paper.

a. Estimate the measure of each angle in your triangle and label it.

b. Add your three estimated angle measures. What do you notice? Do you need to change any of your estimates?

8-87. Read the Math Notes box for this lesson and then find the length of the radius and diameter of each of the following circles.

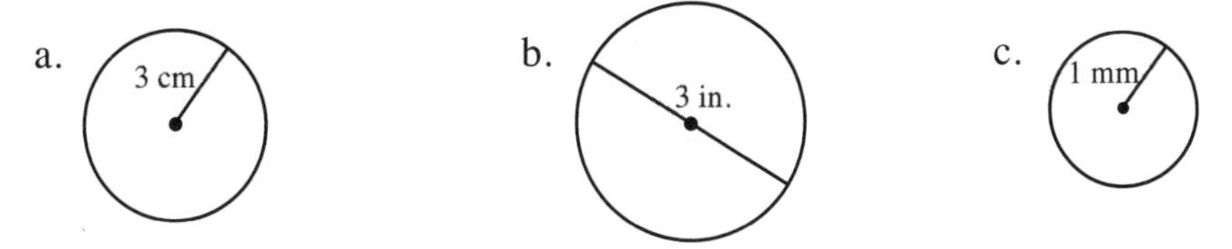

8-88. Tino works at a retail clothing store as a sales clerk and part of his paycheck is based on commission, meaning that it is determined by the value of the clothes that he sells. Each week, he earns $7 an hour plus 15% of his total sales. If Tino works for 18 hours and sells $538 in clothes in a certain week, what is the amount of his commission? What is his total pay for that week?

8-89. Write and solve a proportion for the following problem.

In a recent survey for the student council, Dominique found that 150 students out of a total of 800 students on campus did *not* like soda. If half of the student body was going to attend a dance, how many students could she expect would want soda?

8-90. Find the value of each variable in the following figures. Do not use a protractor. Use the properties of angles to help you.

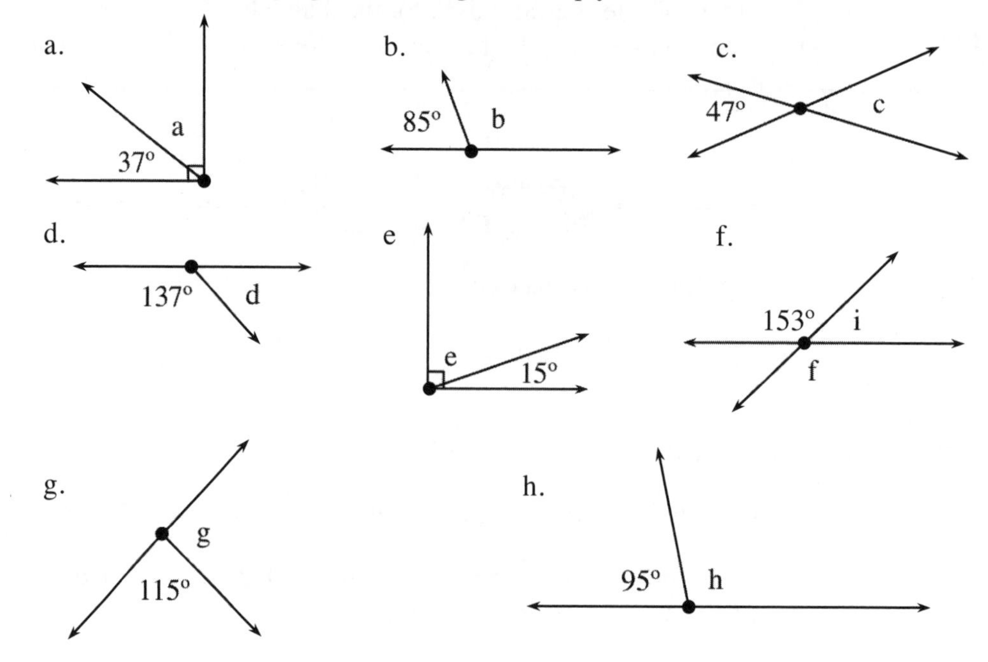

8.3.4 How many triangles can I make?

Building Triangles

Triangles are important shapes. They are the basic building blocks of many architectural designs and structural supports. A tripod stool will tend to be more stable than a chair with four legs. This is because of triangles!

In Lesson 8.3.3 you became familiar with the technology tool for building shapes and gained some basic information about angles in triangles and quadrilaterals. Today, you will do a more in-depth investigation of triangles, you will learn about when a triangle can and cannot be made, and you will discover the necessary condition to create a unique triangle.

8-91. How many different "parts" does a triangle have that can be specified or measured? What are these parts?

8-92. How many different triangles do you think that you can make specifying only two measures to use for the triangle's parts, such as one angle and one side, two angles, or two sides? Work with a partner to investigate this question using the technology tool (or the Lesson 8.3.3 Resource Page materials). Each person will attempt to build a triangle with the specified angle measures and/or side lengths listed below without looking at their partner's drawing. For each triangle that you build and each set of conditions given, do the following:

- Compare the triangle that you built to one that your partner built and decide whether they are the same or not. Are your triangles the same or different? Are there any other possible triangles that can be built using the same conditions? State your conclusion.
- Sketch the triangle(s) on your paper, labeling the given angles or side lengths.

a. One side length 4.5 cm and one angle 135°

b. Two angles: 90° and 60°

c. Two side lengths: 4.5 cm and 7 cm

8-93. Discuss with your team whether or not knowing only two of the six possible measurements for the parts of any triangle is enough information to always draw *exactly* the same triangle. Test your conjecture with more examples until your team is satisfied that you are accurate. Write a summary of your conclusions and your reasons for them.

8-94. Imagine now that three possible measures for a triangle's six parts (3 angles or 3 side lengths) are given. Do you think that everyone will make the same triangle in that case?

a. First, investigate this question for three possible side lengths given. Follow the same instructions as you did in problem 8-92 including building, sketching and labeling the figure(s) you make as well as stating your conclusion for each part. Use the technology tool or the Lesson 8.3.3 Resource Page.

i. 1.5 cm, 5 cm, and 4.5 cm.

ii. 4.5 cm, 5 cm, and 7 cm.

iii. 1.5 cm, 4.5 cm, and 7 cm.

b. At this point, what do you think must be true about the sides of a triangle in order to create at least one triangle? Write down your ideas. Then work with your team to test your ideas by selecting at least 3 more sets of side lengths and trying to build triangles with them.

c. Discuss with your team whether knowing any three possible side lengths for a triangle is enough information for everyone to draw *exactly* the same triangle. Write a summary of your conclusions and your reasons for them.

8-95. Now investigate this same question for angles. That is, do you think that everyone will make the same triangle when given 3 angle measurements?

a. One more time, follow the same instructions as you did in problem 8-92 including building, sketching and labeling the figure(s) you make as well as stating your conclusion for each part. Use the technology tool or the Lesson 8.3.3 Resource Page.

i. $90°, 60°$, and $30°$.

ii. $90°, 45°$ and $45°$.

iii. $135°, 45°$, and $60°$.

b. At this point, what do you think must be true about the angle measurements in order to create at least one triangle? Write down your ideas. Then work with your team to test your ideas by selecting at least 3 more sets of angle measurements and trying to build triangles with them.

c. Discuss with your team whether or not knowing all 3 of the angles of a triangle is enough information for everyone to draw *exactly* the same triangle. Write a summary of your conclusions and your reasons for them.

8-96. In problem 8-94 you found that if you are given three lengths to build the sides of a triangle, then if a triangle can be formed, all the triangles you could make were the same. Suppose you start with two triangles knowing that their three pairs of corresponding sides are the same, as shown in the diagram below.

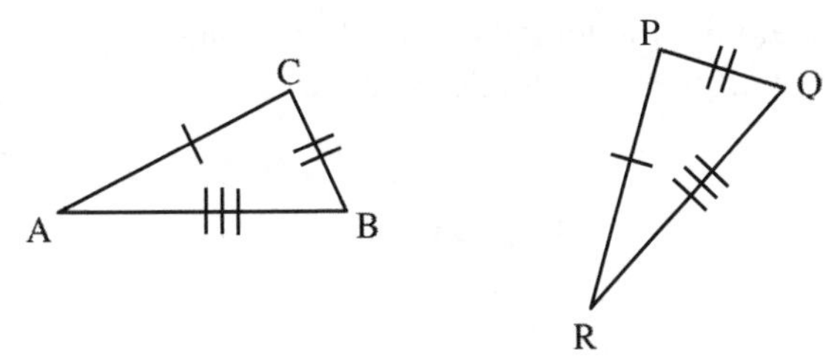

a. Examine the diagram. What do you think the markings indicate? Name the pairs of corresponding sides.

b. What can you say about the two triangles and why? What can you say about their angles? Why?

8-97. LEARNING LOG

In this lesson, you learned a lot of important information about triangles. You learned about the necessary conditions for side lengths and angles to make a triangle. You also learned how to determine if a triangle you create under given conditions would automatically be the same as everyone else's triangle. You will study these concepts in more detail in later math courses.

Make an entry in your Learning Log that summarizes your understanding at this point. Include the following: How much information do you need to make a triangle? Will that given information always create only one triangle, or could it create many triangles? How can you tell how many different triangles can be made, without actually trying to make the triangles? Title your entry "Constructing Triangles" and include today's date.

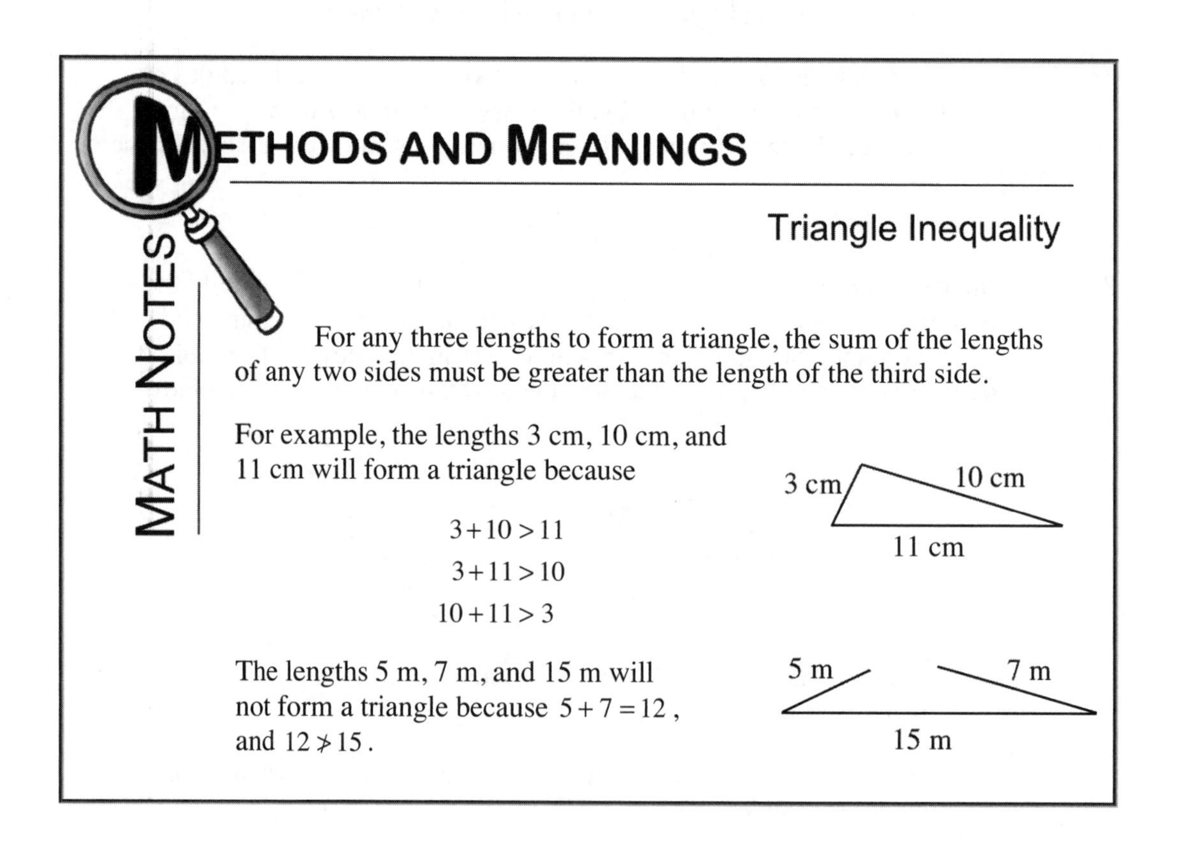

MATH NOTES

METHODS AND MEANINGS

Triangle Inequality

For any three lengths to form a triangle, the sum of the lengths of any two sides must be greater than the length of the third side.

For example, the lengths 3 cm, 10 cm, and 11 cm will form a triangle because

$$3+10>11$$
$$3+11>10$$
$$10+11>3$$

The lengths 5 m, 7 m, and 15 m will not form a triangle because $5+7=12$, and $12 \ngtr 15$.

8-98. You learned in an earlier lesson how to classify an angle by comparing it to a 90° right angle. Find the measure of each angle below and classify it according to its measure.

a. What is the measure of half of a right angle?

b. If the angle at right is made with a right angle added to half of a right angle, what is its measure?

c. Suppose a right angle is divided into three equal angles as shown at right. What is the measure of each angle?

8-99. Gail bought a new baseball cap for \$7.50, which was $\frac{1}{3}$ off the original price. What was the original price?

8-100. Karla's traditional hybrid car gets 35% fewer miles per gallon than Jeenie's solar hybrid car. If Jeenie's car gets 60 miles per gallon, how many miles per gallon does Karla's car get? Calculate Karla's car's mileage in two different ways, using two different scale factors (multipliers).

8-101. Adriel and Gustavo were playing a game with algebra tiles. As they compared them, they were left with the following expressions on their mats. Use legal moves to simplify what is on the mats. Be sure to record your work in a way that others can understand.

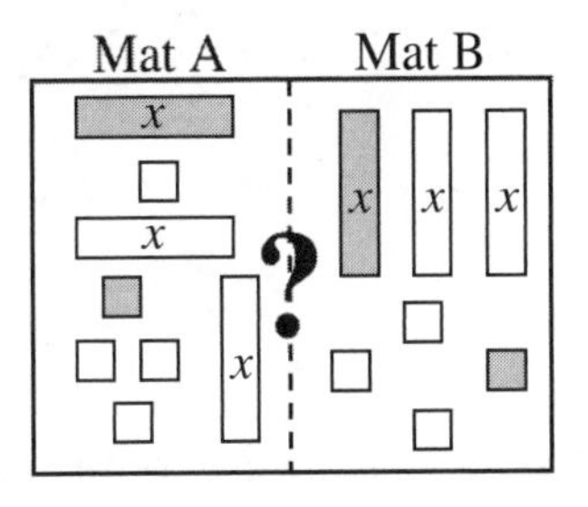

Can you determine which side has the greater value? If so, show why. If not, for what values of x is Mat A larger?

8-102. Find the numbers that belong in the Giant One in each problem to create an equivalent fraction. Copy each problem, and show the values you used within the Giant One.

a. $\frac{7}{12} \cdot \boxed{\frac{\ }{\ }} = \frac{56}{m}$ b. $\frac{8}{3} \cdot \boxed{\frac{\ }{\ }} = \frac{n}{48}$ c. $\frac{20}{26} \cdot \boxed{\frac{\ }{\ }} = \frac{k}{39}$ d. $\frac{20}{42} \cdot \boxed{\frac{\ }{\ }} = \frac{50}{h}$

8-103. A rental car company allows a customer to select any car available on the lot. Currently there are three blue sedans, two tan trucks, two black trucks, four red convertibles, four blue minivans, two black SUVs, and three tan hybrids. What is the probability a customer will select a black vehicle?

8-104. Marley needs to construct a quadrilateral with side lengths of 2, 3, 4, and 5 centimeters. She thinks that there is only one possible quadrilateral that she can make. Is she correct?

8-105. Use a ruler and a protractor to create a triangle with two sides of 3 cm each and an angle measuring 60°.

8-106. Sketch each angle below on your paper, and label each one with its measure in degrees.

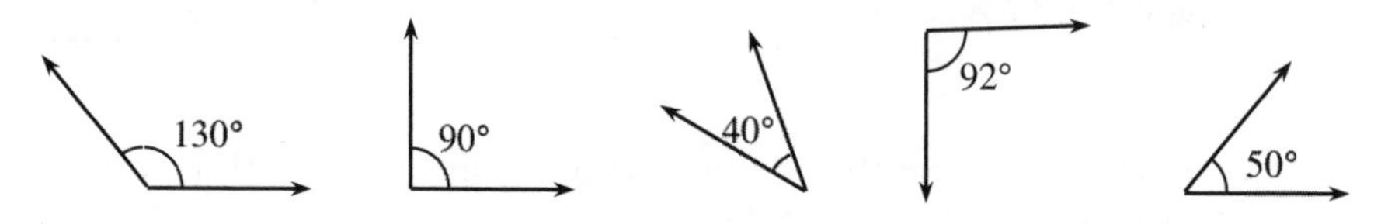

a. Identify whether each angle is an acute, obtuse, or right angle.

b. Which angles could form a complementary pair?

c. Which angles could form a supplementary pair?

8-107. Evaluate each expression.

a. $\frac{2(5+3)}{4}$

b. $\frac{1}{2}(15+3)-10 \div 2$

c. $5\frac{1}{2}-2\frac{1}{4}+\frac{3}{8}$

d. $3+\frac{3}{5}\cdot\frac{1}{4}$

e. $-2+(-5+6)^2$

f. $\frac{3}{4}\cdot\frac{1}{4}+\frac{5}{8}\cdot(-\frac{3}{2})$

8-108. Draw a coordinate graph and plot the following points: $A(-1,-1)$, $B(2,2)$, $C(4,-2)$. Connect the points in order, and then connect point C to point A. Which point could you move to make this an obtuse triangle? (Remember that an obtuse triangle is a triangle with one angle greater than $90°$.) What would be the new point?

8-109. This problem is a checkpoint for solving multi-step equations. It will be referred to as Checkpoint 8.

Solve each equation.

a. $24 = 3x + 3$

b. $6x + 12 = -x - 2$

c. $3x + 3 - x + 2 = x + 5$

d. $5(x - 1) = 5(4x - 3)$

Check your answers by referring to the Checkpoint 8 materials located at the back of your book.

Ideally, at this point you are comfortable working with these types of problems and can solve them correctly. If you feel that you need more confidence when solving these types of problems, then review the Checkpoint 8 materials and try the practice problems provided. From this point on, you will be expected to do problems like these correctly and with confidence.

Chapter 8 Closure What have I learned?

Reflection and Synthesis

The activities below offer you a chance to reflect about what you have learned during this chapter. As you work, look for concepts that you feel very comfortable with, ideas that you would like to learn more about, and topics you need more help with.

① SUMMARIZING MY UNDERSTANDING

This section gives you an opportunity to show your understanding of how variables can be used, one of the main ideas of this chapter.

Team Poster

You have been learning how to use variables and write variable expressions in different situations. You have done this to represent (1) a missing piece of information and (2) a general pattern or rule. You also learned strategies for finding the value of the variable in a specific situation as well as how to use the value given to you to evaluate an expression. This section gives you an opportunity to demonstrate what you know so far about these concepts. Today you and your team will create a poster that illustrates the skills and knowledge that you have developed in this area.

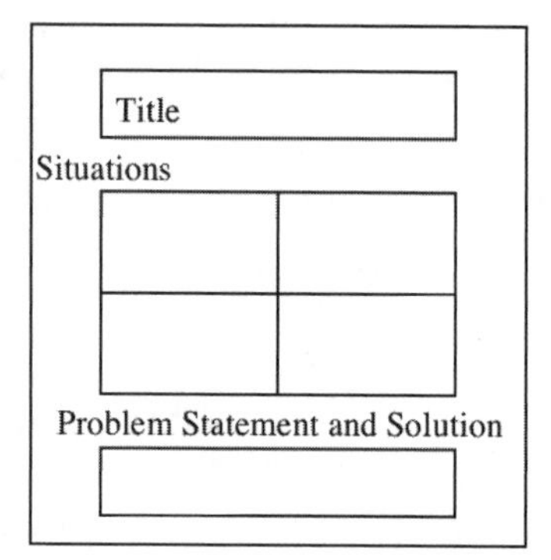

Brainstorm Situations: Follow your teacher's instructions to brainstorm a list of different situations where a variable could be used to answer a question.

Situation Descriptions: Work with your team to think of four different situations for which a variable could be used. Then each person should write a description of one of the situations and suggest a variable to use for the situation. Be sure to provide enough information so that someone unfamiliar with the situation would understand what you mean.

Write a Problem: Follow your teacher's instructions to select one situation randomly. Then work with your team to use that situation to write a problem. Remember that you will need to provide all of the necessary information and details for someone else to be able to solve the problem. Show your problem to your teacher before the next step.

Activity continues on next page. →

① *Activity continued from previous page.*

Solve Your Problem: Now your team should find the answer to your problem. This should include writing a variable expression and then showing how to get the answer. Be sure to include your reasoning for your process and enough of your steps that anyone looking at them will know what you did.

Team Poster: Follow the model above to label and construct the sections of your poster from the pieces that your team has created. Decide together on a title for your poster.

② WHAT HAVE I LEARNED?

Doing the problems in this section will help you to evaluate which types of problems you feel comfortable with and which ones you need more help with.

Solve each problem as completely as you can. The table at the end of this closure section provides answers to these problems. It also tells you where you can find additional help and where to find practice problems like them.

CL 8-110. Without a calculator, simplify each of the following expressions:

a. $20 \div 2 + (-4)(-6)$

b. $5\frac{1}{2} \cdot 1\frac{1}{3}$

c. $(0.4)(0.05)$

d. $\frac{4}{3} \div \frac{5}{8}$

e. $2 + 4(-5) + \frac{1}{2}(3+9)$

f. $2(3 + 4(10-2))$

CL 8-111. Find the missing angles in the diagrams below.

a. 27° 2x° x°

b. 142° t° a° c°

CL 8-112. Write an equation that represents each diagram and find the value of x.

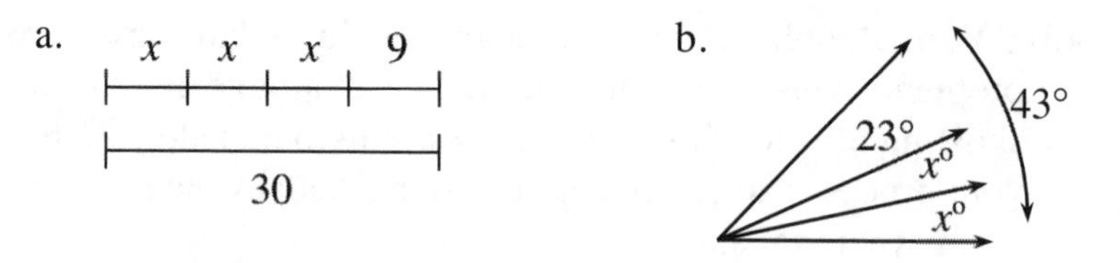

CL 8-113. Solve the proportion $\frac{22}{7} = \frac{5}{x}$ in two different ways. Show your work.

CL 8-114. If baseball were played on Mars, the balls would fly much farther than they do on Earth. One could then speculate that the number of home runs hit would be much greater on Mars. Mike expects that he would hit 50% more home runs if he were playing baseball on Mars. If he hit 76 home runs on Earth, how many home runs does he expect he would hit on Mars?

CL 8-115. Annika is saving money for a trip. She is able to save \$75 a week. Her friend from Iceland, Eva, is also saving money. Eva is able to save 9000 Kronas (Icelandic money) each week. If \$4 is equal to 509 Kronas, who is saving at a greater rate?

CL 8-116. Use the 5-D Process to help you solve the following problem.

Lillian and Isabella went shopping for school supplies. Lillian found her favorite notebook on sale so she bought three of the exact same notebook. Isabella also wanted a notebook. She bought one of the same notebooks that Lillian bought. Both girls started shopping with the same amount of money. If Lillian spent all of her money and Isabella had \$5 left, then how much money did each girl have when she arrived at the store?

CL 8-117. In 1988 the Steering Committee of the Physicians Health Study Research Group released the results of a five-year experiment on over 22,000 male physicians aged 40 to 84. The research on this sample suggested that the participants who took an aspirin every other day had a lower rate of heart attacks.

Problem continues on next page. →

CL 8-117. *Problem continued from previous page.*

a. Can you reasonably conclude from this sample that aspirin reduces heart attacks for all men and women? If you cannot conclude this, why not?

b. Can you reasonably conclude from this sample that aspirin reduces heart attacks for all men? If you cannot conclude this, why not?

c. Can you reasonably conclude from this sample that aspirin reduces heart attacks for all men aged 40 to 84? If you cannot conclude this, why not?

d. Can you reasonably conclude from this sample that aspirin reduces heart attacks for male physicians aged 40 to 84? If you cannot conclude this, why not?

e. Can you reasonably conclude from this sample that aspirin is good for male physicians aged 40 to 84? If you cannot conclude this, why not?

CL 8-118. For each of the problems above, do the following:

- Draw a bar or number line that represents 0 to 10.

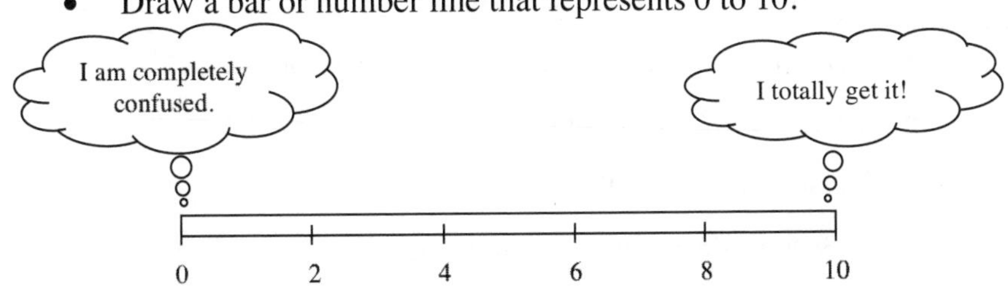

- Color or shade in a portion of the bar that represents your level of understanding and comfort with completing that problem on your own.

If any of your bars are less than a 5, choose *one* of those problems and do one of the following tasks:

- Write two questions that you would like to ask about that problem.
- Brainstorm two things that you DO know about that type of problem.

If all of your bars are at 5 or above, choose one problem and do one of these tasks:

- Write two questions you might ask or hints you might give to a student who was stuck on the problem.
- Make a new problem that is similar and more challenging than that problem and solve it.

③ WHAT TOOLS CAN I USE?

You have several tools and references available to help support your learning: your teacher, your study team, your math book, and your Toolkit, to name only a few. At the end of each chapter, you will have an opportunity to review your Toolkit for completeness. You will also revise or update it to reflect your current understanding of big ideas.

The main elements of your Toolkit should be your Learning Logs, Math Notes, and the vocabulary used in this chapter. Math words that are new appear in bold in the text. Refer to the lists provided below and follow your teacher's instructions to revise your Toolkit, which will help make it useful for you as you complete this chapter and as you work in future chapters.

Learning Log Entries

- Lesson 8.2.2 – Inferences From Random Samples
- Lesson 8.3.1 – Angles
- Lesson 8.3.4 – Constructing Triangles

Math Notes

- Lesson 8.1.2 – Comparing Box Plots
- Lesson 8.2.1 – Type of Samples from a Population
- Lesson 8.2.2 – Random Samples
- Lesson 8.3.1 – Angles
- Lesson 8.3.2 – Angle Relationships
- Lesson 8.3.3 – Circle Vocabulary
- Lesson 8.3.4 – Triangle Inequality

Mathematical Vocabulary

The following is a list of vocabulary found in this chapter. Some of the words have been seen in the previous chapter. The words in bold are words that are new to this chapter. Make sure that you are familiar with the terms below and know what they mean. For the words you do not know, refer to the glossary or index. You might also add these words to your Toolkit so that you can reference them in the future.

acute angle	**adjacent angles**	box plot
cluster sample	**complementary angles**	**construction**
convenience sample	**degree**	histogram
inference	interquartile range (IQR)	mean
median	**measure**	measure of central tendency
population	**protractor**	**obtuse angle**
outlier	quartile	**straight angle**
random sample	**ray**	**representative sample**
right angle	**supplementary angles**	**vertex**
vertical angles	**voluntary response sample**	

Answers and Support for Closure Problems
What Have I Learned?

Problem	Solution	Need Help?	More Practice
CL 8-110.	a. 34 b. $\frac{22}{3}$ or $7\frac{1}{3}$ c. 0.02 d. $\frac{32}{15}$ or $2\frac{2}{15}$ e. −12 f. 70	Lessons 1.2.6, 2.2.5, 2.2.6, and Sections 3.1 and 3.2 MN: 2.2.5, 2.3.1, 3.1.2, 3.2.2, and 3.2.4 LL: 1.2.8, 3.1.1, 3.1.2, 3.2.2, and 3.2.3	Problems CL 4-126, CL 5-155, CL 6-138, 8-9, 8-37, 8-48, 8-62, and 8-107

Problem	Solution	Need Help?	More Practice
CL 8-111.	a. $x = 51°$, $2x = 102°$ b. $a = 142°$, $t = 38°$, $c = 38°$	Lessons 8.3.2, 8.3.3, and 8.3.4 MN: 8.3.1 and 8.3.2 LL: 8.3.1	Problems 8-60, 8-75, 8-90, 8-98, and 8-106
CL 8-112.	a. $x + x + x + 9 = 30$; $x = 7$ b. $x° + x° + 23° = 43°$; $x = 10°$	Lessons 2.2.1 and 2.2.2 MN: 3.2.1	Problems CL 3-134, 8-61, and 8-74
CL 8-113.	$x = \frac{35}{22} \approx 1.59$	Section 7.2 MN: 7.2.2 LL: 7.2.2	Problems 7-100, 7-112, and 8-49 (c)
CL 8-114.	114	Lesson 7.1.7 MN: 7.1.7	Problems CL 7-120, 8-16, and 8-36
CL 8-115.	Annika is saving at a faster rate because she saves $75 a week and Eva saves about $71 a week.	Lesson 4.2.3 MN: 4.2.4	Problems CL 7-122, 8-12, and 8-26
CL 8-116.	Each girl started with $7.50.	Section 5.3 MN: 5.3.3 LL: 5.3.4	Problems CL 5-105, CL7-124, 8-11, 8-27, 8-47, and 8-79
CL 8-117.	a. No; the study did not include women. b. No; the study did not include men of all ages and professions. c. No; the study did not include men of all professions. d. This is probably a reasonable conclusion. e. No; we do not know if there are any other side effects.	Section 8.2 MN: 8.2.1 and 8.2.2 LL: 8.2.2	Problems 8-32, 8-35, and 8-45

9 Circles and Volume

CHAPTER 9 Circles and Volume

Congratulations! You have made it to the last chapter in your math book! Now you will return to geometry, learning how to find the circumference and area of a circle. In Section 9.1, you will also use this concept to find the areas of complicated figures.

In Section 9.2, you will explore how to measure the surface areas and volumes of three-dimensional solids by designing and building cereal boxes. You will visualize what the cut surface of a solid will look like if you slice it at different angles. Finally, you will investigate the volumes of shapes that do not have rectangular bases.

In the course closure and reflection (Section 9.3), you will work with your team to solve challenging problems that allow you to reflect about your learning throughout the course.

Guiding Questions

Think about these questions throughout this chapter:

How are the parts of a circle related?

How can I break this apart?

How much will it hold?

Am I measuring in one, two, or three dimensions?

In this chapter, you will learn how to:

- Calculate the circumferences and areas of circles.
- Find the areas of shapes made up of special quadrilaterals, circles, and triangles.
- Calculate the volumes of some three-dimensional shapes.
- Find the surface areas and volumes of rectangular prisms.

Chapter Outline

Section 9.1	In this section, you will learn about the relationship between the diameter and the circumference of a circle. You will also learn how to calculate the area of a circle from its radius or diameter.
Section 9.2	You will compare how surface area and volume are related by building three-dimensional rectangular prisms. Then you will visualize the shapes made when you slice prisms and use nets to see the surfaces of a prism.
Course Closure and Reflection (Section 9.3)	You will work with your team to solve challenging problems using your learning from the entire course. You will reflect about your learning and how you have been thinking as you have solved problems this year.

9.1.1 What is the multiplier?

Circumference, Diameter, and Pi

You have found *many* proportional relationships in this course. Did you realize that they were so numerous? In future math courses, you will discover that there are other types of relationships that are *not* proportional. Today, however, you will investigate one more, very important proportional relationship: the ratio of the circumference of a circle to its diameter.

9-1. Imagine a regularly sized can of tennis balls. If you were to wrap a string around the can and cut it so that it does not overlap, and then stretch the same piece of string along the can's length, how would the length of string compare to the length of the can? Would it be shorter than the can? Longer? The same length? Discuss this with your team and make a prediction.*

9-2. BUBBLE MADNESS

The idea of the **circumference** of a circle is similar to the idea of the perimeter for other shapes; it is the distance around the circle. Wrapping a string around a circular object is one way to measure its circumference. In this activity, you will investigate the relationship of the circumference of a circle to its **diameter**. The diameter is the length from one side of the circle to the other, through its center.

a. Follow the directions below.

- Obtain a bubble wand, some bubble solution, and construction paper from your teacher.
- Blow a bubble and allow it to land and pop on your construction paper. You will see a circle on your paper. (If this does not produce a clear circle, try catching the bubble you blow with your bubble wand and then placing it on the construction paper.)

Problem continues on next page. →

---

* This problem is adapted from the work of Marilyn Burns.

9-2. *Problem continued from previous page.*

- Wrap a string carefully around this circle and then stretch it along a meter stick to measure the **circumference** of the circle. Make your measurement accurate to the nearest tenth of a centimeter.
- Then use a string and ruler to find the longest measurement across the circle (also accurate to the nearest tenth of a centimeter). This is the **diameter**.

Share tasks so that each person has a chance to blow some bubbles and to measure their circumference and diameter. Take data for at least 8 circles of different sizes.

b. Organize your data in a table and then work with your team to decide on an appropriate scale to graph the data carefully on graph paper.

9-3. WHAT DOES MY GRAPH SHOW?

Discuss the following questions with your team and be prepared to explain your ideas to the class.

a. How can you use your graph to show that the circumference and diameter are related proportionally? (Remember that these are measurements and will thus have some degree of error.)

b. Approximately what is the multiplier between the diameter and the circumference?

9-4. If the diameter of a bubble were 9 cm, predict its approximate circumference without measuring it. Justify your answer in as many ways as you can.

9-5. The ratio of circumference to diameter for circles has been measured with increasing accuracy since before 1650 B.C. The ratio has been found to be equal to π. In English, π is spelled *pi* and is pronounced "pie." It is an **irrational number**, which means that there is no way to write it as a fraction with integers. The value of π is slightly greater than 3. Find the button marked "π" on your calculator.

a. Write down the decimal equivalent for π, accurate to the nearest hundredth.

b. The fraction $\frac{22}{7}$ is often used to approximate π. What is the decimal equivalent of $\frac{22}{7}$, accurate to the nearest hundredth?

9-6. Work with your team to generalize the relationship between circumference and diameter of a circle. In other words, describe how you could calculate the circumference of any circle if you knew the diameter, and how you could find the length of the diameter if you knew the circumference.

9-7. Now return to your prediction from problem 9-1. Discuss it with your team again. Has your prediction changed? Why or why not? Work with your team to test your prediction.

9-8. Scientists have measured the diameter of the earth at the equator to be about 7926 miles.

a. If you were to travel all the way around the earth along the equator, approximately how many miles would you have traveled?

b. **Additional Challenge 1:** If it takes the average human two hours to walk five miles, how long would it take a person to walk around the earth, assuming it is actually possible to do so?

c. **Additional Challenge 2:** Signals that travel across the Internet are often carried through fiber-optic cables and travel at the speed of light, approximately 186,000 miles every second. At this rate, how long would it take an e-mail to travel around the earth?

9-9. LEARNING LOG

Write a Learning Log entry summarizing what you learned about circumference and its relationship to the diameter of a circle. Title this entry "Circumference and Diameter" and label it with today's date.

9-10. Estimate the circumference or diameter for each of the following circles. For each one, give your reasoning.

a. The diameter is 1 cm. What is the circumference?

b. The diameter is 7.2 meters. What is the circumference?

c. The circumference is 1 mile. What is the diameter?

d. The circumference is 12 inches. What is the diameter?

9-11. Imagine that you and your team will be conducting a survey to see how many minutes long lunch should be at your school. Students understand that the longer lunch is, the longer the school day is. Since you cannot ask every student, you will take a sample.

a. You ask every tenth student leaving a school-wide assembly to stop and think about how long he or she would like lunch to be. Do you think this sample is representative of the whole school?

b. These are the answers, in minutes, from the first 20 students:

60 40 50 25 30 15 30 50 50 35 45 25 25 50 25 60 55 60 60 15

Make an inference (a statistical prediction) about the average length *all* students at your school think lunch should be.

9-12. Sasha saved \$850 from her summer job last summer. She put it in an account that earns simple interest each month. After 9 months, her account is worth \$1003. What percent interest did she earn each month?

9-13. Copy the axes below and complete the scales.

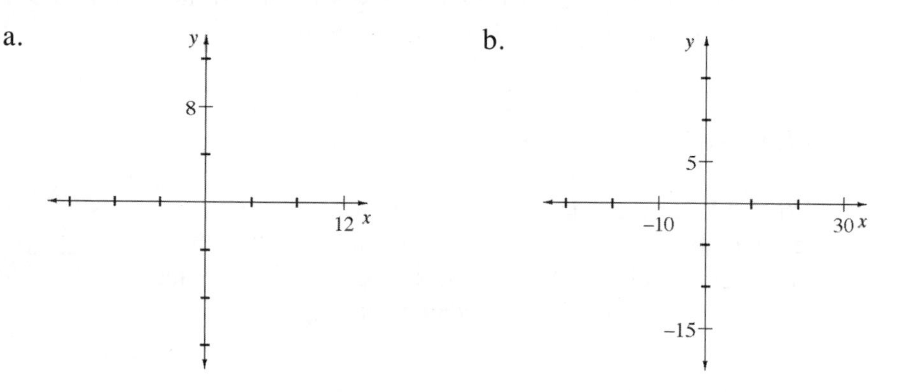

9-14. Janet sells erasers at a price of 8 erasers for 60 cents. She started this table to show the price for different numbers of erasers.

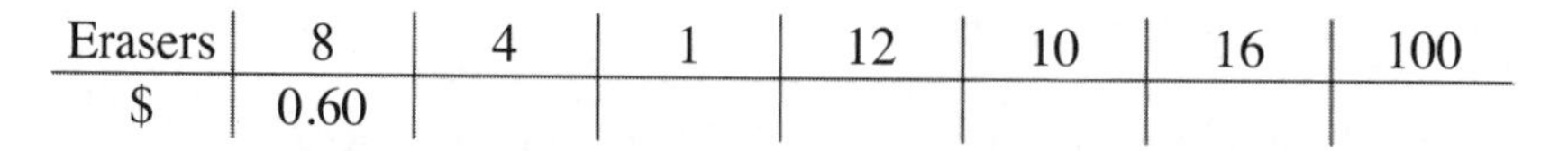

Erasers	8	4	1	12	10	16	100
\$	0.60						

a. Complete her table.

b. Does this situation represent a proportional relationship? Why or why not?

c. Use the information in the table to find the cost of 144 erasers. Write and solve a proportion, if appropriate.

9-15. Jack has 120 songs on his music player. Some are rock, some are jazz, and the rest are classical pieces. If his music player is on random shuffle mode, the probability that it will play a classical piece is $\frac{2}{5}$ and the probability that it will play a jazz piece is $\frac{1}{3}$. How many songs of each type are on Jack's music player?

9-16. Find the circumference of each of the circles described below.

a. Radius of 3 inches

b. Diameter of 27 cm

9-17. The table below shows a list of sampling methods. From what populations are these samples taken? Write down the actual population for each of these sampling techniques.

Method of Sampling	Description of Actual Population
Call every hundredth name in the phone book.	People with phones who have their number listed.
Call people at home at 10 a.m.	
Ask every tenth person who leaves the mall.	
Ask people leaving the bank.	
Mail questionnaires to people.	
Ask everyone on the school bus.	

9-18. A pair of shoes originally costs $42 but is on sale for 33% off. What is the new price? Show how you know.

9-19. The students at Dolan Middle School are competing in after-school activities in which they earn points for helping out around the school. Each team consists of the 30 students in a homeroom. Halfway through the competition, the scores from the students in two of the teams were displayed in the plots at right.

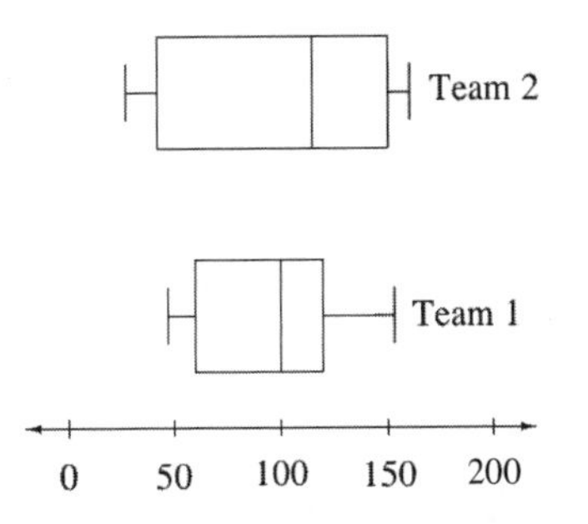

The champion team is the one with the most points when the scores of the 30 students on the team are added. Which team would you rather be on? Explain.

9-20. Copy each problem. Then find the sum, difference, product, or quotient. Remember to show all of your steps.

a. $23.6+12$

b. $16.5+52.43$

c. $46.21-31.2$

d. $27.5-13.11$

e. $4.5(6)$

f. $55\div 2$

9-21. Review the definitions of complementary, supplementary, and vertical angles. Use the information to answer the following questions.

a. Two angles are complementary. If one measures 65°, what is the measure of the other angle?

b. Two angles are supplementary. If one measures 125°, what is the measure of the other angle?

c. Two angles are vertical. If one measures 63°, what is the measure of the other angle?

9.1.2 How can I measure the area?

Area of Circles

The ratio known as π (*pi*, prounounced "pie") was first discovered by the Babylonians nearly 4000 years ago. Over the years, Egyptian, Chinese, and Greek mathematicians also found the constant ratio between the circumference and diameter of a circle by using measurement. The Greek letter π has been used to represent this ratio since the 1700s when it was made popular by the Swiss mathematician Euler (pronounced "oy-ler"). Even though this ratio has been known for many years, the value commonly used for π is still only an approximation.

9-22. ESTIMATING CIRCLE AREA

A circle is different from any shape you have studied so far because it has no sides or corners. This makes it difficult to apply the strategy of decomposing it into rectangles and triangles to find its area. In this situation, estimating its area can be a useful technique. Obtain a Lesson 9.1.2A Resource Page from your teacher.

a. Using the first circle with a **radius** (distance from the center to the circle) of 5 units on the resource page, estimate the area of the circle by counting whole and part squares. When each person in your team has finished his or her own estimate, share your results.

b. Are all of the estimates in your team identical? How can you combine your data as a team to get a new estimate that may be more accurate?

9-23. THE INSIDE OUTSIDE AVERAGE METHOD

While it is convenient to estimate area when shapes are drawn on grid paper, shapes are often not presented in that way. How can other shapes be used to help estimate area? Look carefully at the shape at right (also shown on the resource page).

5

a. How can you find the area of the larger square? What is the area of the larger square?

b. How can you find the area of the smaller square? What is the area of the smaller square?

c. How does the actual area of the circle compare to the area of each square? Is either square a good estimate of the circle's area? Why or why not?

d. Discuss with your team how to use the areas of both the squares to estimate the area of the circle. You might consider using what you have learned about analyzing data. Explain your thinking.

9-24. Julia needs to estimate the area of a circle with a radius of 6 grid units. She decides to use the Inside Outside Average method to make her estimate.

a. On the Lesson 9.1.2A Resource Page, estimate the area of the circle with a radius of 6 grid units by counting whole squares and parts of squares. Share your results with your team.

b. When Julia was calculating the area of the outside square, she started by dividing the large square into four smaller ones. Her picture is at right.

6

To find the area of each small square, Julia multiplied the length times the width:

$$\text{Area} = 6^2 = 36 \text{ sq. grid units}$$

How are the length, width, and area of each small square related to the radius of the circle? How is the area of the outside square related to the radius?

c. Julia divided the inside square into triangles. How is each triangle related to the radius? How is the area of the inside square related to the radius?

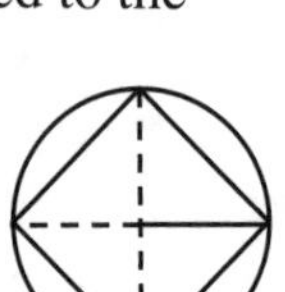

d. If the area of the two squares is related to the radius of the circle, Julia wonders if she can relate her circle estimate back to the radius as well. With your team, look at the estimate for area you have from part (a). How is that area estimate related to the radius of the circle?

9-25. Julia is looking at a new circle with a radius of 10 grid units. So far on her paper, she has written the work at right. What expression should she write to estimate the area of the circle?

Outside area = $4(10)^2$

Inside area = $2(10)^2$

9-26. A FORMULA FOR CIRCLE AREA

By using the Inside Outside Average method for estimating, you discovered that the area of a circle is approximately three times the radius squared. There is another way to decompose and rearrange a circle in order to find a formula for its area. As you go through this process, think about these questions:

- *If a circle is cut up and rearranged into a new shape, is the area of the new shape the same as the area of the circle?*
- *How are the dimensions (base and height) of the new shape related to the circle?*
- *Would this process work for any circle? Does it matter how large the circle is?*

Problem continues on next page. →

9-26. *Problem continued from previous page.*

Take a circle and cut it into 8 equal parts and arrange them like this:

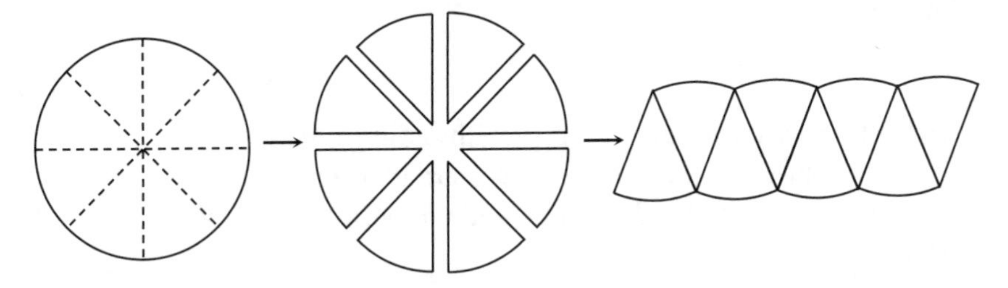

This rearrangement of the circle would look even more like a parallelogram or rectangle if you cut the circle into more pieces:

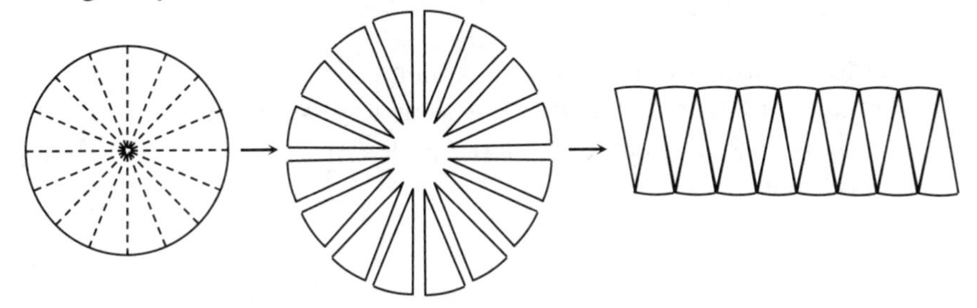

The measurements of this parallelogram are actually related to the original measurements of the circle. The height of the parallelogram is the same as the radius of the circle:

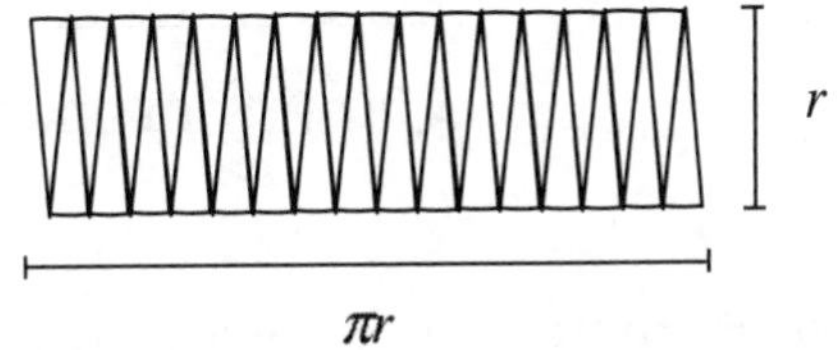

The length of the parallelogram is approximately half of the circumference of the circle. Since the circumference is equal to πd, half of the circumference is equal to:

$$\frac{\pi d}{2} = \frac{\pi(2r)}{2} = \pi r .$$

Substituting these values into the formula for the area of a parallelogram, you get:

$$A = hb = r(\pi r) = r^2\pi .$$

9-27. Calculate the area for the circles with radii (plural of radius) of 5 and 6 grid units using this new method (the formula $A = r^2\pi$) and compare your answers to your team's estimates in problems 9-23 and 9-24. How are the areas using this new method different from the estimates in the Inside Outside Average Method?

9-28. How does the area that you found in problem 9-22 (counting estimate) compare to the calculating the area of a circle with a radius of 5 grid units using the formula
$A = r^2\pi$?

9-29. **Additional Challenge:** A circle with radius 6 inches is cut into four quarters. Those pieces are rearranged into the shape at right. Find the area and the perimeter of the shape.

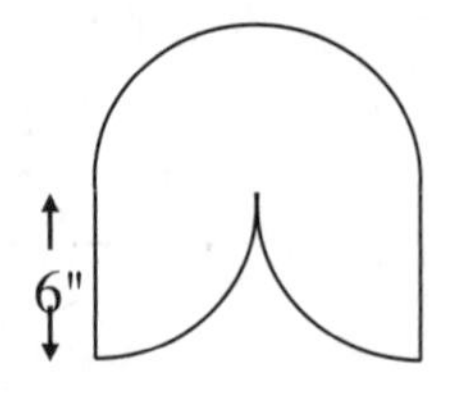

9-30. LEARNING LOG

Write a Learning Log entry that explains how to use the formula for the area of a circle. Include a solved example problem. Title this entry "Area of Circles" and include today's date.

MATH NOTES

METHODS AND MEANINGS

Circumference and Area of Circles

The **circumference** (*C*) of a circle is its perimeter, that is, the "distance around" the circle.

$C = \pi \cdot d$

d

The number π (read "pi") is the ratio of the circumference of a circle to its diameter. That is, $\pi = \frac{\text{circumference}}{\text{diameter}}$. This definition is also used as a way of computing the circumference of a circle if you know the diameter as in the formula $C = \pi d$ where C is the circumference and d is the diameter. Since the diameter is twice the radius (that is, $d = 2r$) the formula for the circumference of a circle using its radius is $C = \pi(2r)$ or $C = 2\pi \cdot r$.

The first few digits of π are 3.141592.

To find the **area** (*A*) of a circle when given its radius (*r*), square the radius and multiply by π. This formula can be written as $A = r^2 \cdot \pi$. Another way the area formula is often written is $A = \pi \cdot r^2$.

9-31. The circle shown at right has a diameter of 20 cm.

a. What measurement do you need to find in order to calculate the area inside the circle?

b. Find the area inside the circle using the formula $A = r^2\pi$. Write your answer as a product of r^2 and π, and as an approximation using $\pi \approx 3.14$.

9-32. Find the area and circumference of the circles in parts (a) and (b) and the radius in part (c). You may want to refer to the Math Notes box in this lesson.

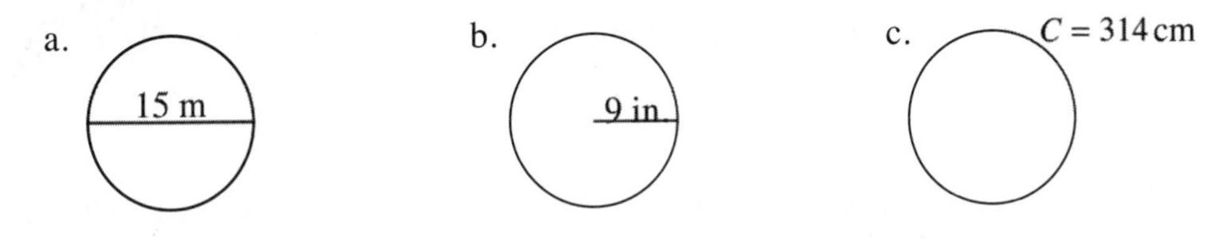

9-33. Use a ruler and a protractor to construct a triangle with two sides of 4 cm and 5.2 cm and an angle measuring 45°.

9-34. For each diagram below, identify each set of angles as complementary, supplementary, or vertical. Then use what you know about the properties of angles to find the measure of each angle labeled with a variable.

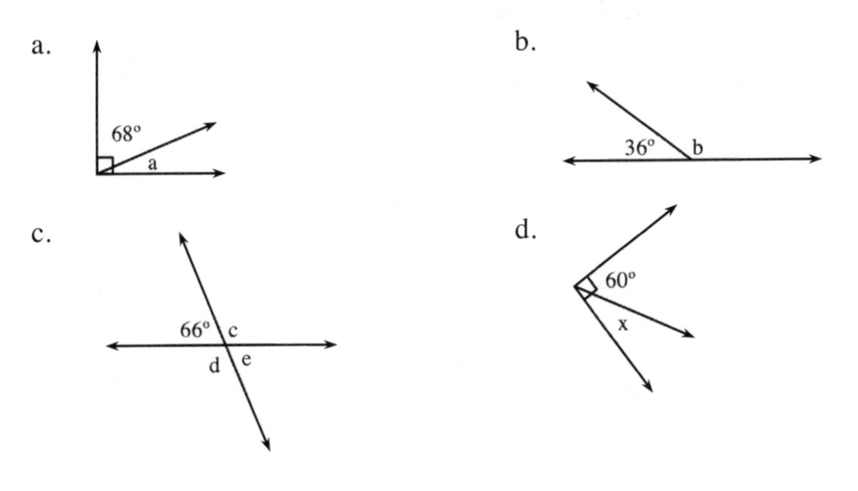

9-35. The Shones' family orchard produces 130 pounds of fruit per tree using traditional farming techniques. They would like to change to biodynamic farming techniques that will increase their crop by 20%. Changing techniques will cost money, but the fruit crop will be larger. Help them decide if they should change by calculating how much they will be able to grow two different ways, using two different scale factors (one multiplier will be greater than one). How many more pounds of fruit per tree will they get?

9-36. Howie and Steve are making cookies for themselves and some friends. The recipe they are using will make 48 cookies, but they only want to make 16 cookies. They have no trouble reducing the amounts of flour and sugar, but the original recipe calls for $1\frac{3}{4}$ cups of butter. Help Howie and Steve determine how much butter they will need.

9-37. Jessica's parents are planning their new house. They received a scale drawing from an architect, and Jessica is trying to figure out how big her bedroom will be. The architect has noted that each $\frac{1}{4}$ inch on his drawing represents one foot of distance in the new house. If the diagram of Jessica's room measures $2\frac{1}{2}$ inches by $4\frac{1}{4}$ inches, what will be the actual dimensions of her new room?

9-38. Stuart is a plumber working on the Garcia family's house. He is working with PVC pipe that has an internal diameter of $\frac{3}{4}$ inch. The thickness of the pipe is $\frac{3}{16}$ inch. What is the exterior (outside) diameter of the pipe?

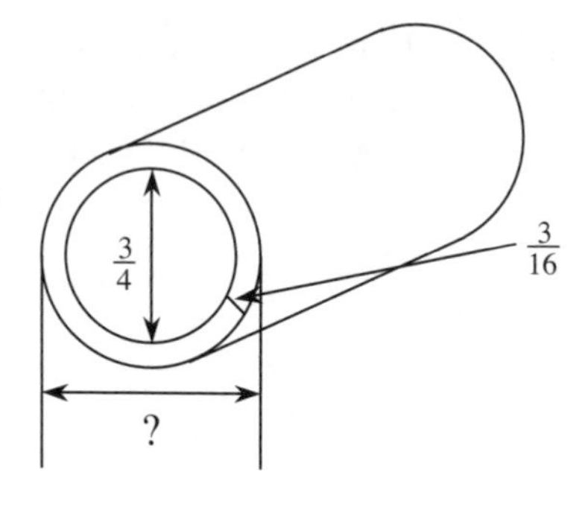

9-39. Quintrell was writing a "Guess My Number" game. He decided to write the clues in a different way. He wrote, *"When 35 is added to my number, the answer is 4 times my original number plus 8. What is my number?"* Use the 5-D Process to find Quintrell's number.

9-40. If m and n are integers, which fractions below are equivalent?

a. $\frac{-m}{n}$ b. $-\frac{m}{n}$ c. $\frac{-m}{-n}$ d. $\frac{m}{-n}$ e. $\frac{m}{n}$

9-41. Thu has a bag with 7 green marbles, 5 blue marbles, and 4 red marbles. For each part below, if the marble selected is replaced before the next marble is drawn, what is the probability that she will draw:

a. A red marble? b. A red or a green marble? c. An orange marble?

9.1.3 What is the area?

Area of Composite Shapes

In this lesson, you will consolidate your understanding of area as you find areas of complicated shapes. As you work on the problems in this lesson, ask your team members these questions:

How can we break this up into shapes that we can find the areas of?

Is there another way to see it?

Can we see the total area as a sum of areas? As a difference of areas?

9-42. Shakira is planning to put a lawn in her backyard by installing sod (rolls of grass) and needs to know how many square feet of sod she should order. Her yard is irregularly shaped and has a fishpond in the center. The dimensions of the lawn she is planning are shaded in the diagram below. All measurements are in feet.

Your Task: Obtain a Lesson 9.1.3A Resource Page from your teacher and work with your team to make a recommendation for how much sod Shakira should order. Can you find more than one way to calculate the area of Shakira's lawn?

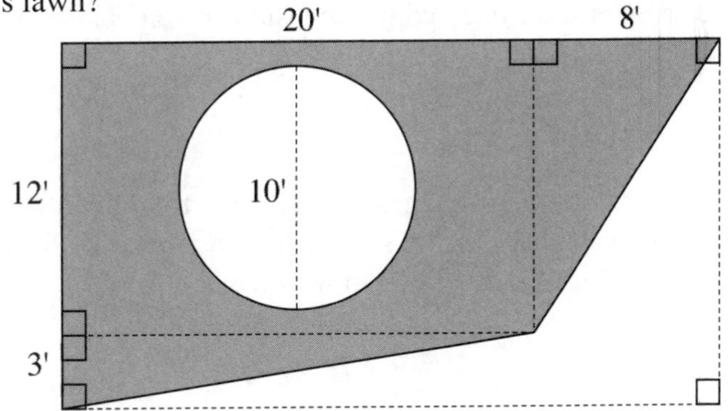

9-43. Find the area of the part of a typical basketball court shaded in the diagram at right.

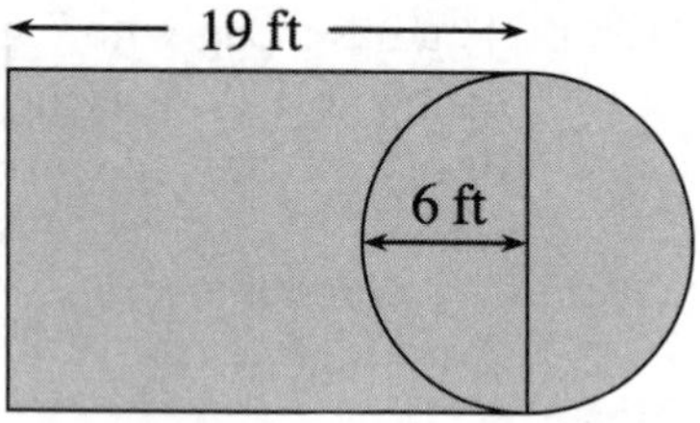

9-44. Gina designs and makes her own clothes. She drew the diagram at right (and also on the Lesson 9.1.3B Resource Page) of the fabric she needs for the front and back of a new shirt. If each unit on the grid represents one inch, how much fabric will she need?

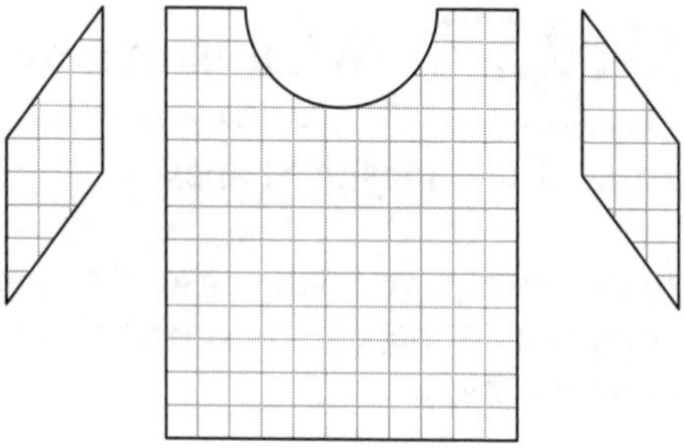

Review & Preview

9-45. The shape at right is composed of a rectangle and a semi-circle (half of a circle).

a. Find the perimeter.

b. Find the area.

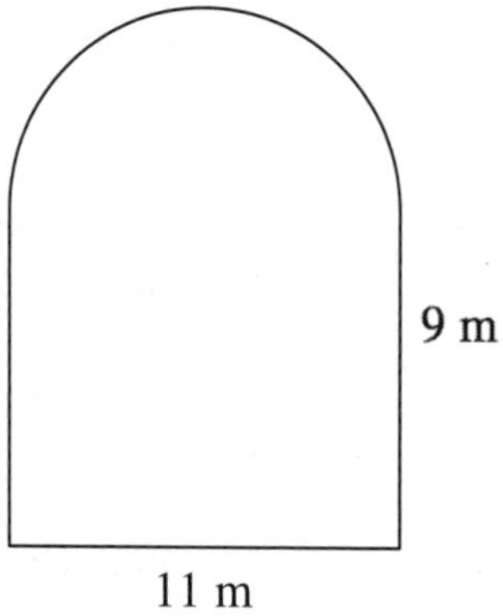

9-46. Draw a parallelogram with a base of 3 cm and a height of 7 cm and show how to calculate its area.

9-47. Find the areas of the circles with dimensions given below.

a. Radius: 4 ft

b. Diameter: 0.6 cm

9-48. Leonard has purchased packages of grid paper for $2.25. If he wants to make a 40% profit on each package he sells to his classmates, by how much should he increase the price? What will the new price be?

9-49. Simplify these expressions.

a. $(x+3.5)2$

b. $23+5x-(7+2.5x)$

c. $3x+4.4-2(6.6+x)$

9-50. Two employees of Frontier Fence Company can install 100 feet of fence in two days.

a. What is the unit rate for one employee?

b. Write a proportion to show the relationship between this rate and 150 feet of fence.

c. At this same rate, how many employees are needed to install 150 feet of fence in one day?

9.2.1 Does surface area affect volume?

Surface Area and Volume

In your work with two-dimensional (flat) shapes, you have described their dimensions, their perimeters, and their areas. For three-dimensional shapes — shapes that have length, width, *and* depth — you can measure the lengths of their edges and calculate the areas of their faces (sides). Three-dimensional shapes can also be described by their volumes, or how much space they enclose. Today you will work with rectangle-based prisms. As you work, keep these questions in mind:

How many cubes would it take to fill it?

How many squares would it take to cover the outside of it?

9-51. PERFECT PACKAGING

Cereal boxes come in different shapes and sizes. Some are tall and skinny, while others are shorter or deeper. The Bravo Breakfast cereal company is considering changing the size of its box. The staff members need some data to help them make the best choice.

The company currently packages its Morning Math Crunch cereal in a box that is 2" deep by 4" wide by 8" tall, as pictured at right. This shape is called a **right rectangular prism** because the top and bottom faces are rectangles that are congruent (same size and shape) and parallel to each other. These are called the **bases**. The other faces (sides of the box) are also rectangles that are perpendicular (at a right angle) to the bases. Use a set of cubes to build a model of this box. Assume that the edge of one cube represents 1" of length on the real cereal box.

a. Describe the box as completely as you can. Include the information below.

- What shapes do you see when you look at the faces of the box?
- What lengths or other measurements can you describe?
- Sketch each shape on your paper, and label it completely.

b. The cardboard sides of the box are called its **faces**. How much cardboard is needed to create all six of the faces of the box? Work with your team to develop a method for calculating this amount. Discuss the kind of units to use. Be ready to explain your method to the class.

c. The number of square units that it takes to cover the outside of an object, like the amount of cardboard you found in part (b), is called the object's **surface area**. The **volume** of a shape is the measure of how much it will hold. Volume is measured in cubic units.

How many cubes did you use to make this model of the cereal box? How many cubic inches of cereal will the box hold?

9-52. The waste-management division at Bravo Breakfast is worried that the box for Morning Math Crunch uses too much cardboard. The waste-management crew wants to make a box that holds the same amount of cereal but uses less cardboard.

a. What measurement of the box is the waste-management division interested in **minimizing** (making as small as possible)? What measurement does the company want to keep the same? What could change?

b. With your team, use the cubes to build different rectangular prisms that will still hold 64 cubic inches of cereal. Each box must be a rectangular prism with exactly six faces. For each prism you create:

- Sketch the prism,
- Label the dimensions on your sketch, and
- Find the surface area.

How many different prisms can you make?

c. Do all of the prisms you built have the same volume? How do you know?

d. Which box will use the smallest amount of cardboard?

9-53. Use cubes to build each prism below. Find the surface area and volume of each shape.

a. 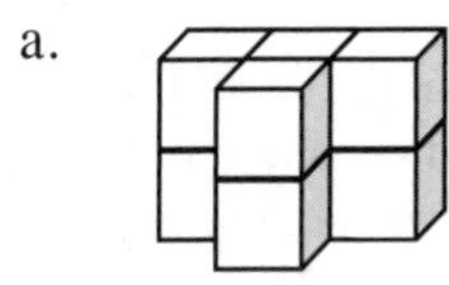

b. 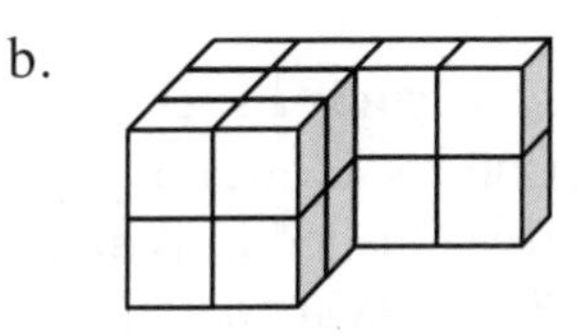

c. Use at least 15 cubes to build a prism of your own design. Sketch the prism and find its surface area and volume.

9-54. LEARNING LOG

Write step-by-step directions explaining to another student how to find the surface area of a prism. You may want to use one of the prisms in problem 9-53 as an example. Give reasons for each step. Record your directions in your Learning Log. Title the entry "Surface Area of a Prism" and label it with today's date.

Methods and Meanings

Math Notes

Polygons, Prisms, and Pyramids

A **polygon** is a two-dimensional closed figure made of straight-line segments connected end to end. The segments may not cross. The point where two sides meet is called a **vertex** (plural: vertices). Polygons are named by the number of sides they have. Polygons with three through ten sides are named and illustrated below.

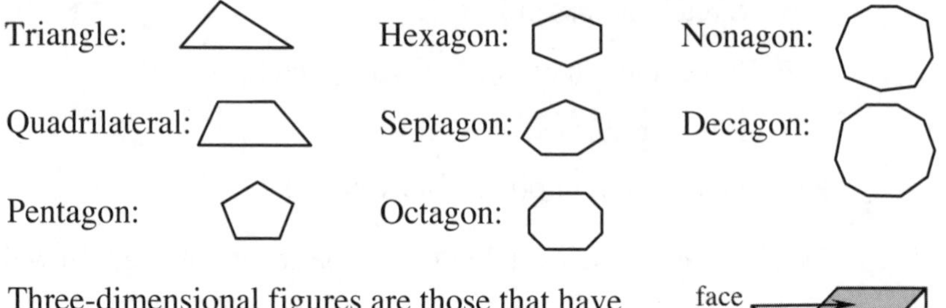

Three-dimensional figures are those that have length, width, and height. If a three-dimensional figure is completely bounded by polygons and their interiors, it is a **polyhedron**. The polygons are called **faces**, and an **edge** is where two faces meet. A cube and a pyramid are each an example of a polyhedron.

face

edges

A **prism** is a special kind of polyhedron that has two congruent (same size and shape), parallel faces called **bases**. The other faces (called **lateral faces**) are parallelograms (or rectangles). No holes are permitted in the solid.

A prism is named for the shape of its base. For example:

triangular prism

pentagonal prism

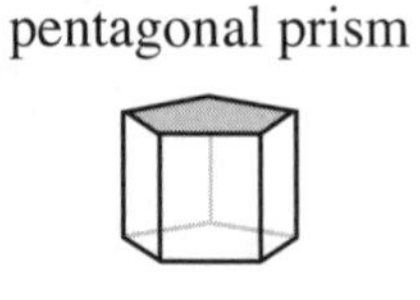

A **pyramid** is a three-dimensional figure with a base that is a polygon. The lateral faces are formed by connecting each vertex of the base to a single point (the vertex of the pyramid) that is above or below the surface that contains the base.

vertex

base

9-55. Read the Math Notes box in this lesson. Use the information to determine whether each shape below is a polygon.

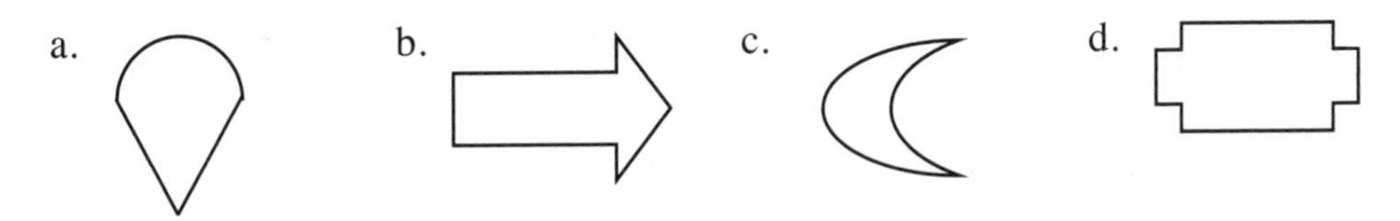

9-56. Find the volume and surface area of each shape below. Assume that the edge of each cube measures 1".

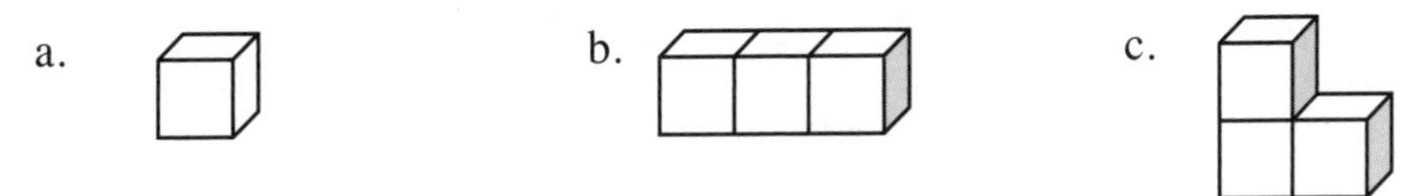

9-57. Red apples cost \$1.20 per pound, and green apples cost \$1.50 per pound.

a. Write an expression to represent the total cost of x pounds of red apples and y pounds of green apples.

b. What is the total cost if you buy 3 pounds of red apples and 2 pounds of green apples?

9-58. Ellen is building a scale model of the space shuttle. A space shuttle is approximately 122 feet long and has a wingspan of 78 feet.

a. How many inches long is the space shuttle?

b. Ellen plans to build her model so that 1 cm on the model represents 10 inches on the space shuttle. Write a proportion to show this relationship for the length of her model. Find how long will her model be (in centimeters)?

c. Write and solve a proportion to find her model's wingspan (in centimeters).

d. Remember that 1 inch is approximately equal to 2.54 cm. How many inches long will her model be?

9-59. Find the area and circumference of a circle with a radius of 7 cm.

9-60. Find the area and perimeter of each shape below. Show your steps and work.

a. All angles are right angles.

b.

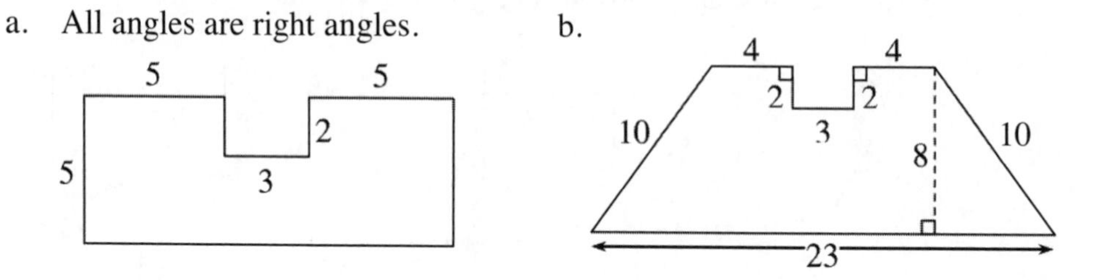

9.2.2 How can I slice it?

Cross Sections

A **cross section** of a three-dimensional solid (an object that has length, width, and height) is the figure obtained when the solid is intersected or "sliced" by a plane (an object that has only length and width, like a flat sheet of paper). Today you will investigate the shapes that can be created by slicing various types of solids.

9-61. Using clay, make a rectangular prism or cube. An example is shown below right. Each person in your team should make a slightly different prism.

a. Use your string to slice the rectangular prism by holding it tightly and pulling it through the solid. An example is shown at right. Place the newly created face made by the slice that came from the inside of the rectangular prism on your paper and trace the resulting shape. What is the name of your shape?

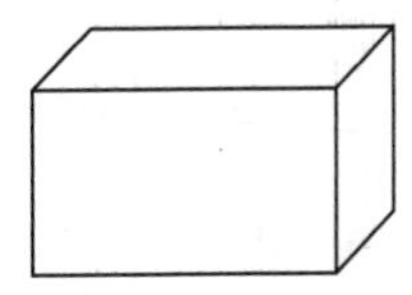

b. Which of the following shapes can you make by slicing your prism in different ways? Before making a new slice, reshape your prism.

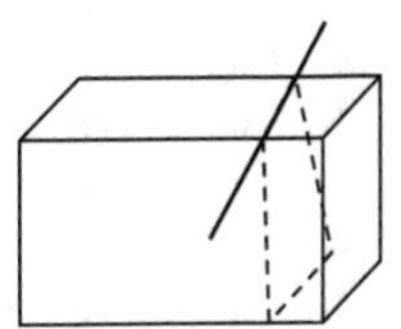

i. Triangle
ii. Square
iii. Rectangle
iv. Trapezoid
v. Parallelogram
vi. Pentagon
vii. Hexagon
viii. Octagon
ix. Circle

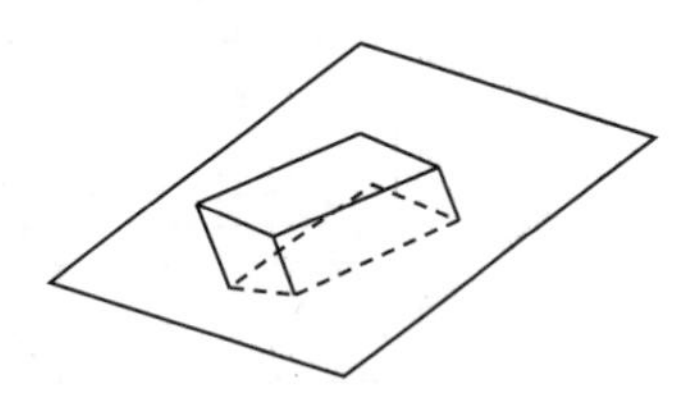

c. Even though each team member had a slightly different rectangular prism, were you able to create the same cross sections? Were there any shapes that one team member could create and another could not?

9-62. Now make a rectangular pyramid. An example is shown at right. Again, each person in your team should make a slightly different pyramid.

a. Use your string as you did in problem 9-61 to slice the pyramid. Place the newly created face that is made by the slice and came from the inside of the pyramid on your paper and trace the resulting shape. What is the name of your shape?

b. What other shapes can you make by slicing your pyramid in different ways? What shapes are impossible to make? How do the types of shapes that you can make with the rectangular pyramid compare to the types of shapes that you made with the rectangular prism?

9-63. CROSS SECTIONS AND VOLUME

In Lesson 9.2.1, you learned that the volume of a solid is found by determining the number of cubes it takes to create the solid.

a. Make a rectangular prism similar to the one you made in problem 9-61. How can you repeatedly slice the prism so that each of the slices that you create is the same size and shape? Discuss this with your team and then slice your prism into equal pieces.

b. Take one of your slices and cut it into cubes of the approximately same size. How many cubes are in one slice?

c. Using the number of cubes from a single slice of the prism and the number of slices you created, how many cubes would it take to build your prism?

d. Find the volume of each prism below. Make sure everyone on your team agrees with the answers.

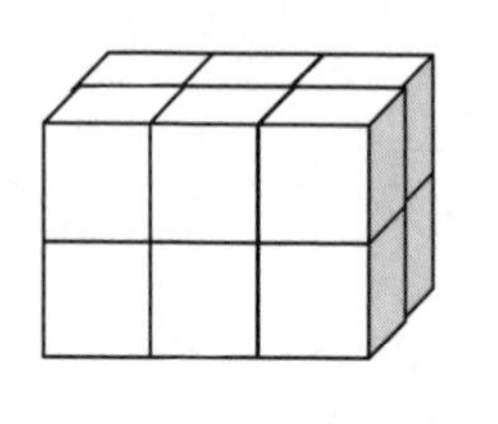

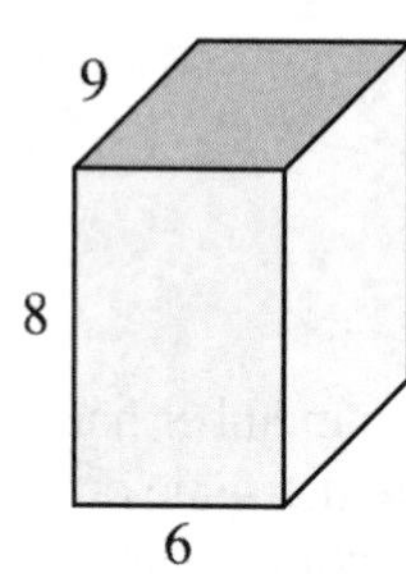

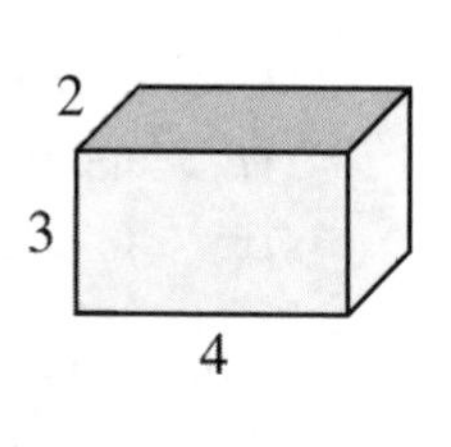

9-64. Sanne made a prism and sliced it into equally sized pieces as you did in problem 9-63, but she is only letting you see the slice shown at right.

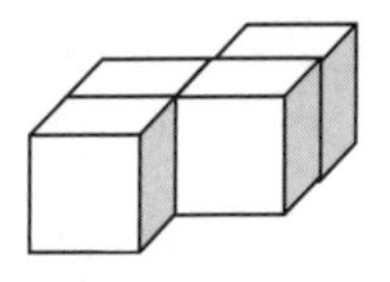

a. Draw a sketch of Sanne's prism.

b. Sanne told you that her prism has 8 slices like this one that are each the same. What is the volume of her prism?

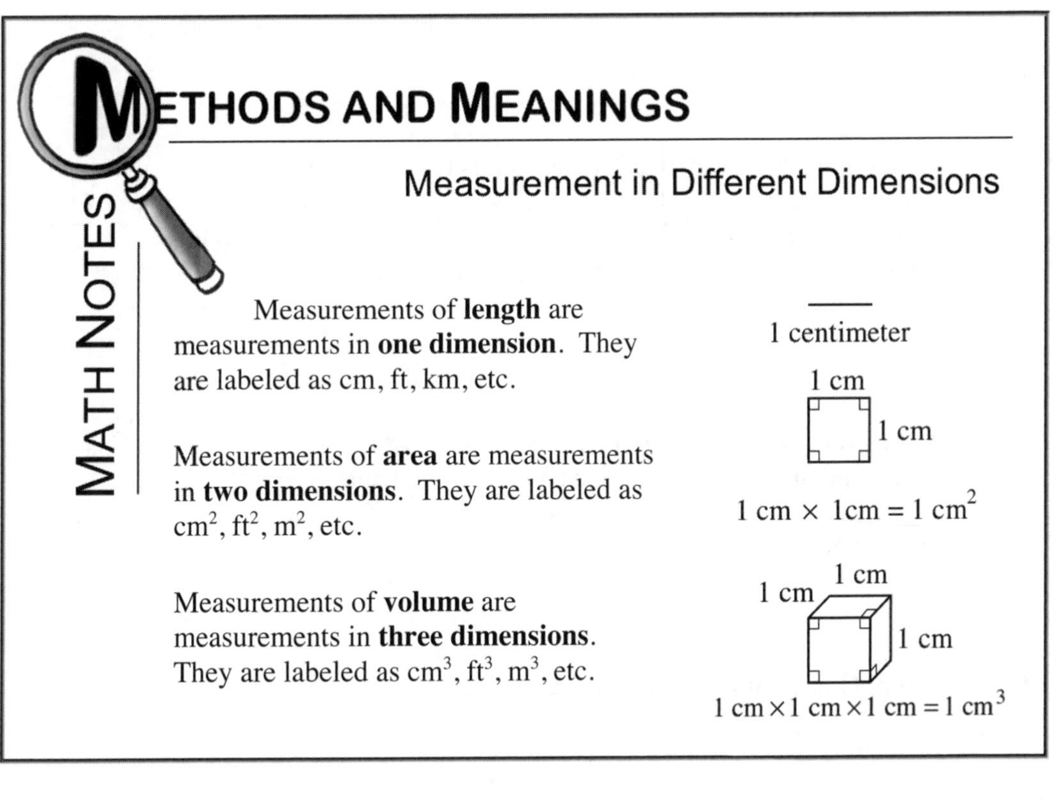

MATH NOTES

METHODS AND MEANINGS

Measurement in Different Dimensions

Measurements of **length** are measurements in **one dimension**. They are labeled as cm, ft, km, etc.

1 centimeter

Measurements of **area** are measurements in **two dimensions**. They are labeled as cm^2, ft^2, m^2, etc.

1 cm, 1 cm

$1 \text{ cm} \times 1\text{cm} = 1 \text{ cm}^2$

Measurements of **volume** are measurements in **three dimensions**. They are labeled as cm^3, ft^3, m^3, etc.

1 cm, 1 cm, 1 cm

$1 \text{ cm} \times 1 \text{ cm} \times 1 \text{ cm} = 1 \text{ cm}^3$

9-65. Use the pyramid shown at right to answer the questions below.

a. If the pyramid were sliced vertically, what would the resulting cross sections look like? Sketch them.

b. If the pyramid were sliced horizontally, what would the resulting cross section look like? Sketch it.

9-66. Use the rectangular prism shown at right to complete parts (a) through (d) below.

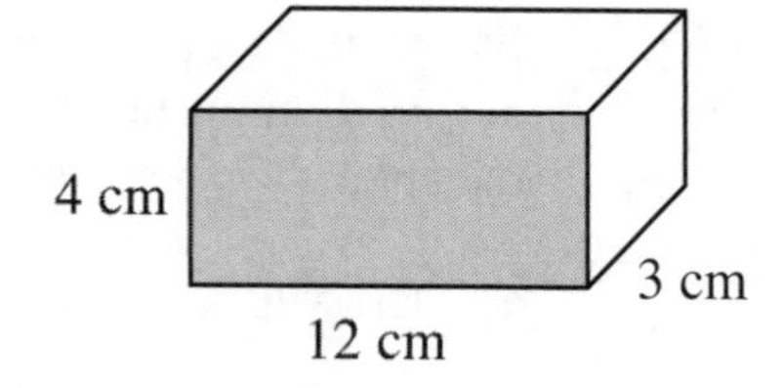

a. Calculate the surface area of the prism. Show all of your subproblems.

b. Explain why the exponent for area units is 2 (that is, cm^2).

c. Calculate the volume of the prism.

d. Explain why the exponent for volume units is a 3 (that is, cm^3).

9-67. James lives in Columbus, OH, and wants to know how far he is from Indianapolis. On his map, the two cities are $1\frac{3}{4}$ inches apart. At the bottom of the map, he sees the scale at right. Write a proportion and then find the distance from Columbus to Indianapolis.

$\frac{1}{4}$ inch
25 miles

9-68. Kenny took some measurements on the front of his house and quickly drew a sketch, which is shown at right. Use his sketch to create a scale drawing of the front of Kenny's house.

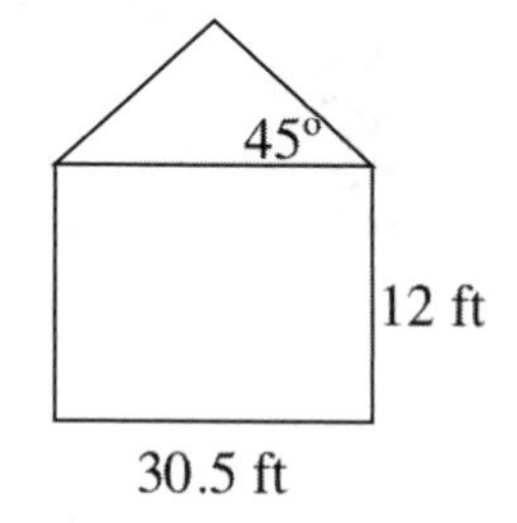

9-69. Simplify each of the following expressions.

a. $3\frac{1}{5} \cdot \frac{7}{4}$ b. $5^3 \cdot \left(-\frac{4}{5}\right)$ c. $2^4 \cdot \frac{5}{8}$ d. $-\frac{1}{2} \cdot 3^2$

e. $-\frac{5}{6} + \left(\frac{1}{2}\right)^2$ f. $\left(-\frac{4}{5}\right)^2 - \frac{3}{50}$ g. $\left(\frac{3}{10}\right)^2 - \left(-\frac{2}{5}\right)^2$ h. $8^2\left(-\frac{7}{8}\right) - \frac{1}{2}$

9-70. Evaluate the inequality $x + 4 < 2x - 3$ for the following values of x. Decide if the given value of x makes the statement true or false. Show all of your work.

a. $x = 4$ b. $x = -2$ c. $x = 7$ d. $x = 9$

9.2.3 How much will fill it?

Volume of a Prism

You have had a lot of practice with finding the area of flat, two-dimensional shapes. Today you will begin using those skills to help you understand shapes with a third dimension. As you work, consider the following questions.

How can we see the shape in layers?

How can we slice the shape so that the layers are identical?

9-71. BIRTHDAY SWEETS

Laverne is making a birthday dessert for her cousin Leslie. She wants to incorporate Leslie's favorite ingredients: cookies and chocolate mousse. She will make the dessert in a special L-shaped pan that is 9.5 cm deep.

First, Laverne is going to make a cookie crust as the bottom layer. The crust will be 1 cm thick so that it is nice and crunchy. She is going to add chocolate mousse on top of the crust until the mousse is 7 cm thick. Finally, she will add a 1.5-cm layer of whipped cream on the mousse and top it with chocolate sprinkles.

a. What area will the dessert cover (in square centimeters) on the pan?

b. Laverne needs to know what quantity of cookies to buy to make the crust layer of the dessert. Does the measurement she needs describe length, area, or volume? Discuss this with your team, and then write down your explanation.

c. One cookie will crush into about 5 cubic centimeters of cookie crumbs. Show Laverne how to find out how many cookies she will need to make the crust layer. Be sure to explain your reasoning. How many cookies should she buy?

9-72. Laverne wants the mousse on top of the crust to be 7 cm thick. Use your answer from part (c) of problem 9-71 to help you figure out how many cubic centimeters of mousse Laverne will need. Explain your reasoning.

9-73. Laverne has 1200 cubic centimeters of whipped cream ready to spread on top of the mousse. Erika looked at Laverne's notes about how much cream she would need and exclaimed, *"You have too much! You will overflow the pan!"*

How could Erika know that Laverne has too much whipped cream? Be prepared to share your ideas with the class. Determine how much extra or how short Laverne is of the amount of whipped cream that she needs.

9-74. Laverne needs to be sure that her finished dessert will be enough to serve everyone.

a. What is the total volume of dessert that Laverne is planning to make? Be ready to share your study team's strategy with the class.

b. If one serving is 285 cm^3, how many people will the dessert serve?

9-75. For the prism at right, find the volume of a layer 1 cm high. Then, find the total volume of the prism. Every face is a rectangle.

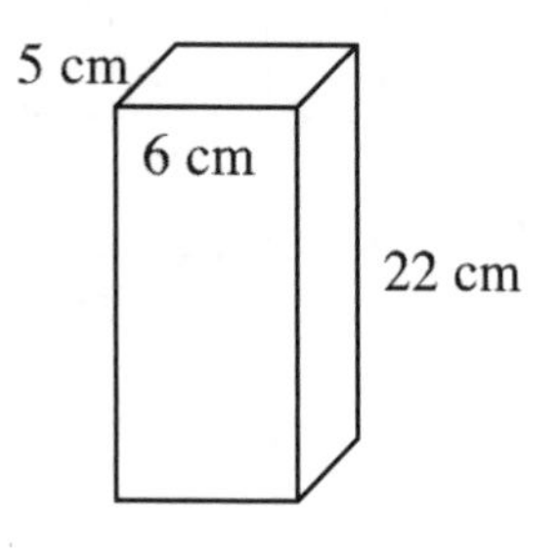

9-76. **Additional Challenge:** When finding the volume of the shape below, Audrey found the volume of the shaded layer first. Here is her work:

$$5 + 20 = 25 \text{, so } 25 \cdot 8 = 200 \text{ ft}^3$$

Then she said, *"The shape is 22 feet high, so there are 22 one-foot-high layers."* She then multiplied and got this answer:

$$22 \cdot 200 = 4400 \text{ ft}^3$$

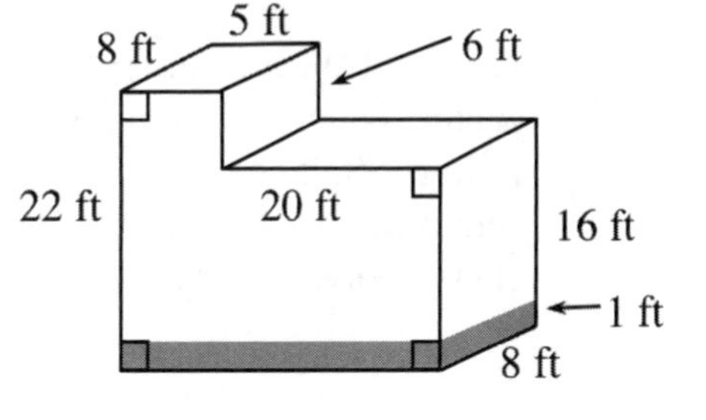

a. What was Audrey's mistake?

b. What is the actual volume of the shape? Explain how you found it.

9-77. Find the surface area and volume of the prism shown at right.

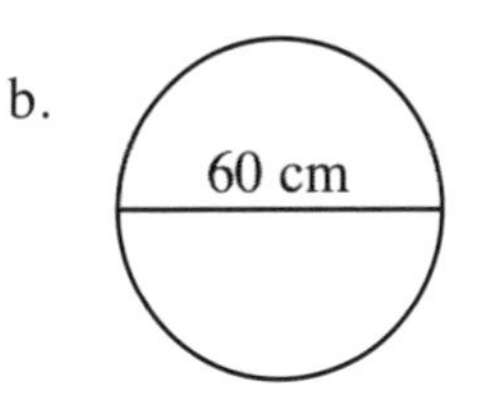

9-78. Find the area of each circle below.

a. radius = 8 cm

b. 60 cm

9-79. Glenda made a scale model of the Empire State Building in New York. The building itself is 1250 feet high, and her scale model is 5 feet high.

a. Write a ratio that compares the heights of the two buildings.

b. If the doorway of Glenda's model is 2 inches wide, how wide would you expect the doorway of the real building to be? Write and solve a proportion.

c. If the real building contains 102 floors, how many floors should Glenda's model contain?

9-80. Simplify each of the following expressions.

a. $8^2 + 7^2$

b. $7^2 \cdot 7 \cdot 7$

c. $\left(\frac{1}{2}\right)^2 + \left(\frac{2}{3}\right)^2$

d. $(2^2 + 6)^2$

e. $-4 \cdot 3^2 - 2$

f. $x - x$

g. $3 \cdot 3 \div 3$

h. $4x + x - 2x$

i. $-2 \cdot 4 \div 4$

9-81. The Wild West Frontier Park now offers an unlimited day pass. For $29.00, visitors can go on as many rides as they want. The original plan charged visitors $8.75 to enter the park plus $2.25 for each ride. Write an equation to determine the number of rides that would make the total cost equal for the two plans. Solve the equation.

9-82. Do girls read more than boys during the summer? Serena's class asked 30 parents to estimate how many pages their child read over the summer. They collected the following data.

Girls: 10 30 230 130 110 240 150 260 60 230 100 20 50 160 90 pages

Boys: 210 100 0 40 260 240 200 220 190 150 50 100 12 140 40 pages

a. Make parallel box plots and compare the center, shape, spread, and outliers.

b. Do girls read more? How many IQRs more do they read? Use the box plots to estimate.

9.2.4 How much will it hold?

Volume of Non-Rectangular Prisms

In this lesson, you will investigate different strategies for finding the volume of non-rectangular prisms. The problems require you to describe how you visualize each shape. As you work with your team, ask each other these questions to focus your discussion:

How can the shape be broken down into simpler shapes?

Can we break the shape into equal layers or slices?

9-83. THE SHELL BOX

Laurel keeps her seashell collection in a small box that is shaped like a rectangular prism with a base of 4" by 3" and height of 5" (see diagram at right). She wants to make a bigger box for her shells, and she has found a pattern that she likes. The pattern has two sides that are pentagons, and the finished box will look like a miniature house (see picture at right). Use the net on the Lesson 9.2.4 Resource Page to construct a paper model of Laurel's new box.

a. Calculate the volume of Laurel's original small box. What method did you use?

b. Laurel was trying to figure out the volume of the new box.

One of her friends said, *"Why don't you find the volume of one layer and then figure out how many layers there would be?"*

Another friend said, "*What if you separated the pentagon into two parts, so that you have a rectangular prism and a prism with a triangle base? Then you could find the volume of the two parts separately and put them back together.*"

Talk about each of these strategies with your team. Could Laurel use these ideas to find the volume of her new box?

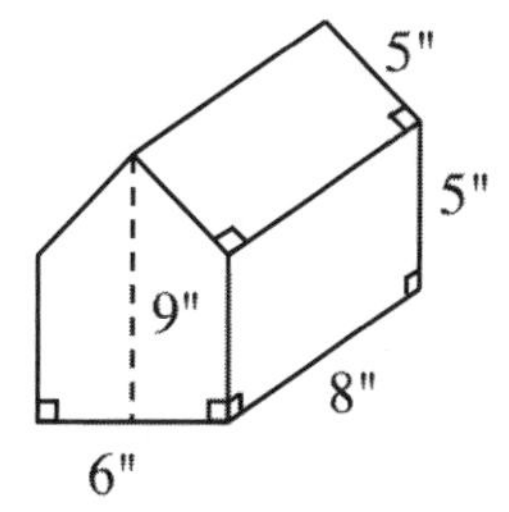

c. Work with your team to calculate the volume of Laurel's new box. Show your thinking clearly and be prepared to share your method with the class.

9-84. Find the volume of the prism at right using any method you choose. Be prepared to explain your reasoning.

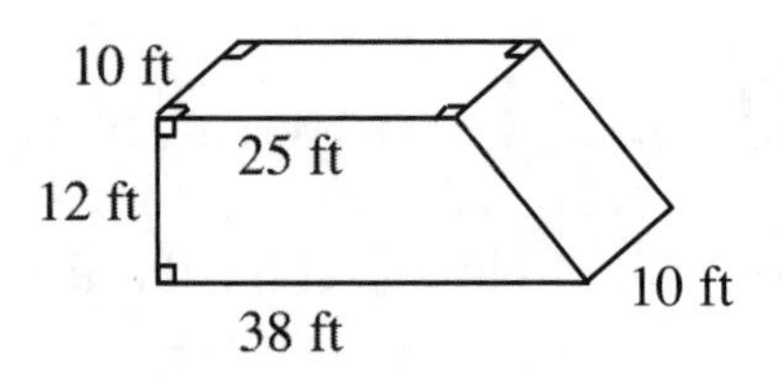

9-85. Bryan was looking at the prism in problem 9-84 with his team. He wondered how they could slice the prism horizontally into layers that would all be the same size.

a. If the team slices the shape so that the bottom layer has the 10 ft by 38 ft rectangle as its base, will each layer be equal in size?

b. How could the team turn or tip the shape so that if the shape is sitting on a table and is cut horizontally, each layer will be the same size and shape? Which face will rest on the table?

c. When does it make sense to tip the shape in order to see the layers? Discuss this question with your team and summarize your conclusion on your paper.

9-86. LEARNING LOG

The method for finding the volume of a prism is commonly described as "finding the area of the base, then multiplying by the height." Discuss with your study team how this strategy works. How does the area of the base help to find the volume? Does it matter which face is the base? Why do you multiply by the height? Record your conclusions in your Learning Log. Title the entry, "Volume of a Prism," and label it with today's date.

MATH NOTES

Volume of a Prism

The **volume** of a prism can be calculated by dividing the prism into layers that are each one unit high. To calculate the total volume, multiply the volume of one layer by the number of layers it takes to fill the shape. Since the volume of one layer is the area of the base (B) multiplied by 1 (the height of that layer), you can use the formula below to compute the volume of a prism.

If h = height of the prism,

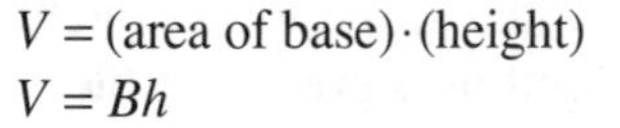

$V = (\text{area of base}) \cdot (\text{height})$

$V = Bh$

Example:

Area of base = (2 in.)(3 in.) = 6 in.^{2}

(Area of base)(height) = (6 in.^{2})(4 in.) = 24 in.^{3}

Volume = 24 in.^{3}

4 in.
2 in.
3 in.

9-87. Is each shape below a prism? If so, identify the shape that is the base. If not, explain why not.

a. b. c. d.

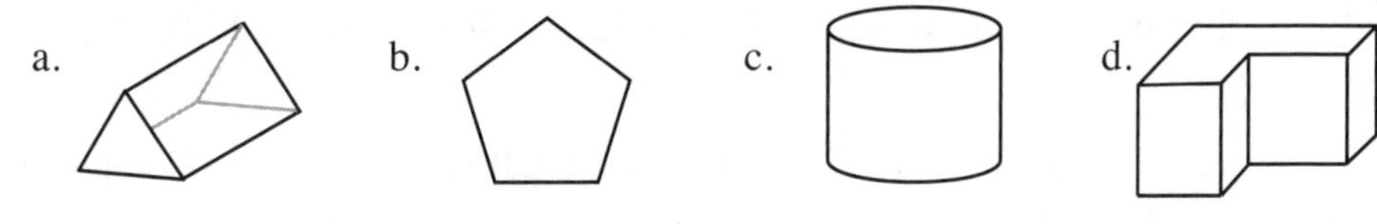

9-88. Find the volume of a 1-unit-high layer of each prism below. Then find the total volume and the surface area of each figure.

a. A rectangular prism

10 m
10 m
50 m

b. A triangle-based prism

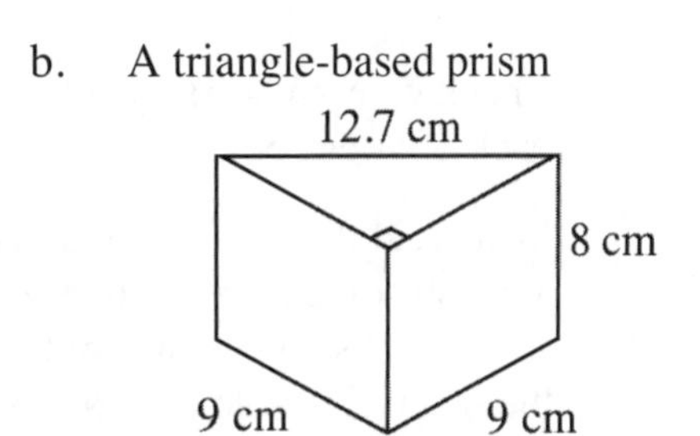

9-89. Use the prism shown at right to answer the questions below.

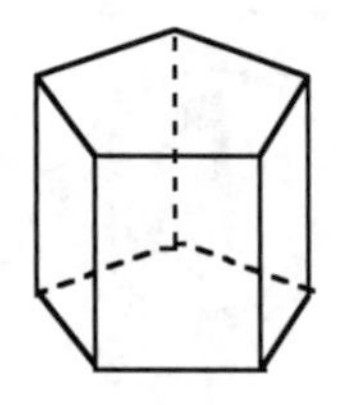

a. If the prism were sliced vertically, sketch the resulting cross section.

b. If the prism were sliced horizontally, sketch the resulting cross section.

9-90. Find the area and circumference of a circle that has a diameter of 17 mm. Write your answers in terms of π and as a decimal approximation.

9-91. A bag of marbles contains only the colors red and green.

a. If the probability of getting a red marble is $\frac{1}{3}$, what is the probability of getting a green marble?

b. If there are 24 marbles in the bag, how many are green?

c. What is the probability of drawing two marbles that are red? Note: The first marble is not replaced before drawing the second. Write your answer as a fraction and as a percent.

d. What is the probability of drawing two red marbles if the first one is replaced before the second one is drawn? Write your answer as a fraction and as a percent.

9-92. This problem is a checkpoint for unit rates and proportions. It will be referred to as Checkpoint 9.

In parts (a) and (b), compute the unit rate. In parts (c) and (d), solve the proportion.

a. Tina drove 108 miles and used 4.5 gallons of gasoline. Compute the miles per gallon.

b. If 17 oranges cost $3.23, compute the cost per orange.

c. $\frac{x}{12} = \frac{20}{30}$

d. $\frac{13}{40} = \frac{m}{100}$

Check your answers by referring to the Checkpoint 9 materials located at the back of your book.

Ideally, at this point you are comfortable working with these types of problems and can solve them correctly. If you feel that you need more confidence when solving these types of problems, then review the Checkpoint 9 materials and try the practice problems provided. From this point on, you will be expected to do problems like these correctly and with confidence.

Chapter 9 Closure What have I learned?

Reflection and Synthesis

The activities below offer you a chance to reflect about what you have learned during this chapter. As you work, look for concepts that you feel very comfortable with, ideas that you would like to learn more about, and topics you need more help with.

① WHAT HAVE I LEARNED?

Doing the problems in this section will help you to evaluate which types of problems you feel comfortable with and which ones you need more help with.

Solve each problem as completely as you can. The table at the end of this closure section provides answers to these problems. It also tells you where you can find additional help and where to find practice problems like them.

CL 9-93. Find the area and circumference of a circle with a radius of 6.5 cm.

CL 9-94. Find the surface area and volume of each solid below.

a. All angles are right angles.

b. Right prism with base area = 48 cm^2

CL 9-95. Find the surface area and volume of a prism with a square base, sides of 8 inches, and a height of 12 inches.

CL 9-96. Jamie bought a music player on sale for $65. The original price was $80. What percent discount did she receive?

CL 9-97. Manuela found a great deal on pens at 3 for $0.99. It was such a good deal that she decided to buy two-dozen pens. How much did she pay for all of the pens?

CL 9-98. Shawn's science class has a ratio of 4:5, girls to boys.

a. What is the ratio of boys to girls?

b. What is the ratio of boys to total students?

c. What percent of the class is boys?

d. What fraction of the class is girls?

CL 9-99. Casey was building a rectangular pen for his pigs. He has 62 feet of fencing. The length of his pen is 9 feet longer than the width. Write and solve an equation to find the dimensions of the pen.

CL 9-100. Solve the following equations.

a. $12 = \frac{6}{7}x$	b. $3x + (-4) = 2x + 9$	c. $3x - 8 = 4x + (-2)$
d. $2(x - 3) = 1 - 3x$	e. $\frac{38}{6} = \frac{x}{18}$	f. $\frac{9}{x} = \frac{85}{10}$

CL 9-101. For each of the problems above, do the following:

- Draw a bar or number line that represents 0 to 10.

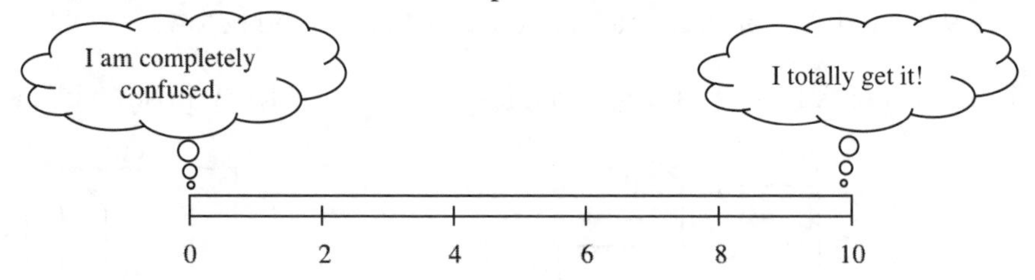

- Color or shade in a portion of the bar that represents your level of understanding and comfort with completing that problem on your own.

If any of your bars are less than a 5, choose *one* of those problems and do one of the following tasks:

- Write two questions that you would like to ask about that problem.
- Brainstorm two things that you DO know about that type of problem.

If all of your bars are a 5 or above, choose one of those problems and do one of these tasks:

- Write two questions you might ask or hints you might give to a student who was stuck on the problem.
- Make a new problem that is similar and more challenging than that problem and solve it.

② WHAT TOOLS CAN I USE?

You have several tools and references available to help support your learning: your teacher, your study team, your math book, and your Toolkit, to name only a few. At the end of each chapter, you will have an opportunity to review your Toolkit for completeness. You will also revise or update it to reflect your current understanding of big ideas.

The main elements of your Toolkit should be your Learning Logs, Math Notes, and the vocabulary used in this chapter. Math words that are new appear in bold in the text. Refer to the lists provided below and follow your teacher's instructions to revise your Toolkit, which will help make it useful for you as you complete this chapter and as you work in future chapters.

Learning Log Entries

- Lesson 9.1.1 – Circumference and Diameter
- Lesson 9.1.2 – Area of Circles
- Lesson 9.2.1 – Surface Area of a Prism
- Lesson 9.2.4 – Volume of a Prism

Math Notes

- Lesson 9.1.2 – Circumference and Area of Circles
- Lesson 9.2.1 – Polygons, Prisms, and Pyramids
- Lesson 9.2.3 – Measurement in Different Dimensions
- Lesson 9.2.4 – Volume of a Prism

Mathematical Vocabulary

The following is a list of vocabulary found in this chapter. Some of the words have been seen in the previous chapter. The words in bold are words that are new to this chapter. Make sure that you are familiar with the terms below and know what they mean. For the words you do not know, refer to the glossary or index. You might also add these words to your Toolkit so that you can reference them in the future.

area	base	**circumference**
cross section	degree	**diameter**
edge	**face**	inference
irrational number	**lateral faces**	measurement
polygon	**polyhedron**	**pi (π)**
pyramid	**right rectangular prism**	**surface area**
vertex	**volume**	

Answers and Support for Closure Problems
What Have I Learned?

Note: MN = Math Note, LL = Learning Log

Problem	Solution	Need Help?	More Practice
CL 9-93.	$A \approx 132.7 \text{ cm}^2$ $C \approx 40.8 \text{ cm}$	Lessons 9.1.1 and 9.1.2 MN: 9.1.2 LL: 9.1.1, 9.1.2	Problems 9-10, 9-16, 9-31, 9-32, 9-47, 9-59, 9-78, and 9-90
CL 9-94.	a. SA = 1512 ft^2 V = 2744 ft^3 b. SA = 572 cm^2 V = 672 cm^3	Section 9.2 MN: 9.2.1, 9.2.3, and 9.2.4 LL: 9.2.1 and 9.2.4	Problems 9-56, 9-77, and 9-88
CL 9-95.	Surface area = 512 in.^2 Volume = 768 in.^3	Section 9.2 MN: 9.2.1, 9.2.3, and 9.2.4 LL: 9.2.1 and 9.2.4	Problems 9-56, 9-77, and 9-88
CL 9-96.	About 19%	Lesson 7.1.7 MN: 7.1.7	Problems CL 7-120, CL 8-114, 9-18, 9-35, and 9-48
CL 9-97.	$7.92	Lessons 7.2.1 and 7.2.2 MN: 7.2.2 LL: 7.2.2	Problems CL 7-118, 9-14, 9-36, 9-50, 9-58, 9-67, 9-79, and 9-92
CL 9-98.	a. 5:4 b. 5:9 c. About 56% d. $\frac{4}{9}$	Lessons 5.1.1 and 5.1.2 MN: 5.1.1 and 5.1.2	Problems 5-18, 5-62, and 9-79

Problem	Solution		Need Help?	More Practice
CL 9-99.	$2x+2(x+9)=62$ OR $4x+18=62$ The dimensions of the pen are 11 feet by 20 feet.		Section 5.3 and Lesson 6.2.4 MN: 5.3.3 and 6.2.4 LL: 5.3.4	Problems CL 6-144, CL 7-124, CL 8-116, and 9-81
CL 9-100.	a. $x=14$ c. $x=-6$ e. $x=114$	b. $x=13$ d. $x=\frac{7}{5}=1.4$ f. $x=\frac{90}{85}\approx 1.06$	Lessons 7.1.4, 7.1.5, and 7.1.6 MN: 7.1.6 LL: 7.1.5	Problems CL 7-121 and 9-92

9.3.1 How much should it cost?

Volume and Scaling

Have you ever made choices about which size of an item (such as a pizza or bottle of juice) to buy? If so, you may have considered which size was priced to give you the most for your money. In this lesson, you will work with your team as you analyze pricing of popcorn at a popular movie theater.

9-102. The Maverick Movie Theater sells a small tub of popcorn for $1.

a. To keep its prices proportional to the amount of popcorn offered, what should the theater charge for the large tub shown at right? Show how you found your answer.

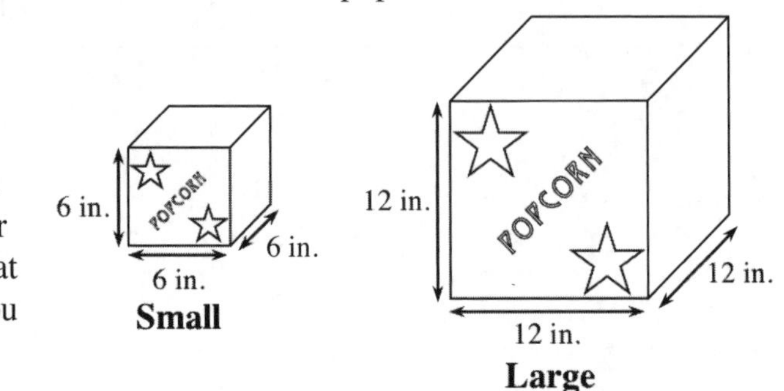

b. The medium-sized tub is a prism with a square base of 9 inches and a height of 12 inches. It currently costs $6 and is not selling well. The owner wants you to decide if this price is fair, as compared to the prices of the other sizes of popcorn tubs. How much should the medium tub cost if the owner wants it priced the same per cubic inch as the small tub? Write a note to the owner that explains whether the medium-sized tub is priced proportionally.

c. Customers have complained that the large tub is too wide to carry into the theater without spilling. The owner wants to change the base to be a 10-inch square instead. To keep the same volume, the owner thinks that the new tub will need to be 14 inches tall. She reasons that if the width gets two inches shorter, the height should grow by two inches.

Do you agree? If so, show how you know. If not, determine the new height of the tub.

d. The owner decided to create a new size that is 50% wider and 50% taller than the small tub. The owner plans to charge 50% more. Is this a good decision? If not, what should the owner charge and what percent increase is this price? Justify your answer.

Problem continues on next page. →

9-102. *Problem continued from previous page.*

e. The owner wants to offer a tub of popcorn that would cost \$6. She wants you to design the tub. Assume that the price should be proportional with the amount of popcorn in the small tub of popcorn. While the box can have any length, width, and height, be sure to make it a reasonable design for someone to hold and for the employees to fill with popcorn.

Draw a diagram of your box with all measurements labeled.

9-103. MAKING CONNECTIONS

When you solved the previous problem, you needed to use your knowledge about several different mathematical ideas.

a. With your team, do the following:

- Use colors to mark parts of your solution that used particular mathematical ideas. (For example, did you measure lengths? Did you draw quadrilaterals?)
- Label each mathematical idea with words in the margin of your paper.

b. Contribute your ideas to a class discussion. Did any other teams identify mathematical ideas that you used but had not noticed? If so, add these to your notes. Then write each mathematical idea on an index card.

c. How are these different mathematical ideas connected in this problem? Work with your team and follow your teacher's instructions to make a concept map. You will need to find ways to show or explain each of the connections you find.

9-104. BECOMING MATHEMATICALLY PROFICIENT

During this course, you have been asked lots of different kinds of questions. The purpose of many of the questions is to help you think in new ways.

This book focuses on helping you use some very specific Mathematical Practices. The Mathematical Practices are different ways to approach a mathematics problem, pull it apart, and work on it. They include ways you communicate mathematics to your teammates and teacher. They are what make you a mathematician, not just a number cruncher!

Problem continues on next page. →

9-104. *Problem continued from previous page.*

Two of the Mathematical Practices you may have used in this lesson, for example, are **make sense of problems and persevere in solving them** and **construct viable arguments and critique the reasoning of others**. Below, you will learn more about what these mean.

a. With your team, read and discuss the descriptions below.

Make sense of problems and persevere in solving them:

Making sense of problems and persevering in solving them means that you can solve realistic problems that are full of different kinds of mathematics. These types of problems are not routine, simple, or typical. Instead, they combine lots of math ideas and real-life situations.

In this course, you made sense of such problems and persevered in solving them on a daily basis. You carried out investigations that were not simply "word problems." By making sense of a problem, rather than being told how to solve it step-by-step, you developed a deeper understanding of mathematics. You also learned how to carry out mathematical procedures fluently and efficiently.

In addition to learning and using problem-solving strategies, you had to stick with challenging problems, trying different strategies and using all of the resources available to you.

Construct viable arguments and critique the reasoning of others:

An important practice of mathematics is to **construct viable arguments and critique the reasoning of others**. In this course, you regularly shared information, opinions, and expertise with your study team. You took turns talking, listening, contributing, arguing, asking for help, checking for understanding, and keeping each other focused.

During this process, you learned to use higher-order thinking. "Critical thinking" is another way to describe "higher-order thinking." It can be difficult to learn, but it is extremely valuable. Learning how to think critically helped you understand concepts more deeply. It allowed you to apply newfound ideas in all sorts of problems, not just the specific concept you happened to be working on.

Problem continues on next page. →

9-104. *Problem continued from previous page.*

You and your study teams used higher-order, critical-thinking skills any time you provided clarification, built on each other's ideas, analyzed a problem by breaking it into smaller parts, came to agreement during a discussion, and productively criticized each other's ideas.

Justifying and critiquing was a part of your daily classwork, not an occasional assignment. For each problem, you were expected to communicate your mathematical findings in writing, in oral presentations, or in poster presentations in a clear and convincing manner.

b. How did you **make sense of problems and persevere in solving them** when you solved problem 9-102? Be ready to explain your ideas.

c. How did you **construct viable arguments and critique the reasoning of others** while doing problem 9-102? How is **critiquing the reasoning of others** important in problems such as this one?

d. Work with your team to brainstorm other problems in this course in which you **made sense of problems and persevered in solving them** and **constructed viable arguments and critiqued the reasoning of others**. Be ready to share your ideas with the class.

9.3.2 What is the best design?

Using Multiple Math Ideas to Create an Interior Design

Have you ever helped to decide how furniture should be arranged in a room? Or have you seen something that you liked and wondered if it would fit in your space? In this lesson, you will use several math ideas you have learned in this course to help figure out how to place furniture in a particular room. Then you will discuss what you have learned in this course that helps you solve complex problems like this one.

9-105. DELIGHTFUL DESIGN

Laura is moving into a new bedroom. She is trying to decide how to arrange her furniture in her new room, but the only information she has about the size of her room is from the scale drawing shown at right.

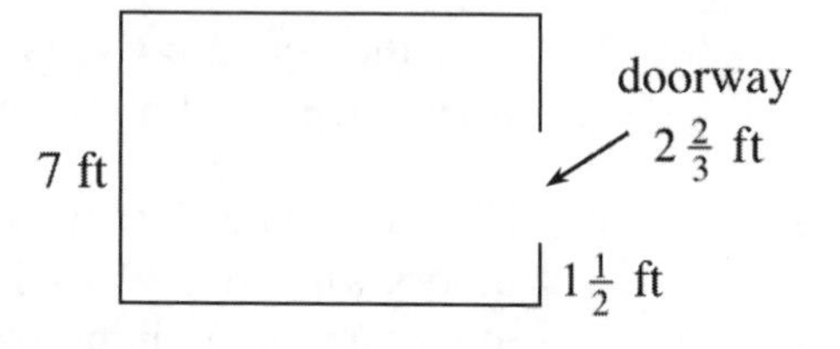

She has four pieces of bedroom furniture, with the dimensions given below.

Bed: 40 in. × 74 in.

Nightstand: 24 in. × 18 in.

Dresser: 26 in. × 18 in.

Desk: 52 in. × 22 in.

a. To plan the arrangement of the furniture, Laura needs to know the dimensions of the room. Find the missing wall measurements of Laura's bedroom.

b. Laura wants to draw a floor plan to make it easier to imagine how the furniture will fit into the space. Work with your team to decide on a scale factor, and draw a floor plan of Laura's bedroom on graph paper.

c. Laura wants to make paper cut-outs to represent her furniture so that she can arrange them on her floor plan. Each member of your team should choose one piece of furniture and draw a reduced version. (Be sure to reduce by the same amount as you did for your floor plan.) Then cut out the reduced pieces of furniture and move them around the floor plan to create an arrangement that Laura could use for her room.

d. How much walking space will Laura have in her bedroom? In other words, what is the area that is not covered with furniture?

9-106. MAKING CONNECTIONS

When you solved this problem, you needed to use your learning about several different math ideas.

a. Discuss this with your team.

 - Use colors to mark parts of your solution that used particular math ideas. (For example, did you add portions? Did you calculate measures of central tendency, such as mean or median?)
 - Label each math idea with words in the margin of your paper.

b. Contribute your ideas to a class discussion. Did any other teams identify math ideas that you used but had not noticed? If so, add these to your notes. Then write each math idea on an index card.

c. How are these different math ideas connected in this problem? Work with your team and follow your teacher's instructions to make a concept map. Work with your team to find ways to show or explain each of the connections you think of.

9-107. BECOMING MATHEMATICALLY PROFICIENT

During this course, you have been asked lots of different kinds of questions. The purpose of many of the questions is to help you think in new ways.

This book focuses on helping you use some very specific Mathematical Practices. The Mathematical Practices are different ways to approach a mathematics problem, pull it apart, and work on it. They include ways you communicate mathematics to your teammates and teacher. They are what make you a mathematician, not just a number cruncher!

Two of the Mathematical Practices you may have used in this lesson, for example, are **look for and make use of structure** and **look for and express regularity in repeated reasoning.** Below, you will learn more about what these mean.

Problem continues on next page. →

9-107. *Problem continued from previous page.*

a. With your team, read and discuss the descriptions below.

Look for and make use of structure:

Looking for and making use of structure has been an important part of this course. Since you are working to develop a deep, conceptual understanding of mathematics, you often use this practice to bring closure to an investigation. There are many concepts that you have learned by looking at the underlying structure of a math idea and thinking about how it connects to other ideas you have already learned.

One example of when you looked at the underlying structure of a math idea is when you learned to simplify with the "Giant One." The "Giant One" was a structure to use in arithmetic with fractions, where the numerator and denominator are the same, giving you a value of 1.

By being involved in the actual development of math concepts, you gain a deeper understanding of mathematics than you would if you were simply told what they are and how to do related problems.

Look for and express regularity in repeated reasoning:

Look for and express regularity in repeated reasoning means that when you are faced with an investigation of a new mathematical concept, you sometimes look for a simpler or related problem. This strategy can help expand your ability to solve increasingly complex problems.

For example, you **looked for and expressed regularity in repeated reasoning** when you expanded the reasoning from simple probability situations to more complicated ones such as compound independent and dependent situations.

b. How did **looking for and making use of structure** help you solve problem 9-105? Be ready to explain your ideas.

c. Sometimes you **look for and express regularity in repeated reasoning** to help explain mathematics and to explain your thinking. How did **looking for regularity in repeated reasoning** help you make your scale drawing in problem 9-105?

d. Work with your team to brainstorm other problems in this course in which you **looked for and expressed regularity in repeated reasoning** and **looked for and made use of structure**. Be ready to share your ideas with the class.

9.3.3 How can I use ratios?

Applying Ratios

Fish biologists need to keep track of fish populations in the waters they monitor. They want to know, for example, how many striped bass there are in San Francisco Bay. This number changes throughout the year as fish move in and out of the bay to spawn. Therefore, biologists need a way to gather current data quickly and inexpensively.

Today you and your team will model how scientists might make an estimate of the number of fish in a body of water using an application of ratios.

9-108. ESTIMATING FISH POPULATIONS TEAM CHALLENGE

Your team will be given a "lake" (paper bag) with "fish" (beans). Do you think that you can find out how many fish are in your lake?

Your Task: Determine the number of fish in your lake as accurately as possible *without* actually counting the fish. Then count the fish to determine the accuracy of your method.

Discussion Points

What are you supposed to find? Explain this in your own words.

How do you think fish biologists determine the population of fish in a lake?

What information can you gather to help you answer this question?

What tools will you need?

Can you use ratios to determine the number of fish in your lake? Why or why not?

9-109. Since it is impossible to count every animal, biologists use a process called "tag and recapture" to help them estimate the size of a population. Tag and recapture involves collecting a sample of animals, tagging them, and releasing them back into the wild. Later, biologists collect a new sample of the animals and count the number first-time captures and recaptures in the sample. Then they use the data to estimate the population size.

Your team's task is to use the tag-and-recapture process to estimate the number of "fish" (beans) in your "lake" (paper bag).

a. How many fish do you think are in your lake? Make an estimate.

b. Use the "net" (small cup) to collect an initial sample. Carefully count the number of fish in the sample and record the data.

c. To tag the fish, either replace each fish in the sample with a fish of a different color or mark both sides of each captured fish with a pen. Add these tagged fish to the lake. Be careful not to let any of the fish jump out onto the floor! If you replaced the fish with fish of different colors, then put the original fish from your sample aside. Do not return them to the lake, or else this will increase the number of fish in the lake.

d. Gently shake the bag to mix the fish thoroughly. Then collect another sample. Count the number of tagged and untagged fish in this new sample. Record the information on your paper. Then return the entire sample to the lake.

e. Look over the data you have collected so far. How many tagged fish are in the lake? How many tagged fish were in the second sample? What was the total number of fish in the second sample? Use this data and equivalent ratios to determine the total number of fish in the lake.

f. Repeat the process outlined in parts (d) and (e) to get a second estimate of the total number of fish in the lake. Is this second estimate close to the first?

g. **Extension:** Your solutions represent two estimates for the fish population of your lake. While it is important to get an accurate count, each time you net a sample, it costs taxpayers $500 for your time and equipment. So far, your samples have cost a total of $1000. If you think your estimate is accurate at this point, record it on the class table with your cost. If you think you should try another sample for better accuracy, do the same steps as before. Draw as many samples as you need, but remember that each sample costs $500.

h. Count the fish in your lake to find the actual population. Then record your team's data on the class table. Use the mean of your estimates to represent your overall estimate of fish in the lake.

i. Was your estimate close? Was it better than your estimate from part (a)? If not, what might have affected it? Do you think that this method of counting populations is accurate? Why or why not?

9-110. MAKING CONNECTIONS

When you solved this problem, you needed to use your knowledge about several different mathematical ideas.

a. With your team do the following:

- Use colors to mark parts of your solution that used particular mathematical ideas. (For example, did you measure lengths? Did you draw quadrilaterals?)
- Label each mathematical idea with words in the margin of your paper.

b. Contribute your ideas to a class discussion. Did any other teams identify mathematical ideas that you used but had not noticed? If so, add these to your notes. Then write each mathematical idea on an index card.

c. How are these different mathematical ideas connected in this problem? Work with your team and follow your teacher's instructions to make a concept map. You will need to find ways to show or explain each of the connections you find.

9-111. BECOMING MATHEMATICALLY PROFICIENT

During this course, you have been asked lots of different kinds of questions. The purpose of many of the questions is to help you think in new ways.

This book focuses on helping you use some very specific Mathematical Practices. The Mathematical Practices are different ways to approach a mathematics problem, pull it apart, and work on it. They include ways you communicate mathematics to your teammates and teacher. They are what make you a mathematician, not just a number cruncher!

Two of the Mathematical Practices you may have used in this lesson, for example, are **model with mathematics** and **use appropriate tools**. Below, you will learn more about what these mean.

a. With your team, read and discuss the descriptions below.

Model with mathematics:

When you **model with mathematics**, you are not wearing fancy clothes on a runway in New York! Mathematical modeling is what you do when you work with situations that involve multiple representations. For example, in this course, you frequently modeled different relationships and patterns using tables, graphs, equations, and words or diagrams.

Problem continues on next page. →

9-111. *Problem continued from previous page.*

In creating these models, you often first make assumptions, then make predictions, and finally check to see if your predictions make sense in the context of the problem.

In situations involving the variability of data, you learned that although a model may not be perfect, it can still be very useful for describing data and making predictions. You also found that a calculator or computer can help you model situations more efficiently than doing the work by hand.

Use appropriate tools strategically:

Throughout this course, you had to **use appropriate tools strategically**. In a typical lesson, you had many different tools available to you. Examples of tools include rulers, scissors, diagrams, graph paper, blocks, tiles, and calculators. However, you were not usually told which specific tools to use to solve any particular problem.

Sometimes, different teams decided to use different tools to solve the same problem. Thus, you often shared your solution strategies with the whole class. Frequently, this included a discussion about which tools were most efficient and productive to solve a given problem.

As you continued to do more and more sophisticated mathematics throughout the course, you were introduced to other tools, such as computer applications.

b. How did you **model with mathematics** while doing problem 9-109? How is **modeling** important in problems such as this one?

c. How did you **use appropriate tools strategically** when you solved problem 9-109? Be ready to explain your ideas.

d. Work with your team to brainstorm other problems in this course in which you **modeled with mathematics** and **used appropriate tools strategically**. Be ready to share your ideas with the class.

Core Connections, Course 2
Checkpoint Materials

Notes to Students (and their Teachers)

Students master different skills at different speeds. No two students learn exactly the same way at the same time. At some point you will be expected to perform certain skills accurately. Most of the Checkpoint problems incorporate skills that you should have been developing in grades 5 and 6. If you have not mastered these skills yet it does not mean that you will not be successful in this class. However, you may need to do some work outside of class to get caught up on them.

Starting in Chapter 1 and finishing in Chapter 9, there are 9 problems designed as Checkpoint problems. Each one is marked with an icon like the one above and numbered according to the chapter that it is in. After you do each of the Checkpoint problems, check your answers by referring to this section. If your answers are incorrect, you may need some extra practice to develop that skill. The practice sets are keyed to each of the Checkpoint problems in the textbook. Each has the topic clearly labeled, followed by the answers to the corresponding Checkpoint problem and then some completed examples. Next, the complete solution to the Checkpoint problem from the text is given, and there are more problems for you to practice with answers included.

Remember, looking is not the same as doing! You will never become good at any sport by just watching it, and in the same way, reading through the worked examples and understanding the steps is not the same as being able to do the problems yourself. How many of the extra practice problems do you need to try? That is really up to you. Remember that your goal is to be able to do similar problems on your own confidently and accurately. This is your responsibility. You should not expect your teacher to spend time in class going over the solutions to the Checkpoint problem sets. If you are not confident after reading the examples and trying the problems, you should get help outside of class time or talk to your teacher about working with a tutor.

Checkpoint Topics

1. Area and Perimeter of Polygons
2. Multiple Representations of Portions
3. Multiplying Fractions and Decimals
5 Order of Operations
6. Writing and Evaluating Algebraic Expressions
7A. Simplifying Expressions
7B. Displays of Data: Histograms and Box Plots
8. Solving Multi-Step Equations
9. Unit Rates and Proportions

Checkpoint 1

Problem 1-141

Area and Perimeter of Polygons

Answers to problem 1-141: a. 96 cm^2, 40 cm; b. 22 in.^{2}, 25.05 in.; c. 144 cm^2, 52 cm; d. 696.67 m^2, 114.67 m

Area is the number of square units in a flat region. The formulas to calculate the area of several kinds of polygons are:

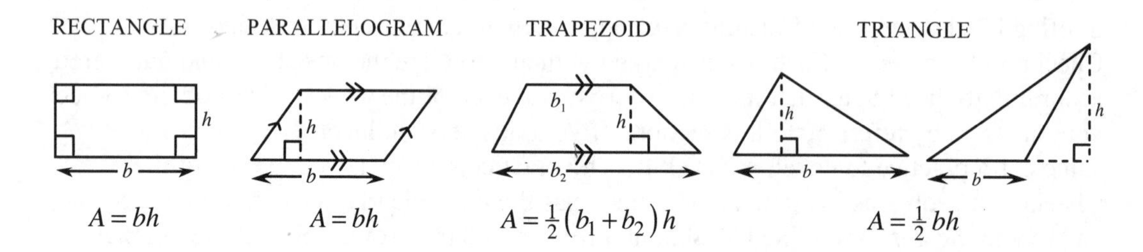

Perimeter is the distance around a figure on a flat surface. To calculate the perimeter of a polygon, add together the length of each side.

Example 1:
Compute the area and perimeter.

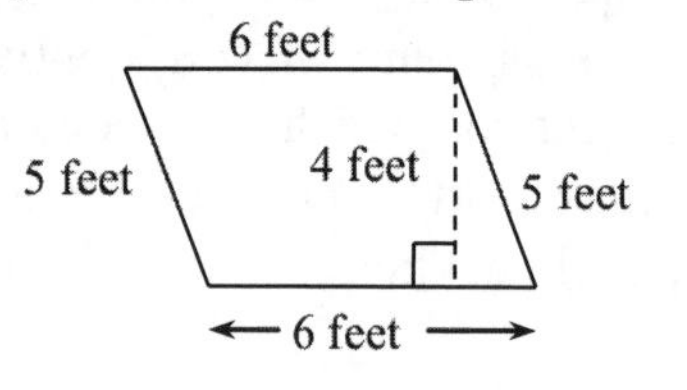

parallelogram

$A = bh = 6 \cdot 4 = 24 \text{ feet}^2$

$P = 6 + 6 + 5 + 5 = 22 \text{ feet}$

Example 2:
Compute the area and perimeter.

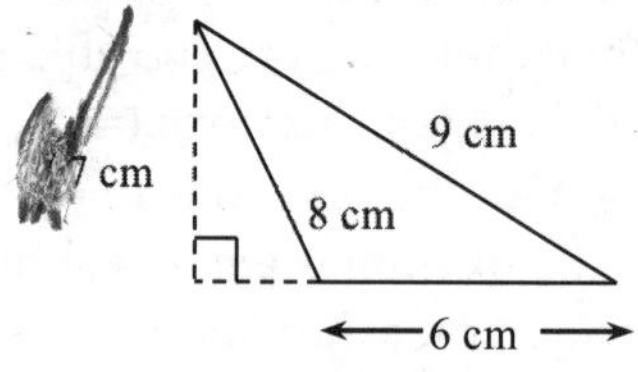

triangle

$A = \frac{1}{2}bh = \frac{1}{2} \cdot 6 \cdot 7 = 21 \text{ cm}^2$

$P = 6 + 8 + 9 = 23 \text{ cm}$

Now we can go back and solve the original problem.

a. Rectangle: $A = bh = 12 \cdot 8 = 96 \text{ cm}^2$; $P = 8 + 8 + 12 + 12 = 40 \text{ cm}$

b. Triangle: $A = \frac{1}{2}bh = \frac{1}{2} \cdot 11 \cdot 4 = 22 \text{ in.}^2$; $P = 11 + 9.05 + 5 = 25.05 \text{ in.}$

c. Parallelogram: $A = bh = 16 \cdot 9 = 144 \text{ cm}^2$; $P = 16 + 16 + 10 + 10 = 52 \text{ cm}$

d. Trapezoid: $A = \frac{1}{2}(b_1 + b_2)h = \frac{1}{2}(25 + 44.67) \cdot 10 = 696.67 \text{ m}^2$;
$P = 21 + 25 + 24 + 44.67 = 114.67 \text{ m}$

Here are some more to try. Find the area and perimeter of each figure.

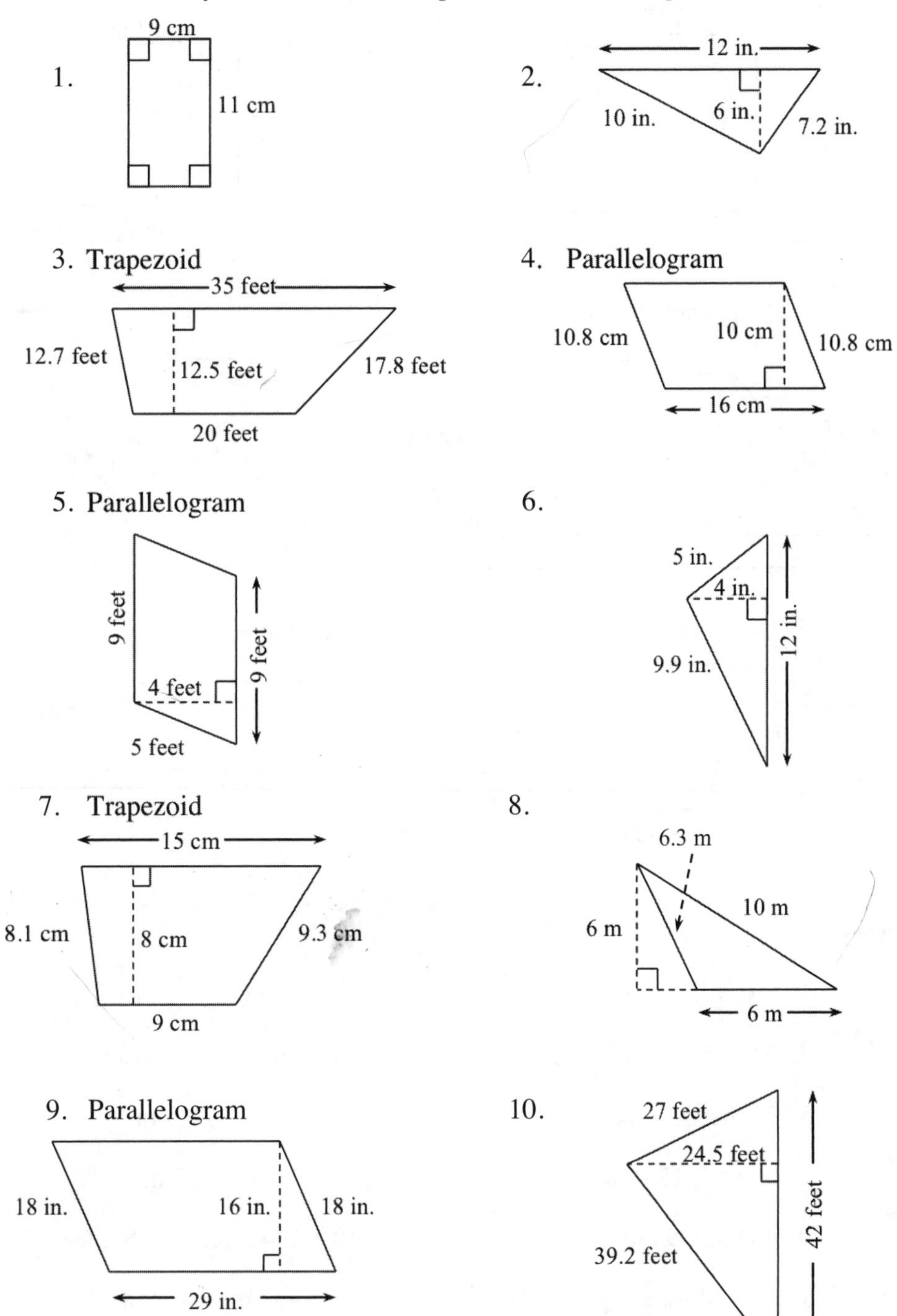

11.

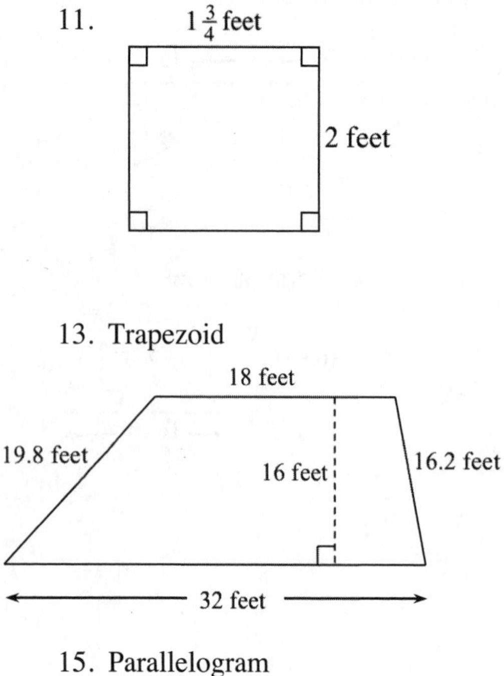

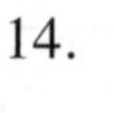

12. Trapezoid

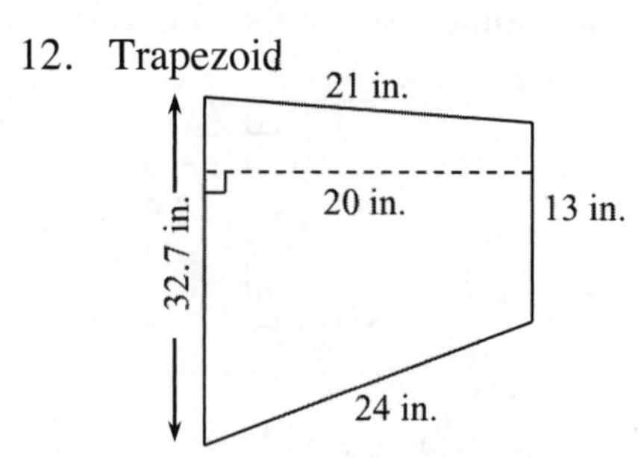

13.

14.

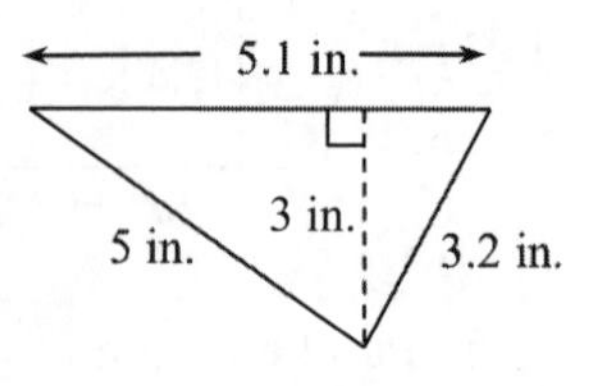

15. Parallelogram

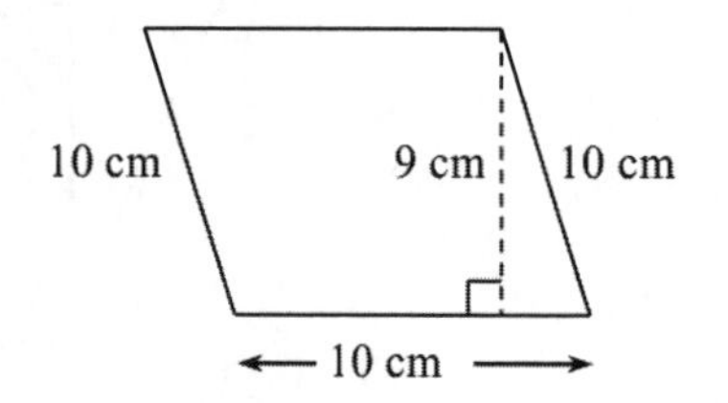

16. Trapezoid

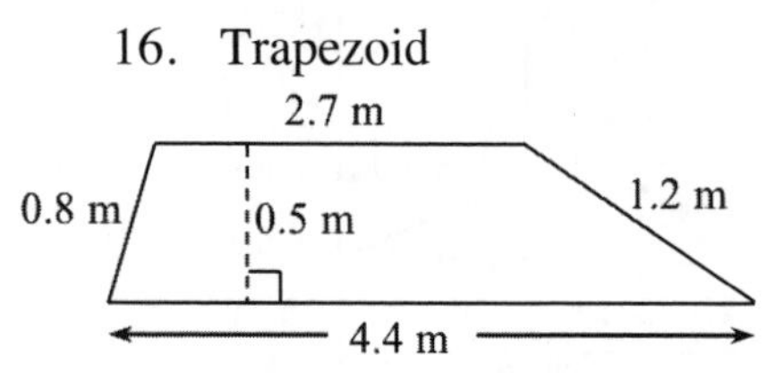

Answers:

1. 99 cm^2, 40 cm
2. 36 in.^{2}, 29.2 in.
3. 343.75 feet^2, 85.5 feet
4. 160 cm^2, 53.6 cm
5. 36 feet^2, 28 feet
6. 24 in.^{2}, 26.9 in.
7. 96 cm^2, 41.4 cm
8. 18 m^2, 22.3 m
9. 464 in.^{2}, 94 in.
10. 514.5 feet^2, 108.2 feet
11. $\frac{14}{4} = 3\frac{1}{2}$ feet^2, $\frac{30}{4} = 7\frac{1}{2}$ feet
12. 457 in.^{2}, 90.7 in.
13. 400 feet^2, 86 feet
14. 7.65 in.^{2}, 13.3 in.
15. 90 cm^2, 40 cm
16. 1.78 m^2, 9.1 m

Checkpoint 2

Problem 2-120

Multiple Representations of Portions

Answers to problem 2-120: a. 43%, $\frac{43}{100}$, b. $\frac{9}{10}$, 0.9, 90%, c. $\frac{39}{100}$, 0.39, d. 64%, 0.64

Portions of a whole may be represented in various ways as represented by this web. Percent means "per hundred" and the place value of a decimal will determine its name. Change a fraction in an equivalent fraction with 100 parts to name it as a percent.

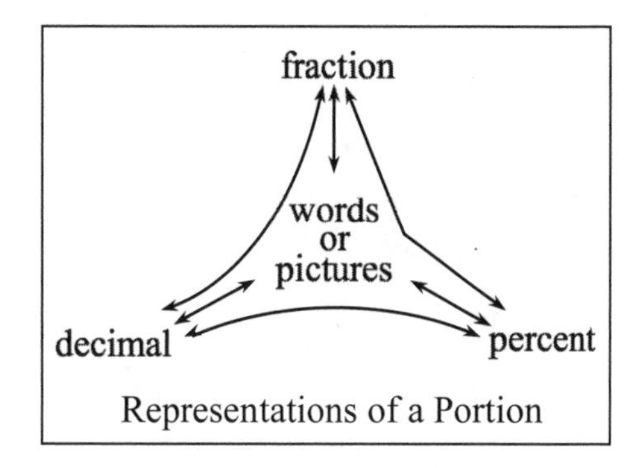

Representations of a Portion

Example 1: Name the given portion as a fraction and as a percent. 0.3

Solution: The digit 3 is in the tenths place so $0.3 = \text{three tenths} = \frac{3}{10}$.

On a diagram or a hundreds grid, 3 parts out of 10 is equivalent to 30 parts out of 100 so $\frac{3}{10} = \frac{30}{100} = 30\%$.

Example 2: Name the given portion as a fraction and as a decimal. 35%

Solution: $35\% = \frac{35}{100}$ = thirty-five hundredths = 0.35; $\frac{35}{100} = \frac{7}{20}$

Now we can go back and solve the original problem.

a. 0.43 is forty-three hundredths or $\frac{43}{100} = 43\%$

b. nine tenths is $\frac{9}{10} = \frac{9}{10} \cdot \frac{10}{10} = \frac{90}{100} = 90\%$; $\frac{9}{10} = 0.9$

c. $39\% = \frac{39}{100}$ = thirty-nine hundredths = 0.39

d. $\frac{16}{25} = \frac{16}{25} \cdot \frac{4}{4} = \frac{64}{100} = 0.64 = 64\%$

Here are some more to try. For each portion of a whole, write it as a percent, fraction, and a decimal.

1. 6%
2. 0.35
3. $\frac{1}{4}$
4. $\frac{2}{5}$
5. 0.16
6. 87%
7. $\frac{13}{25}$
8. 21%
9. $\frac{7}{50}$
10. 0.050
11. 65%
12. 3.7%
13. $\frac{7}{10}$
14. 0.66
15. $\frac{19}{20}$
16. 20%
17. 0.23
18. 1.0
19. 135%
20. $\frac{77}{100}$

Answers:

1. $\frac{6}{100} = \frac{3}{50}, 0.06$
2. $35\%, \frac{35}{100} = \frac{7}{20}$
3. $25\%, 0.25$
4. $40\%, 0.4$
5. $16\%, \frac{16}{100} = \frac{4}{25}$
6. $\frac{87}{100}, 0.87$
7. $52\%, 0.52$
8. $\frac{21}{100}, 0.21$
9. $14\%, 0.14$
10. $5\%, \frac{5}{100} = \frac{1}{20}$
11. $\frac{13}{20}, 0.65$
12. $\frac{37}{1000}, 0.037$
13. $70\%, 0.7$
14. $66\%, \frac{66}{100} = \frac{33}{50}$
15. $95\%, 0.95$
16. $\frac{20}{100} = \frac{1}{5}, 0.2$
17. $23\%, \frac{23}{100}$
18. $100\%, \frac{100}{100} = \frac{1}{1}$
19. $\frac{135}{100} = 1\frac{35}{100} = 1\frac{7}{20}, 1.35$
20. $77\%, 0.77$

Checkpoint 3

Problem 3-110

Multiplying Fractions and Decimals

Answers to problem 3-110: a. $\frac{9}{20}$, b. $\frac{1}{5}$, c. $4\frac{2}{9}$, d. $7\frac{1}{5}$, e. 12.308, f. 0.000208

To multiply fractions, multiply the numerators and then multiply the denominators. To multiply mixed numbers, change each mixed number to a fraction greater than one before multiplying. In both cases, simplify by looking for factors than make "one."

To multiply decimals, multiply as with whole numbers. In the product, the number of decimal places is equal to the total number of decimal places in the multiplied numbers. Sometimes zeros need to be added to place the decimal point.

Example 1: Multiply $\frac{3}{8}\cdot\frac{4}{5}$

Solution:

$\frac{3}{8}\cdot\frac{4}{5}\Rightarrow\frac{3\cdot4}{8\cdot5}\Rightarrow\frac{3\cdot\cancel{4}}{2\cdot\cancel{4}\cdot5}\Rightarrow\frac{3}{10}$

Example 2: Multiply $3\frac{1}{3}\cdot2\frac{1}{2}$

Solution:

$3\frac{1}{3}\cdot2\frac{1}{2}\Rightarrow\frac{10}{3}\cdot\frac{5}{2}\Rightarrow\frac{10\cdot5}{3\cdot2}\Rightarrow\frac{5\cdot\cancel{2}\cdot5}{3\cdot\cancel{2}}\Rightarrow\frac{25}{3}$ or $8\frac{1}{3}$

Note that we are simplifying using Giant Ones but no longer drawing the Giant One.

Example 3: Multiply 12.5 · 0.36

Solution:

12.5	(one decimal place)
×0.36	(two decimal places)
750	
3750	
4.500	(three decimal places)

Now we can go back and solve the original problem.

a. $\frac{2}{3}\cdot\frac{2}{5}\Rightarrow\frac{2\cdot2}{3\cdot5}\Rightarrow\frac{4}{15}$

b. $\frac{7}{10}\cdot\frac{2}{7}\Rightarrow\frac{\cancel{7}\cdot\cancel{2}}{5\cdot\cancel{2}\cdot\cancel{7}}\Rightarrow\frac{1}{5}$

c. $2\frac{1}{3}\cdot2\frac{1}{2}\Rightarrow\frac{7}{3}\cdot\frac{5}{2}\Rightarrow\frac{7\cdot5}{3\cdot2}\Rightarrow\frac{35}{6}$ or $5\frac{5}{6}$

d. $1\frac{1}{3}\cdot2\frac{1}{6}\Rightarrow\frac{4}{3}\cdot\frac{13}{6}\Rightarrow\frac{2\cdot\cancel{2}\cdot13}{3\cdot\cancel{2}\cdot3}\Rightarrow\frac{26}{9}$ or $2\frac{8}{9}$

e.

2.71
×4.5
1355
10840
12.195

f.

0.35
×0.0007
0.**000**245

Here are some more to try. Multiply the fractions and decimals below.

1. $0.08 \cdot 4.7$
2. $0.21 \cdot 3.42$
3. $\frac{4}{7} \cdot \frac{1}{2}$
4. $\frac{5}{6} \cdot \frac{3}{8}$
5. $\frac{8}{9} \cdot \frac{3}{4}$
6. $\frac{7}{10} \cdot \frac{3}{4}$
7. $3.07 \cdot 5.4$
8. $6.57 \cdot 2.8$
9. $\frac{5}{6} \cdot \frac{3}{20}$
10. $2.9 \cdot 0.056$
11. $\frac{6}{7} \cdot \frac{4}{9}$
12. $3\frac{1}{7} \cdot 1\frac{2}{5}$
13. $\frac{2}{3} \cdot \frac{5}{9}$
14. $\frac{3}{5} \cdot \frac{9}{13}$
15. $2.34 \cdot 2.7$
16. $2\frac{1}{3} \cdot 4\frac{4}{5}$
17. $4\frac{3}{5} \cdot \frac{1}{2}$
18. $\frac{3}{8} \cdot \frac{5}{9}$
19. $0.235 \cdot 0.43$
20. $421 \cdot 0.00005$

Answers:

1. 0.376
2. 0.7182
3. $\frac{2}{7}$
4. $\frac{5}{16}$
5. $\frac{2}{3}$
6. $\frac{21}{40}$
7. 16.578
8. 18.396
9. $\frac{1}{8}$
10. 0.1624
11. $\frac{8}{21}$
12. $4\frac{2}{5}$
13. $\frac{10}{27}$
14. $\frac{27}{65}$
15. 6.318
16. $11\frac{1}{5}$
17. $2\frac{3}{10}$
18. $\frac{5}{24}$
19. 0.10105
20. 0.02105

Checkpoint 5

Problem 5-148

Order of Operations

Answers to problem 5-148: a: 20, b: –4

In general, simplify an expression by using the **Order of Operations**:

- Evaluate each exponential (for example, $5^2 = 5 \cdot 5 = 25$).
- Multiply and divide each term from left to right.
- Combine like terms by adding and subtracting from left to right.

But simplify *the expressions in parentheses* or any other expressions of grouped numbers first. Numbers above or below a "fraction bar" are considered grouped. A good way to remember is to circle the terms like in the following example. Remember that terms are separated by + and – signs.

Example 1: Simplify $12 \div 2^2 - 4 + 3(1+2)^3$

$$12 \div 2^2 - 4 + 3(1+2)^3$$

Simplify within the circled terms: Be sure to perform the exponent operations before dividing.
$12 \div 2^2 = 12 \div 2 \cdot 2 = 3$

$$3 - 4 + 3(3)^3$$

Then perform the exponent operation: $3^3 = 3 \cdot 3 \cdot 3 = 27$

$$3 - 4 + 3(27)$$

Next, multiply and divide left to right: $3(27) = 81$

$$3 - 4 + 81$$

Finally, add and subtract left to right: $3 - 4 = -1$

$$-1 + 81$$

$$80$$

Example 2: Simplify $-3^2 - \frac{2+7}{3} + 8 \div \left(\frac{1}{2}\right)$

$$-3^2 - \frac{2+7}{3} + 8 \div \left(\frac{1}{2}\right)$$

Simplify within the circled terms: $-3^2 = -3 \cdot 3 = -9$

$\frac{2+7}{3} = \frac{9}{3} = 3 \quad 8 \div \frac{1}{2} = 8 \cdot \frac{2}{1} = 16$

Then add and subtract, left to right.

$$-9 - 3 + 16$$
$$-12 + 16$$
$$4$$

Now we can go back and solve the original problem.

a.
$$16 - 2^3 \div 8 + 5$$
$$16 - 2 \cdot 2 \cdot 2 \div 8 + 5$$
$$16 - 4 \cdot 2 \div 8 + 5$$
$$16 - 8 \div 8 + 5$$
$$16 - 1 + 5$$
$$15 + 5$$
$$20$$

b.
$$(-2+6)^2 - \left(\tfrac{3}{2}\right) \cdot 14 + 1$$
$$(4)^2 - \tfrac{42}{2} + 1$$
$$16 - 21 + 1$$
$$-5 + 1$$
$$-4$$

Here are some more to try.

1. $10 \cdot \frac{1}{2} + (-6)(-3)$
2. $\frac{-5+(-6)\left(\frac{2}{3}\right)}{-3}$
3. $(6-8)(9-10)-(4+2)(6+3)$
4. $\frac{-84}{36-12(-5)}$
5. $\frac{1}{2}(6-2)^2 - 4 \cdot 3$
6. $3\left(2(1+5)+8-3^2\right)$
7. $(8+12) \div 4 - 6$
8. $-6^2 + 4 \cdot 8$
9. $18 \cdot 3 \div 3^3$
10. $10 + 5^2 - 25$
11. $20 - (3^3 \div 9) \cdot 2$
12. $100 - (2^3 - 6) \div 2$
13. $85 - (4 \cdot 2)^2 - 3$
14. $22 + (3 \cdot 2)^2 \div 2$
15. $16 + 11(-2)^2 - 25\left(\frac{2}{5}\right)$
16. $54 \div 3^2 + \left(\frac{4}{3}\right)\left(\frac{27}{2}\right) - 1^2$
17. $2(3-1)^3 \div 8$
18. $(7^2 - 1) \div 4 + 2$
19. $-3 \cdot 2 \div (-2-4)$
20. $-3 \cdot 2 \div -2 - 4$
21. $12 + 3\left(\frac{8-2}{12-9}\right) - 2\left(\frac{9-1}{19-15}\right)$
22. $15 + 4\left(\frac{11-2}{9-6}\right) - 2\left(\frac{12-4}{18-10}\right)$
23. $32 \div 16 - 8 \cdot 25\left(\frac{1}{2}\right)^2$
24. $36 + 16 \cdot \left(\frac{1}{4}\right) - (50 \div 25)^2$

Answers:

1. 23
2. 3
3. –52
4. $-\frac{7}{8}$
5. –4
6. 33
7. –1
8. –4
9. 2
10. 10
11. 14
12. 99
13. 18
14. 40
15. 50
16. 23
17. 2
18. 14
19. 1
20. –1
21. 14
22. 25
23. –48
24. 36

Checkpoint 6

Problem 6-139

Writing and Evaluating Algebraic Expressions

Answers to problem 6-139: a. $x+6$, b. $y-5$, c. $2x+3$, d. $5y$, e. 11; 3; 13; 40

There are some vocabulary words that are frequently used to represent arithmetic operations.

Addition is often suggested by: sum, increased, more than, greater than, total

Subtraction is often suggested by: difference, decreased by, less than, smaller than

Multiplication is often suggested by: product, times, twice, double

Division is often suggested by: quotient, divided by, shared evenly

Examples

Five more than *m*:
Five more than a number, increases a number by 5 so it would be $m+5$.

Three less than *x*:
Three less than a number makes the number smaller by 3 so it would be $x-3$.

Triple *m*:
Tripling a number is the same as multiplying the number by 3 so it would be $3m$.

Five divided by *x*:
Division is usually written as a fraction so it would be $\frac{5}{x}$.

To evaluate an algebraic expression means to calculate the value of the expression when the variable is replaced by a numerical value.

Examples

Evaluate $2x-5$ if $x=7$ Solution: $2x-5 \Rightarrow 2 \cdot 7-5=14-5=9$

Evaluate $\frac{6}{x}+9$ if $x=2$ Solution: $\frac{6}{x}+9 \Rightarrow \frac{6}{2}+9=3+9=12$

Now we can go back and solve the original problem. Part (e) is included with the writing of the expression.

a. Six more suggests adding 6 so it would be $x+6$; if $x=5$ then $x+6 \Rightarrow 5+6=11$.

b. Five less suggests subtracting 5 so it would be $y-5$; if $y=8$ then $y-5 \Rightarrow 8-5=3$.

c. Twice a number suggests multiplication by 2 and then increasing by 3 means to add 3 to the previous product so it would be $2x+3$; if $x=5$ then $2x+3 \Rightarrow 2 \cdot 5+3=13$.

d. Product suggests multiply so it would be $5y$; if $y=8$ then $5y \Rightarrow 5 \cdot 8=40$.

Here are some more to try. For problems 1 through 16 write an algebraic expression. For problems 17 through 24 evaluate the expression for the given values.

1. 5 greater than m
2. Double s
3. 7 less than t
4. 6 more than y
5. 14 divided by b
6. m subtracted from a
7. x divided among 5
8. The product of 7 and e
9. The sum of d and l
10. 6 times c
11. The product of x, y, and w
12. h times 8, added to j
13. 4 divided by p, increased by 7
14. Half of r
15. Three times q increased by 5
16. Two less than triple n
17. $4x-3$ if $x=5$
18. $7d$ if $d=10$
19. $2xy+1$ if $x=3$, $y=4$
20. $4+8g$ if $g=6$
21. $4b+12$ if $b=11$
22. $\frac{9g}{27}$ if $g=3$
23. $mw+h$ if $m=5, w=8, h=6$
24. $\frac{y}{z}+7$ if $y=4, z=2$

Answers:

1. $m+5$
2. $2s$
3. $t-7$
4. $y+6$
5. $\frac{14}{b}$
6. $a-m$
7. $\frac{x}{5}$
8. $7e$
9. $d+l$
10. $6c$
11. xyw
12. $8h+j$
13. $\frac{4}{p}+7$
14. $\frac{r}{2}$
15. $3q+5$
16. $3n-2$
17. 17
18. 70
19. 25
20. 52
21. 56
22. 1
23. 46
24. 9

Checkpoint 7A

Problem 7-50

Simplifying Expressions

Answers to problem 7-50: a. $2x^2+x-10$, b. $x^2-9x+11$

Like terms are two or more terms that are exactly the same except for their coefficients. That is, they have the same variable(s), with corresponding variable(s) raised to the same power. Like terms can be combined into one quantity by adding and/or subtracting the coefficients of the terms. Terms are usually listed in the order of decreasing powers of the variable. Combining like terms, one way of simplifying expressions, using algebra tiles is shown in the first two examples.

Example 1:

Simplify $(2x^2+4x+5)+(x^2+x+3)$ means combine $2x^2+4x+5$ with x^2+x+3.

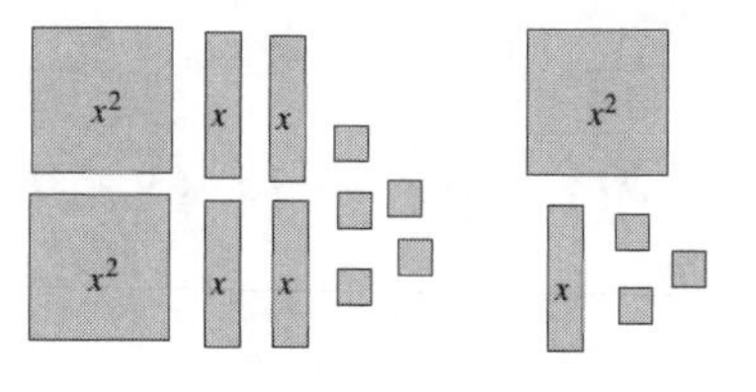

$$(2x^2+4x+5)+(x^2+x+3) = 3x^2+5x+8$$

Example 2:

Simplify $x^2+3x-4+2(2x^2-x)+3$.

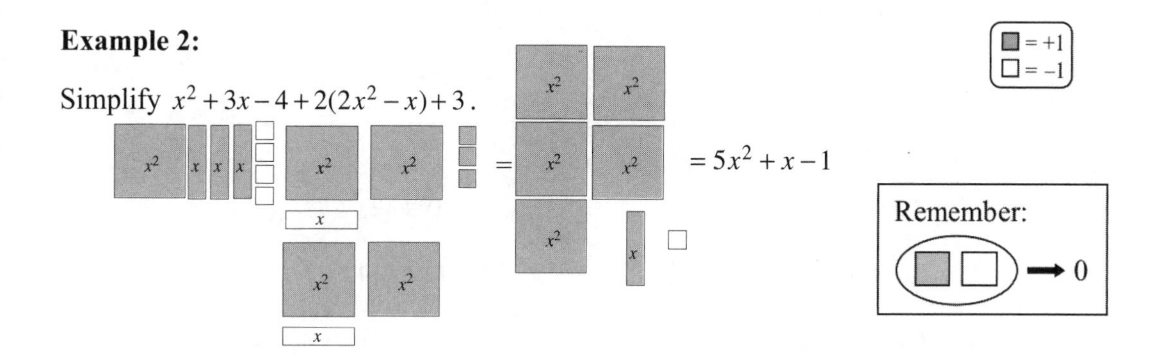

Now we can go back and solve the original problem.

a. $4x^2+3x-7+-2x^2-2x+(-3)$

$(4x^2-2x^2)+(3x-2x)+(-7+(-3))$

$2x^2+x-10$

b. $-3x^2-2x+5+4x^2-7x+6$

$(-3x^2+4x^2)+(-2x-7x)+(5+6)$

$x^2-9x+11$

Here are some more to try.

1. $(x^2+3x+4)+(x^2+3x+2)$
2. $x^2+4x+3+x^2+2x+5$
3. $2x^2+2x-1+x^2-4x+5$
4. $3x^2-x+7-3x^2+2x+(-4)$
5. $2x^2+4x+(-3)+x^2-3x+5$
6. $4x^2+2x-8+(-2x^2)+5x+1$
7. $-4x^2+2x+8-3x^2+5x-3$
8. $3x^2+2(4x+1)-2x^2+4x+5$
9. $3(5x^2+4x)-7+2x+3$
10. $3x^2-4x+2+4(2x^2+2x)$
11. $-2(3x^2-x+2)+3x-1$
12. $2(x^2-2x)+7+5(x^2+4x)-3$
13. $2x^2-3(x-3)+5x^2-4x$
14. $-3x+3(x^2+2)+(-x)-4$
15. $(x^2+3x+2)-(x^2-3x-2)$
16. $(2x^2-5x)-(x^2+7x)$
17. $(5x+6)-(x^2-5x+6)$
18. $4a+2b+3c-6a+3b-6c$
19. $3c+4a-7c+5b-(-4a)+7$
20. $-5a+6b-7c-(3c-4b-a)$

Answers:

1. $2x^2+6x+6$
2. $2x^2+6x+8$
3. $3x^2-2x+4$
4. $x+3$
5. $3x^2+x+2$
6. $2x^2+7x-7$
7. $-7x^2+7x+5$
8. $x^2+12x+7$
9. $15x^2+14x-4$
10. $11x^2+4x+2$
11. $-6x^2+5x-5$
12. $7x^2+16x+4$
13. $7x^2-7x+9$
14. $3x^2-4x+2$
15. $6x+4$
16. x^2-12x
17. $-x^2+10x$
18. $-2a+5b-3c$
19. $8a+5b-7c+7$
20. $-4a+10b-10c$

Checkpoint 7B

Problem 7-117

Displays of Data: Histograms and Box Plots

Answers to problem 7-117:

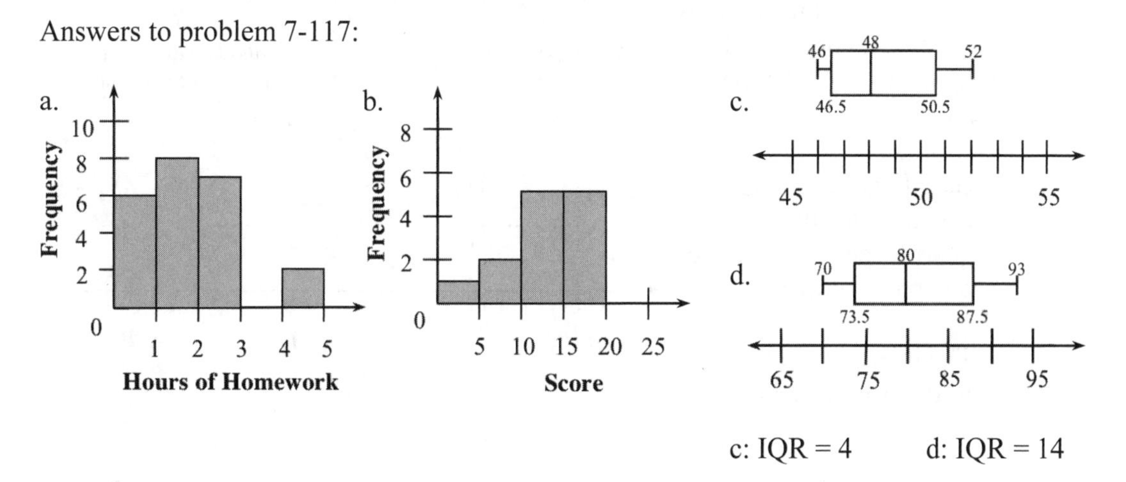

c: IQR = 4 d: IQR = 14

Histograms

A histogram is a method of showing data. It uses a bar to show the frequency (the number of times something occurs). The frequency measures something that changes numerically. (In a bar graph the frequency measures something that changes by category.) The intervals (called bins) for the data are shown on the horizontal axis and the frequency is represented by the height of a rectangle above the interval. The labels on the horizontal axis represent the lower end of each interval or bin.

Example: Sam and her friends weighed themselves and here is their weight in pounds: 110, 120, 131, 112, 125, 135, 118, 127, 135, and 125. Make a histogram to display the information. Use intervals of 10 pounds.

Solution:

See histogram at right. Note that the person weighing 120 pounds is counted in the next higher bin.

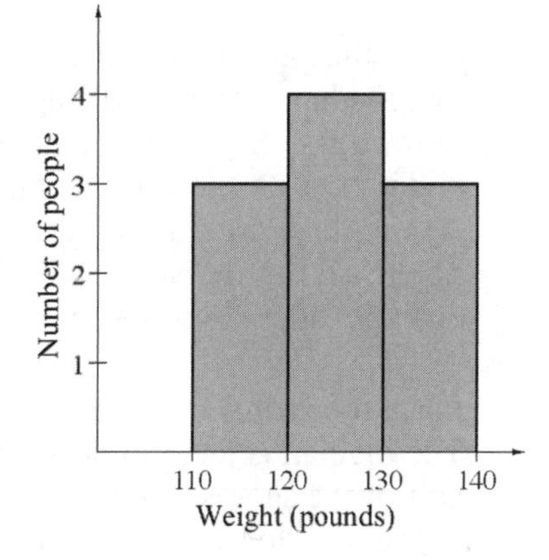

Box Plots

A box plot displays a summary of data using the median, quartiles, and extremes of the data. The box contains the "middle half" of the data. The right segment represents the top 25% of the data and the left segment represent the bottom 25% of the data.

Example: Create a box plot for the set of data given in the previous example.

Solution: Place the data in order to find the median (middle number) and the quartiles (middle numbers of the upper half and the lower half.)

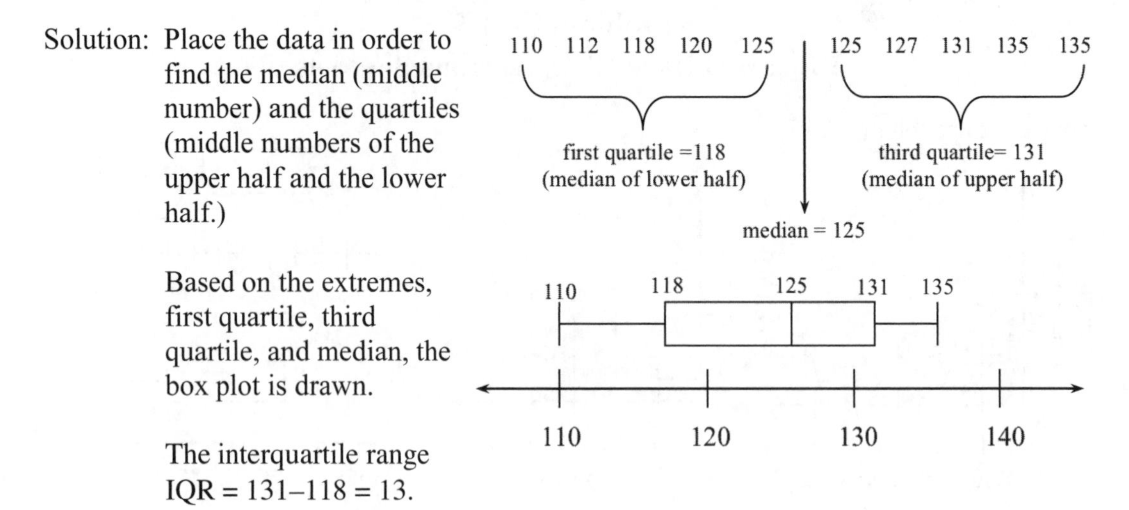

Based on the extremes, first quartile, third quartile, and median, the box plot is drawn.

The interquartile range IQR = 131–118 = 13.

Now we can go back to the original problem.

a. The 0–1 bin contains the six students who do less than one hour of homework. The 1–2 bin contains the 10 students who do at least one hour but less than two hours. The 2–3 bin contains the seven students who do at least two hours but less than three hours. There are no students who do at least three hours and less than four. Two students did four hours and less than five. See the histogram above.

b. The 0–5 bin contains two scores less than 5 points. The 5–10 bin contains the two scores of a least five but less than 10. The 10–15 bin contains the eight scores at least 10 but less than 15. The 15–20 bin contains the seven scores at least 15 but less than 20. See the histogram above.

c. Place the ages in order: 46, 46, 47, 47, 48, 49, 50, 51, 52.
The median is the middle age: 48. The first quartile is the median of the lower half of the ages. Since there are four lower-half ages, the median is the average of the middle two: $\frac{46+47}{2} = 46.5$. The third quartile is the median of the upper half ages. Again, there are four upper-half ages, so average the two middle ages: $\frac{50+51}{2} = 50.5$. The interquartile range is the difference between the third quartile and the first quartile: 50.5–46.5 = 4. See the box plot above.

d. Place the scores in order: 70, 72, 75, 76, 80, 82, 85, 90, 93.
The median is the middle score: 80. The lower quartile is the median of the lower half of the scores. Since there are four lower-half scores, the median is the average of the middle two: $\frac{72+75}{2} = 73.5$. The third quartile is the median of the upper half of the scores. Again, there are four upper-half scores, so average the two middle ages: $\frac{85+90}{2} = 87.5$. The interquartile range is the difference between the third quartile and the first quartile: 87.5–73.5 = 14. See the box plot above.

Here are some more to try. For problems 1 through 6, create a histogram. For problems 7 through 12, create a box plot. State the quartiles and the interquartile range.

1. Number of heads showing in 20 tosses of three coins:
   2, 2, 1, 3, 1, 0, 2, 1, 2, 1, 1, 2, 0, 1, 3, 2, 1, 3, 1, 2

2. Number of even numbers in 5 rolls of a dice done 14 times:
   4, 2, 2, 3, 1, 2, 1, 1, 3, 3, 2, 2, 4, 5

3. Number of fish caught by 7 fishermen:
   2, 3, 0, 3, 3, 1, 5

4. Number of girls in grades K-8 at local schools:
   12, 13, 15, 10, 11, 12, 15, 11, 12

5. Number of birthdays in each March in various 2nd grade classes:
   5, 1, 0, 0, 2, 4, 4, 1, 3, 1, 0, 4

6. Laps jogged by 15 students:
   10, 15, 10, 13, 20, 14, 17, 10, 15, 20, 8, 7, 13, 15, 12

7. Number of days of rain:
   6, 8, 10, 9, 7, 7, 11, 12, 6, 12, 14, 10

8. Number of times a frog croaked per minute:
   38, 23, 40, 12, 35, 27, 51, 26, 24, 14, 38, 41, 23, 17

9. Speed in mph of 15 different cars:
   30, 35, 40, 23, 33, 32, 28, 37, 30, 31, 29, 33, 39, 22, 30

10. Typing speed of 12 students in words per minute:
    28, 30, 60, 26, 47, 53, 39, 42, 48, 27, 23, 86

11. Number of face cards pulled when 13 cards are drawn 15 times:
    1, 4, 2, 1, 1, 0, 0, 2, 1, 3, 3, 0, 0, 2, 1

12. Height of 15 students in inches:
    48, 55, 56, 65, 67, 60, 60, 57, 50, 59, 62, 65, 58, 70, 68

Answers:

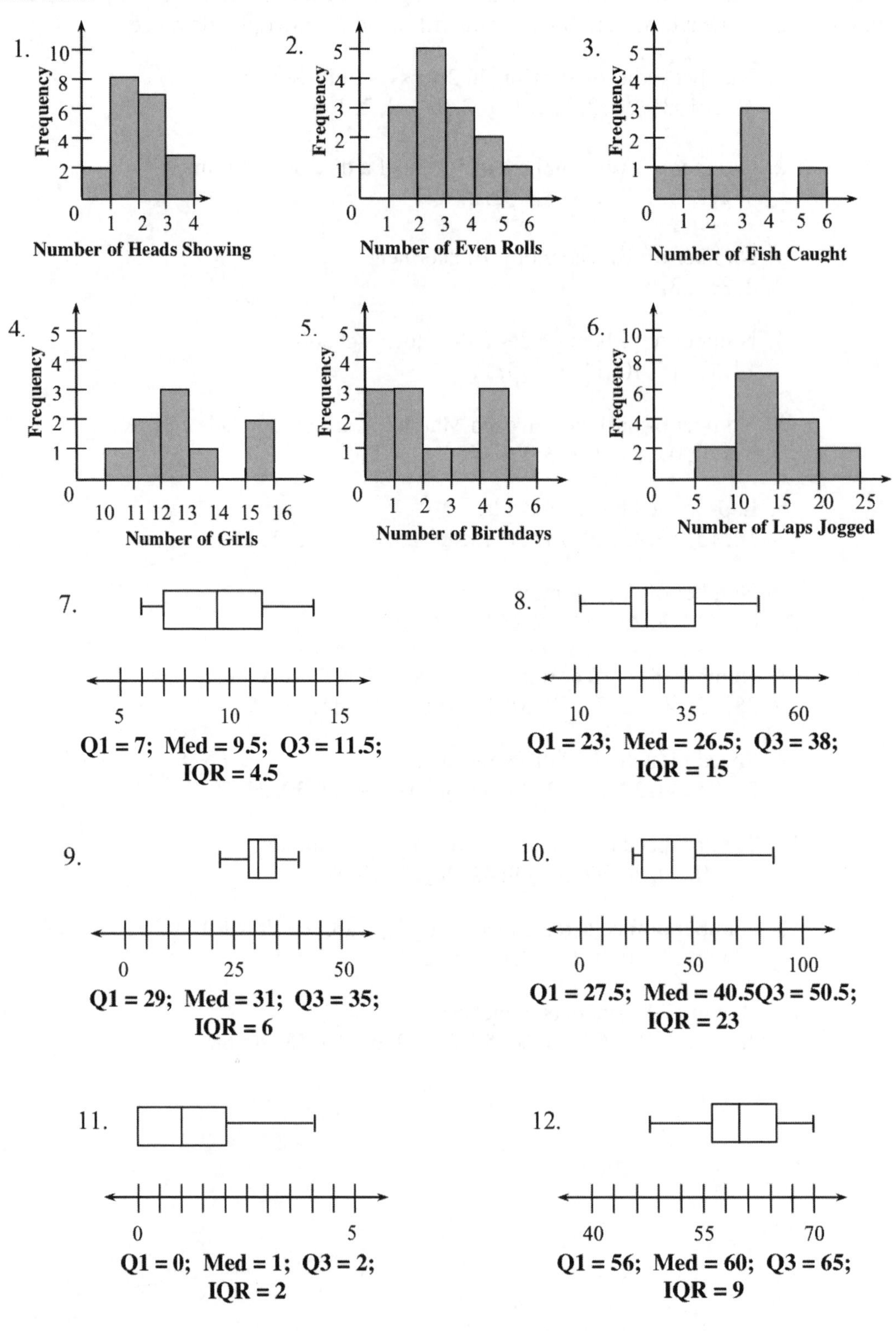
1.
Frequency
Number of Heads Showing
2.
Frequency
Number of Even Rolls
3.
Frequency
Number of Fish Caught
4.
Frequency
Number of Girls
5.
Frequency
Number of Birthdays
6.
Frequency
Number of Laps Jogged
7.
Q1 = 7; Med = 9.5; Q3 = 11.5;
IQR = 4.5
8.
Q1 = 23; Med = 26.5; Q3 = 38;
IQR = 15
9.
Q1 = 29; Med = 31; Q3 = 35;
IQR = 6
10.
Q1 = 27.5; Med = 40.5Q3 = 50.5;
IQR = 23
11.
Q1 = 0; Med = 1; Q3 = 2;
IQR = 2
12.
Q1 = 56; Med = 60; Q3 = 65;
IQR = 9

Checkpoint 8

Problem 8-109

Solving Multi-Step Equations

Answers to problem 8-109: a: $x = 7$, b: $x = -2$, c: $x = 0$, d: $x = \frac{2}{3}$

A general strategy for solving equations is to first simplify each side of the equation. Next isolate the variable on one side and the constants on the other by adding equal values on both sides of the equation or removing balanced sets or zeros. Finally determine the value of the variable–usually by division.

Note: When the process of solving an equation ends with different numbers on each side of the equal sign (for example, $2 = 4$), there is *no solution* to the problem. When the result is the same expression or number on each side of the equation (for example, $x+2=x+2$) it means that *all numbers* are solutions.

Example 1: Solve $3x+3x-1=4x+9$

Solution		
	$3x+3x-1=4x+9$	problem
	$6x-1=4x+9$	simplify by combining like terms
	$2x=10$	add 1, subtract $4x$ on each side
	$x=5$	divide by 2

Example 2: Solve $-2x+1+3(x-1)=-4+-x-2$

Solution		
	$-2x+1+3(x-1)=-4+-x-2$	problem
	$-2x+1+3x-3=-x-6$	distribute the 3 on the left side
	$x-2=-x-6$	simplify by combining like terms
	$2x=-4$	add x, add 2 to each side
	$x=-2$	divide by 2

Now we can go back and solve the original problem.

a. $24 = 3x+3$
$21 = 3x$
$7 = x$

b. $6x+12=-x-2$
$6x=-x-14$
$7x=-14$
$x=-2$

c. $3x+3-x+2=x+5$
$2x+5=x+5$
$2x=x$
$x=0$

d. $5(x-1)=5(4x-3)$
$5x-5=20x-15$
$5x=20x-10$
$-15x=-10$
$x=\frac{-10}{-15}=\frac{2}{3}$

Here are some more to try.

1. $2x+3=-7$
2. $-3x-2=-1$
3. $3x+2+x=x+5$
4. $4x-2-2x=x-5$
5. $2x-3=-x+3$
6. $1+3x-x=x-4+2x$
7. $4-3x=2x-6$
8. $3+3x-x+2=3x+4$
9. $-x-3=2x-6$
10. $-4+3x-1=2x+1+2x$
11. $-x+3=6$
12. $5x-3+2x=x+2+x$
13. $2x-7=-x-1$
14. $-2+3x=x-2-4x$
15. $-3x+7=x-1$
16. $1+2x-4=-3+x$
17. $3(x+2)=x+2$
18. $2(x-2)+x=5$
19. $10=x+5+x$
20. $-x+2=x-5-3x$
21. $3x+2-x=x-2+x$
22. $4x+12=2x-8$
23. $3(4+x)=x+6$
24. $6-x-3=4(x-2)$

Answers:

1. $x=-5$
2. $x=-\frac{1}{3}$
3. $x=1$
4. $x=-3$
5. $x=2$
6. $x=5$
7. $x=2$
8. $x=1$
9. $x=1$
10. $x=-6$
11. $x=-3$
12. $x=1$
13. $x=2$
14. $x=0$
15. $x=2$
16. $x=0$
17. $x=-2$
18. $x=3$
19. $x=2\frac{1}{2}$
20. $x=-7$
21. no solution
22. $x=-10$
23. $x=-3$
24. $x=2\frac{1}{5}$

Checkpoint 9

Problem 9-92

Unit Rates and Proportions

Answers to problem 9-92: a: 24 mpg; b: \$0.19; c: $x = 8$; d: $m = 32.5$

A rate is a ratio comparing two quantities and a unit rate has a denominator of one after simplifying. Unit rates or proportions may be used to solve ratio problems. Solutions may also be approximated by looking at graphs of lines passing through the origin and the given information.

Example 1: Judy's grape vine grew 15 inches in 6 weeks. What is the unit growth rate (inches per week)?

Solution: The growth rate is $\frac{15 \text{ inches}}{6 \text{ weeks}}$. To create a unit rate we need a denominator of "one." $\frac{15 \text{ inches}}{6 \text{ weeks}} = \frac{x \text{ inches}}{1 \text{ week}}$. Solve by using a Giant One: $\frac{15 \text{ inches}}{6 \text{ weeks}} = \frac{6}{6} \cdot \frac{x \text{ inches}}{1 \text{ week}} \Rightarrow 2.5 \frac{\text{inches}}{\text{week}}$

Example 2: Bob's favorite oatmeal raisin cookie recipe use 3 cups of raisins for 5 dozen cookies. How many cups are needed for 40 dozen cookies?

Solution: The rate is $\frac{3 \text{ cups}}{5 \text{ dozen}}$ so the problem may be written as this proportion: $\frac{3}{5} = \frac{c}{40}$.

One method of solving the proportion is to use a Giant One:

$$\frac{3}{5} = \frac{c}{40} \Rightarrow \frac{3}{5} \cdot \frac{8}{8} = \frac{24}{40} \Rightarrow c = 24$$

Another method is to think about unit rates. Since the unit rate is $\frac{3}{5}$ cup per dozen, one could also take the unit rate and multiply by the number of units needed: $\frac{3}{5} \cdot 40 = 24$.

Using either method the answer is 24 cups of raisins.

Now we can go back and solve the original problem.

a. $\frac{108 \text{ miles}}{4.5 \text{ gallons}} = \frac{4.5}{4.5} \cdot \frac{x \text{ miles}}{1 \text{ gallon}} \Rightarrow 24 \frac{\text{miles}}{\text{gallon}}$

b. $\frac{\$3.23}{17 \text{ oranges}} = \frac{17}{17} \cdot \frac{x}{1 \text{ orange}} \Rightarrow 0.19 \frac{\$}{\text{orange}}$

c. Using a Giant One:

$\frac{x}{12} \cdot \frac{2.5}{2.5} = \frac{2.5x}{30} = \frac{20}{30} \Rightarrow 20 = 2.5x \Rightarrow x = 8$

d. Using the Giant One

$\frac{13}{40} \cdot \frac{2.5}{2.5} = \frac{32.5}{100} \Rightarrow m = 32.5$

Here are some more to try. For problems 1 through 8 find the unit rate. For problems 17 through 24 solve the proportion.

1. Typing 544 words in 17 minutes (words per minute)
2. Taking 92 minutes to run 10 miles (minutes per mile)
3. Reading 258 pages in 86 minutes (pages per minute)
4. Falling 385 feet in 35 seconds (feet per second)
5. Buying 15 boxes of cereal for $39.75 ($ per box)
6. Drinking 28 bottles of water in 8 days (bottles per day)
7. Scoring 98 points in a 40 minute game (points per minute)
8. Planting 76 flowers in 4 hours (flowers per hour)

9. $\frac{3}{8}=\frac{x}{50}$	10. $\frac{2}{5}=\frac{x}{75}$	11. $\frac{7}{9}=\frac{14}{x}$	12. $\frac{24}{25}=\frac{96}{x}$
13. $\frac{15}{9}=\frac{12}{x}$	14. $\frac{45}{60}=\frac{x}{4}$	15. $\frac{4}{7}=\frac{18}{x}$	16. $\frac{8}{9}=\frac{72}{x}$
17. $\frac{3}{5}=\frac{x}{17}$	18. $\frac{17}{30}=\frac{51}{x}$	19. $\frac{5}{8}=\frac{16}{x}$	20. $\frac{3}{22}=\frac{15}{x}$
21. $\frac{1}{5}=\frac{x}{27}$	22. $\frac{x}{11}=\frac{8}{15}$	23. $\frac{14}{17}=\frac{x}{34}$	24. $\frac{12}{15}=\frac{36}{x}$

Answers:

1. $32\,\frac{\text{words}}{\text{minute}}$	2. $9.2\,\frac{\text{minutes}}{\text{mile}}$	3. $3\,\frac{\text{pages}}{\text{minute}}$	4. $11\,\frac{\text{feet}}{\text{second}}$
5. $2.65\,\frac{\text{dollars}}{\text{box}}$	6. $3.5\,\frac{\text{bottles}}{\text{day}}$	7. $2.45\,\frac{\text{points}}{\text{minute}}$	8. $19\,\frac{\text{flowers}}{\text{hour}}$
9. $x=18.75$	10. $x=30$	11. $x=18$	12. $x=100$
13. $x=7.2$	14. $x=3$	15. $x=31.5$	16. $x=81$
17. $x=10.2$	18. $x=90$	19. $x=25.6$	20. $x=110$
21. $x=5.4$	22. $x=5\frac{13}{15}$	23. $x=28$	24. $x=45$

Puzzle Investigator Problems

Dear Students,

Puzzle Investigator problems (PIs) present you with an opportunity to investigate complex, interesting problems. Their purpose is to focus on the process of solving complex problems. **You will be evaluated on your ability to show, explain, and justify your work and thoughts**. Save *all* of your work, including what does not work, in order to write about the processes you used to reach your answer.

Completion of a Puzzle Investigator problem includes four parts:

- **Problem Statement:** State the problem clearly in your own words so that anyone reading your paper will understand the problem you intend to solve.
- **Process and Solutions:** Describe in detail your thinking and reasoning as you work from start to finish. Explain your solution and how you know it is correct. Add diagrams when it helps your explanation. Include what you do that does not work and changes you make along the way. If you do not complete this problem, describe what you do know and where and why you are stuck.
- **Reflection:** Reflect about your learning and your reaction to the problem. What mathematics did you learn from it? What did you learn about your math problem solving strategies? Is this problem similar to any other problems you have done before? If yes, how?
- **Attached work:** Include all your work and notes. Your scratch work is important because it is a record of your thinking. Do not throw anything away.

PI-1. LONG DISTANCE

The odometer (which measures the distance traveled) on Mario's parents' car reads 28,882 when his father fills it up. Since Mario's family is going on vacation, his father set the trip odometer to 0 so he will know how many miles long the trip is. To keep Mario and his sister busy during the trip, he gives them the following problems.

a. Mario noticed that there are only 2 different digits in the number 28,882. How far will the car need to travel before all the digits are different? What is that number?

b. The numbers 101, 1221, and 1357531, among many others, are all **palindromes** because their digits read the same left-to-right as they do right-to-left. When are the next five times that the digits of the car odometer will be a palindrome?

c. When is the next time that both the car odometer and the trip odometer will be a palindrome?

PI-2. CROSSED PATHS

Sandra left her home at 6 a.m. Saturday and hiked all day to a cottage at the top of the mountain. She arrived at 6 p.m. and spent the night in the cottage. The next morning she left the cottage at 6 a.m. and hiked home by the same trail, arriving at 6 p.m.

Both days she was on the trail for 12 hours, but sometimes stopped to eat, swim, or gather flowers. This means that she was not traveling at the same speed the entire time.

Must it be true that there is at least one point along the trail that Sandra passed at exactly the same time on each of the two days? Or is it possible that she was never at any place on Sunday at the exact same time she had been there on Saturday?

Your Task: Decide if there must be at least one point on the trail that Sandra passed at exactly the same time both days. Then explain your reasoning in a way that will convince someone else that your decision is correct.

PI-3. CROSSING OVER

Elizabeth, Brian, Dean, and Leslie want to cross a bridge. They all begin on the same side and have only 17 minutes to get everyone across to the other side.

To complicate matters, it is nighttime and there is only one flashlight. A maximum of two people can cross at one time. Any group that crosses, either 1 or 2 people, must have the flashlight with them. The flashlight must be walked back and forth; it cannot be thrown.

Each student walks at a different speed. A pair must walk together at the rate of the slower student's pace.

Elizabeth:	1 minute to cross
Brian:	2 minutes to cross.
Dean:	5 minutes to cross.
Leslie:	10 minutes to cross.

For example, if Elizabeth and Leslie walk across first, 10 minutes have elapsed when they get to the other side of the bridge. If Leslie returns across the bridge with the flashlight, a total of 20 minutes has passed, and you have failed the mission.

Your Task: Find a strategy that can get everyone across in 17 minutes. Use diagrams and words to help clearly explain your strategy.

PI-4. TOURNAMENT

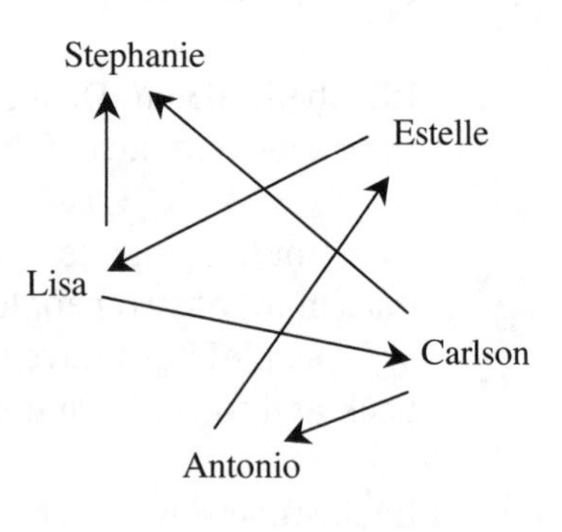

Five friends decided to have a video game competition. Each person is scheduled to play everyone other person.

After several games, Stephanie started a diagram to show which pairs have played and who has won so far. The arrows in her diagram point from the winner to the loser. For example, when Lisa and Carlson played, Lisa won.

a. How many more games need to be played? Show how you know.

b. Stephanie's diagram can help you predict the winner of future matches! For each pair below, who do you think will win? If you think it is equally likely that either player will win, explain why. Use Stephanie's diagram to support your answer.

   i. Stephanie and Antonio   *ii.* Estelle and Carlson

c. Is there always a winner? For example, is it possible to have a tournament with five friends where everyone wins and loses two games? If it is possible, draw a diagram for a different tournament with five friends so that each person wins and loses 2 games. If it is not possible, explain why it cannot be done.

d. How many games would be played in a tournament of 6 friends if each person played every other person exactly once? What if there were 10 friends?

PI-5. POLYOMINOES!

Polyominoes are shapes made of some number of unit squares. This is why a game using rectangular pieces made with two squares is called "dominoes" (which can be referred to as 2-ominoes). Below are all the possible 3-ominoes and 4-ominoes.

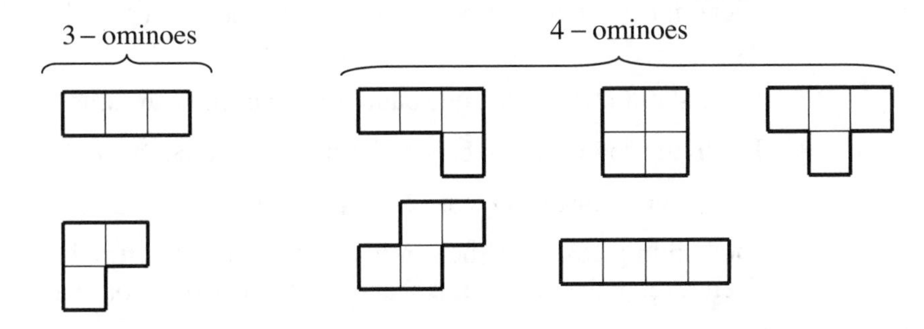

a. It turns out there are 12 different 5-ominoes! Draw them. For two designs to be different, one design should not be able to be turned or flipped or slid onto another so that it will match exactly.

b. It turns out that 9 of the 5-ominoes can be created by adding a single square to one of the 4-ominoes. Which 4-omino would that be? Use diagrams to show how the 5-ominoes are formed.

c. Using the 2×2 square, four 4-ominoes can be put together to make a 4×4 square, as shown at right. Will this work for the other 4-ominoes? Form 4×4 squares using four of the same 4-omino. Are there any 4-ominoes that will not form a square?

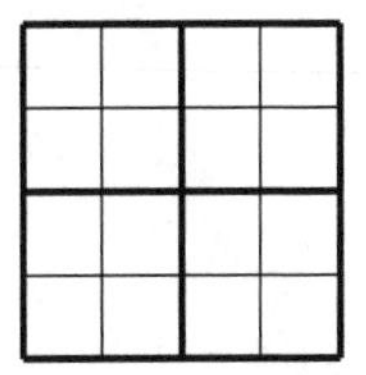

d. The cross shape at right can be tiled using four copies of one 5-omino. In fact, it turns out that there are several different 5-ominoes that can do this. See how many ways you can find to do it.

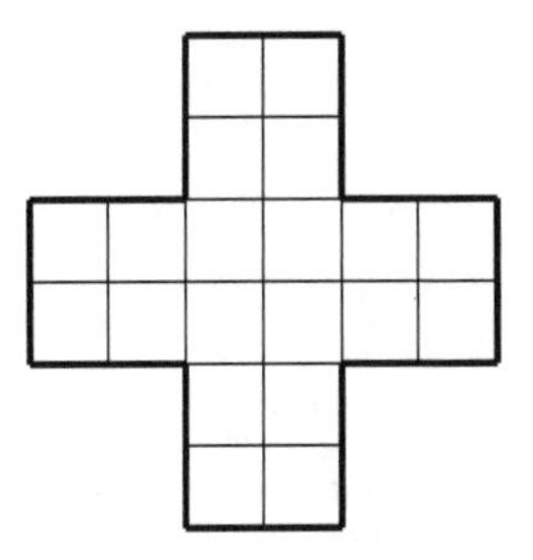

PI-6. DESIGNING AN APARTMENT

Ms. Speedi wants to build her dream house and would like you to design it. According to local zoning laws, she is limited to a one-story house with a maximum area of 1,000 square feet. (This is the maximum area of the floor.) She also has some personal requirements for this house:

- There must be two bedrooms with a combined area of at least 250 square feet.
- There should be at least one bathroom near the bedrooms.
- The living room cannot be smaller than 200 square feet.
- The kitchen must be at least 220 square feet.
- The building costs are cheaper when the entire structure is rectangular. Therefore, make the overall shape of Ms. Speedi's house a rectangle.

a. Design a possible layout of Ms. Speedi's dream house. Make sure your design meets the zoning law (with a maximum area of 1,000 square feet) and Ms. Speedi's personal requirements.

b. On graph paper, draw a scaled blueprint of Ms. Speedi's house. Provide details that help others understand your design like the front door, windows, and interior doors. Add furniture if you like.

c. What are the benefits of your design over others? What are the drawbacks? What assumptions did you make for your design? Did you need to make any difficult decisions?

PI-7. SQUARES GALORE

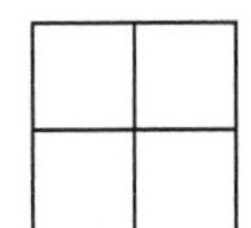

How many squares do you see at right? Can you identify more than 4 squares? How can we know when we have found all the squares? The puzzles below will help you investigate these questions.

a. How many squares can you find on an 8×8 checkerboard, like the one shown at right? (By the way, there are more than 65 squares.) Organize your work so that you can find patterns that help you to determine how many 1×1 squares, 2×2 squares, and so on, that you can find.

b. Use your patterns from part (a) to figure out how many squares would be in a design made with square tiles if it is 30 tiles wide and 30 tiles long. Can you do this without drawing a diagram?

c. Is there a square made up of square tiles (like the checkerboard) that has only 75 squares overall? What about one that has 120 squares overall? If it is possible, show the square design and explain how you found it. If it is not possible, explain why that design cannot exist.

PI-8. PASCAL'S TRIANGLE

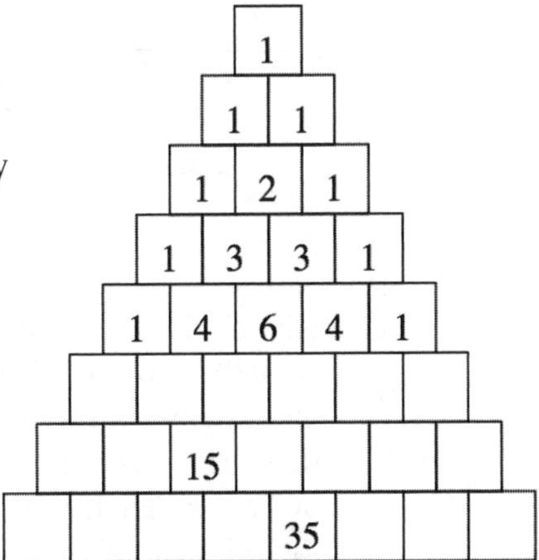

The number pattern started at right is called **Pascal's Triangle**. While it looks like a simple arrangement of numbers, it has many interesting patterns within it. In this challenge, you will learn more about the hidden patterns of Pascal's Triangle.

a. Using the PI-8 Resource Page (which you can download at www.cpm.org), use the patterns to complete the missing numbers. Some of the numbers are given so you can check your work.

b. What is the sum of the 20th row of the triangle? Can you find this without extending the triangle? Explain how you found your answer.

c. Using a see-through highlighter, color in the squares that contain odd numbers. Describe the pattern that emerges.

d. Find at least three other patterns in Pascal's Triangle that you have not described so far.

PI-9. TILING THE LAUNDRY ROOM

Travis is planning to tile his laundry room with large L-shaped tiles made with 3 squares. (See an example at right.) According to his floor plan, the room is a 4 ft.$\times 4$ ft. square. There is a drain in the floor that cannot be covered and is shaded in the diagram.

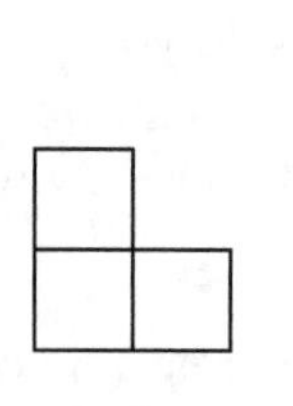

Tile

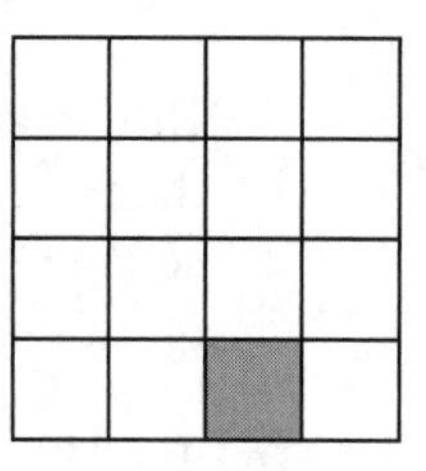

Laundry Room Floor

a. Show one way that Travis could tile his floor using his L-shaped tiles without breaking tiles and so that no tiles overlap or cover the drain. Use colors to help distinguish the tiles in your diagram. Is there more than one way to tile his floor?

b. While at the store, Travis suddenly worried that his diagram is wrong and he cannot remember where the drain is located. Does it matter? Can the floor be tiled no matter where the drain is located? Test the different possible locations of the drain (listed below) and write a short note to Travis about what you discovered.

i. Drain is located in the middle

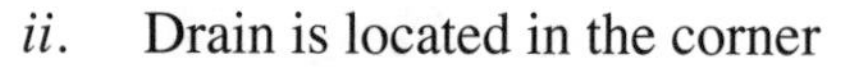

ii. Drain is located in the corner

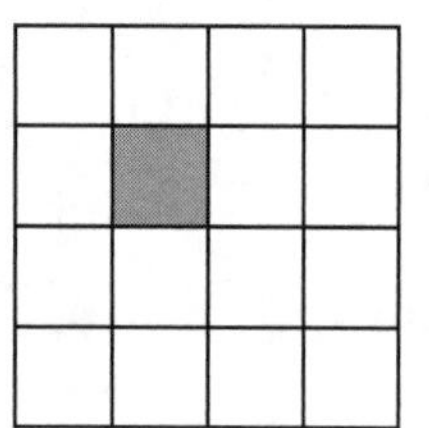

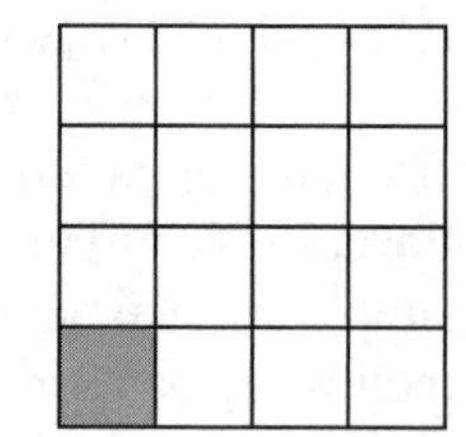

c. Uh oh! Travis came home with his tiles and found out that his floor is actually a 5 ft.$\times 5$ ft. square and the drain is in the corner. (This is why measurements should always be checked twice!) Luckily, he bought extra tiles. However, can this floor be tiled? Using graph paper, draw a diagram of Travis' laundry room floor and find a way he can tile his floor with the same L-shaped tiles.

d. Given that his laundry room is a 5 ft.$\times 5$ ft. square, does it matter where the drain is located? Find at least one more location (not in the corner) for the drain that would allow Travis to tile the floor. Also find at least one location for the drain that would not allow the floor to be tiled without breaking a tile.

PI-10. WAY TO GO!

The map at right shows the streets in Old Town. Assume Jacqueline is standing at the corner of A and 1st Streets. Assume Jacqueline will only walk South or East. The shaded rectangles represent large buildings. Assume Jacqueline will not pass through any buildings.

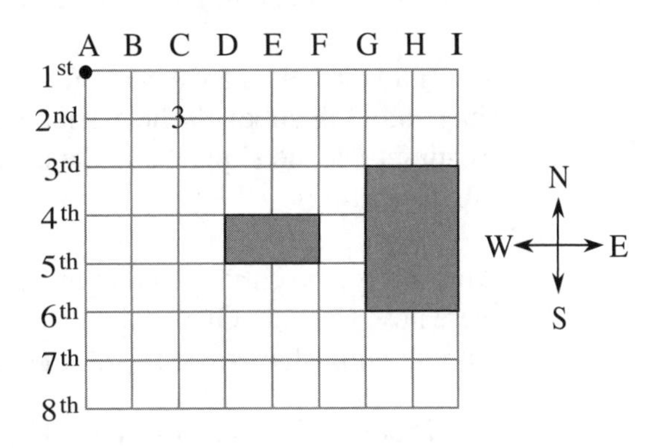

a. The number "3" at the intersection of C and 2nd Streets means that there are three different ways she can get there from her starting position. What are those three ways? Describe them in words.

b. How many different ways can she walk to the corner of F and 4th Streets?

c. How many different ways can she walk to the corner of D and 5th Streets?

d. Explain how you can use your answers to parts (b) and (c) to find the number of ways she can walk to the corner of F and 5th Streets. Why does this make sense?

e. Find the number of different ways she can walk to the corner of I and 8th Streets.

f. How could you change the map so that Jacqueline has only 7 ways to get to the corner of D and 3rd streets? You can remove blocks or add them.

PI-11. WITH OR WITHOUT FROSTING

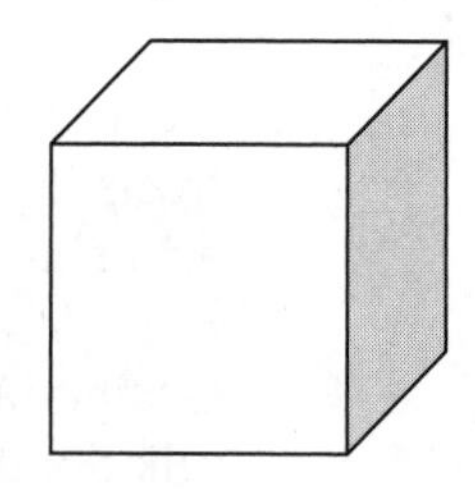

Mr. Hamada baked a cake for his class that was in the shape of a big cube. As he carried the cake over to the frosting table, he slipped and the cake fell into a large tub of frosting!

Amazingly, the cake stayed in one piece, but all 6 sides were now frosted. One student suggested the cake be cut into cube-shaped pieces, all the same size.

a. There are 32 students in Mr. Hamada's class and he does not want more than 100 pieces of cake. If Mr. Hamada cuts the cake into cube-shaped pieces, all the same size, how many pieces of cake should he cut so that everyone could have a piece? (Note: You might want to use small blocks to explore this question.)

b. A student noticed that some pieces have no frosting, while others have 1, 2, or 3 sides frosted. How many of each type of piece can Mr. Hamada offer?

c. There were many students that wanted a piece with frosting on 3 sides, so Mr. Hamada changed his mind and decided to cut the cake into 125 cube-shaped pieces, all the same size. Did this increase the number of pieces with frosting on 3 sides? Why or why not?

PI-12. CANDY SALES

For a fundraiser, each math club member must sell 30 candy bars each day for a week. Although they all sold the same type of candy, the members could choose their price to compete for top sales member.

Alfredo decided to sell three candy bars for $1, earning $10 per day, while June sold hers at the rate of two for $1, earning her $15 per day.

One day, both Alfredo and June were on a field trip, so they asked Bomani to sell their candy bars for them. Bomani agreed and promised he would not change their prices. Bomani decided that instead of offering three for $1 and two for $1, he would put them together and sell the 60 candy bars at the rate of five for $2.

When Alfredo and June returned, Bomani handed them the money he had earned for the day, $24. Alfredo and June were angry and demanded the dollar they were sure Bomani stole! Bomani is now confused... what happened?

Your Task: Discover what really happened to the extra dollar, and write a letter to Alfredo and June before this scene turns really ugly.

PI-13. TO TELL THE TRUTH

Alicia, Ben, Cassie, and Daryl shared some birthday cake before going into the living room to work on their homework. During the rest of the afternoon, each one of them left the room by themselves for a few minutes.

When they finished their homework, they went into the kitchen and discovered that the rest of the cake was missing. Below are their statements:

Alicia: "*Ben ate it!*"

Cassie: "*I didn't eat it!*"

Ben: "*Daryl must have eaten it.*"

Daryl: "*Ben is lying.*"

a. If only one of these statements is a lie, who ate the rest of the cake? Explain how you know which statement is false.

b. If only one of the above statements is the truth, who ate the rest of the cake? Explain how you know which statement is true.

c. While sorting out this mess, Ben's dad said, "What I am saying is not true." Is this statement true or false? Explain.

PI-14. SECRET CODE

Arianna wants to send a secret code through her computer. By using a two-digit number for every letter, she can build secret words with numbers. For example, using her code below, "SECRET" becomes "180402170419."

A	B	C	D	E	F	G	H	I	J	K	L	M
00	01	02	03	04	05	06	07	08	09	10	11	12
N	O	P	Q	R	S	T	U	V	W	X	Y	Z
13	14	15	16	17	18	19	20	21	22	23	24	25

a. To answer the question "who is your favorite mathematician," Arianna wrote 00170207081204030418. Decipher her message. Remember that every pair of numbers represents a letter.

b. To send secret messages through computers, the numeric codes must be changed so that they only contain the digits 0 and 1. These are called **binary codes**, and use the base-2 number system. The base-2 number system counts in sets of 2 instead of sets of 10. The first 12 counting numbers in base-2 are shown in the table below. Based on this counting system, how would you write "12" in base-2? What about 15? 16?

Base 10:	00	01	02	03	04	05	06	07	08	09	10	11
Base 2:	00	01	10	11	100	101	110	111	1000	1001	1010	1011

c. To make a computer code for the entire alphabet, plus a code for a space and a code for an exclamation point, you will need the base-2 equivalents for the numbers 0 through 27. The codes will have 5 digits so that every letter has the same number of digits. Copy and complete the table below.

A = 00	00000	H = 07		O = 14	01110	V = 21	
B = 01	00001	I = 08		P = 15		W= 22	10110
C = 02	00010	J = 09		Q = 16		X = 23	
D = 03	00011	K = 10		R= 17		Y = 24	
E = 04	00100	L = 11		S = 18	10010	Z = 25	
F = 05		M = 12		T = 19		= 26	
G = 06		N = 13	01101	U = 20		! = 27	11011

d. To send the message "NOSE," Arianna's computer would change 13141804 to 01101011101001000100. What would be the computer code for "MATH"?

e. Decipher Arianna's secret message below. Remember that every 5 digits is a letter.

0111110100110011100101011001001101000101101000110111011

Glossary

5-D Process An organized method to solve problems. The 5 D's stand for Describe/Draw, Define, Do, Decide, and Declare. This is a problem-solving strategy for which solving begins by making a prediction about the answer or one element of it (a trial), and then confirming whether the result of the trial is correct. If not, information is gained about how close the trial is to the correct value, so that adjustments to the trial value may be made. Being organized is extremely important to the success of this method, as well as writing a usable table. The 5-D Process leads to writing equations to represent word problems. (p. 295)

absolute value The absolute value of a number is the distance of the number from zero. Since the absolute value represents a distance, without regard to direction, absolute value is always non-negative. Thus, the absolute value of a negative number is its opposite, while the absolute value of a non-negative number is just the number itself. The absolute value of x is usually written "$|x|$." For example, $|-5| = 5$ and $|22| = 22$. (p. 89)

acute angle An angle with a measure greater than 0° and less than 90°. An example is shown at right. (p. 460)

acute triangle A triangle with all three angle measures less than 90°.

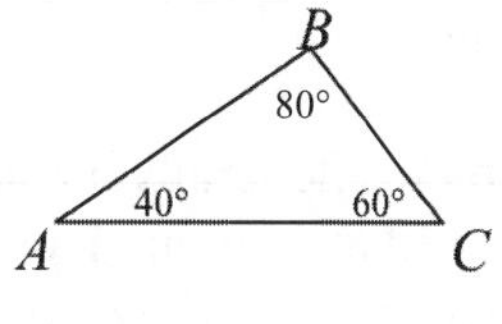

addition (+) An operation that tells how many objects there are when two sets are combined. The result is the number of objects in the two sets together which is called a sum. In arithmetic, the word "object" usually means "number."

additive identity The number 0 is called the additive identity because adding 0 to any number does not change the number. For example, 7 + 0 = 7. (p. 96)

Additive Identity Property The Additive Identity Property states that adding zero to any expression leaves the expression unchanged. That is, $a + 0 = a$. For example, $-2 + 0 = -2$.

additive inverse The number you need to add to a given number to get a sum of 0. For example, the additive inverse of –3 is 3. It is also called the opposite. (p. 96)

Additive Inverse Property The Additive Inverse Property states that for every number a there is a number $-a$ such that $a = -a = 0$. For example, the number 5 has an additive inverse of –5; 5 + (–5) = 0. The additive inverse of a number is often called its opposite. For example, 5 and –5 are opposites.

adjacent angles For two angles to be adjacent, they must satisfy these three conditions: (1) The two angles must have a common side; (2) They must have a common vertex; and (3) They can have no interior points in common. This means that the common side must be between the two angles; no overlap between the angles is permitted. In the example at right, $\measuredangle ABC$ and $\measuredangle CBD$ are adjacent angles. (p. 466)

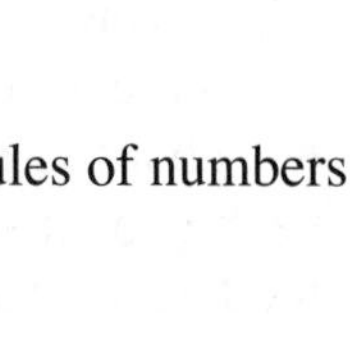

algebra A branch of mathematics that uses variables to generalize the rules of numbers and numerical operations.

algebra tiles An algebra tile is a manipulative whose area represents a constant or variable quantity. The algebra tiles used in this course consist of large squares with dimensions x-by-x; rectangles with dimensions x-by-1; and small squares with dimensions 1-by-1. These tiles are named by their areas: x^2, x, and 1, respectively. The smallest squares are called "unit tiles." In this text, shaded tiles will represent positive quantities while unshaded tiles will represent negative quantities. (p. 220)

algebraic expression See *expression*.

algorithm A fixed rule for carrying out a mathematical procedure. For example, to find the average of a set of values, find the sum of the values and divide by the number of values.

angle Generally, an angle is formed by two rays that are joined at a common endpoint. Angles in geometric figures are usually formed by two segments that have a common endpoint (such as the angle shaded in the figure at right). Also see *acute angle*, *obtuse angle*, and *right angle*. (p. 460)

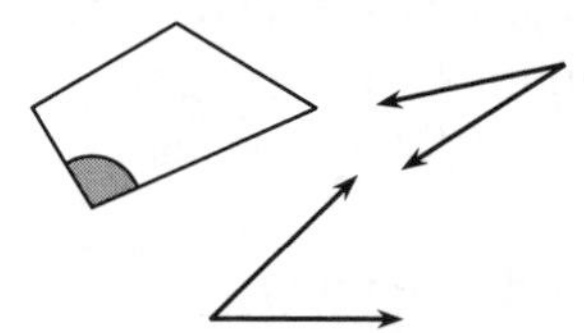

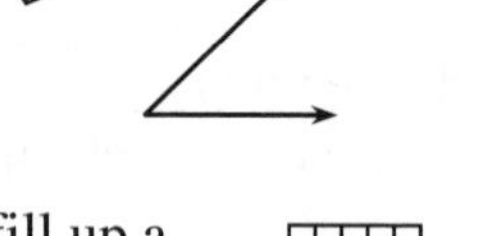

area For this course, area is the number of square units needed to fill up a region on a flat surface. In later courses, the idea will be extended to cones, spheres, and more complex surfaces. Also see *surface area*. (p. 10)

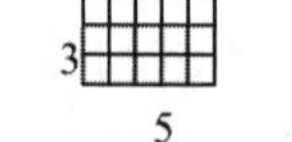

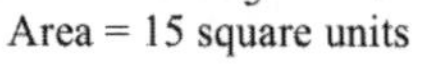

area model An area model or diagram is one way to represent the probabilities of the outcomes for a sequence of two events. The total area is 1, and the probabilities are represented by proportional parts. In the example, P(S) and P(not S) are the dimensions of the right side of the rectangle. The probabilities that A will occur or not occur are the dimensions of the top of the rectangle. The area of each part is the probability of each possible sequence of two events. (p. 281)

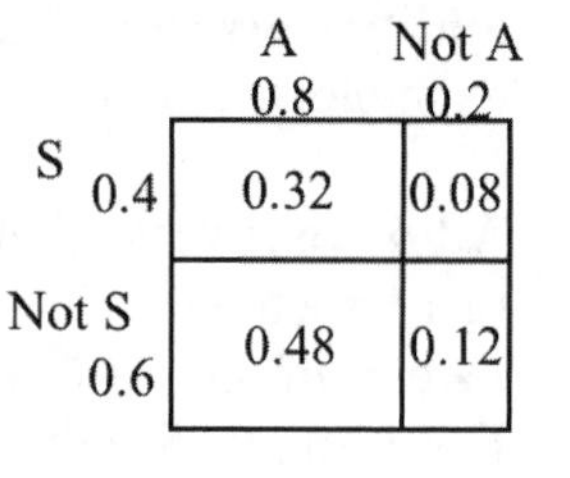

area of a triangle To find the area of a triangle, multiply the length of the base b by the height h and divide by two: $A = \frac{1}{2}bh$. (p. 10)

Associative Property of Addition The Associative Property of Addition states that if a sum contains terms that are grouped, then the sum may be grouped differently with no effect on the total, that is, $a+(b+c)=(a+b)+c$. For example, $3+(4+5)=(3+4)+5$. (p. 190)

Associative Property of Multiplication The Associative Property of Multiplication states that if a product contains terms that are grouped, then the product may be grouped differently with no effect on the result, that is, $a(bc)=(ab)c$. For example, $2\cdot(3\cdot 4)=(2\cdot 3)\cdot 4$. (p. 190)

average The sum of given values divided by the number of values used in computing the sum. For example, the average of 1, 4, and 10 is $(1+4+10)/3$. See *mean*. (p. 13)

axis (plural: axes) On a coordinate plane, two number lines that meet at right angles at the origin (0, 0). The x-axis runs horizontally and the y-axis runs vertically.

bar graph A bar graph is a set of rectangular bars that have height proportional to the number of data elements in each category. Each bar stands for all of the elements in a single distinguishable category (such as "red"). Usually all of the bars are the same width and separated from each other. Also see *histogram*.

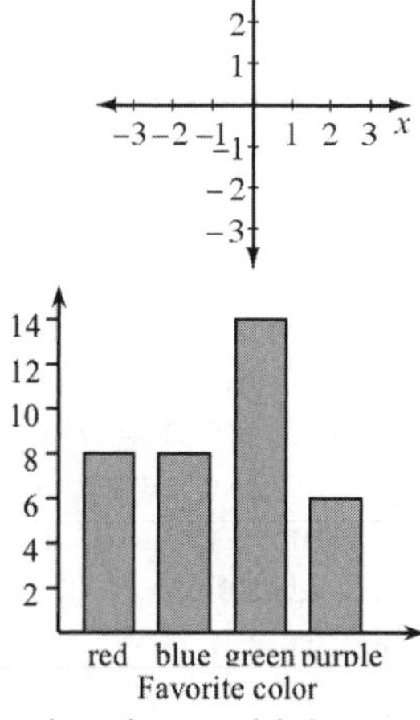

base of a geometric figure (a) The base of a triangle: any side of a triangle to which a height is drawn. There are three possible bases in each triangle. (b) The base of a trapezoid: either of the two parallel sides. (c) The base of a parallelogram (including rectangle, rhombus, and square): any side to which a height is drawn. There are four possible bases. (d) The base of a three-dimensional figure. Also see *prism* and *pyramid*.

base of an exponent When working with an exponential expression in the form b^a, b is called the base. For example, 2 is the base in 2^5. (5 is the exponent, and 32 is the value.) See *exponent*.

bin An interval on a histogram.

boundary point The endpoint or endpoints of a ray or segment on a number line where an inequality is true, marked with a solid dot. For strict inequalities (that is, inequalities involving < or >), the point is not part of the solution, and is marked with an open dot. Boundary points may be found by solving the equality associated with the given inequality. For example, the solution to the equation $2x=6$ is $x=3$, so the inequality $2x\geq 6$ has a boundary point at 3. A boundary point is also sometimes called a "dividing point." (p. 336)

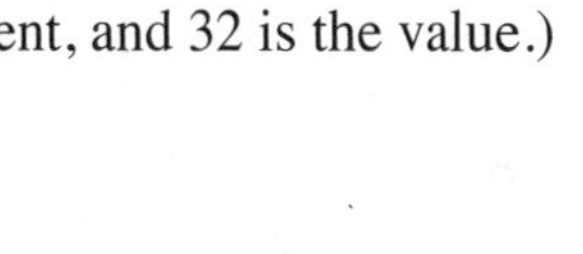

box plot A graphic way of showing a summary of data using the median, quartiles, and extremes of the data. (p. 404)

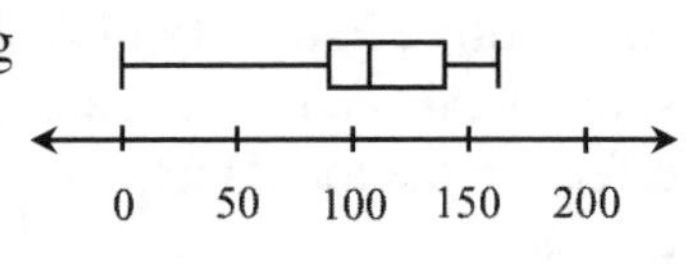

center of a circle On a flat surface, the fixed point from which all points on the circle are equidistant. *See* circle.

center of a data distribution Numbers that locate or approximate the center of a data set. Two of the ways to measure the center of a data set are the mean and the median. When dealing with measures of center, it is often useful to consider the distribution of the data. For symmetric distributions with no outliers, the mean can represent the middle, or "typical" value, of the data well. However, in the presence of outliers or non-symmetrical data distributions, the median may be a better measure. *Also see* mean and median. (pp. 13, 19, 393)

certainty When an event will definitely happen. The probability of a certain event is 1.

chord A line segment with its endpoints on a circle. A chord that passes through the center of a circle is called a "diameter." *See* circle. (p. 471)

circle The set of all points on a flat surface that are the same distance from a fixed point. If the fixed point (center) is O, the symbol $\odot O$ represents a circle with center O. If r is the length of a circle's radius and d is the length of its diameter, the circumference of the circle is $C = 2\pi r$ or $C = \pi d$. The area of the circle is $A = \pi r^2$. (p. 471)

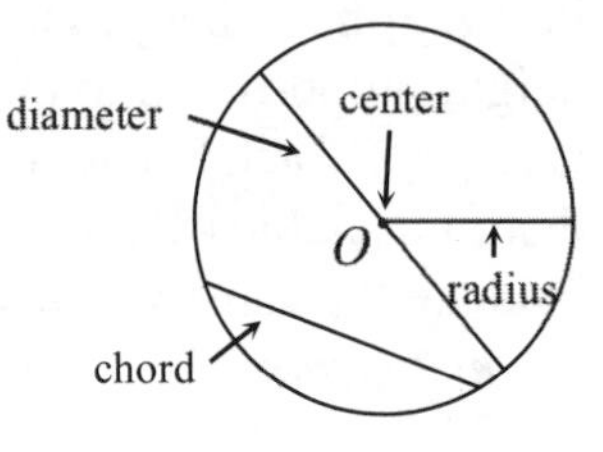

circumference The perimeter (distance around) of a circle. (p. 498)

cluster sample A subgroup of the population that has the similar characteristic of interest as that of the whole population. A cluster sample is one way to obtain a representative sample. (p. 450)

coefficient (numerical) A number multiplying a variable or product of variables. For example, –7 is the coefficient of $-7x$. (p. 331)

combination histogram and box plot A way to visually represent a distribution of data. The box plot is drawn with the same x-axis as the histogram.

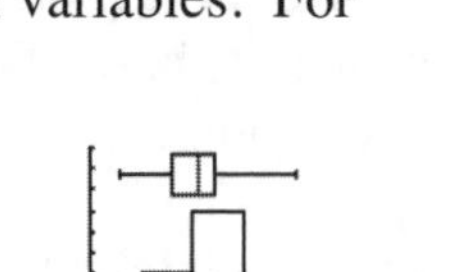

combining like terms Combining two or more like terms simplifies an expression by summing constants and summing those variable terms in which the same variables are raised to the same power. For example, combining like terms in the expression $3x + 7 + 5x - 3 + 2x^2 + 3y^2$ gives $8x + 4 + 2x^2 + 3y^2$. When working with algebra tiles, combining like terms involves putting together tiles with the same dimensions. (p. 444)

common Shared.

common factor A common factor is a factor that is the same for two or more terms. For example, x^2 is a common factor for $3x^2$ and $-5x^2y$.

common multiple A number that is a multiple of the two or more numbers. For example, 24 and 48 are common multiples of 3 and 8.

Commutative Property of Addition The Commutative Property of Addition states that if two terms are added, then the order may be reversed with no effect on the total. That is, $a+b=b+a$. For example, $7+12=12+7$. (p. 190)

Commutative Property of Multiplication The Commutative Property of Multiplication states that if two expressions are multiplied, then the order may be reversed with no effect on the result. That is, $ab=ba$. For example, $5\cdot8=8\cdot5$. (p. 190)

comparison symbol See *inequality symbol.*

compass In this course, a compass is tool used to draw circles. (p. 469)

complement The complement of an event is the set of all outcomes in the sample space that are not included in the event. (p. 265)

complementary angles Two angles whose measures add up to 90°. Angles T and V are complementary because $m\measuredangle T+m\measuredangle V=90°$. Complementary angles may also be adjacent, like $\measuredangle ABC$ and $\measuredangle CBD$ in the diagram at far right. (p. 466)

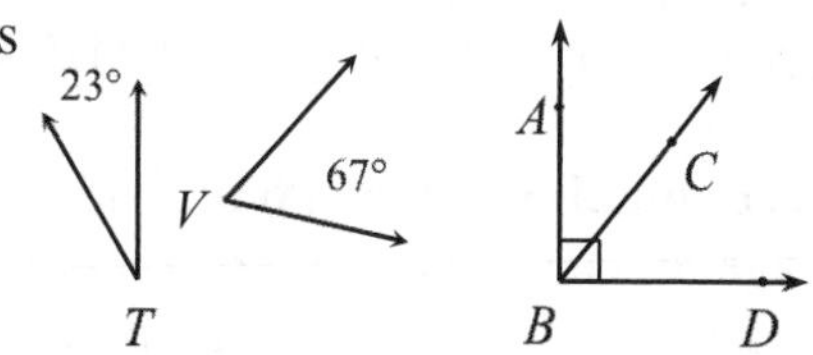

complex fraction A fraction with a fraction in the numerator and/or denominator.

composite number A number with more than two factors.

composite shape A shape made of several simpler shapes. (p. 501)

compound event A compound event in probability is an outcome that depends on two or more other events. For example, finding the probability that both a red ball and also a blue block are drawn from a bag in two draws. (p. 271, 277)

congruent Two shapes are congruent if they have exactly the same shape and size. Congruent shapes are similar and have a scale factor of 1.

conjecture An educated guess that often results from noticing a pattern.

consecutive integers Integers that are in order without skipping any integers. For example, 8, 9, and 10 are consecutive integers. (p. 302)

constant of proportionality (k) In a proportional relationship, equations are of the form $y = kx$, where k is the constant of proportionality. (p. 210)

constant term A number that is not multiplied by a variable. In the expression $2x + 3(5 - 2x) + 8$, the number 8 is a constant term. The number 3 is not a constant term, because it is multiplied by a variable inside the parentheses. (p. 226, 331)

construction (geometric) In mathematics, it is the process of using a straightedge and compass to create geometric diagrams. (p. 469)

convenience sample A subgroup of the population for which it was easy to collect data. A convenience sample is not a random sample. (p. 450)

coordinate The number corresponding to a point on the number line or an ordered pair (x, y) that corresponds to a point in a two-dimensional coordinate system. In an ordered pair, the x-coordinate appears first and the y-coordinate appears second. For example, the point $(3, 5)$ has an x-coordinate of 3. See *ordered pair*.

coordinate graph (system) A system of graphing ordered pairs of numbers on a coordinate plane. An ordered pair represents a point, with the first number giving the horizontal position relative to the x-axis and the second number giving the vertical position relative to the y-axis. Also see *ordered pair*. (p. 87)

corresponding parts Points, sides, edges, or angles in two or more figures that are images of each other with respect to a transformation. If two figures are congruent, then the corresponding parts of the figures are congruent to each other. See *ratio of similarity* and *congruent*. (p. 194)

counterexample An example showing that a statement has at least one exception; that is, a situation in which the statement is false. For example, the number 4 is a counterexample to the statement that all even numbers are greater than 7.

cross section The intersection of a three-dimensional solid and a plane. (p. 509)

cube A polyhedron of six faces, each of which is a square. (p. 504)

cubic unit A cube, each of whose edges measure 1 unit in length. Volume is measured in cubic units.

data display A visual way for organizing information. Data displays used in this course are bar graphs, box plots, dot plots, histograms, scatter plots, stem-and-leaf plots, and Venn diagrams.

decimal point The dot separating the whole number from the decimal portion, that is, the ones and tenths places in a decimal number.

degree A unit for measuring angles. Usually denoted by ° (the degree symbol). There are 360° in one full rotation. (p. 457)

denominator The lower part of a fraction, which expresses into how many equal parts the whole is divided.

dependent events Two events are dependent if the outcome of one event affects the probability of the other event. For example, if one card is drawn out of a deck of cards, then the probability that the first card is red is $\frac{26}{52} = \frac{1}{2}$ because 26 of the 52 cards are red. However, the probability of the second card now depends on the result of the first selection. If the first card was red, then there are now 25 red cards remaining in a deck of 51 cards, and the probability that the second card is red is $\frac{25}{51}$. The second event (selecting the second card) is dependent on the first event (selecting the first card). (p. 266)

diameter A line segment drawn through the center of a circle with both endpoints on the circle. The length of a diameter is usually denoted d. Note that the length of a circle's diameter is twice the length of its radius. *See* circle. (p. 471)

difference The result of subtraction.

dimensions The dimensions of a figure that is a flat region or space tell how far that the figure extends in each direction. For example, the dimensions of a rectangle might be 16 cm wide by 7 cm high. (p. 511)

Distributive Property For any a, b, and c, $a(b+c) = ab + ac$. For example, $10(7+2) = 10 \cdot 7 + 10 \cdot 2$. (p. 116)

dividend A quantity to be divided. (See *divisor*.)

divisible A number is divisible by another if the remainder of the division is zero.

division (÷) The inverse operation to multiplication, or the operation that creates equal groups.

divisor The quantity by which another quantity is to be divided. dividend/divisor = quotient + remainder (if there is any).

dot plot A way of displaying data that has an order and can be placed on a number line. Dot plots are generally used when the data is discrete (separate and distinct) and numerous pieces of data fall on most values.

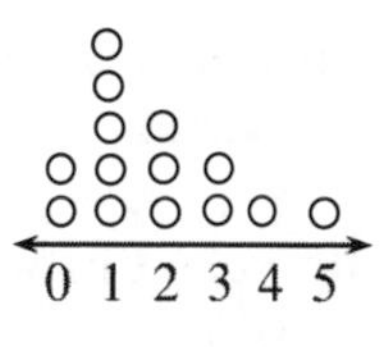

double-peaked See *shape (of a data display).*

edge In three dimensions, a line segment formed by the intersection of two faces of a polyhedron. (p. 506)

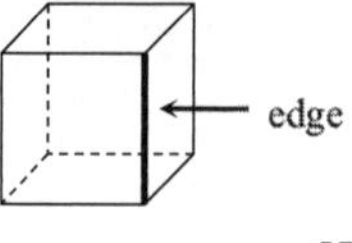

endpoint A point that mark the ends of a line segment or ray. (p. 460)

enlarge To make larger. (p. 399)

enlargement ratio The ratio of similarity comparing a figure to a similar larger figure is often called the enlargement ratio. This ratio shows by what factor the first figure is enlarged to get the second figure.

equal ($=$) Two quantities are equal when they have the same value. For example, when $x=4$, the expression $x+8$ is equal to the expression $3x$ because the values of the expressions are the same.

equally likely Outcomes or events are considered to be equally likely when they have the same probability.

equation A mathematical sentence in which two expressions have an "equals" sign ($=$) between them indicating that they have an equal value. For example, the equation $7x+4.2=-8$ states that the expression $7x+4.2$ has the value -8. In this course, an equation is often used to represent a rule relating two quantities.

Equation Mat An Equation Mat puts two Expression Mats side-by-side to find the value(s) which make the expressions equal. Legal moves are used to find the value(s) that makes the expressions equal. For example, the Equation Mat at right represents the equation $2(x+1)-1=x+4$. The two sides of the mat are equal when $x=3$. Also see *"legal" moves*. (p. 339)

equilateral A polygon is equilateral if all of its sides have equal length. The word "equilateral" comes from "equi" (meaning "equal") and "lateral" (meaning "side"). Equilateral triangles not only have sides of equal length, but also angles of equal measure. However, a polygon with more than three sides may be equilateral without having congruent angles. For example, see the rhombus at right.

equivalent expressions Two expressions are equivalent if they have the same value. For example, $2+3$ is equivalent to $1+4$. (p. 88)

equivalent fractions Two fractions are equivalent if they have the same numerical value. For example, 3/6 and 5/10 are equivalent fractions. (p. 48)

equivalent ratios Two ratios are equivalent if they have the same value when simplified. (p. 249)

evaluate (an expression) To find the numerical value of. To evaluate an expression, substitute the value(s) given for the variable(s) and perform the operations according to the Order of Operations. For example, evaluating $2x + y - 10$ when $x = 4$ and $y = 3$ gives the value 1. Also see *expression*. (p. 143)

event One or more results of an experiment. (p. 40)

experimental probability The probability based on data collected in experiments. The experimental probability of an event is defined to be $\frac{\text{number of successful outcomes in the experiment}}{\text{total number of outcomes in the experiment}}$. (p. 40)

exponent In an expression of the form b^a, a is called the exponent. For example, in the expression 2^5, 5 is called the exponent (2 is the base, and 32 is the value). The exponent indicates how many times to use the base as a multiplier. For example, in 2^5, 2 is used 5 times: $2^5 = 2 \cdot 2 \cdot 2 \cdot 2 \cdot 2 = 32$. For exponents of zero, the rule is: for any number $x \neq 0$, $x^0 = 1$. (p. 137)

expression An expression is a combination of individual terms separated by plus or minus signs. Numerical expressions combine numbers and operation symbols; algebraic (variable) expressions include variables. For example, $4 + (5 - 3)$ is a numerical expression. In an algebraic expression, if each of the following terms, $6xy^2$, 24, and $\frac{y-3}{4+x}$, are combined, the result may be $6xy^2 + 24 - \frac{y-3}{4+x}$. An expression does not have an "equals" sign. (p. 137, 331)

Expression Comparison Mat An Expression Comparison Mat puts two Expression Mats side-by-side so they can be compared to see which represents the greater value. For example, in the Expression Comparison Mat at right, Mat A represents –3, while Mat B represents –2. Since $-2 > -3$ Mat B is greater. (p. 319)

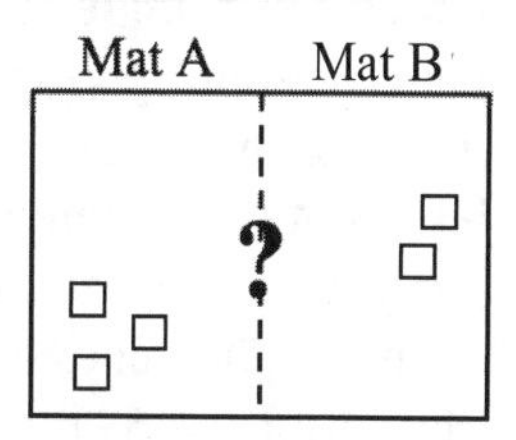

Expression Mat An organizing tool used to visually represent an expression with algebra tiles. (p. 230)

face One of the flat surfaces of a polyhedron, including the base(s). (p. 506)

factor (1) In arithmetic: when two or more integers are multiplied, each of the integers is a factor of the product. For example, 4 is a factor of 24, because $4 \cdot 6 = 24$.
(2) In algebra: when two or more algebraic expressions are multiplied together, each of the expressions is a factor of the product. For example, x^2 is a factor of $-17x^2y^3$, because $(x^2)(-17y^3) = -17x^2y^3$. (3) To factor an expression is to write it as a product. For example, the factored form of $3x - 18$ is $3(x - 6)$. (p. 331, 341)

fair game A game in which each player has an equally likely chance of winning. (p. 9)

family of fractions All fractions that are equivalent to each other form a family of fractions. See *equivalent fractions*. (p. 249)

first quartile (Q1) The median of the lower half of an ordered set of data is the lower quartile. (p. 387)

formula An equation that shows a mathematical relationship.

fraction The quotient of two quantities in the form $\frac{a}{b}$ where b is not equal to 0.

Fraction Busters "Fraction Busting" is a method of simplifying equations involving fractions that uses the Multiplicative Property of Equality to rearrange the equation so that no fractions remain. To use this method, multiply both sides of an equation by the common denominator of all the fractions in the equation. The result will be an equivalent equation with no fractions. For example, when given the equation $\frac{x}{7}+2=\frac{x}{3}$, we can multiply both sides by the "Fraction Buster" 21. The resulting equation, $3x+42=7x$, is equivalent to the original but contains no fractions. (p. 408)

fraction greater than one A fraction in which the numerator is greater than the denominator.

frequency The number of times that something occurs within an interval or data set.

generic rectangle A type of diagram used to visualize multiplying expressions without algebra tiles. Each expression to be multiplied forms a side length of the rectangle, and the product is the sum of the areas of the sections of the rectangle. For example, the generic rectangle at right may be used to multiply $(2x+5)$ by $(x+3)$. (p. 86, 190)

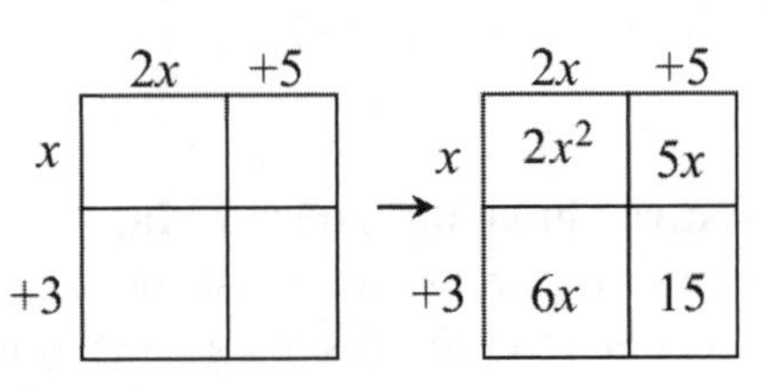

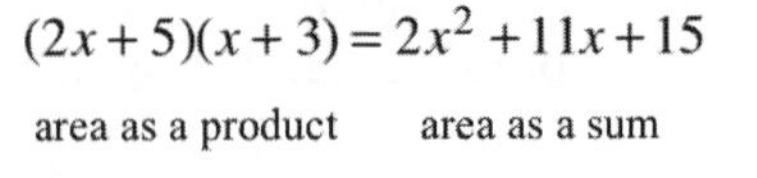

Giant One A fraction that is equal to 1. Multiplying any fraction by a Giant One will create a new fraction equivalent to the original fraction. (p. 48)

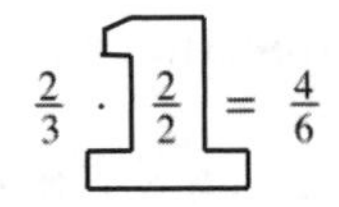

graph A graph represents numerical information in a visual form. The numbers may come from a table, situation (pattern), or rule (equation or inequality). Most of the graphs in this course show points, lines, and/or curves on a two-dimensional coordinate system like the one at right or on a single axis called a number line (see diagram below right).

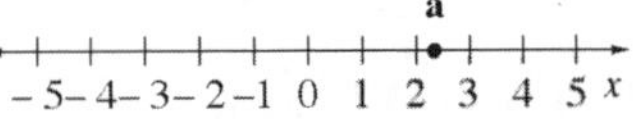

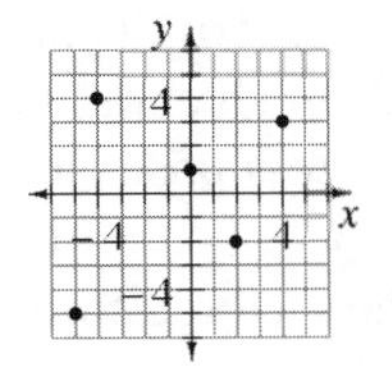

graphic organizer (GO) A visual representation of concepts or ideas you have learned. It helps with brainstorming and/or organizing information. It can make connections between ideas more clear. Examples are concept maps, charts, and Venn diagrams.

greater than One expression is greater than another if its value is larger. We indicate this relationship with the greater than symbol ">". For example, $4 + 5$ is greater than $1 + 1$. We write $4 + 5 > 1 + 1$. (p. 322)

greatest common factor (GCF) For integers, the greatest positive integer that is a common factor of two or more integers. For example, the greatest common factor of 28 and 42 is 14. (p. 322)

height (a) Triangle: the length of a segment that connects a vertex of the triangle to a line containing the opposite base (side) and is perpendicular to that line. (b) Trapezoid: the length of any segment that connects a point on one base of the trapezoid to the line containing the opposite base and is perpendicular to that line. (c) Parallelogram (includes rectangle, rhombus, and square): the length of any segment that connects a point on one base of the parallelogram to the line containing the opposite base and is perpendicular to that line. (d) Pyramid and cone: the length of the segment that connects the apex to a point in the plane containing the base of a figure and is perpendicular to that plane. (e) Prism or cylinder: the length of a segment that connects one base of the figure to the plane containing the other base and is perpendicular to that plane.

hexagon A polygon with six sides. (p. 506)

histogram A way of displaying data that is much like a bar graph in that the height of the bars is proportional to the number of elements. The difference is that each bar of a histogram represents the number of data elements in a range of values, such as the number of people who weigh from 100 pounds up to, but not including, 120 pounds. Each range of values should have the same width. Also see *bar graph*. (p. 382)

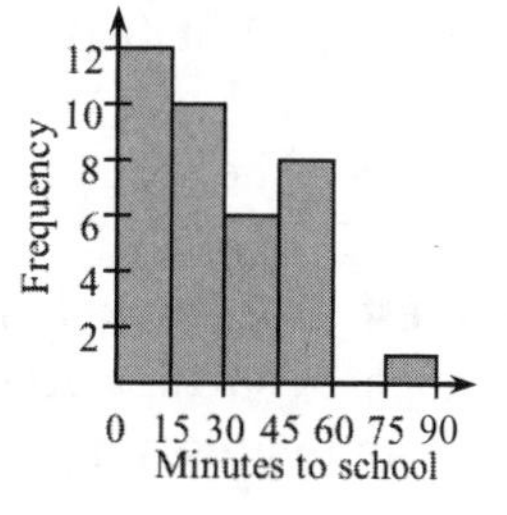

horizontal Parallel to the horizon. The x-axis of a coordinate graph is the horizontal axis. (p. 121)

hundredths grid A square with an area of 1 unit in which each side is divided into tenths. The area of each small square is $\frac{1}{10}$ by $\frac{1}{10}$ or $\frac{1}{100}$. (p. 154)

Identity Property of Addition The Identity Property of Addition states that adding zero to any expression leaves the expression unchanged. That is, $a + 0 = a$. For example, $7 + 0 = 7$, and $-2y + 0 = -2y$.

Identity Property of Multiplication The Identity Property of Multiplication states that multiplying any expression by 1 leaves the expression unchanged. That is, $a(1) = a$. For example, $437x \cdot 1 = 437x$. (p. 46)

impossibility An event with a probability of zero.

improper fraction *See* fraction greater than one.

independent events If the outcome of a probabilistic event does not affect the probability of another event, then the events are independent. For example, assume that a normal six-sided die is being rolled twice to determine the probability of rolling a 1 twice. The result of the first roll does not affect the probability of rolling a 1 on the second roll. Since the probability of rolling a 1 on the first roll is $\frac{1}{6}$ and the probability of rolling a 1 on the second roll is also $\frac{1}{6}$, then the probability of rolling two 1s in a row is $\frac{1}{6} \cdot \frac{1}{6} = \frac{1}{36}$. (p. 266)

inequality An inequality consists of two expressions on either side of an inequality symbol. For example, the inequality $7x + 4.2 < -8$ states that the expression $7x + 4.2$ has a value less than –8. (p. 336)

inequality symbols The symbol ≤ read from left to right means "less than or equal to," the symbol ≥ read from left to right means "greater than or equal to," and the symbols < and > mean "less than" and "greater than," respectively. For example, "$7 < 13$" means that 7 is less than 13. (p. 322)

inference A statistical prediction. (p. 455)

integers The set of numbers $\{\ldots, -3, -2, -1, 0, 1, 2, 3, \ldots\}$. (p. 91)

interest An amount paid which is a percentage of an initial value (principal). For example, a savings account may offer 4% annual interest rate, which means they will pay $4.00 in interest for a principal of $100 kept in the account for one year. (p. 417)

interquartile range (IQR) A way to measure the spread of data. It is calculated by subtracting the first quartile from the third quartile. (p. 387)

interval A set of numbers between two given numbers. (p. 121)

inverse operation An operation that undoes another operation. For example, multiplication is the inverse operation for division.

irrational numbers The set of numbers that cannot be expressed in the form $\frac{a}{b}$, where a and b are integers and $b \neq 0$. For example, π and $\sqrt{2}$ are irrational numbers. (p. 490)

isosceles trapezoid A trapezoid with two (non-parallel) sides of equal length.

isosceles triangle A triangle with two sides of equal length.

lateral face A (flat) sides of a polyhedron. It is always a polygon. (p. 506)

least common multiple (LCM) The smallest common multiple of a set of two or more integers. For example, the least common multiple of 4, 6, and 8 is 24.

"legal" moves When working with an Equation Mat or Expression Comparison Mat, there are certain "legal" moves you can make with the algebra tiles that keep the relationship between the two sides of the mat intact. For example, removing an x tile from the positive region of each side of an equation mat is a legal move; it keeps the expressions on each side of the mat equal. The legal moves are those justified by the properties of the real numbers. (p. 340)

less than (1) One expression is less than another if its value is not as large. This relationship is indicated with the less than symbol "$<$." For example, $1+1$ is less than $4+5$, so the comparison is written as $1+1<4+5$. (2) Sometimes the comparison is made that one amount is a certain quantity less than another amount. For example, a student movie ticket might cost two dollars *less than* an adult ticket. (p. 322)

like terms Two or more terms that contain the same variable(s), with corresponding variables raised to the same power. For example, $5x^2$ and $2x^2$ are like terms. See *combining like terms*. (p. 226)

line A line is an undefined term in geometry. A line is one-dimensional and continues without end in two directions. A line is made up of points and has no thickness. A line may be named with a letter (such as l), but also may be labeled using two points on the line, such as $\overleftrightarrow{AB}$ shown the right.

A B

line segment The portion of a line between two points. A line segment is named using its endpoints. For example, the line segment at right may be named either $\overline{AB}$ or $\overline{BA}$.

A B

lowest common denominator (LCD) The smallest common multiple of the denominators of two or more fractions. For example, the LCD of $\frac{5}{12}$ and $\frac{3}{8}$ is 24.

lowest terms of a fraction A fraction for which the numerator and the denominator have no common factor greater than one.

mean The mean, or average, of several numbers is one way of defining the "middle" of the numbers. To find the average of a group of numbers, add the numbers together then divide by the number of numbers in the set. For example, the average of the numbers 1, 5, and 6 is $(1+5+6)\div 3=4$. The mean is generally the best measure of central tendency when there are not outliers in the data set. See *average*. (p. 13)

measure of central tendency Mean and median are measures of central tendency, reflecting special statistical information about a set of data. See *center (of a data distribution)*. (p. 19)

measurement For the purposes of this course, a measurement is an indication of the size or magnitude of a geometric figure. For example, an appropriate measurement of a line segment would be its length. Appropriate measurements of a square would include not only the length of a side, but also its area and perimeter. The measure of an angle represents the number of degrees of rotation from one ray to the other about the vertex. (p. 511)

median The middle number of an ordered set of data. If there is no distinct middle, then the average of the two middle numbers is the median. The median is generally more accurate than the mean as a measure of central tendency when there are outliers in the data set. (p. 19)

mixed number (fraction) A number that consists of an integer and a fraction. For example, $3\frac{3}{8}$.

multiple The product of a whole number and any other (nonzero) whole number. For example, 15 is a multiple of 5.

multiple representations of a portion See *portions web*.

multiplication $(\cdot)$ An operation that reflects repeated addition. For example, $3 \cdot 4 = 4 + 4 + 4$.

multiplicative identity The number 1 is called the multiplicative identity because multiplying any number by 1 does not change the number. For example, $7(1) = 7$. (p. 48)

Multiplicative Identity Property The Multiplicative Identity Property states that multiplying any expression by 1 leaves the expression unchanged. That is, $a(1) = a$. For example, $437x \cdot 1 = 437x$. (p. 175)

multiplicative inverse The multiplicative inverse for a non-zero number is the number we can multiply by to get the multiplicative identity, 1. For example, for the number 5, the multiplicative inverse is $\frac{1}{5}$; for the number $\frac{2}{3}$ the multiplicative inverse is $\frac{3}{2}$. (p. 160)

multiplier The number you can multiply by in order to increase or decrease an amount. See *scale factor*. (p. 187)

mutually exclusive Two events are mutually exclusive if they have no outcomes in common. (p. 275)

negative number A negative number is a number less than zero. Negative numbers are graphed on the negative side of a number line, which is to the left of the origin. (p. 91)

net A drawing of each of the faces of a prism or pyramid, as if it were cut along its edges and flattened out.

number line A diagram representing all real numbers as points on a line. All real numbers are assigned to points. The numbers are called the coordinates of the points and the point for which the number 0 is assigned is called the origin. Also see *boundary point*. (p. 91)

numerator The number above the bar in a fraction that tells the numbers of parts in relationship to the number of parts in the whole.

obtuse angle Any angle that measures between (but not including) 90° and 180°. (p. 460)

obtuse triangle A triangle with one obtuse angle.

octagon A polygon with eight sides. (p. 506)

one-dimensional Something that does not have any width or depth. Lines and curves are one-dimensional. (p. 511)

operation A mathematical process such as addition, subtraction, multiplication, division, raising to a power, or taking a root.

opposite (of a number) The same number but with the opposite sign (+ or –). The additive inverse.

Order of Operations The specific order in which certain operations are to be carried out to evaluate or simplify expressions: parentheses (or other grouping symbols), exponents (powers or roots), multiplication and division (from left to right), and addition and subtraction (from left to right). (p. 137)

ordered pair Two numbers written in order as follows: (x, y). The primary use of ordered pairs in this course is to represent points in an xy-coordinate system. The first coordinate (x) represents the distance from the x-axis. The second coordinate (y) represents the distance from the y-axis. For example, the ordered pair (3, 5) represents the point shown in bold at right.

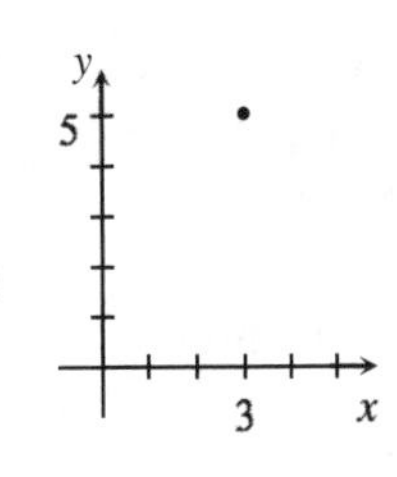

origin The point on a coordinate plane where the x-axis and y-axis intersect is called the origin. This point has coordinates $(0,0)$. The point assigned to zero on a number line is also called the origin. See *axis*.

outcome Possible result in an experiment or consequence of an action. (p. 40, 266)

outlier A number in a set of data that is much larger or much smaller than the other numbers in the set. (p. 393)

parallel Two or more straight lines on a flat surface that do not intersect (no matter how far they are extended) are parallel. The matching arrows on the parallelogram (see below) indicate that those segments are parallel.

parallel box plot A way to visually compare multiple data distributions by drawing each of their box plots on the same axis. (p. 444)

parallelogram A quadrilateral with two pairs of parallel sides. (p. 10)

pentagon A polygon with five sides. (p. 506)

percent (%) A ratio that compares a number to 100. Percents are often written using the "%" symbol. For example, 0.75 is equal to $\frac{75}{100}$ or 75%. (p. 23)

percent ruler A diagram like the one shown at right. It is used to visually aid in determining an amount that is a percent of a whole. (p. 292)

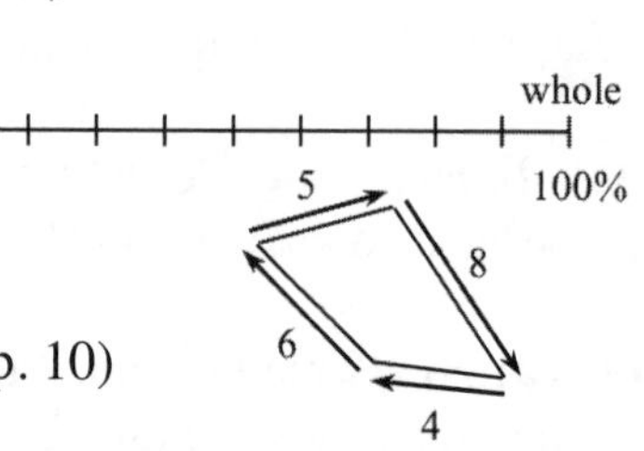

perimeter The distance around a figure on a flat surface. (p. 10)

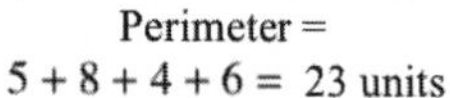

perpendicular Two rays, line segments, or lines that meet (intersect) to form a right angle (90°) are called perpendicular. A line and a flat surface may also be perpendicular if the line does not lie on the flat surface but intersects the surface and forms a right angle with every line on the flat surface passing through the point of intersection. A small square at the point of intersection of two lines or segments indicates that the lines form a right angle and are therefore perpendicular.

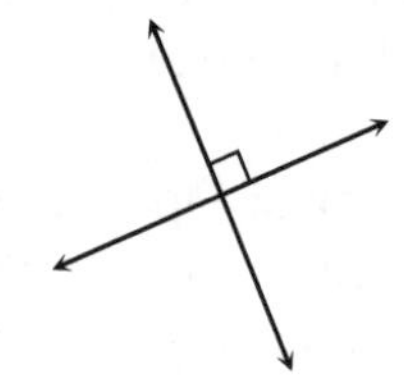

pi (π) The ratio of the circumference (C) of the circle to its diameter (d). For every circle, $\pi = \frac{\text{circumference}}{\text{diameter}} = \frac{C}{d}$. Numbers such as 3.14, 3.14159, or $\frac{22}{7}$ are approximations of π. (p. 498)

place value The number assigned to each place that a digit occupies.

plane A plane is a two-dimensional flat surface that extends without end. It is made up of points and has no thickness. (p. 509)

point An exact location in space. In two dimensions, an ordered pair specifies a point on a coordinate plane. See *ordered pair*.

polygon A two-dimensional closed figure of three or more line segments (sides) connected end to end. Each segment is a side and only intersects the endpoints of its two adjacent sides. Each point of intersection is a vertex. At right are two examples of polygons. (p. 506)

polyhedron A three-dimensional figure with no holes for which all faces are polygons. (p. 506)

population A collection of objects or group of people about whom information is gathered. (p. 450)

portion A part of something; a part of a whole.

portions web The web diagram at right illustrates that fractions, decimals, and percents are different ways to represent a portion of a number. Portions may also be represented in words, such as "four fifths" or "seven fourths," or as diagrams.

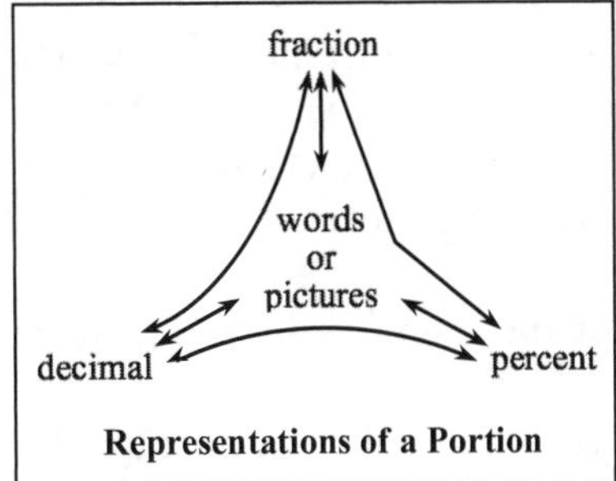

Representations of a Portion

positive numbers Numbers that are greater than zero. (p. 91)

power A number or variable raised to an exponent in the form x^n. See *exponent*.

prime factor A factor that is a prime number. (p. 52)

prime factorization The expression of a number as the product of prime factors.

prime number A positive integer with exactly two factors. The only factors of a prime number are 1 and itself. For example, the numbers 2, 3, 17, and 31 are all prime. (p. 52)

principal Initial investment or capital. An initial value. (p. 417)

prism A three-dimensional figure that consists of two parallel congruent polygons (called *bases*) and a vertical surface containing segments connecting each point on each side of one base to the corresponding point on the other base. The lateral surface of a prism consists of parallelograms. (p. 506)

probability A number that represents how likely an event is to happen. When a event has a finite number of equally-likely outcomes, the probability that one of those outcomes, called A, will occur is expressed as a ratio and written as: $P(A) = \frac{\text{number of successful outcomes}}{\text{total number of possible outcomes}}$. For example, when flipping a coin, the probability of getting tails, $P(\text{tails})$, is 1/2 because there is only one tail (successful outcome) out of the two possible equally likely outcomes (a head and a tail). Probability may be written as a ratio, decimal, or percent. A probability of 0 (or 0%) indicates that the occurrence of that outcome is impossible, while a probability of 1 (or 100%) indicates that the event must occur. Events that "might happen" will have values somewhere between 0 and 1 (or between 0% and 100%). (p. 40)

probability table *See area model.*

probability tree Tree diagrams are useful for representing possible outcomes of probability experiments. For example, the tree diagram at right represents the possible outcomes when a coin is flipped twice.

product The result of multiplying. For example, the product of 4 and 5 is 20.

proportion An equation stating that two ratios (fractions) are equal. For example, the equation at right is a proportion. A proportion is a useful type of equation to set up when solving problems involving proportional relationships. (p. 210)

$$\frac{68 \text{ votes for Mr. Mears}}{100 \text{ people surveyed}} = \frac{34 \text{ votes for Mr. Mears}}{50 \text{ people surveyed}}$$

proportional equation An equation stating that two ratios (fractions) are equal. (p. 210)

proportional relationship Two values are in a proportional relationship if a proportion may be set up that relates the values. (p. 210)

proportions web The web diagram at right illustrates the connections between different representations of the same proportional relationship. (p. 212)

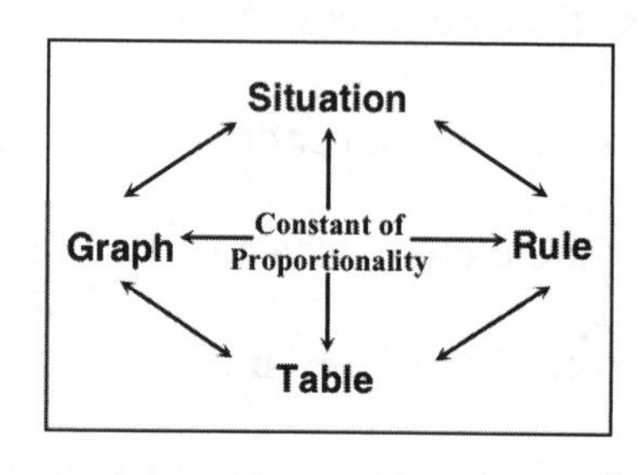

protractor A geometric tool used for physically measuring the number of degrees in an angle. (p. 458)

pyramid A three-dimensional figure with a base that is a polygon. The lateral faces are formed by connecting each vertex of the base to a single point (the vertex of the pyramid) that is above or below the surface that contains the base. (p. 506)

quadrants The coordinate plane is divided by its axes into four quadrants. The quadrants are numbered as shown in the first diagram at right. When graphing data that has no negative values, sometimes a graph that shows only the first quadrant is used.

quadrilateral A polygon with four sides. The shape at right is a quadrilateral. (p. 506)

quartile Along with the median, the quartiles divide a set of data into four groups of the same size. Also see *box plot*. (p. 387)

quotient The result of a division problem. (p. 162)

radius (plural: radii) A line segment drawn from the center of a circle to a point on the circle. (p. 471)

random An event is random if its result cannot be known (and can only be guessed) until the event is completed. For example, the flip of a fair coin is random because the coin can either land on heads or tails and the outcome cannot be known for certain until after the coin is flipped.

random number A number generated by a process whose outcome does not follow any sort of pattern and thus the number cannot be predicted.

random number generator A computational device designed to generate a set of numbers that lack any pattern. (p. 259)

random sample A sample which was chosen as a result of a random process. A random sample can represent the whole population well. (p. 455)

range The range of a set of data is the difference between the highest and lowest values. (p. 387)

rate A ratio comparing two quantities, often a comparison of time. For example, miles per hour.

ratio A ratio compares two quantities by division. A ratio may be written using a colon, but is more often written as a fraction. For example, the comparison may be made of the ratio of female students in a particular school to the total number of students in the school. This ratio could be written as 1521:2906 or as the fraction shown at right. (p. 214)

$$\frac{\text{1521 female students}}{\text{2906 total students}}$$

ratio of similarity The ratio of any pair of corresponding sides of two similar figures. This means that once it is determined that two figures are similar, all of the pairs of corresponding sides of the figures have the same ratio. For example, for the similar triangles $\triangle ABC$ and $\triangle DEF$ at right, the ratio of similarity is $\frac{5}{11}$. The ratio of similarity may also be called the linear scale factor. (p. 194)

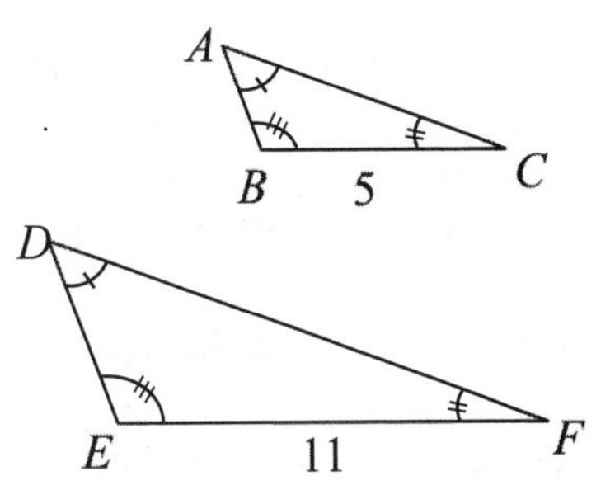

rational numbers Numbers that may be expressed in the form $\frac{a}{b}$, where a and b are integers and $b \neq 0$. For example, 0.75 is a rational number because 0.75 may be expressed in the form $\frac{3}{4}$. (p. 70)

ray A ray is part of a line that starts at one point and extends without end in one direction. In the example at right, ray $\overrightarrow{AB}$ is part of $\overleftrightarrow{AB}$ that starts at A and contains all of the points of $\overleftrightarrow{AB}$ that are on the same side of A as point B, including A. Point A is the endpoint of $\overrightarrow{AB}$. (p. 460)

reciprocals The reciprocal of a nonzero number is its multiplicative inverse, that is, the reciprocal of x is $\frac{1}{x}$. For a number in the form $\frac{a}{b}$, where a and b are non-zero, the reciprocal is $\frac{b}{a}$. The product of a number and its reciprocal is 1. For example, the reciprocal of 12 is $\frac{1}{12}$, because $12 \cdot \frac{1}{12} = 1$. (p. 160)

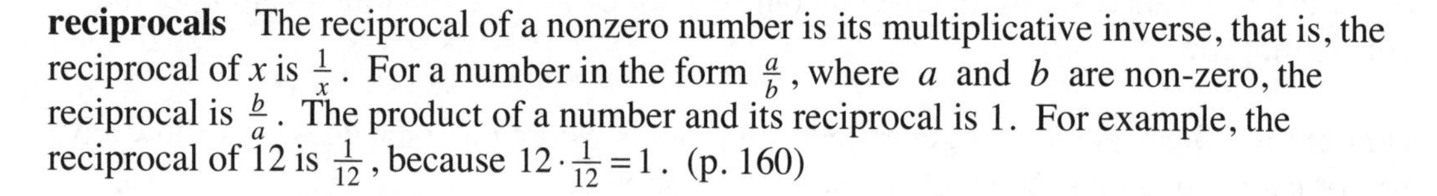

rectangle A quadrilateral with four right angles. (p. 10)

reduce To make smaller. (p. 399)

regular polygon A polygon is regular if the polygon is a convex polygon with congruent angles and congruent sides. For example, the shape at right is a regular hexagon.

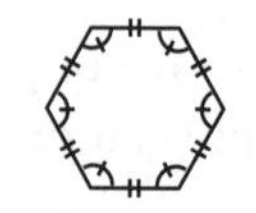
REGULAR HEXAGON

repeating decimal A repeating decimal is a decimal that repeats the same sequence of digits forever from some point onward. For example, 4.56073073073... is a decimal for which the three digits 073 continue to repeat forever. Repeating decimals are always the decimal expansions of rational numbers. (p. 81)

representative sample A subgroup of the population that has the similar characteristic of interest as that of the whole population. Representative samples are usually the result of random sampling. (p. 450)

remainder The amount left over when the divisor does not divide the dividend exactly. For example $63 \div 5$ is 12 with a remainder of 3.

rewrite To rewrite an equation or expression is to write an equivalent equation or expression. Rewriting could involve using the Distributive Property, combining like terms, or using Fraction Busters. We usually rewrite in order to change expressions or equations into more useful forms or sometimes, just simpler forms. (p. 146)

rhombus A quadrilateral with four congruent sides. Also see *equilateral*.

right angle An angle that measures 90°. A small square is used to note a right angle, as shown in the example at right.

right triangle A triangle that has one right angle. The side of a right triangle opposite the right angle is called the "hypotenuse," and the two sides adjacent to the right angle are called "legs."

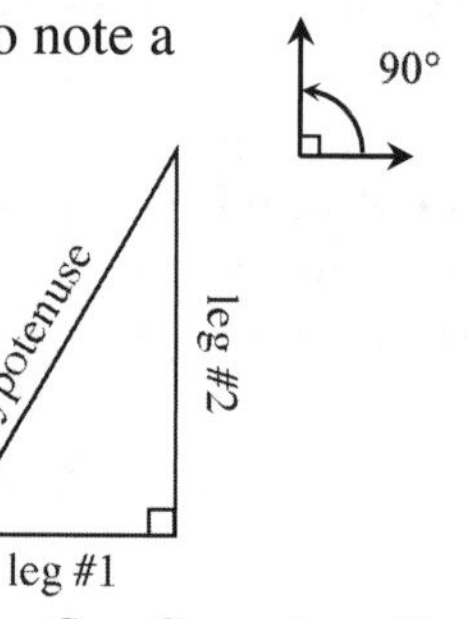

round (a number) To express an approximate value of a number that is exact to a given decimal place. For example, if the number 1234.56 is 1235 when rounded to the nearest whole number and is 1200 when rounded to the nearest 100.

rule A rule is an equation or inequality that represents the relationship between two numerical quantities. A rule is often used to represent the relationship between quantities in a table, a pattern, a real-world situation, or a graph.

sample A subset (group) of a given population with the same characteristics as the whole population. (p. 450)

sample space The collection of all possible outcomes of an event. (p. 400)

scale (scaling) The ratio between a length of the representation (such as a map, model, or diagram) and the corresponding length of the actual object. For example, the map of a city may use one inch to represent one mile. (p. 36)

scale drawing A drawing that shows a real object with accurate sizes except they have all been reduced or enlarged by a certain amount (called the scale factor). (p. 192)

scale factor A ratio that compares the sizes of the parts of one figure or object to the sizes of the corresponding parts of a similar figure or object. In this course it is also referred to as the multiplier. (p. 194)

scale on axes The scale on an axis tells you what number each successive tick mark on the axis represents. A complete graph has the scale marked with numbers on each axis. Each axis should be scaled so that each interval represents the same amount. (p. 121)

scalene triangle A triangle with no congruent sides. (p. 293)

scatter plot Two related sets of data may have the corresponding values of the sets listed as ordered pairs. If these ordered pairs are graphed in the coordinate plane, then the result is a scatter plot.

set A collection of items.

shape (of a data display) Statisticians use the following words to describe the overall shape of a data distribution: symmetric, skewed, single-peaked, double-peaked, and uniform. Examples are shown below. (p. 393)

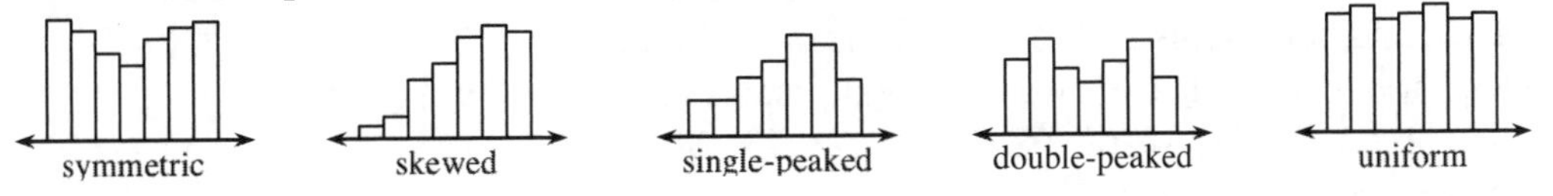

side of an angle One of the two rays that form an angle.

similar figures Similar figures have the same shape but are not necessarily the same size. For example the two triangles at right are similar. In similar figures, the measures of corresponding angles are equal and the ratio of the corresponding sides lengths are equal. (p. 194)

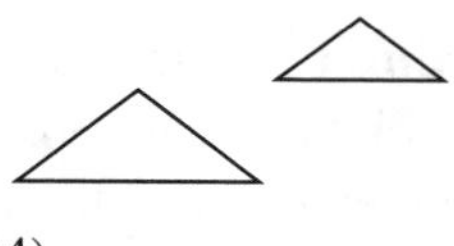

simple interest Interest paid on the principal alone. (p. 417)

simplify To simplify an expression is to write a less complicated expression with the same value. A simplified expression has no parentheses and no like terms. For example, the expression $3-(2x+7)-4x$ may be simplified to $-4-6x$. When working with algebra tiles, a simplified expression uses the fewest possible tiles to represent the original expression. (p. 226)

simulation (probability) When conducting an experiment with an event that is unrealistic to perform, a simulation can be used. A simulation is a similar experiment that has the same probabilities as the original experiment. (p. 259)

single-peaked See *shape (of a data display)*. (p. 393)

skewed (data display) See *shape (of a data display)*. (p. 393)

solution The number or numbers that when substituted into an equation or inequality make the equation or inequality true. For example, $x = 4$ is a solution to the equation $3x = 12$ because $3x$ equals 12 when $x = 4$. (p. 363)

solve To find all the solutions to an equation or an inequality. The solution(s) may be number(s), variable(s), or an expression. (p. 340)

spread (data display) A measure of the amount of variability in a data set. Three ways to measure spread are the range, the mean absolute deviation, and the interquartile range. (p. 387)

square A quadrilateral with four right angles and four congruent sides.

square

square units The units used to describe the measure of an area in the form of 1×1 unit squares.

stem-and-leaf plot A frequency distribution that arranges data so that all digits except the last digit in each piece of data are in the stem, the last digit of each piece of data are the leaves, and both stems and leaves are arranged in order from least to greatest. The example at right displays the data: 49, 52, 54, 58, 61, 61, 67, 68, 72, 73, 73, 73, 78, 82, 83, 108, 112, and 117. (p. 382)

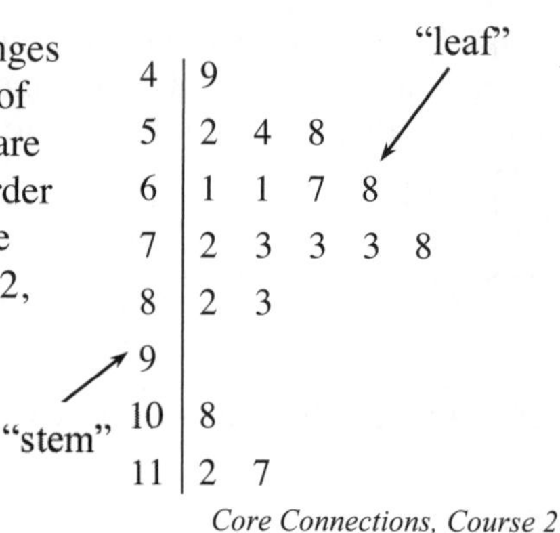

stoplight icon The icon (shown at right) will appear periodically throughout the text. Problems that display this icon contain errors of some type. (p. 43)

straight angle An angle that measures 180°. This occurs when the rays of the angle point in opposite directions, forming a line. (p. 460)

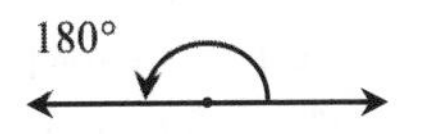

straightedge A tool used as a guide to draw lines, rays, and segments. (p. 469)

subproblems A problem solving strategy that breaks a problem into smaller parts that must be solved in order to solve the original, more complex problem.

substitution Replacing one symbol with a number, a variable, or another algebraic expression of the same value. Substitution does not change the value of the overall expression. For example, suppose that the expression $13x-6$ must be evaluated for $x=4$. Since x has the value 4, 4 may be substituted into the expression wherever x appears, giving the equivalent expression $13(4)-6$. (p. 143)

subtraction (–) An operation that gives the difference between two numbers. (p. 147)

sum The result of adding two or more numbers. For example, the sum of 4 and 5 is 9.

Super Giant One A Giant One in which either or both the numerator and denominator are fractions. (p. 165)

supplementary angles Two angles a and b for which $a+b=180°$. Each angle is called the supplement of the other. In the example at right, angles A and B are supplementary. Supplementary angles are often adjacent. For example, since $\measuredangle LMN$ is a straight angle, then $\measuredangle LMP$ and $\measuredangle PMN$ are supplementary angles because $m\measuredangle LMP + m\measuredangle PMN = 180°$. (p. 466)

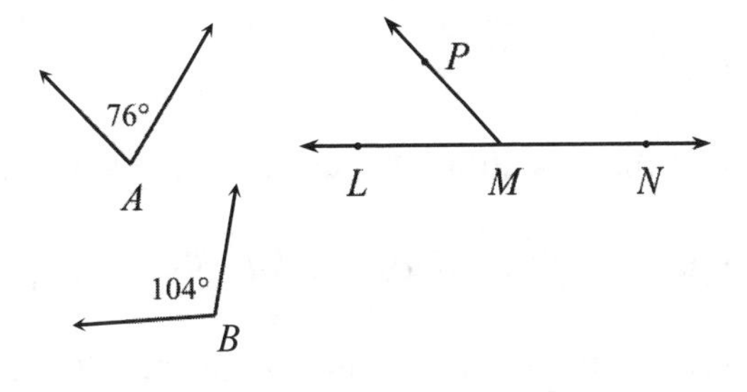

surface area The sum of all the area(s) of the surface(s) of a three-dimensional solid. For example, the surface area of a prism is the sum of the areas of its top and bottom bases, and its vertical surfaces (lateral faces). (p. 503)

symmetric See *shape (of a data display)*. (p. 393)

systematic list A list created by following a system (organized process). When finding probabilities, a systematic list helps to find all outcomes of a sample space or event. (p. 277)

term A term is a single number, variable, or the product of numbers and variables, such as –45, $1.2x$, and $3xy^2$. (p. 137)

terminating decimal A terminating decimal is a decimal that has only a finite number of non-zero digits, such as 4.067. Terminating decimals are a particular kind of repeating decimal for which the repeating portion is zeros, so the example could be written 4.0670000000... but it is not necessary to write the zeros at the end. (p. 81)

theoretical probability A calculated probability based on the possible outcomes when each outcome has the same chance of occurring: (number of successful outcomes)/(total number of possible outcomes). (p. 40)

third quartile (Q3) The median of the upper half of an ordered set of data. (p. 387)

three-dimensional An object that has height, width, and depth. (p. 511)

tick mark A symbol that shows that a number line has been divided into intervals of equal length. See *number line*.

trapezoid A quadrilateral with at least one pair of parallel sides. (p. 10)

triangle A polygon with three sides. (p. 506)

triangle inequality In a triangle with side lengths a, b, and c, c must be less than the sum of a and b and greater than the difference of a and b. In the example at right, a is greater than b (that is, $a > b$), so the possible values for c are all numbers such that $c > a - b$ and $c < a + b$. (p. 476)

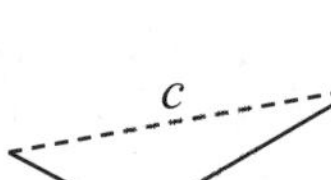

two-dimensional An object having length and width. (p. 511)

uniform See *shape (of a data display)*. (p. 393)

unit of measure A standard quantity (such as a centimeter, second, square foot, or gallon) that is used to measure and describe an object. A single object may be measured using different units of measure. For example, a pencil may be 80 mm long, meaning that the pencil is 80 times as long as a unit of 1 mm. However, the same pencil is 8 cm long, so that the pencil is the same length as 8 cm laid end-to-end. This is because 1 cm is the same length as 10 mm.

unit rate A rate with a denominator of one when simplified. (p. 214)

variability *See* spread.

variable A symbol used to represent one or more numbers. In this course, letters of the English alphabet are used as variables. For example, in the expression $3x-(8.6xy+z)$, the variables are x, y, and z. (p. 220)

variable expression See *expression*.

vertex (plural: vertices) (1) For a two-dimensional geometric shape, a vertex is a point where two or more line segments or rays meet to form a "corner," such as in a polygon or angle. (2) For a three-dimensional polyhedron, a vertex is a point where the edges of the solid meet. (p. 460, 506)

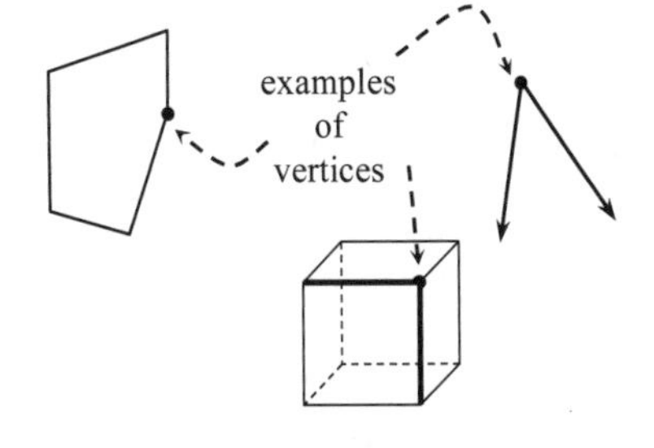

vertical At right angles to the horizon. On a coordinate graph, the y-axis runs vertically. (p. 121)

vertical angles The two opposite (that is, non-adjacent) angles formed by two intersecting lines. "Vertical" is a relationship between pairs of angles, so one angle cannot be called vertical. Angles that form a vertical pair are always congruent. (p. 466)

volume A measurement of the size of the three-dimensional region enclosed within an object. Volume is expressed as the number of $1\times1\times1$ unit cubes (or parts of cubes) that fit inside a solid. (p. 511)

voluntary response sample A subgroup of the population that chose to respond to a survey. A voluntary response sample is not a random sample. (p. 450)

***x*-axis** The horizontal number line on a coordinate graph. See *axis*.

***x*-coordinate** In an ordered pair, (x, y), that represents a point in the coordinate plane, x is the value of the x-coordinate. That is, the distance from the y-axis that is needed to plot the point. (p. 87)

***y*-axis** The vertical number line on a coordinate graph. See *axis*.

***y*-coordinate** In an ordered pair, (x, y), that represents a point in the coordinate plane, y is the value of the y-coordinate. That is, the distance from the x-axis that is needed to plot the point. (p. 87)

zero pair Two quantities whose sum is zero. A number and its opposite make a zero pair because their sum is 0. (p. 231)

Index
Student Version

Many of the pages referenced here contain a definition or an example of the topic listed, often within the body of a Math Notes box. Others contain problems that develop or demonstrate the topic. It may be necessary to read the text on several pages to fully understand the topic. Also, some problems listed here are good examples of the topic and may not offer any explanation. The page numbers below reflect the pages in the Student Version. References to Math Notes boxes are bolded.

E

S

Common Core State Standards for Mathematics

Mathematics | Grade 7

In Grade 7, instructional time should focus on four critical areas: (1) developing understanding of and applying proportional relationships; (2) developing understanding of operations with rational numbers and working with expressions and linear equations; (3) solving problems involving scale drawings and informal geometric constructions, and working with two- and three-dimensional shapes to solve problems involving area, surface area, and volume; and (4) drawing inferences about populations based on samples.

(1) Students extend their understanding of ratios and develop understanding of proportionality to solve single- and multi-step problems. Students use their understanding of ratios and proportionality to solve a wide variety of percent problems, including those involving discounts, interest, taxes, tips, and percent increase or decrease. Students solve problems about scale drawings by relating corresponding lengths between the objects or by using the fact that relationships of lengths within an object are preserved in similar objects. Students graph proportional relationships and understand the unit rate informally as a measure of the steepness of the related line, called the slope. They distinguish proportional relationships from other relationships.

(2) Students develop a unified understanding of number, recognizing fractions, decimals (that have a finite or a repeating decimal representation), and percents as different representations of rational numbers. Students extend addition, subtraction, multiplication, and division to all rational numbers, maintaining the properties of operations and the relationships between addition and subtraction, and multiplication and division. By applying these properties, and by viewing negative numbers in terms of everyday contexts (e.g., amounts owed or temperatures below zero), students explain and interpret the rules for adding, subtracting, multiplying, and dividing with negative numbers. They use the arithmetic of rational numbers as they formulate expressions and equations in one variable and use these equations to solve problems.

(3) Students continue their work with area from Grade 6, solving problems involving the area and circumference of a circle and surface area of three-dimensional objects. In preparation for work on congruence and similarity in Grade 8 they reason about relationships among two-dimensional figures using scale drawings and informal geometric constructions, and they gain familiarity with the relationships between angles formed by intersecting lines. Students work with three-dimensional figures, relating them to two-dimensional figures by examining cross-sections. They solve real-world and mathematical problems involving area, surface area, and volume of two- and three-dimensional objects composed of triangles, quadrilaterals, polygons, cubes, and right prisms.

(4) Students build on their previous work with single data distributions to compare two data distributions and address questions about differences between populations. They begin informal work with random sampling to generate data sets and learn about the importance of representative samples for drawing inferences.

7 Grade 7 Overview

Ratios and Proportional Relationships

- Analyze proportional relationships and use them to solve real-world and mathematical problems.

The Number System

- Apply and extend previous understandings of operations with fractions to add, subtract, multiply, and divide rational numbers.
- Know that there are numbers that are not rational and approximate them by rational numbers.

Expressions and Equations

- Use properties of operations to generate equivalent expressions.
- Solve real-life and mathematical problems using numerical and algebraic expressions and equations.

Geometry

- Draw, construct and describe geometrical figures and describe the relationships between them.
- Solve real-life and mathematical problems involving angle measure, area, surface area, and volume.
- Solve real-life and mathematical problems involving volume of cylinders, cones, and spheres.

Statistics and Probability

- Use random sampling to draw inferences about a population.
- Draw informal comparative inferences about two populations.
- Investigate chance processes and develop, use, and evaluate probability models.

Mathematical Practices

1. Make sense of problems and persevere in solving them.
2. Reason abstractly and quantitatively.
3. Construct viable arguments and critique the reasoning of others.
4. Model with mathematics.
5. Use appropriate tools strategically.
6. Attend to precision.
7. Look for and make use of structure.
8. Look for and express regularity in repeated reasoning.

Grade 7

Ratios and Proportional Relationships 7.RP

Analyze proportional relationships and use them to solve real-world and mathematical problems.

1. Compute unit rates associated with ratios of fractions, including ratios of lengths, areas and other quantities measured in like or different units. *For example, if a person walks 1/2 mile in each 1/4 hour, compute the unit rate as the complex fraction* $^{1/2}/_{1/4}$ *miles per hour, equivalently 2 miles per hour.*
2. Recognize and represent proportional relationships between quantities.
   a. Decide whether two quantities are in a proportional relationship, e.g., by testing for equivalent ratios in a table or graphing on a coordinate plane and observing whether the graph is a straight line through the origin.
   b. Identify the constant of proportionality (unit rate) in tables, graphs, equations, diagrams, and verbal descriptions of proportional relationships.
   c. Represent proportional relationships by equations. *For example, if total cost t is proportional to the number n of items purchased at a constant price p, the relationship between the total cost and the number of items can be expressed as* $t = pn$.
   d. Explain what a point (x, y) on the graph of a proportional relationship means in terms of the situation, with special attention to the points (0, 0) and $(1, r)$ where r is the unit rate.
3. Use proportional relationships to solve multistep ratio and percent problems. *Examples: simple interest, tax, markups and markdowns, gratuities and commissions, fees, percent increase and decrease, percent error.*

The Number System 7.NS

Apply and extend previous understandings of operations with fractions to add, subtract, multiply, and divide rational numbers.

1. Apply and extend previous understandings of addition and subtraction to add and subtract rational numbers; represent addition and subtraction on a horizontal or vertical number line diagram.
   a. Describe situations in which opposite quantities combine to make 0. *For example, a hydrogen atom has 0 charge because its two constituents are oppositely charged.*
   b. Understand $p + q$ as the number located a distance $|q|$ from p, in the positive or negative direction depending on whether q is positive or negative. Show that a number and its opposite have a sum of 0 (are additive inverses). Interpret sums of rational numbers by describing real-world contexts.
   c. Understand subtraction of rational numbers as adding the additive inverse, $p - q = p + (-q)$. Show that the distance between two rational numbers on the number line is the absolute value of their difference, and apply this principle in real-world contexts.
   d. Apply properties of operations as strategies to add and subtract rational numbers.
2. Apply and extend previous understandings of multiplication and division and of fractions to multiply and divide rational numbers.
   a. Understand that multiplication is extended from fractions to rational numbers by requiring that operations continue to satisfy the properties of operations, particularly the distributive property, leading to products such as $(-1)(-1) = 1$ and the rules for multiplying signed numbers. Interpret products of rational numbers by describing real-world contexts.
   b. Understand that integers can be divided, provided that the divisor is not zero, and every quotient of integers (with non-zero divisor) is a rational number. If p and q are integers, then $-(p/q) = (-p)/q = p/(-q)$. Interpret quotients of rational numbers by describing real world contexts.

c. Apply properties of operations as strategies to multiply and divide rational numbers.
d. Convert a rational number to a decimal using long division; know that the decimal form of a rational number terminates in 0s or eventually repeats.

3. Solve real-world and mathematical problems involving the four operations with rational numbers.[1]

Expressions and Equations 7.EE

Use properties of operations to generate equivalent expressions.

1. Apply properties of operations as strategies to add, subtract, factor, and expand linear expressions with rational coefficients.
2. Understand that rewriting an expression in different forms in a problem context can shed light on the problem and how the quantities in it are related. *For example, $a + 0.05a = 1.05a$ means that "increase by 5%" is the same as "multiply by 1.05."*

Solve real-life and mathematical problems using numerical and algebraic expressions and equations.

3. Solve multi-step real-life and mathematical problems posed with positive and negative rational numbers in any form (whole numbers, fractions, and decimals), using tools strategically. Apply properties of operations to calculate with numbers in any form; convert between forms as appropriate; and assess the reasonableness of answers using mental computation and estimation strategies. *For example: If a woman making $25 an hour gets a 10% raise, she will make an additional 1/10 of her salary an hour, or $2.50, for a new salary of $27.50. If you want to place a towel bar 9 3/4 inches long in the center of a door that is 27 1/2 inches wide, you will need to place the bar about 9 inches from each edge; this estimate can be used as a check on the exact computation.*
4. Use variables to represent quantities in a real-world or mathematical problem, and construct simple equations and inequalities to solve problems by reasoning about the quantities.
   a. Solve word problems leading to equations of the form $px + q = r$ and $p(x + q) = r$, where p, q, and r are specific rational numbers. Solve equations of these forms fluently. Compare an algebraic solution to an arithmetic solution, identifying the sequence of the operations used in each approach. *For example, the perimeter of a rectangle is 54 cm. Its length is 6 cm. What is its width?*
   b. Solve word problems leading to inequalities of the form $px + q > r$ or $px + q < r$, where p, q, and r are specific rational numbers. Graph the solution set of the inequality and interpret it in the context of the problem. *For example: As a salesperson, you are paid $50 per week plus $3 per sale. This week you want your pay to be at least $100. Write an inequality for the number of sales you need to make, and describe the solutions.*

Geometry 7.G

Draw, construct, and describe geometrical figures and describe the relationships between them.

1. Solve problems involving scale drawings of geometric figures, including computing actual lengths and areas from a scale drawing and reproducing a scale drawing at a different scale.
2. Draw (freehand, with ruler and protractor, and with technology) geometric shapes with given conditions. Focus on constructing triangles from three measures of angles or sides, noticing when the conditions determine a unique triangle, more than one triangle, or no triangle.
3. Describe the two-dimensional figures that result from slicing three-dimensional figures, as in plane sections of right rectangular prisms and right rectangular pyramids.

[1] Computations with rational numbers extend the rules for manipulating fractions to complex fractions.

Solve real-life and mathematical problems involving angle measure, area, surface area, and volume.

4. Know the formulas for the area and circumference of a circle and use them to solve problems; give an informal derivation of the relationship between the circumference and area of a circle.
5. Use facts about supplementary, complementary, vertical, and adjacent angles in a multi-step problem to write and solve simple equations for an unknown angle in a figure.
6. Solve real-world and mathematical problems involving area, volume and surface area of two- and three-dimensional objects composed of triangles, quadrilaterals, polygons, cubes, and right prisms.

Statistics and Probability 7.SP

Use random sampling to draw inferences about a population.

1. Understand that statistics can be used to gain information about a population by examining a sample of the population; generalizations about a population from a sample are valid only if the sample is representative of that population. Understand that random sampling tends to produce representative samples and support valid inferences.
2. Use data from a random sample to draw inferences about a population with an unknown characteristic of interest. Generate multiple samples (or simulated samples) of the same size to gauge the variation in estimates or predictions. *For example, estimate the mean word length in a book by randomly sampling words from the book; predict the winner of a school election based on randomly sampled survey data. Gauge how far off the estimate or prediction might be.*

Draw informal comparative inferences about two populations.

3. Informally assess the degree of visual overlap of two numerical data distributions with similar variabilities, measuring the difference between the centers by expressing it as a multiple of a measure of variability. *For example, the mean height of players on the basketball team is 10 cm greater than the mean height of players on the soccer team, about twice the variability (mean absolute deviation) on either team; on a dot plot, the separation between the two distributions of heights is noticeable.*
4. Use measures of center and measures of variability for numerical data from random samples to draw informal comparative inferences about two populations. *For example, decide whether the words in a chapter of a seventh-grade science book are generally longer than the words in a chapter of a fourth-grade science book.*

Investigate chance processes and develop, use, and evaluate probability models.

5. Understand that the probability of a chance event is a number between 0 and 1 that expresses the likelihood of the event occurring. Larger numbers indicate greater likelihood. A probability near 0 indicates an unlikely event, a probability around 1/2 indicates an event that is neither unlikely nor likely, and a probability near 1 indicates a likely event.
6. Approximate the probability of a chance event by collecting data on the chance process that produces it and observing its long-run relative frequency, and predict the approximate relative frequency given the probability. *For example, when rolling a number cube 600 times, predict that a 3 or 6 would be rolled roughly 200 times, but probably not exactly 200 times.*
7. Develop a probability model and use it to find probabilities of events. Compare probabilities from a model to observed frequencies; if the agreement is not good, explain possible sources of the discrepancy.

a. Develop a uniform probability model by assigning equal probability to all outcomes, and use the model to determine probabilities of events. *For example, if a student is selected at random from a class, find the probability that Jane will be selected and the probability that a girl will be selected.*

b. Develop a probability model (which may not be uniform) by observing frequencies in data generated from a chance process. *For example, find the approximate probability that a spinning penny will land heads up or that a tossed paper cup will land open-end down. Do the outcomes for the spinning penny appear to be equally likely based on the observed frequencies?*

8. Find probabilities of compound events using organized lists, tables, tree diagrams, and simulation.

   a. Understand that, just as with simple events, the probability of a compound event is the fraction of outcomes in the sample space for which the compound event occurs.

   b. Represent sample spaces for compound events using methods such as organized lists, tables and tree diagrams. For an event described in everyday language (e.g., "rolling double sixes"), identify the outcomes in the sample space which compose the event.

   c. Design and use a simulation to generate frequencies for compound events. *For example, use random digits as a simulation tool to approximate the answer to the question: If 40% of donors have type A blood, what is the probability that it will take at least 4 donors to find one with type A blood?*